REVISED EDITION

TRIGONOMETRY

BY

N. J. LENNES
Professor of Mathematics
University of Montana

AND

A. S. MERRILL
Professor of Mathematics
University of Montana

HARPER & BROTHERS
New York and London

Trigonometry *is a complete re-*
vision of Plane Trigonometry.

CONTENTS

EDITOR'S PREFACE TO THE FIRST EDITION

[As a tribute to the distinguished editor of the first edition of the books of this series, this preface is retained in this revised edition. It is much to be regretted that his services are no longer available.]

THERE are several reasons why this book is not "just another trigonometry." It has been many years in the making and its essential features have had numerous trials in the classroom. It will be found to be a teachable book, and one whose flexibility will commend itself to the independent and thoughtful teacher.

The editor would call especial attention to the very careful pagination, which is so often neglected in our textbooks; to the importance of the cumulative reviews which may be used with telling effect on the students whose habits of thinking have not been well organized; and to the provisions made for the stronger students who will do far more than the rank and file of the class if properly encouraged.

In particular, the editor would commend to teachers the fruitful opportunities open to the leaders of a class in trigonometry for individual reading and study and subsequent reports to the undergraduate Mathematical Club which should be a feature of every college department of mathematics. Topics for such reports will be found in the later chapters of this text and will be suggested at many points in the "Historical Sketch." Such club activities have undergone a rapid growth during the past few years and scores of colleges have found them to be stimulating and effective adjuncts to the regular class work. For further reference to this subject see an address by Professor H. E. Hawkes of Columbia University in the *American Mathematical Monthly* for October, 1918, and the reports and club topics by Professor R. C. Archibald of Brown University in every issue of the *Monthly* for 1918.

H. E. SLAUGHT

UNIVERSITY OF CHICAGO

AUTHORS' PREFACE

EXAMINATION of textbooks, and correspondence with large numbers who used this text in its first edition, reveal the entirely expected result that the texts, and the courses in trigonometry given in this country, may be divided into three classes:

(a) Those in which trigonometric computation is treated completely from the start, with the development of only such formulas as are needed for this purpose; this being followed by the usual trigonometric analysis.

(b) Those in which general definitions are introduced at the start and in which trigonometric analysis precedes the computational work.

(c) Those in which an attempt is made to compromise between (a) and (b).

When it was decided to reset this book completely, the authors were set free to adopt any plan that they wished. Following their own preference, and at the same time giving full heed to the suggestions of teachers from about fifty schools selected at random among those who used the first edition, alternative (a) was unhesitatingly adopted. The result is the order of topics now found in this book.

Order of Topics.—Part One, the first 94 pages, deals with the solution of triangles based on the minimum of theoretical apparatus that is needed for this purpose. Chapter VII, the first chapter of Part Two, deals with trigonometric identities, this chapter being followed in order by chapters on Variation of Trigonometric Functions, Inverse Functions and Trigonometric Equations, De Moivre's Theorem, Exponential and Hyperbolic Functions, Miscellaneous Work on Trigonometric Identities, Miscellaneous Supplementary Material, Spherical Trigonometry, and a Historical Sketch.

Those who wish to begin the study of trigonometry with the computation of triangles will in the main also wish to follow the order of this book in Part Two. Part One will be adequate for schools in which trigonometry is to serve the purpose of general plane surveying, such as schools of forestry, some technical schools, and other schools that teach this subject as a means to indirect measuring. In many college classes that allot a relatively small amount of time to trigonometry, Part One will be supplemented by Chapter VII, dealing with identities in a more elementary way, and by parts of Chapters VIII and IX. From the above it seems apparent that the order of this book can be followed with equal propriety whether the course is to be very brief, or much more extended as is now the case in some of our institutions.

It is believed that the subject as treated in this book, when all its chapters are included, will be found to be entirely adequate for the strongest course now given as an introduction to this subject in our colleges and technical schools.

Aside from the program as to order of topics described above, which is now adopted more definitely than in the first edition, the characteristics of the first edition have in the main been retained. We again call special attention to:

(a) The matter of paging, (b) the arrangement of exercises and problems (these have been replaced almost completely by new ones), (c) the cumulative reviews, (d) the provision for stronger students, (e) the historical sketch, (f) answers to odd-numbered problems, which are now included, (g) the complete list of the formulas on plane trigonometry (pages 186–188) that are developed in the whole book.

General Characteristics.—Effort has been made to attain simplicity and clarity of statement and at the same time rigor and completeness of proof. In some cases where complete proof of a general theorem is necessarily of considerable length and complexity, the proof is made under specified limitations, which are removed later. Thus the addition formulas are first proved under the limitation that all angles involved are positive and less than 180°.

More than ordinary attention has been given to the matter of paging. Pages 106, 107 are typical. On these two pages the formulas for $\sin (A \pm B)$, $\cos (A \pm B)$ are proved. Thus the student has this naturally related material before him without obscuring part of it by turning the page. On pages 74, 75 the law of sines is proved, solving triangles by means of this law is developed, the form of computation given, and exercises are provided. On pages 78, 79 the law of tangents and its uses are given, together with appropriate exercises. The study of the table of logarithms of numbers begins on page 38, where reference is made only to logarithms of numbers between 300 and 350, which are found on the opposite page. Similar remarks apply to the pages of tables reproduced on pages 41 and 49 and their study on the opposite pages, and also to the page of natural functions (page 25) and the study and use of it on the page opposite. In only a very few cases in the latter part of the book is a page turned in the middle of a proof or a discussion. While this arrangement causes a considerable amount of thought and labor in organizing the material in the first place, and not a little trouble and expense in adjusting the proof in the final paging, they are believed to be justified and even obligatory. Are not the students and teachers in our schools entitled to the same standard of convenience in the instruments they use that is now so rigorously maintained in providing industrial appliances and arrangements?

Arrangement of Exercises and Problems.—Exercises and problems are in nearly all instances provided in two or three groups marked A, B, C. These groups are intended to be of equal difficulty and equally adapted for first use. By this arrangement it is possible to assign different sets to different sections and in successive years. This saves the teacher the trouble of selecting from very long lists that are usually given. These groups of exercises and problems are usually followed by more general lists which on the whole are more difficult and which may be used as extra work for the stronger students. In the case of unusually able classes these may be used to the exclusion of the other groups.

Cumulative Reviews.—On pages 169–174 there is a series of cumulative reviews, the purpose of which is stated briefly on page 168. These reviews are in no sense reviews of the chapters at the end of which it is suggested they be given. For the purpose of organizing them an analysis was made of the essential elements that are brought into the course and of the recurrence of these elements in the course itself. They were then arranged to supplement these recurrences so that the course itself together with the reviews should give each element properly spaced reviews or "relearnings," which we now know are necessary for relatively permanent retention. This arrangement is comparatively novel in textbooks, and in order not to obtrude it upon teachers who do not wish to make use of it, the reviews are placed in a group near the end of the book, instead of at separate points in the main body of the text.

Provision for Stronger Students Made Possible.—Besides the more general exercises and problems that are given in separate groups in the main body of the book, a series of topics near the end may be used as special assignments for able students who are candidates for the highest grades. Pages 175–178 provide work related to surveying. Students interested in physics or engineering may read pages 178–181 and solve the problems given. The miscellaneous theorems and problems in the final list beginning on page 182 are on the whole more difficult than the early part of the book, and also of more general mathematical interest.

Again, Chapters X, XI ("De Moivre's Theorem," and "Exponential and Hyperbolic Functions") may be assigned for special reports by unusual students. In our own institution such reports have been made before the Mathematics Club, which is an organization of undergraduates interested in mathematics. One of the weaknesses of our college teaching seems to be that the students get but little practice in mastering a subject from the printed page. Certainly the ablest students should be led to do this at an early stage.

Different Courses for Which This Book Is Adapted.—This has been mentioned, in part, above. A minimum core of Chapters I to VII will be studied in all except the briefest courses, with the single exception that some may wish to omit Chapter II, in which right triangles are computed by means of the natural functions and without the use of logarithms. This minimum core may be enlarged in a variety of ways by selections from Chapters VIII to XIII. In a technical school sections dealing with the variation of the functions, the slide-rule, the problems related to physics, and problems from the final list will naturally be selected. If the interest is primarily in pure mathematics a somewhat different selection will be made, depending largely upon the taste of the instructor. It is believed that the material provided is adequate for all demands which can reasonably be made upon an elementary text such as the present, while at the same time topics of specialized interest have not been introduced into the early parts.

Historical Sketch.—Instead of isolated notes in the body of the text, a historical sketch is given in a separate chapter at the end of the book. This makes possible a continuous story showing something of the development of the subject as a whole, and at the same time makes easily accessible information about any particular topic. The sweep of the story, and some of the causal relations between its parts, become more apparent than they can possibly be from isolated notes.

N. J. L.
A. S. M.

INTRODUCTION

THE word **trigonometry**, derived from two Greek words *trigonon*, triangle, and *metron*, measure, is the name of a branch of mathematics whose most elementary part deals with the relations of the sides and angles of a triangle and with the applications of these relations in the solution of problems. It is this part of trigonometry that we shall study in Part One of this book. The great practical importance of this part of our study lies in the fact that it enables us to measure distances indirectly, which in practice is very different from measuring them directly.

1. Direct measurement of straight lines.—The distance between two points on a sheet of paper can be measured directly by using a graduated ruler. You may be able to determine such a distance within a 32d of an inch and possibly somewhat closer.

A surveyor can measure rather easily and fairly accurately the straight-line distance between two points on the earth's surface if they are not very far apart and if they are connected by a straight path that he can traverse. In surveying, however, the distances that are required are horizontal distances. If a building lot is inclined to the horizontal, as is the line *AB* in the figure, then the surveyor must find the length of the horizontal line *AC*, for this is the width of the lot that is available for building.

In simple cases this horizontal distance is sometimes found by starting, as at *B* in the figure, holding the tape horizontal to the point *D*, then dropping a vertical line to *E*, then holding the tape horizontal to *F*, and so on, each time noting the length of the horizontal line. The sum of the lines *BD*, *EF*, *GH* is equal to the required distance *CA*. In practice this is clumsy and laborious, and some other method must be found.

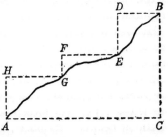

1

2. The distance between two mountain peaks.—Suppose we are engaged in making a fundamental survey of mountainous country. We have to find the distance accurately between two mountain peaks some twenty miles apart, the error permitted being about four inches to the mile, which is the case in the U. S. Coast and Geodetic survey.

To measure this distance by direct use of the surveyor's steel tape, or by any other direct means, is in practice almost impossible. If you start down the mountain side from the peak A, you may encounter precipices hundreds of feet high. Gorges may make it necessary to turn aside from the direction toward the peak B, and at times B will be invisible from where you are and there will be some trouble knowing exactly in what direction to go. At the bottom of the valley there is a river some hundreds of feet wide and measuring its width directly will be a real difficulty. All the time that you are overcoming these difficulties, you must be certain that in every mile of horizontal distance you measure you do not get a result that is four inches too great or too small. As you reflect on the details of this process you will be impressed with the almost impossible character of the task.

3. The distance from the shore to an island.—An accurate map is to be made of a coastal region such as that between Seattle and Alaska. An island lies some ten miles from the shore and the distance must be known with only a small margin of error. How are we to find it? We cannot even start measuring the distance directly. Anchored boats might be placed at the ends of our measuring tape as we proceed, but they will not remain as still as would

be required for our purpose. Even the most securely anchored ship will drift around by a considerable distance. Here, then, we encounter a difficulty even greater than that in finding the distance between the mountain peaks. On the map that we are to make (that has been made) there are literally a thousand such distances. Beyond question they must be measured by some indirect method.

4. Distances to the moon, sun, and stars, and their sizes.— Whether the knowledge sought is of practical value or not, and whether or not the quest for it is such as sensible men should undertake, the fact remains that huge amounts of effort and millions in money have been expended in learning the proportions of our solar system—the distances to the moon, sun, and planets, and the sizes of these bodies. Certainly, here we are beyond any possibility of direct measurements. No man has gone more than about 14 miles from the earth's surface, while the distance to the moon is about 240,000 miles and the distance to the sun some 400 times as great as to the moon. The distance to the outermost planet is more than 40 times as great as to the sun, and the distance to the nearest fixed star is over a quarter million times as great as that to the sun.

We now know that the diameter of the moon is a little over one-fourth that of the earth, while the sun is so large that a string of 110 beads, each the size of our earth, would about reach through the sun along a diameter. We know that the diameters of Mercury, Venus, and Mars are less than that of our earth, while the diameters of Jupiter, Saturn, Uranus, and Neptune are much greater. The outlying little planet Pluto is probably just a little larger than the earth. We know that among the fixed stars our sun is among the smaller and that some of them have diameters hundreds of times that of the sun.

5. What we shall learn about indirect measurement.— In the extremely delicate work that is needed in much of our surveying here on the surface of this earth, and in the still more delicate work that is done in making astronomical measurements, there is much that we cannot learn about in an elementary course in trigonometry. But we shall learn the fundamental ideas that are involved, and we shall also learn much about how these ideas are used in solving problems that no one on this earth had ever solved until less than 500 years ago. Brilliant as were the ancient Greeks and some of the Egyptians and others, these problems remained unsolved by them. As may be seen in the Historical Sketch at the end of this book, they did considerable toward the creation of trigonometry, but they did not go far enough actually to solve the problems we are now considering. All this is astounding when we reflect on the hundreds of thousands of years that man has lived in this world.

6. How our ideas and our outlook have changed.—It is of course not pretended that the information we are describing is due solely, perhaps not even mainly, to the perfecting of trigonometry. But trigonometry has been indispensable. It has been as necessary as any important part of an automobile is to its success (the wheels, for example). Excellent instruments were equally necessary, instruments that cannot be made except where science and the mechanic arts are highly developed and where a need for them has become pressing.

Let us now look at the change that has been made possible through the subject we are about to study—a subject without which the change could not have come about. Primitive men, and some who had what we call a fairly highly developed civilization, thought of this earth as flat, a plain made for the abode of man. "The four corners of the earth" gave this view Biblical sanction. The moon and sun were small affairs—made to light us by night and by day. The early Greeks thought of the sun as carried across the sky daily by the sun god Helios (Apollo). The stars were minor affairs. The earth, the home of man, was the center of it all. Even in the middle ages there were fierce debates as to which was farther away from us, the moon or the sun.

What a contrast to our present outlook! The sun is now one of many billions of stars in our galaxy. Then beyond our galaxy there are millions of other galaxies, possibly as large as our own. From the point of view of our galaxy, our earth is a mere mote floating in almost vacant space, reflecting perhaps at times a faint gleam of that flood of light that our sun sheds over the vast ocean of empty space that surrounds it. On that mote, infinitesimal man lives his brief life.

Beyond a shadow of a doubt this vast change in our understanding of our surroundings and of ourselves must influence our lives profoundly. If we are intelligent, if we are curious to learn something about that which has influenced our lives so deeply and is daily so influencing them, we shall be interested to learn to understand one of the elements that has made this change possible. And especially we shall be interested to see how simple and elementary are the ideas that are involved.

It should be mentioned that some of the ancients, especially among the early Greeks, held views about the earth more like those we now hold.   They did believe the earth to be round, but their ideas about the moon, sun, planets, and stars were quite primitive.   Trigonometry existed only in rudimentary form, precision instruments for observation were not in existence, and these early correct ideas did not lead to that extension of observation and computation that were necessary definitely to overcome the crude ideas just described.   The result was that the rank and file held to these primitive beliefs for another two thousand years.

7. Measuring distances indirectly by using similar triangles.

Example 1.   This is a true story: Some boys undertook to find the distance across a lake without measuring it directly.   The lake was frozen over near their shore and they carried out their operations on the ice.   Their problem was to find the distance between A and B as shown in the figure.

At A and C they laid off right angles using a carpenter's square.   Then they stretched a string from A to C and sighted from D to B so that the points D, E, and B were in a straight line, as were also A, E, and C. The two right triangles DCE and BAE were now easily seen to be similar. The value of AB was found as shown at the right.   The lines

$$AB/AE = DC/CE$$
$$AB = AE \times DC/CE$$

(segments) AE, DC, and CE were then measured, and the length of AB was found by performing the computation indicated in the formula.

TOPICS FOR STUDY AND DISCUSSION

1. How is it known that the two triangles DCE and BAE are similar?

2. State the theorem in plane geometry used in the above indirect measurement.   See page 10.

3. Discuss the practical difficulty in getting the angles A and C exactly right angles.   How would you sight along the side of a square lying on the ice?

4. Why was a string stretched from A to C?   Describe fully how you would place the point E.

5. Suppose these boys found the distance from A to B to be 4767 feet. Would you feel certain that the distance was not 4800 feet or possibly 4750 feet?   Would you be certain that they were not wrong by 100 feet?   Would the result of their work be of any real practical importance?   Do you suppose these boys were anxious to know this distance or did they do this work simply as a "stunt"?   Did these boys proceed according to correct ideas?

Example 2. In the figure the points B and C lie on opposite sides of a mountain, and the lines AB and AC are on flat ground. The problem is to find the distance from B to C.

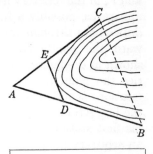

We know from geometry that if $AE/AC = AD/AB$, then the line DE is parallel to BC, and the triangles ADE and ABC are similar. Since C cannot be seen from B, we cannot measure the angle B and hence cannot lay off the angle D directly. However, we can measure AB, AC, and AD and compute AE and thus locate the line DE.

Then we compute BC by using the formula at the right.

$$AE/AC = AD/AB$$
$$AE = AC \times AD/AB$$

You will notice that this problem has been made simple by placing the long lines AB and AC on level ground. In practice this would usually not be

$$BC/DE = AB/AD$$
$$BC = DE \times AB/AD$$

the case and this simple method would be more difficult to use. However, the measurements and the placing of the points D and E would be less difficult than the operations in Example 1 on page 5. Note that in this example we do not need to lay off any angle equal to a given angle; without instruments this is a difficult thing to do when working in the field.

8. The plane-table.—The plane-table consists of a drawing board that can be mounted on a tripod and leveled or put in any desired slanting position. On top of this drawing board is placed an apparatus for sighting on a distant point, and a straightedge for drawing lines.

The plane-table, simple as it is, is a very effective instrument for mapping, and the results can be made so accurate that the errors are not visible to the eye on a map of ordinary size. The method of using it is as follows.

The operator sets up his table at a point (station) A (see figure on page 7), and marks a point on the drawing paper that is fastened to the board. He then selects points, as B, C, D, E, and F, in the territory he is mapping. By means of his sighting apparatus, possibly a little telescope, and the straight-edge he draws lines through the point A pointing in the directions toward the points B, C, etc., as shown in the figure. Then he carries the plane-table to the point (station) B and arranges it so that the line AB on his paper points to his first station. Then he selects an arbitrary point on this line and marks it B. This point will represent on his map the station at which he is now working. Then he draws lines through B in the directions toward C, D, E, and F. The points at which the lines meet will be the points on his map that represent the corresponding stations in the territory that he is mapping.

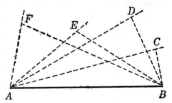

Note that not a single line or angle has been measured and still the resulting map is accurate—as accurate as is the accuracy of the drawing of the lines in the required directions. The accuracy of the map is due to the fact that the triangles in it are similar to the triangles formed by lines passing through the stations in the territory that correspond to the points on the map.

However, we do not yet know the scale of the map. To find that, we must measure the distance between two of the stations and the length of the corresponding line on the map. If the line AB on the map was taken two feet long and the distance between the stations A and B on the ground is 2000 feet, then the scale of the map is 1:1000. By measuring the distance between any two points on the map we can now find the distance between the corresponding stations in the territory represented by it. All we need to do is to use a simple proportion. However, the accuracy obtained by this method is far from satisfying the requirements of a high-grade survey.

TOPICS FOR STUDY AND DISCUSSION

1. What are the theorems from plane geometry that are used in Example 2 on page 6?

2. Discuss the use of the plane-table in constructing a map. How can the scale of this map be found? What theorem of geometry is involved in the making of this map?

9. Using the tape and the transit.—In measuring distances directly, the surveyor uses a steel tape, or chain, on which feet and inches are marked. The tape is usually 100 feet long. Care is taken to go in a straight line and to mark off sharply the end of each 100 feet as it is measured. When high accuracy is required, a distance may be measured several times and the average of the different measurements used.

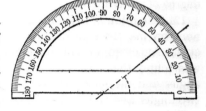

In making drawings a *protractor* may be used to lay off angles as shown in the figure. But for work in the field a much more elaborate instrument called a *transit*, or *theodolite*, is used. This instrument is equipped with a telescope for seeing distant objects more clearly, and admits of very easy and accurate measurement of angles. In fact, in surveying direct measuring of angles is very easy, while direct measurement of straight lines is very difficult. For this reason only a single line is measured directly even in a survey extending over hundreds of miles, while hundreds of angles are measured directly.

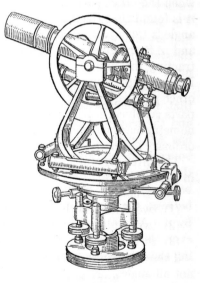

10. Units of angular measure.—For the purpose of surveying, the main unit of angle is the **degree,** which is one 90th of a right angle. A degree is divided into 60 equal parts called **minutes,** and a minute is divided into 60 equal parts called **seconds.** The word minute is derived from the Latin word *minutus* meaning little, and the word second is derived from two Latin words meaning "second minute" part, contracted into the one word "second." Degrees, minutes, and seconds are written °, ′, ″, respectively. Thus 47 degrees, 32 minutes, and 57 seconds is written 47°32′57″.

11. Need of additional theory.—Without the ideas, or theory, of similar triangles, the indirect measurements described on pages 5 to 7 would be impossible. Furthermore, the methods suggested there may lead to practical difficulties so great that desired accuracy is impossible. We will begin trigonometry proper by building up theories which will enable us to make these indirect measurements more easily and with a greater degree of accuracy.

12. The relation of geometry and trigonometry.—Plane trigonometry may be regarded as a direct extension of plane geometry. An example will make this clear: In plane geometry it was found that two triangles are equal if, for instance, two angles and the included side in one are equal, respectively, to two angles and the included side of the other.

This means that if in the triangle ABC, $\angle A$, $\angle B$, and side AB are fixed, then the whole triangle is fixed. Hence it should be possible to find $\angle C$, side AC, and side BC when the other parts are given. In geometry it is found that the sum of the angles of a triangle is 180° (two right angles). Hence if $\angle A$ and $\angle B$ are given, $\angle C$ can be found by subtracting the sum of $\angle A$ and $\angle B$ from 180°.

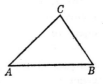

But geometry gives no method for finding AC and BC when the other parts are given. The problem of finding these unknown parts is solved in trigonometry. From this point of view trigonometry may be regarded as a series of devices by means of which ordinary geometry is made available for practical application.

The three general theorems on the equality of triangles found in geometry are:

Two triangles are equal if

(1) two sides and the included angles are equal, respectively,

(2) two angles and the included sides are equal, respectively,

(3) three sides are equal, respectively.

These theorems show that a triangle is fixed if three parts, not all angles, are given.[1]

The main problem related to the measurements of the triangle consists in finding formulas (rules) by means of which the unknown parts of a triangle may be computed when the known parts are sufficient to determine it.

---

[1] For a necessary modification of this statement, see page 76.

13. The theorems of geometry used in trigonometry.—The theorems of which immediate use is made are in part:

(1) If the angles of one triangle are equal, respectively, to the angles of another, the triangles are similar.

(2) If two triangles are similar, the corresponding sides form a proportion.

(3) The sum of the acute angles of a right triangle is equal to one right angle.

(4) If in a right triangle one angle is 30°, then the side opposite this angle is half the hypotenuse.

(5) If two angles of a triangle are equal, the sides opposite them are equal.

(6) The square of the hypotenuse of a right triangle is equal to the sum of the squares of the sides.

(7) The line from the vertex of an isosceles triangle to the middle point of the base is perpendicular to the base.

(8) If the two sides of an angle are perpendicular, respectively, to the two sides of another angle, then the angles are equal or supplementary.

(9) The square of a side opposite an acute angle of a triangle is equal to the sum of the squares of the other two sides, minus twice the product of one of these sides and the projection of the other one upon it.

(10) The square of a side opposite an obtuse angle of a triangle is equal to the sum of the squares of the other two sides plus twice the product of one of these sides and the projection of the other one upon it.

(11) The area of a triangle is equal to one-half of the product of its base and altitude.

(12) A tangent to a circle is perpendicular to the radius drawn to the point of tangency.

(13) An angle inscribed in a circle is measured by one-half the intercepted arc.

(14) A circle may be circumscribed about a regular polygon of any number of sides.

(15) Tangents to a circle from a point outside it are equal.

(16) The bisectors of the angles of a triangle intersect in the center of the inscribed circle.

(17) The perpendicular bisectors of the sides of a triangle intersect in the center of the circumscribed circle.

CHAPTER I

TRIGONOMETRIC FUNCTIONS OF ACUTE ANGLES

THE right triangle occurs in many problems, not only in pure mathematics, but also in applications in surveying and in the physical sciences. Since the angles of a right triangle, except the right angle, are acute we will begin our work with a study of acute angles.

14. The six trigonometric functions for acute angles.—Consider a given acute angle A. On either side of the angle, select any point B, and from B drop a perpendicular BC to the other side. In the right triangle thus formed, designate CB (the side opposite A) by a, AC (adjacent to A but opposite B) by b, and AB, the hypotenuse (opposite C), by c.

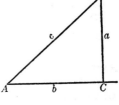

There are six ratios of these sides when taken in pairs, namely a/c, b/c, a/b, c/a, c/b, b/a. These are called, respectively, the **sine, cosine, tangent, cosecant, secant,** and **cotangent** of the angle A. The names of these ratios, also called trigonometric functions, are usually abbreviated, as shown in the following equations.

$$\sin A = \frac{\text{opposite side}}{\text{hypotenuse}} = \frac{a}{c} \quad [1] \qquad \csc A = \frac{\text{hypotenuse}}{\text{opposite side}} = \frac{c}{a} \quad [4]$$

$$\cos A = \frac{\text{adjacent side}}{\text{hypotenuse}} = \frac{b}{c} \quad [2] \qquad \sec A = \frac{\text{hypotenuse}}{\text{adjacent side}} = \frac{c}{b} \quad [5]$$

$$\tan A = \frac{\text{opposite side}}{\text{adjacent side}} = \frac{a}{b} \quad [3] \qquad \cot A = \frac{\text{adjacent side}}{\text{opposite side}} = \frac{b}{a} \quad [6]$$

Notice that these six functions are arranged in pairs so that in each pair either function is the reciprocal of the other. Thus in $\sin A = a/c$ and $\csc A = c/a$, each is the reciprocal of the other. Similarly $\cos A = b/c$ and $\sec A = c/b$ are reciprocals each of the other, as are also $\tan A = a/b$ and $\cot A = b/a$.

These functions are also called the **trigonometric ratios.**

11

15. Trigonometric functions depend on angles only.—In the figure take any two points B and B' on one side of the angle A and draw perpendiculars BC and $B'C'$ to the other side. Then the two triangles ABC and $AB'C'$ are similar right triangles; hence

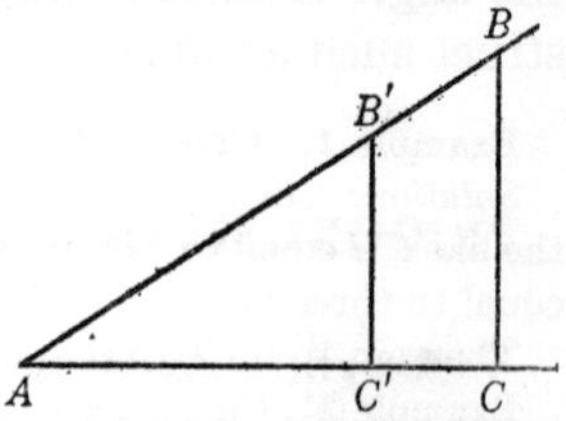

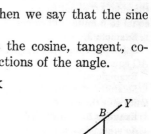

$$\sin A = CB/AB = C'B'/AB'$$

That is, the value of sin A does not depend upon the position of the perpendicular BC, but upon the size of the angle. This is what we mean when we say that the sine is a **function of** the angle.

In the same way we can see that the cosine, tangent, cotangent, secant, and cosecant are functions of the angle.

SIGHT WORK

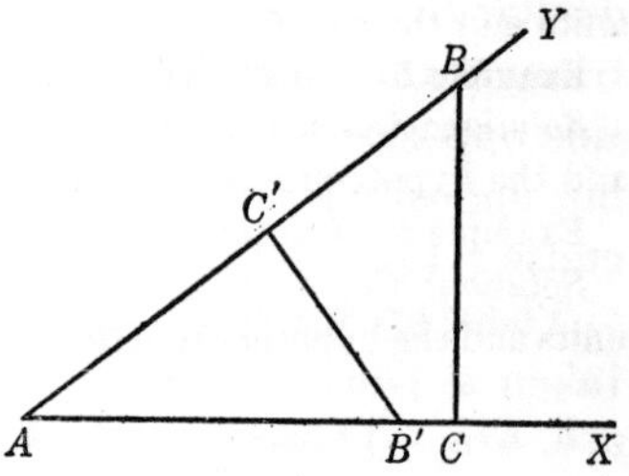

1. In the figure, BC is perpendicular to AX and $B'C'$ is perpendicular to AY. Then sin $A = CB/AB$ and also sin $A = C'B'/AB'$. Are these ratios equal?

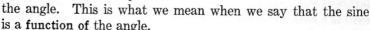

Suggestion: Are triangles ABC and $AB'C'$ similar?

(1) Do we obtain the same value for sin A no matter on which side of the angle the point B is taken? Why?

(2) Do we obtain the same value of cos A no matter on which side of the angle the point B is taken? Why?

(3) Ask and answer similar questions for tan A, cot A, sec A, csc A.

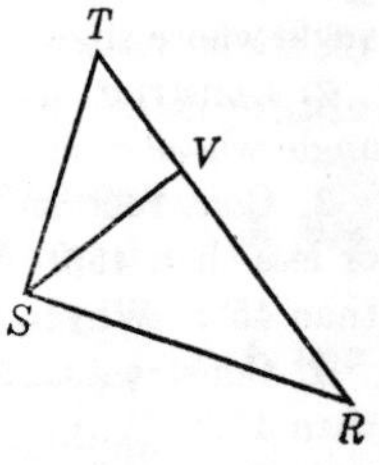

2. In the figure, $\angle RST = 1$ rt $\angle$ and $\angle SVT = 1$ rt $\angle$. Give the six functions of $\angle R$ in terms of RS, SV, and VR.

3. In the same figure give the six functions of $\angle T$ in terms of TS, SR, and RT and also in terms of TS, SV, and VT.

4. Give the six functions of $\angle VSR$.

5. Give the six functions of $\angle TSV$.

Using the figure at the right, show that $\angle A = \angle A'$ if any pair of the trigonometric functions are equal.

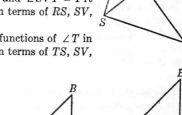

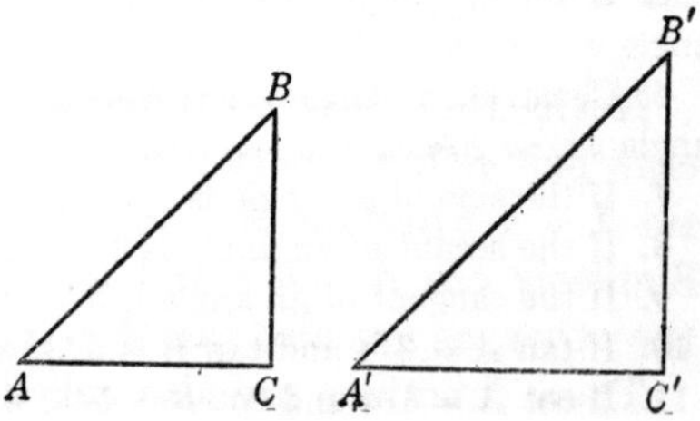

16. Construction of an acute angle having given one of its six functions.—If one of the six functions of an acute angle is given, the angle is thereby fixed and we shall now show how to construct such an angle.

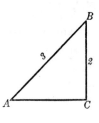

Example 1. Construct an angle whose sine is 2/3.
Solution: Construct a right triangle ABC, making the line CB equal to two units and the hypotenuse AB equal to three units.
Then $\sin A = CB/AB = 2/3$.

Example 2. Construct an angle whose cosine is 2/5.
Solution: Construct a right triangle ABC, making the side AC equal to 2 units and the hypotenuse AB equal to 5 units. Then $\cos A = AC/AB = 2/5$.

Example 3. Construct an angle whose tangent is 4/3.
Solution: Construct a right triangle ABC, making CB equal to 4 units and AC equal to 3 units. Then $\tan A = CB/AC = 4/3$.

Example 4. Construct an angle whose cotangent is 3/7.
Solution: Construct a right triangle ABC, making the side AC equal to 3 units and the side CB equal to 7 units. Then $\cot A = AC/CB = 3/7$.

Example 5. Construct an angle whose secant is 6/5.
Solution: Construct a right triangle ABC, making side AC equal to 5 units and the hypotenuse AB equal to 6 units. Then $\sec A = AB/AC = 6/5$.

Example 6. Construct an angle whose cosecant is 7/4.
Solution: Construct a right triangle ABC, making the side CB equal to 4 units and the hypotenuse AB equal to 7 units. Then $\csc A = AB/CB = 7/4$.

EXERCISES

1. Construct an angle whose sine is 3/7. Is it possible to construct an angle whose sine is 4/3? Why?

2. Construct an angle whose cosine is 3/4. Is it possible to construct an angle whose cosine is 4/3? Why?

3. Construct an angle whose tangent is 3/5. Is this angle greater than or less than 45°? Why? Is an angle whose tangent is 5/3 greater or less than 45°? Why?

4. Construct an angle whose cotangent is 4/3. Is this angle greater or less than 45°? Why?

5. Construct an angle whose secant is 7/3. Is it possible to construct an angle whose secant is less than 1? Why?

6. Construct an angle whose cosecant is 3/2. Is it possible to construct an angle whose cosecant is less than 1? Why?

7. If the sine of an angle is 3/5 what is its cosecant?

8. If the secant of an angle is 3/2 what is its cosine?

9. If the tangent of an angle is 5/3 what is its cotangent?

10. If $\tan A = 3/4$ and $\tan B = 5/3$, which is greater, A or B?

11. If $\cot A = 3/4$ and $\cot B = 5/3$, which is greater, A or B?

17. Cofunctions of complementary angles.

—Two angles are **complementary** if their sum is one right angle, or 90°. The two acute angles in a right triangle are complementary. That is, in the figure $\angle A$ is a complement of $\angle B$, and $\angle B$ is a complement of $\angle A$.

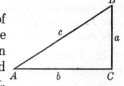

As suggested by the names, the cosine of an angle is called the **cofunction** of the sine of the angle. Similarly, the cotangent of an angle is the cofunction of the tangent and the cosecant is the cofunction of the secant. Reciprocally, the sine is the cofunction of the cosine, the tangent is the cofunction of the cotangent, and the secant is the cofunction of the cosecant.

Since in the above figure

$$\sin A = a/c = \cos B, \ \tan A = a/b = \cot B, \ \sec A = c/b = \csc B,$$

we have the general rule:

A function of an angle is the cofunction of the complement of the angle.

Hence we have,

$\sin A = \cos (90° - A)$, [7] $\cos A = \sin (90° - A)$, [8]
$\tan A = \cot (90° - A)$, [9] $\cot A = \tan (90° - A)$, [10]
$\sec A = \csc (90° - A)$, [11] $\csc A = \sec (90° - A)$. [12]

SIGHT WORK

In these exercises it is assumed that all angles are acute and that hence the rules obtained above apply.

1 If the sum of two angles is 90°, what is the relation between the sine of one of them and the cosine of the other?

2. If the tangent of one of two angles is equal to the cotangent of the other, what is the relation between these angles?

3. If the sum of two angles is 90°, what is the relation between the secant of one of them and the cosecant of the other?

4. Find the value of x if $\sin (2x - 20°) = \cos (3x + 10°)$.

Suggestion: Since $\sin (2x - 20°) = \cos (3x + 10°)$ it follows that $2x - 20° + 3x + 10° = 90°$.

5. Find A if $\sin A = \cos 3A$.

6. Find A if $\sin \frac{2}{3} A = \cos 2A$.

7. Find A if $\sec 4A = \csc 3A$.

8. Find x if $\tan (5x + 15°) = \cot (7x - 20°)$.

9. Find x if $\sec (2x + 40°) = \csc (5x - 30°)$.

10. Find A and B if $\sin A = \cos B$ and if $A - B = 20°$.
11. Find A and B if $\sin A = \cos 2B$ and if $B + 10° = A$.
12. Find A and B if $\tan 3A = \cot B$ and $A - B = 10°$.
13. Find A and B if $\cot (A + 10°) = \tan B$ and $A - B = 40°$.
14. Find A and B if $\tan (B - 20°) = \cot 5A$ and $4A - B = 25°$.
15. Find x and y if $\sec (x + 18°) = \csc (y + 40°)$ and $5x - 2y = 20°$.
16. Find x and y if $\csc (x - 50°) = \sec (y - 10°)$ and $x - y = 20°$.
17. Find x and y if $\sec (4x - 24°) = \csc (x - y + 18°)$ and $x + y = 48°$.

18. Functions of 30°, 45°, 60°.—If in the right triangle ABC, $\angle A = 45°$, then $\angle B = 45°$, and $AC = CB$. If $CB = a$, then $AB^2 = a^2 + a^2$, and $AB = a\sqrt{2}$.

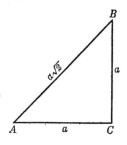

Hence $\sin 45° = \dfrac{a}{a\sqrt{2}} = \dfrac{1}{\sqrt{2}} = \frac{1}{2} \times \sqrt{2}$.

In the equilateral triangle $AB'B$, C is the middle point of $B'B$. Then using this figure, we have $\angle CAB = 30°$, $\angle B = 60°$.

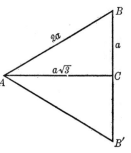

If $AB = 2a$, then $CB = a$, and $AC = a\sqrt{3}$. Then we have $\sin 30° = a/2a = 1/2$, $\cos 30° = a\sqrt{3}/2a = \sqrt{3}/2$. Also $\sin 60° = a\sqrt{3}/2a = \sqrt{3}/2$, $\cos 60° = a/2a = 1/2$.

19. Table of functions of 30°, 45°, 60°.—The following table will help in remembering sine, cosine, and tangent of 30°, 45°, 60°.

Angle	30°	45°	60°
Sine	$\frac{1}{2}$	$\frac{1}{2}\sqrt{2}$	$\frac{1}{2}\sqrt{3}$
Cosine	$\frac{1}{2}\sqrt{3}$	$\frac{1}{2}\sqrt{2}$	$\frac{1}{2}$
Tangent	$\frac{1}{3}\sqrt{3}$	1	$\sqrt{3}$

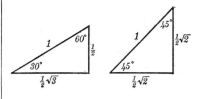

EXERCISE

Using the figure, show that the values given above are correct.

The sines may be remembered by noticing that for 30°, 45°, 60° they are in order 1/2 of $\sqrt{1}$, of $\sqrt{2}$, of $\sqrt{3}$; or $\sqrt{1}/2$, $\sqrt{2}/2$, $\sqrt{3}/2$. The cosines of these angles are the same numbers with the order reversed. The tangent may be remembered by noticing that $\sqrt{3} = \tan 60°$, while $\frac{1}{3}\sqrt{3} = \tan 30°$.

20. Approximate, or rounded, numbers.—If we count a small number of objects we get an exact number. Thus we can find the exact number of people in a room or the exact number of dollars in a cash drawer. In counting a very large number of objects we are in some cases not so certain. Thus the 1930 U. S. Census gives the number of people in the United States as 122,775,046. Clearly the number at any one instant of time is not known within many thousands. While the census was being taken scores of thousands were born and other scores of thousands died. Still other scores of thousands were missed by the enumerators, and some may have been counted twice. To the nearest thousand the population was 122,775,000; to the nearest ten thousand it was 122,780,000; and to the nearest hundred thousand, 122,800,000. In 122,800,000 the number is "rounded" to four figures, in 122,780,000 it is rounded to five figures.

In measuring and weighing, the results are always approximate. Thus a piece of steel may be found to be 8.473 inches long. This means simply that we assert we know that the length is certainly as near 8.473 inches as it is to either 8.472 inches or 8.474 inches. The number expressing the actual length may be regarded as rounded to 8.473.

21. Significant part of a number.—If we omit all zeros at the beginning and end of a number, then the remaining figures are usually regarded as the significant part of the number. Thus 12278 is the significant part in 122,780,000 if this number is regarded as the nearest approximation in ten thousands. On the other hand, in 470 the zero is significant if it is intended to assert that this number is correct to the nearest unit; that is, if we wish to assert that the number is greater than or equal to 469.5 and less than 470.5.

In a table the final zeros are always significant, since it is asserted that the figures are correct to the last decimal shown. In any decimal the last figures should be intended to be significant and hence all zeros at the end should be significant.

In recording large measurements that cannot be accurate, the final zeros are not significant. In such cases it is usually stated that the error is a certain amount or a certain fraction of the amount measured. Unless it is clear from the context or from an explicit statement that a final zero in a whole number is significant, it should be regarded as not significant.

22. Operating with rounded numbers.—Suppose the dimensions of a room are given as 17.8 feet by 26.3 feet. If w is the width and l is the length of the room, then the record of these measurements asserts that the width is greater than 17.75 and less than 17.85 ($17.75 < w < 17.85$) and l is greater than 26.25 and less than 26.35 ($26.25 < l < 26.35$).

The products as given at the right show that the area is, say, between 466 and 471.

$$17.75 \times 26.25 < wl < 17.85 \times 26.35$$
$$465.9375 < wl < 470.3475$$

If we multiply the numbers as they stand we get 468.14, which we may round off to 468. This shows that a

$$17.8 \times 26.3 = 468.14$$

product of two numbers rounded to 3 figures may be rounded fairly safely to 3 figures.

In operating with rounded numbers the following rules may be used.

The sum of rounded numbers should be rounded to the number of decimals contained in the number having the smallest number of decimals in the numbers added.

To multiply two approximate numbers with the same number of significant figures round off the product so it will have the same number of significant figures as the factors. If the factors have different numbers of significant figures, round off the one with the larger number so it will have the same number as the smaller. If one of two factors is exact and the other rounded, round off the product to the same number of significant figures as the rounded factor.

To divide rounded numbers having the same number of significant figures round the quotient to this number of significant figures. If the dividend and divisor do not have the same number of significant figures, round off one of them so these numbers will be equal.

When we work with numbers rounded to three figures we say we have three-place accuracy; when we work with numbers rounded to four figures, we have four-place accuracy, and so on. When working with angles, three-place accuracy corresponds to an accuracy within 5 minutes of angle, four-place accuracy corresponds to accuracy within 1 minute of angle, and five-place to accuracy within 5 seconds of angle.

23. Finding trigonometric functions from a graph.—In the ruled quarter circle below the radius is 100 small units. If the radius is regarded as the unit, the small spaces will represent .01, and the horizontal and vertical distances can then be read roughly to the nearest thousandth.

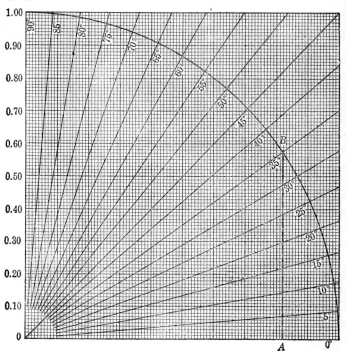

Consider the angle 35° (*AOB*) that is marked in the figure. The sine of this angle is *AB* ÷ *OB*. But *OB* = 1. Hence the sine is *AB*. It appears from the figure that *AB* = 0.573 or possibly 0.574. It also appears that *OA* = 0.818 very nearly. From the table on page 25 you may find that, correct to three places of decimals, these values are as shown at the right. You see that in case of the sine the reading of the graph gave

$$\sin 35° = 0.574 \text{ (graph)}$$
$$\sin 35° = 0.574 \text{ (table)}$$

$$\cos 35° = 0.818 \text{ (graph)}$$
$$\cos 35° = 0.819 \text{ (table)}$$

a result correct to three decimals and that the cosine was one off in the last place.

EXERCISE

1. Using the above figure, make a table of sines and cosines for 5°, 10°, 15°, 20°, . . . Then check your results against the table on page 25.

CHAPTER II

SOLUTION OF RIGHT TRIANGLES BY MEANS OF NATURAL FUNCTIONS

WE KNOW from geometry that a right triangle is determined by any two elements besides the right angle, provided at least one of them is a side.

Thus, the right triangle ABC with sides a, b, c is determined by each of the pairs of elements: a, b; a, c; b, c; a, $\angle A$; b, $\angle A$; c, $\angle A$; etc. (Notice that the triangle is not determined by $\angle A$, $\angle B$.) We shall now obtain formulas by means of which the remaining parts of a right triangle may be computed when enough parts are given to determine it.

24. An illustrative problem.—In order to show how some of the ideas already developed may apply to a practical situation, consider the problem of finding the height (CB in the figure) to which a rod (AB) 22 feet long will reach up a vertical wall, if it is known that the rod makes an angle ($\angle CAB$) of 35° with the horizontal line AC.

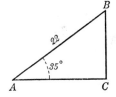

From the definitions on page 11, we have
$$\sin 35° = CB/AB = CB/22$$

Therefore, $CB = 22 \sin 35°$
From page 18, $\sin 35° = .574$, hence $CB = 22 \times .574 = 12.628$ (feet).

Note that .574 is greater than .5735 and less than .5745. Hence we know that the true product lies between $22 \times .5735 = 12.617$ and $22 \times .5745 = 12.639$. Hence we are fairly safe in saying that $CB = 12.62$. Certainly $CB = 12.628$ states more than we know, and if rounded to 12.63 is not our best value. That is, the four-figure number gives a better answer than the five-figure number.

19

25. Selection of formulas.—The work of computing may be reduced to a minimum by the proper selection of formulas. Unless logarithms are used (see page 33), care should be taken to obtain formulas which require multiplication rather than division, since the latter operation is more laborious. This is illustrated below.

All formulas used in finding unknown parts of a right triangle are obtained from the fundamental relations:

(1) $\sin A = a/c$,   (2) $\cos A = b/c$

(3) $\tan A = a/b$,   (4) $\csc A = c/a$

(5) $\sec A = c/b$,   (6) $\cot A = b/a$

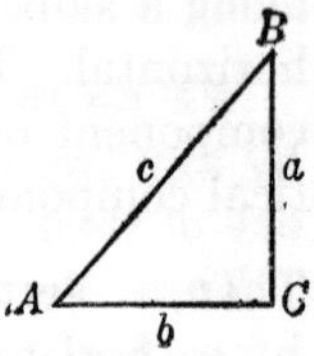

To find a we notice that it is contained in (1), (3), (4), and (6) above and we have

(1) $a = c \sin A$ (2) $a = b \tan A$

(3) $a = c/\csc A$ (4) $a = b/\cot A$

Here we use (1) rather than (3) and (2) rather than (4), since (1) and (2) lead to multiplication, while (3) and (4) lead to division.

Again b is contained in (2), (3), (5), and (6) above, and we find

(1) $b = c \cos A$ (2) $b = a/\tan A$

(3) $b = c/\sec A$ (4) $b = a \cot A$

Here we use (1) rather than (3) and (4) rather than (2).

Finally, c is contained in (1), (2), (4), and (5) above and we find

(1) $c = a/\sin A$ (2) $c = b/\cos A$

(3) $c = a \csc A$ (4) $c = b \sec A$

Here we would use (3) rather than (1), and (4) rather than (2). However, secants and cosecants are usually not given in the tables, since these are the reciprocals of the cosine and the sine, respectively. Hence, if we are not using logarithms, we are compelled to carry out the long divisions by numbers containing several figures. This shows one of the important advantages in using logarithms. (See page 33.)

The above are the formulas that you will actually use in practice. However, as you become acquainted with your subject you will see them directly from the definitions and you will not need to remember them.

26. Formulas in frequent use.—The two formulas

$a = c \sin A$ (side opposite = hypotenuse × sine)
$b = c \cos A$ (side adjacent = hypotenuse × cosine)

are in frequent use in the further study of trigonometry and also in its applications in surveying and in mechanical problems.

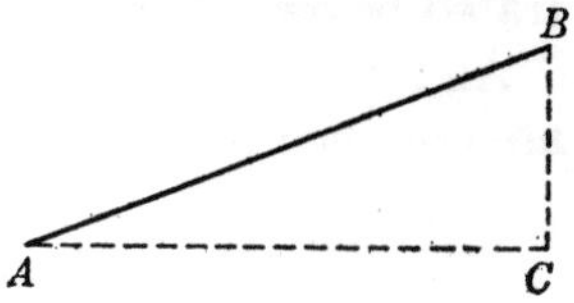

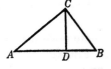

Suppose that in the figure, AB lies along a slope of a hill and that AC is horizontal. Then AC is the horizontal component of AB and CB is the vertical component, while $\angle A$ is the incline.

Then,   vertical component = length × sine of incline,
         horizontal component = length × cosine of incline.

The tangent of A is the **slope** of the line.

SIGHT WORK

1. State each of the following formulas in words.

(1) $a = c \sin A$,   (2) $a = b \tan A$,   (3) $b = c \cos A$
(4) $b = a \cot A$,   (5) $c = a \csc A$,   (6) $c = b \sec A$

(1) may be stated thus: *The side opposite either acute angle of a right triangle equals the hypotenuse times the sine of that angle.*

In the figure the triangles ABC, ADC, and BDC, are right angled. In each of the following give the most convenient formula for finding the part required.

	Given	Required		Given	Required
2.	$\angle A, AD$	DC	**17.**	$\angle A, DC$	AD
3.	$\angle B, BD$	DC	**18.**	$\angle ACD, AC$	AD
4.	$\angle ACD, AD$	DC	**19.**	$\angle DCB, CB$	CD
5.	$\angle DCB, CD$	DB	**20.**	$\angle A, AC$	AD
6.	$\angle A, AB$	AC	**21.**	$\angle B, BC$	BD
7.	$\angle B, AC$	AB	**22.**	$\angle B, AB$	AC
8.	$\angle DCB, DB$	CD	**23.**	$\angle A, AD$	AC
9.	$\angle A, AC$	CB	**24.**	$\angle ACD, AD$	AC
10.	$\angle B, BC$	AB	**25.**	$\angle B, BD$	BC
11.	$\angle ACD, CD$	AD	**26.**	$\angle DCB, CD$	BC
12.	$\angle B, DC$	BD	**27.**	$\angle A, AB$	CB
13.	$\angle A, CB$	AC	**28.**	$\angle B, AC$	CB
14.	AC, BC	$\tan A$	**29.**	DB, DC	$\tan B$
15.	AB, AC	$\cos A$	**30.**	DB, BC	$\cos B$
16.	AC, BC	$\cot A$	**31.**	BC, CD	$\cos \angle DCB$

27. Use of tables in computing.—In solving triangles by means of the trigonometric functions, use is made of tables giving these functions for various angles. Such tables have been worked out for every minute of angle from 0° to 90° and in some cases for every second of angle.

Part of such a table is given here.

Angle	Sin	Cos	Tan	Cot	Sec	Csc
30°	.5000	.8660	.5774	1.7321	1.1547	2.0000
31°	.5150	.8572	.C009	1.6643	1.1666	1.9416
32°	.5299	.8480	.6249	1.6003	1.1792	1.8871
33°	.5446	.8387	.6494	1.5399	1.1924	1.8361
34°	.5592	.8290	.6745	1.4826	1.2062	1.7883
35°	.5736	.8192	.7002	1.4281	1.2208	1.7434
36°	.5878	.8090	.7265	1.3764	1.2361	1.7013
37°	.6018	.7986	.7536	1.3270	1.2521	1.6616
38°	.6157	.7880	.7813	1.2799	1.2690	1.6243
39°	.6293	.7771	.8098	1.2349	1.2868	1.5890

The first column to the left in the table indicates the number of degrees in the angle. The next column gives the sines of these angles, and the next gives the cosines, and so on.

The use of these tables may be illustrated by means of examples:

Example 1. Find sin 32°, cos 35°, tan 37°, cot 38°.

Solution: To find the sin 32° we look in the column headed Sin and in the line in which 32° stands and find the number .5299. Hence sin 32° = .5299. Similarly, we find cos 35° = .8192, tan 37° = .7536, and cot 38° = 1.2799.

Example 2. If $\angle A = 38°$ and $c = 17$, find a.

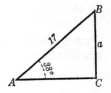

Solution: Since sin $A = a/c$, we obtain
$a = c \times \sin A = 17 \times \sin A$.
We now find in the table that sin 38° = .6157.
Hence $a = 17 \times .6157 = 10.4669$.

Example 3. If $\angle A = 31°$ and $c = 25$, find b.

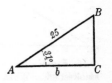

Solution: Since cos $A = b/c$ we have $b = c \times \cos A$, and hence $b = 25 \times .8572 = 21.43$.

Example 4. If $\angle A = 34°$ and $b = 12$, find c.

Solution: Since sec $A = \dfrac{c}{b}$, we have $c = b \times \sec A = 12 \times 1.2062 = 14.474$.

28. Approximate character of tables and results.—With very few exceptions the numbers given in tables such as the one on page 22 are approximations. Sin 30° = .5 exactly and csc 30° = 2 exactly, but all the other numbers given in this table are approximations. Hence most of the results obtained by using such a table are only approximately correct; the closeness of the approximations depends upon the number of decimals in the table.

The following Example shows another kind of approximation which is of importance in trigonometry.

Example. Find the angle A to the nearest degree if sin A = .5774.

Solution: Since sin 35° = .5736 and sin 36° = .5878, it follows that angle A lies between 35° and 36°. Further, since .5774 is nearer to .5736 than it is to .5878, we conclude that $\angle A$ is nearer 35° than 36°. Hence $\angle A$ to the nearest degree is 35°.

Later we shall learn to compute angles to the nearest minute and in some cases even to the nearest second.

EXERCISES

In the following exercises find the length of lines to the nearest one-hundredth. Each example refers to this figure. The given lengths are to be regarded as exact.

1. $\angle A$ = 31°, c = 18, find a.
2. $\angle A$ = 37°, c = 24, find b.
3. $\angle A$ = 38°, a = 65, find b.
4. $\angle A$ = 35°, a = 42, find c.

5. $\angle A$ = 39°, b = 16, find a.
6. $\angle A$ = 33°, b = 38, find c.
7. $\angle A$ = 34°, c = 3.4, find a.
8. $\angle A$ = 32°, a = 1.34, find c.

In the following six examples find the required angle to the nearest degree.

9. a = 13, b = 19, find $\angle A$.
10. a = 34, b = 28, find $\angle B$.
11. a = 36, c = 56, find $\angle A$.

12. a = 39, c = 46, find $\angle B$.
13. b = 65, c = 81, find $\angle A$.
14. b = 5.7, c = 9.2, find $\angle B$.

15. To find the height of a tree CB the line CA is measured, and also the angle CAB. Find the height if $\angle ACB$ = 90°, CA = 135 feet, and $\angle A$ = 31°.

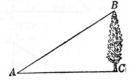 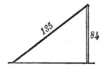 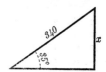

16. From a point 84 feet above the ground a steel cable is fastened to a smokestack. What angle does this rope make with the ground if it is 135 feet long?

17. A boy's kite string is 340 feet long and makes an angle of 35° with the ground. Find the vertical height of the kite.

29. Finding functions of angles up to 45°.—The table on the page opposite gives four trigonometric functions for every degree of angle between 0° and 90°. The larger tables that will finally be used in practice give the functions for every minute of angle. However, the essential points to be mastered are the same in those tables as in the briefer one given here. (See Tables, pages 74–91.)

For all the angles up to 45° the number of degrees is indicated in the first column to the left. The functions sine, cosine, tangent, cotangent occur in columns in order from left to right. For example, to find cot 37° we look down the left column to 37° and then across the page to the column headed Cot at the top. That is, cot 37° = 1.3270.

30. Finding functions of angles between 45° and 90°.—For angles between 45° and 90° the number of degrees is given in the column to the right of the page. The column containing sines of angles less than 45° contains cosines of angles greater than 45°. Thus sin 40° is the cosine of 50°. The columns of tangents and cotangents are similarly related. This follows from the fact that *cofunctions of complementary angles are equal.* (See page 14.) The column marked Sin above is marked Cos below, the one marked Cos above is marked Sin below, and the same for Tan and Cot.

Thus, tan 65° = cot 25°, sin 72° = cos 18°, etc.

SIGHT WORK

From the table on page 25 find:

1. sin 13°.	6. cos 29°.	11. cos 57°.	16. cot 17°.
2. cos 42°.	7. cot 81°.	12. tan 54°.	17. sin 38°.
3. sin 63°.	8. tan 67°.	13. cot 39°.	18. sin 68°.
4. tan 42°.	9. cos 79°.	14. cos 63°.	19. tan 18°.
5. sin 17°.	10. sin 84°.	15. tan 45°.	20. cot 10°.

Find the angle *A* to the nearest degree for each of the following.

21. sin A = .4846.	26. cot A = 1.9820.	31. cot A = 2.6420.
22. cos A = .3942.	27. tan A = .3902.	32. tan A = 1.9364.
23. tan A = 1.2782.	28. cot A = .9372.	33. cot A = 2.5628.
24. cot A = 1.6710.	29. sin A = .7381.	34. tan A = 2.14202.
25. tan A = 1.4920.	30. cos A = .7381.	35. sin A = .1948.

Using the table, compare the following and explain.

36. sin 63°, cos 27°.	38. tan 41°, cot 49°.	40. cot 13°, tan 77°.
37. cos 35°, sin 55°.	39. cot 33°, tan 57°.	41. tan 34°, cot 56°.

TABLE OF SINES, COSINES, AND TANGENTS

Angle	Sin	Cos	Tan	Cot	Angle
1°	.0175	.9998	.0175	57.2900	89°
2°	.0349	.9994	.0349	28.6363	88°
3°	.0523	.9986	.0524	19.0811	87°
4°	.0698	.9976	.0699	14.3007	86°
5°	.0872	.9962	.0875	11.4301	85°
6°	.1045	.9945	.1051	9.5144	84°
7°	.1219	.9925	.1228	8.1443	83°
8°	.1392	.9903	.1405	7.1154	82°
9°	.1564	.9877	.1584	6.3138	81°
10°	.1736	.9848	.1763	5.6713	80°
11°	.1908	.9816	.1944	5.1446	79°
12°	.2079	.9781	.2126	4.7046	78°
13°	.2250	.9744	.2309	4.3315	77°
14°	.2419	.9703	.2493	4.0108	76°
15°	.2588	.9659	.2679	3.7321	75°
16°	.2756	.9613	.2867	3.4874	74°
17°	.2924	.9563	.3057	3.2709	73°
18°	.3090	.9511	.3249	3.0777	72°
19°	.3256	.9455	.3443	2.9042	71°
20°	.3420	.9397	.3640	2.7475	70°
21°	.3584	.9336	.3839	2.6051	69°
22°	.3746	.9272	.4040	2.4751	68°
23°	.3907	.9205	.4245	2.3559	67°
24°	.4067	.9135	.4452	2.2460	66°
25°	.4226	.9063	.4663	2.1445	65°
26°	.4384	.8988	.4877	2.0503	64°
27°	.4540	.8910	.5095	1.9626	63°
28°	.4695	.8829	.5317	1.8807	62°
29°	.4848	.8746	.5543	1.8040	61°
30°	.5000	.8660	.5774	1.7321	60°
31°	.5150	.8572	.6009	1.6643	59°
32°	.5299	.8480	.6249	1.6003	58°
33°	.5446	.8387	.6494	1.5399	57°
34°	.5592	.8290	.6745	1.4826	56°
35°	.5736	.8192	.7002	1.4281	55°
36°	.5878	.8090	.7265	1.3764	54°
37°	.6018	.7986	.7536	1.3270	53°
38°	.6157	.7880	.7813	1.2799	52°
39°	.6293	.7771	.8098	1.2349	51°
40°	.6428	.7660	.8391	1.1918	50°
41°	.6561	.7547	.8693	1.1504	49°
42°	.6691	.7431	.9004	1.1106	48°
43°	.6820	.7314	.9325	1.0724	47°
44°	.6947	.7193	.9657	1.0355	46°
45°	.7071	.7071	1.0000	1.0000	45°
Angle	Cos	Sin	Cot	Tan	Angle

31. Variation of trigonometric functions.—For some purposes it is important to notice how the trigonometric functions change as the angle changes. By looking at the table on page 25 it may be seen that as the angle increases from 1° to 89° the sine increases from .0175 to .9998. So we say that the sine is an **increasing** function of the angle. Moreover, the sine increases more rapidly when the angle is small. Thus, when the angle changes from 1° to 2° the sine increases from .0175 to .0349, or by the amount .0174. But when the angle increases from 88° to 89° the sine increases from .9994 to .9998, or by the amount .0004.

In the same way we find that the tangent is also an increasing function, but that it increases more rapidly as the angle grows larger. Thus when the angle increases from 1° to 2° the tangent increases by .0174; but when the angle increases from 88° to 89° the tangent increases by 28.6537. When the angle increases from 89° toward 90° the tangent grows large beyond all bounds. For a more complete treatment of this point, see page 117.

Again looking at the table on page 25 we see that the cosine grows smaller as the angle increases, the cosine of 1° being .9998 and the cosine of 89° being .0175. That is, the cosine is a **decreasing** function of the angle. When the angle is near zero, the cosine decreases very slowly, and then decreases more rapidly as the angle grows larger. Compare the decrease between 1° and 2° and between 88° and 89°.

32. Interpolation.—The meaning of this word will be made clear by means of examples:

Example 1. Using the table on page 25 find the value of sin 43° 30′.

From the table we find sin 44° and 43° as shown at the right. For the purpose of subtracting we place sin 44° above sin 43°. The difference is .0127, which is the amount by which the sine changes as the angle changes from 43° to 44°. Since 43° 30′ is half way from 43° to 44°, we assume that the sine is half way from sin 43° to sin 44°. So we find half the difference and add it to sin 43°, which gives .6884 as the sine of 43° 30′. We say we find sin 43° 30′ by *interpolating* (placing between) between sin 43° and sin 44°.

sin 44° =	.6947
sin 43° =	.6820
Difference =	.0127
Half diff. =	.0064
sin 43° 30′ =	.6884

The correctness of sin 43° 30′ thus obtained may be checked by turning to page 90 of the Tables, where sin 43° 30′ is given to five places as .68835.

Example 2. Find sin 43° 15′. The process is exactly the same as in Example 1 except that now we take ¼ of the difference and add it to sin 43°. On page 90 of the Tables we find that sin 43°15′ = .68518, which is correct to five places. Hence, again interpolation gives the result correct to four places.

To find sin 43° 45′ we add ¾ of the difference to sin 43°. To find sin 43° 10′ we add ⅙ of the difference, and so on.

Example 3. Find cos 27° 50′.

Find cos 27° and cos 28° as shown at the right. Since the cosine decreases we put the cosine of the smaller angle first. Since 50′ is ⅚ the way from 27° to 28° we take ⅚ of the difference between cos 27° and cos 28°, and then *subtract* this from cos 27°. We subtract because the cosine decreases as the angle goes from 27° to 28°. Check the result by comparing with cos 27° 50′, page 84 of the Tables.

Example 4. Find A if sin A = .5894. From the table we find that .5894 lies between sin 36° and sin 37°. The difference between these is .0140. The difference between sin 36° and sin A is .0016. Hence A lies .0016/.0140 or 4/35 the distance from 36° to 37°. That is $\angle A$ is 4/35 of one degree greater than 36°. But 4/35 of 1° is 4/35 × 60 minutes or 6.9′. So we find that $\angle A$ = 36° 7′, correct to the nearest minute. Check the result by comparing sin 36° 7′ on page 88 of the Tables. Is 36° 7′ too large or too small?

sin 44°	= .6947
sin 43°	= .6820
Diff.	= .0127
¼ of diff.	= .0032
sin 43° 15′	= .6852

cos 27°	= .8910
cos 28°	= .8829
Diff.	= .0081
⅚ of diff.	= .0067
cos 27° 50′	= .8843

sin 37°	= .6018
sin 36°	= .5878
Diff.	= .0140
sin A	= .5894
sin 36°	= .5878
Diff.	= .0016
4/35 × 60	= 6.9
A = 36° 7′	

EXERCISES

Find the following by interpolating in the table on page 25.

1. sin 21° 30′	7. cos 37° 10′	13. sin 17° 10′
2. sin 14° 15′	8. cos 58° 50′	14. cos 39° 50′
3. sin 64° 45′	9. tan 24° 30′	15. tan 54° 45′
4. sin 81° 35′	10. tan 63° 50′	16. cos 70° 50′
5. cos 64° 30′	11. tan 76° 15′	17. cot 2° 20′
6. cos 18° 15′	12. tan 83° 50′	18. tan 85° 50′

Find the angle A to the nearest minute.

19. sin A = .3479	25. cos A = .3842	31. tan A = .6714
20. sin A = .4996	26. cos A = .4348	32. tan A = 1.2626
21. sin A = .7387	27. cos A = .7290	33. tan A = 4.1048
22. sin A = .8492	28. cos A = .8126	34. tan A = 6.2987
23. cot A = 1.3926	29. sec A = .3104	35. cot A = 0.1472
24. tan A = 0.1317	30. cot A = 2.4102	36. cos A = 0.1472

33. Solving a triangle.—Solving a triangle consists in finding the numerical measures of the parts not given. The method has been shown in various examples on page 20, when the part to be found is indicated. When more than one part is required, attention should be paid to the form of procedure. Consider the solution of the following example.

Example. Solve the triangle ABC, given $A = 62°$, $b = 75.31$, $C = 90°$.

Solution: $\tan A = \dfrac{a}{b},$ $\qquad\qquad\qquad \cos A = \dfrac{b}{c}$

Hence $\quad a = b \tan A$ $\qquad\qquad\qquad c = \dfrac{b}{\cos A}$

Substituting $a = 75.31 \times 1.8807 = 141.64$ $\qquad c = \dfrac{75.31}{.4695}$

$$c = 160.40$$

These results are very nearly correct to four *significant* digits. We may check by the relation $a^2 + b^2 = c^2$.

$$\begin{aligned} a^2 &= 141.6^2 = 20050.6 \\ b^2 &= 75.31^2 = \underline{5671.6} \\ a^2 + b^2 &= 25722.2 \\ c^2 &= 25728.2 \end{aligned}$$

This shows approximately a check to the expected four places.

With a five-place table these results are $a = 141.64$, $c = 160.41$, which shows the closeness obtained by using a four-place table.

EXERCISES

In each of the following solve the right triangle ABC, with sides a, b, c, if $\angle C$ is the right angle. Use the table on page 25. Assume that the measures given for the sides are exact; find the unknown sides to four significant digits.

1. $a = 8$,	$b = 12$		13. $b = 5.35$,	$B = 17°$
2. $a = 29$,	$b = 17$		14. $b = 254$,	$B = 59°$
3. $a = 62$,	$c = 75$		15. $c = 92.2$,	$A = 42°$
4. $a = 15$,	$c = 50$		16. $c = 7.53$,	$A = 71°$
5. $a = 28$,	$A = 46°$		17. $c = 8.05$,	$B = 57°$
6. $a = 3.15$,	$A = 68°$		18. $c = 54.6$,	$B = 38°$
7. $a = 0.93$,	$B = 14°$		19. $A = 52°$,	$b = 17.4$
8. $a = 7.85$,	$B = 74°$		20. $B = 31°$,	$c = 62.8$
9. $b = 92$,	$c = 180.6$		21. $a = 37.1$,	$c = 87.2$
10. $b = 3.6$,	$c = 7.8$		22. $b = 5.22$,	$c = 17.4$
11. $b = 8.4$,	$A = 53°$		23. $a = 8.04$,	$B = 43°$
12. $b = 35.8$,	$A = 81°$		24. $B = 27°$,	$b = 54.7$

34. Use of a more extended table.—On pages 74 to 91 of the set of Tables values are given of the sine, cosine, tangent and cotangent for every minute of angle, from 1° to 90°. This permits the use of more accurate data and insures more accurate results when used in the solution of triangles. An example will be solved to show how the table may be used:

Example. Solve the right triangle ABC, if $A = 19° 35'$, $c = 31.70$, and $C = 90°$.
Solution:

$$\sin A = \frac{a}{c} \qquad\qquad \cos A = \frac{b}{c}$$

$$
\begin{aligned}
a &= c \sin A & b &= c \cos A \\
&= 31.70 \times .33518 & &= 31.70 \times .94215 \\
&= 10.625 & &= 29.866
\end{aligned}
$$

These results are almost certainly correct to four significant figures; they may be checked by the relation $a^2 + b^2 = c^2$. The point to be noted is that the values of sin 19° 35' and cos 19° 35' are found directly from the table.

When one of the parts to be found is an angle, the result may be obtained directly from the table to the nearest minute.

Example. In $\triangle ABC$, $a = 71.84$, $b = 62.25$, $C = 90°$. Find A.
Solution:

$$\tan A = \frac{a}{b} = \frac{71.84}{62.25} = 1.1541, \text{ nearly}$$

From page 91, tan 49° 5' = 1.1538
               tan 49° 6' = 1.1544

Hence A is almost exactly halfway between 49° 5' and 49° 6', slightly closer to 49° 5'.

EXERCISES

Solve the right triangle ABC with $C = 90°$, other parts as shown. Make use of the more elaborate table of natural functions. Compute angles to the nearest minute, sides correct to four significant digits.

1. $a = 8.57,$	$A = 58° 12'$		**11.** $b = 120.05,$	$B = 68° 47'$
2. $a = 176.1,$	$B = 76° 42'$		**12.** $b = 0.1860,$	$A = 21° 12'$
3. $c = 1815,$	$A = 29° 5'$		**13.** $c = 2.15,$	$B = 67° 1'$
4. $a = 272.3,$	$b = 159.4$		**14.** $b = 267.5,$	$a = 127.8$
5. $b = 763.7,$	$c = 892.5$		**15.** $a = 763,$	$c = 972$
6. $b = 1.131,$	$A = 50° 37'$		**16.** $a = 21.31,$	$B = 82° 9'$
7. $a = 256.0,$	$c = 763.3$		**17.** $b = 0.0132,$	$c = 0.0275$
8. $c = 21.52,$	$B = 81° 38'$		**18.** $c = 7284,$	$A = 5° 21'$
9. $b = 0.01317,$	$B = 36° 11'$		**19.** $a = 118.21,$	$A = 46° 58'$
10. $c = 11.113,$	$A = 18° 41'$		**20.** $c = 2773.5,$	$B = 70° 40'$

35. Angles of elevation and of depression.—In many problems in practical measuring, the angle between a horizontal line and a line from the observer to an elevated (or depressed) object is measured.

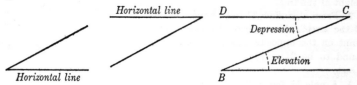

If in the last figure the observer is at B, then he measures the angle of elevation of the point C, and if he stands at C, then he measures the angle of depression of B.

Angles of elevation and angles of depression occur frequently in practical surveying. Thus, the height of a tree, of a building, or of a mountain may be obtained by finding its angle of elevation from a given point, when certain additional data are also known or may be found without ascending the object whose height is to be measured.

Similarly, the depth of a canyon may be measured by an observer standing above it at a point from which the bottom of the canyon may be seen by simply measuring the angle of depression from the point where he is standing and obtaining certain other data which can be found without descending the canyon. For this problem, see example 7, page 183.

36. The solution of problems.—When a trigonometric problem is given in story form, the first step in the solution is to construct a figure. The manner in which the principles of trigonometry may then be applied will become evident.

Example. From the top of a tower 221 feet high, the angle of depression of an object on the horizontal plane through the foot of the tower is found to be 28° 55′. Find the distance from the foot of the tower to the object.

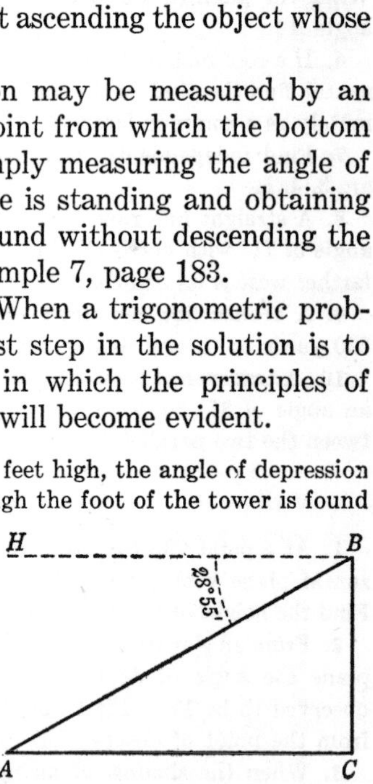

Solution: In the figure let CB represent the tower, A the position of the object. Then HBA is the angle of depression. Evidently,

$$\angle A = HBA = 28°\ 55'.$$

Then we have,

$$\tan 28°\ 55' = \frac{221}{AC}, \qquad AC = \frac{221}{\tan 28°\ 55'} = \frac{221}{.5524} = 400.1\ \text{ft.}$$

PROBLEMS: GROUP A

1. At a point 175 feet from the base of a tree and in the same horizontal plane with its base, the angle of elevation of the top is 38° 20′.   Find the height of the tree.

2. From a window 37 feet above one side of the street, the angle of depression of **a** point on the opposite side of the street is found to be 21°.   Find the width of the street.

3. A pole 55 feet tall casts a shadow 63 feet long.   Find to the nearest degree the angle of elevation of the sun.

4. A rope 73 feet long reaches from the top of a flag pole to a point 25 feet from its base and in the same horizontal plane with its base.   Find the height of the flag pole.

5. The pitch of a roof is CD/AB (see figure). When the pitch of a roof is $\frac{1}{3}$, what is the size of angle A?

6. If a roof makes an angle of 35° with the horizontal, find the pitch of the roof.   Express approximately as a common fraction.

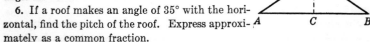

7. Find independently the acute angles of a right triangle whose sides are 3, 4, 5.

8. A straight line runs in a northwesterly direction so that it makes an angle of 71° with north (N. 71° W.) for a distance of 35 miles.   How much farther west is its end than its initial point?

9. A broken line runs from A due north 350 yards to B, then due east 520 yards to C, and finally due south 780 yards to D.   Find angle ADC.

10. A transversal between two parallel lines is 2.46 inches long and makes an angle of 37° 30′ with one of the lines.   Find the shortest distance between the two parallel lines.

GROUP B

1. At a point 205 feet from the base of a flag pole and in the same horizontal plane with its base, the angle subtended by the flag pole is 39°. Find the height of the flag pole.

2. From an elevation of 165 feet above a level plane the angle of depression of an object is observed to be 19°.   Find the air-line distance from the point of observation to the object.

3. When the shadow of an upright pole 12 feet high is found to be 10 feet 4 inches on a horizontal plane, what is the angle of elevation of the sun?

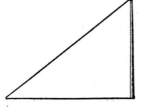

4. A kite string 275 feet long makes an angle of 28° with the horizontal. Assuming that the string is straight, find the height of the kite.

5. Using the definition of pitch given in example 5 of Group A, find the pitch of a roof in which the angle between the roof and the horizontal is 38° 40′. Express approximately as a simple common fraction.

6. If a roof is 30 feet wide and the ridge pole is 9 feet above the level of the eaves, find the pitch of the roof.

7. In example 6, find the angle which the roof makes with the horizontal.

8. The base of a triangle is 28. One side makes an angle of 25° with the base and its length is 18. Find the altitude of the triangle.

9. While rowing across a river 400 yards wide, a boat is carried downstream 55 yards. Find the angle between the course of the boat and the line directly across the river.

10. A diving board 13 feet long makes an angle of 20° with the horizontal. The lower end is 1 foot 6 inches above the surface of the water. How high above the water is the upper end?

GROUP C

1. When the angle of elevation of the sun is 41°, the length of the shadow of a tree on level ground is 65 feet. Find the height of the tree.

2. From the top of a tower 185 feet high the angle of depression of an object in the plane of its base is 27°. Find the air-line distance from the top of the tower to the object.

3. A ladder reaches to the top of a 12-foot fence when its base is 4½ feet from the base of the fence and in the same horizontal plane. Find the angle which the ladder makes with the horizontal.

4. A stretch of straight road runs up a hill at an angle of 11° 30′ with the horizontal for a distance of 350 feet. Find the difference in altitude of the two ends.

5. Using the definition of pitch as given in example 5 of Group A, find the angle which a roof makes with the horizontal when the pitch is 7/20.

6. Find the pitch of a roof which makes an angle of 31°. Express approximately as a simple common fraction.

7. A ship travels 90 miles in a straight line which runs 21° 30′ east of due north. Find how much farther north it is at the end of its run than at the start.

8. A ship is traveling in a northeasterly direction making an angle of 28° with north (N. 28° E.) with a velocity of 18 miles per hour. Find its velocity in a due north direction.

9. A boy walks 5 blocks due east, then 8 blocks north, and finally 12 more blocks east. The blocks are all of the same length. Find the direction from his starting point to his destination.

10. A brace 4 feet 6 inches long runs from the lowest to the highest of 5 shelves spaced one foot apart. What angle does it make with each shelf?

CHAPTER III

LOGARITHMS

IN APPLYING the formulas of trigonometry to the solution of problems, long computations occur frequently. The laboriousness of these computations is greatly reduced by the use of logarithms, which enable us to replace multiplication and division respectively by addition and subtraction.

37. Definition of logarithms.—The index of the power to which a given number called the **base** must be raised to equal a second number is called the **logarithm** of the second number.

That is, x is the logarithm of N to the base a if

$$a^x = N \text{ (exponential notation).}$$

This is denoted by writing

$$x = \log_a N \text{ (logarithmic notation).}$$

Thus, since $2^4 = 16$, $4 = \log_2 16$; since $10^2 = 100$, $2 = \log_{10} 100$; since $10^3 = 1000$, $3 = \log_{10} 1000$. In general if $y^z = k$, then $z = \log_y k$.

38. The base.—In developing a table of logarithms the same base must be used for all numbers. While any positive number except 1 might be used as a base, in practice the number 10 is the only one used for tables designed as aids in computation.

39. Systems of logarithms.—The system of logarithms having 10 as its base is called the **Common System of Logarithms.** Another system, called the *Napierian* or *Natural* System, is used for theoretical purposes. Its base cannot be expressed exactly in decimal notation. To seven decimal places it is 2.7182818. This base is usually denoted by e.[1]

In this book the common system only is used. Since the base of all logarithms in that system is 10, the base will be omitted in our notation. Thus log N is understood to mean $\log_{10} N$. If $x = \log N$, it is understood that $10^x = N$.

---

[1] The use of 10 as the base of logarithms for practical computation is natural, since it fits more smoothly into our decimal number system than any other base. The reason for using e as a base for theoretical purposes cannot be explained here. It becomes apparent when we come to study the calculus.

40. Laws of exponents.—Since logarithms are exponents, they have the properties (that is, they obey the laws) of exponents. The following laws of exponents are needed in developing the rules for logarithmic computation.

(1) $a^x \cdot a^y = a^{x+y}$	(4) $\sqrt[y]{a^x} = a^{x/y}$
(2) $a^x \div a^y = a^{x-y}$	(5) $a^{-x} = \dfrac{1}{a^x}$
(3) $(a^x)^y = a^{xy}$	(6) $a^0 = 1$

Thus,

(1') $2^2 \cdot 2^3 = 2^{2+3} = 2^5$	(4') $\sqrt[3]{2^6} = 2^{\frac{6}{3}} = 2^2$
(2') $2^5 \div 2^2 = 2^{5-2} = 2^3$	(5') $2^{-3} = \dfrac{1}{2^3}$
(3') $(2^2)^3 = 2^{2\cdot 3} = 2^6$	(6') $2^0 = 1$

41. Logarithm of a product.—The logarithm of a product is the sum of the logarithms of the factors.

Take 10 as the base and assume that

$$M = 10^x, \ N = 10^y.$$

Then, $\log M = x, \ \log N = y.$

By the laws of exponents $MN = 10^x \cdot 10^y = 10^{x+y}.$

Hence $x + y = \log MN.$

That is, $\log MN = \log M + \log N.$

Similarly, if $P = 10^z$

$$MNP = 10^x \cdot 10^y \cdot 10^z = 10^{x+y+z}$$

and $\log (MNP) = \log M + \log N + \log P.$

This law evidently holds for any base and for any number of factors. Hence we have the rule:

To find the logarithm of a product, find the sum of the logarithms of the factors.

42. Logarithm of a quotient.—The logarithm of a quotient equals the logarithm of the dividend minus the logarithm of the divisor.

If M and N are the same as in the preceding paragraph, we have

$$\frac{M}{N} = \frac{10^x}{10^y} = 10^{x-y}.$$

That is, $\log \dfrac{M}{N} = x - y = \log M - \log N.$

Hence, we have the rule:

To find the logarithm of a quotient, subtract the logarithm of the divisor from the logarithm of the dividend.

43. Logarithm of a power.—The logarithm of a power of a number equals the logarithm of the number multiplied by the index of the power.

If $M = 10^x$, then $M^y = (10^x)^y = 10^{xy}$. Hence, the logarithm of M^y is xy, or $\log M^y = y \log M$, and we have the rule:

To find the logarithm of a power of a number multiply the logarithm of the number by the index of the power.

44. Logarithm of a root.—The rule of the preceding paragraph holds also when the index of the power is a fraction.

By (4) of §40, $\sqrt[q]{M} = M^{\frac{1}{q}}$. Hence by the rule of §43, $\log \sqrt[q]{M} = \log M^{\frac{1}{q}} = \frac{1}{q} \log M$, and we have the rule:

To find the logarithm of a root of a number, divide the logarithm of the number by the index of the root.

45. Negative and zero logarithms.—From (5) and (6) of §40, two important results regarding logarithms are obtained.

If the base a of the system of logarithms used is greater than 1, as in the common system, then a^x, where x is positive (whether integral or fractional), is always greater than 1, and $1/a^x$ is accordingly less than 1. Consequently if

$$M = \frac{1}{a^x} = a^{-x}, \text{ then, } \log M = -x.$$

That is,

The logarithm of any positive number less than 1 is negative.
From (6) of §40, $10° = 1$, and hence, $\log 1 = 0$.

SIGHT WORK

1. Given, $\log 43 = 1.63347$ and $\log 76 = 1.88081$, find $\log (43 \times 76)$ and also $\log (76 \div 43)$.

2. Given, $\log 21 = 1.32222$, $\log 186 = 2.26951$, and $\log 324 = 2.51055$, find $\log (21 \times 186 \times 324)$.

3. From the logarithms given in example 2, find $\log \dfrac{324 \times 186}{21}$.

Suggestion: First find $\log 324 \times 186$.

4. Using the same logarithms find $\log \sqrt[3]{\dfrac{324 \times 21}{186}}$.

5. From the logarithms in example 2, find $\log \sqrt[3]{186 \times 21}$.

6. Given, $\log 1.06 = 0.02531$, find $\log (1.06)^{16}$.

7. Given $\log 1.06 = 0.02531$, find $\log (1.06)^{\frac{1}{12}}$.

46. Approximate logarithms.—The logarithms of all rational numbers other than 1, 10, 100 . . . and their reciprocals, can be given only approximately by means of decimals or common fractions. The closeness of the approximation depends upon the number of decimal places used. (See page 42.)

Different tables are used for different purposes. Thus there are tables with four, five, six, seven, and even ten or more places.

47. Characteristic and mantissa.—The integral part of a logarithm is called the **characteristic** and the decimal part is called the **mantissa**.

> Thus, in the logarithm 3.78104, 3 is the characteristic, and .78104 is the mantissa.

Tables of logarithms give the mantissas. The word logarithm is often used when we refer to the mantissa only.

48. Rule for characteristics.—From the following table many important inferences may be drawn. Note that the equations in the second column follow immediately from those in the first.

10^4	=	10,000	log	10,000	= 4
10^3	=	1000	log	1000	= 3
10^2	=	100	log	100	= 2
10^1	=	10	log	10	= 1
10^0	=	1	log	1	= 0
10^{-1}	=	.1	log	.1	= -1
10^{-2}	=	.01	log	.01	= -2
10^{-3}	=	.001	log	.001	= -3
10^{-4}	=	.0001	log	.0001	= -4

From this table it is evident that if a number lies between 1000 and 10,000, its logarithm lies between 3 and 4, and may be written as 3 + a fraction. Such a number has 4 digits preceding the decimal point. Similarly, a number between 100 and 1000 has 3 digits and its logarithm is 2 + a fraction. Again, the logarithm of a number of 1 digit is 0 + a fraction. Hence we have:

RULE I. *If a number is greater than 1, the characteristic of its logarithm is positive and is one less than the number of digits preceding the decimal point.*[1]

Again, from the table it is evident that if a number lies between 1 and .1, its logarithm lies between −1 and 0; it may thus be written as −1 + a fraction. For a number lying be-

---

[1] Zero is here regarded as a positive number.

tween .1 and .01, the logarithm is between −2 and −1, and may be written as −2 + a fraction. Now any number between .1 and .01, as .0831 or .01001, has one zero immediately following the decimal point, while a number between 1 and .1 has no zero immediately following the decimal point. Continuing in this way, it appears that the characteristic of the logarithm of a number having *two* zeros immediately following the decimal point is −3; for one having three such zeros, it is −4; and so on. Hence we have:

RULE II. *If a positive number is less than 1, the characteristic of its logarithm is negative, and is numerically one greater than the number of zeros immediately following the decimal point.*

49. Ways of writing negative characteristics.—Using a table of logarithms and Rule II above, we find that, for instance, in the logarithm of .0347 the mantissa is .54033 and the characteristic is −2. Since the mantissa is positive the whole logarithm could not be written −2.54033, because this would mean that the whole number is negative. Two methods are in current use for writing logarithms with negative characteristics. This logarithm is usually written in one of the forms $\bar{2}.54033$ or 8.54033 − 10. In $\bar{2}.54033$ the minus sign above the 2 indicates that it only is negative.

In 8.54033 − 10 the characteristic, −2, has been divided into a positive part, 8, and a negative part, −10. Using this second notation and omitting the −10 we have log .347 = 9.54033, log .0347 = 8.54033, log .00347 = 7.54033. From this we can find another form of Rule II above:

RULE II'. *The sum of the positive part of the characteristic and the number of zeros immediately following the decimal point is 9.*

This rule is easily remembered, and is convenient in practice. We must of course remember the −10 in the logarithm.

If some number other than 10 were used as a base of the system of logarithms, 2 for instance, the characteristic could not be found by any such simple rules. For numbers between 2 and 4 the characteristic would be 1, for numbers between 4 and 8 the characteristic would be 2, for numbers between 8 and 16 the characteristic would be 3, and so on. For numbers between 1024 and 2048 the characteristic would be 11. The inconvenience of such a system for practical use is obvious.

50. Numbers having the same mantissa.—From the table on page 39 we have

$$\log \ 347 \ = 2.54033.$$

Since, $\qquad 3470 \ = 347 \times 10,$

it follows that $\quad \log 3470 \ = \log 347 + \log 10 \ (\S41)$

$$= 2.54033 + 1 = 3.54033.$$

Also, $\qquad\qquad 34.7 = 347 \div 10$

and hence $\quad \log \quad 34.7 = \log 347 - \log 10 \ (\S42)$

$$= 2.54033 - 1 = 1.54033$$

In this manner the following table is easily constructed:

$$\log \quad 3.47 = 0.54033 \qquad \log \quad .347 = \overline{1}.54033$$
$$\log \quad 34.7 \ = 1.54033 \qquad \log \quad .0347 = \overline{2}.54033$$
$$\log \quad 347 \ \ = 2.54033 \qquad \log \ .00347 = \overline{3}.54033$$
$$\log \ 3470 \ = 3.54033 \qquad \log .000347 = \overline{4}.54033$$

Hence we conclude that *the logarithms of numbers having the same significant parts have the same mantissa.*

SIGHT WORK

Given, log 1784 = 3.25139, find the logarithms of 178.4, 17.84, 1.784, 0.1784, .01784, 17840.

51. Logarithms that are read directly from table.—In the table on the page opposite, the first column to the left is the *number column.* The other columns contain mantissas.

To avoid crowding the page, repetition of numbers is avoided in printing. Thus in the first column of logarithms, 48 is omitted from all numbers between 48001 and 49136. These figures must be supplied when using the table.

Example 1. Find log 33.7.

Solution: In the line of 337 and in the first column we find 763. Looking at the next full five-place number above in this column, we find that the complete mantissa is 52763. Hence, by §48, log 33.7 = 1.52763.

Example 2. Find log 327.8.

Solution: In the line of 327 and in the column that has the figure 8 at the top we find 561, before which 51 must be supplied. Hence 51561 is the required mantissa, and log 327.8 = 2.51561.

In the first column of logarithms are the logarithms of numbers with three significant figures. The other columns contain logarithms of numbers with four significant figures, the particular column depending upon the fourth figure of the number whose logarithm is sought. Thus, log 3172 is in the column headed 2, log 3217 is in the column headed 7, and so on.

Logarithms 300–350

Numbers 300–350		Logs 47712–54518										
N	**0**	**1**	**2**	**3**	**4**	**5**	**6**	**7**	**8**	**9**		**P.P.**
300	47 712	47 727	47 741	47 756	47 770	47 784	47 799	47 813	47 828	47 842		**15**
301	857	871	885	900	914	929	943	958	972	986	1	1.5
302	48 001	48 015	48 029	48 044	48 058	48 073	48 087	48 101	48 116	48 130	2	3.0
303	144	159	173	187	202	216	230	244	259	273	3	4.5
304	287	302	316	330	344	359	373	387	401	416	4	6.0
305	430	444	458	473	487	501	515	530	544	558	5	7.5
306	572	586	601	615	629	643	657	671	686	700	6	9.0
307	714	728	742	756	770	785	799	813	827	841	7	10.5
308	855	869	883	897	911	926	940	954	968	982	8	12.0
309	996	49 010	49 024	49 038	49 052	49 066	49 080	49 094	49 108	49 122	9	13.5
310	49 136	49 150	49 164	49 178	49 192	49 206	49 220	49 234	49 248	49 262		**14**
311	276	290	304	318	332	346	360	374	388	402	1	1.4
312	415	429	443	457	471	485	499	513	527	541	2	2.8
313	554	568	582	596	610	624	638	651	665	679	3	4.2
314	693	707	721	734	748	762	776	790	803	817	4	5.6
315	831	845	859	872	886	900	914	927	941	955	5	7.0
316	969	982	996	50 010	50 024	50 037	50 051	50 065	50 079	50 092	6	8.4
317	50 106	50 120	50 133	147	161	174	188	202	215	229	7	9.8
318	243	256	270	284	297	311	325	338	352	365	8	11.2
319	379	393	406	420	433	447	461	474	488	501	9	12.6
320	50 515	50 529	50 542	50 556	50 569	50 583	50 596	50 610	50 623	50 637		
321	651	664	678	691	705	718	732	745	759	772		
322	786	799	813	826	840	853	866	880	893	907		
323	920	934	947	961	974	987	51 001	51 014	51 028	51 041		
324	51 055	51 068	51 081	51 095	51 108	51 121	135	148	162	175		
325	188	202	215	228	242	255	268	282	295	308		
326	322	335	348	362	375	388	402	415	428	441		
327	455	468	481	495	508	521	534	548	561	574		
328	587	601	614	627	640	654	667	680	693	706		
329	720	733	746	759	772	786	799	812	825	838		
330	51 851	51 865	51 878	51 891	51 904	51 917	51 930	51 943	51 957	51 970		**13**
331	983	996	52 009	52 022	52 035	52 048	52 061	52 075	52 088	52 101	1	1.3
332	52 114	52 127	140	153	166	179	192	205	218	231	2	2.6
333	244	257	270	284	297	310	323	336	349	362	3	3.9
334	375	388	401	414	427	440	453	466	479	492	4	5.2
335	504	517	530	543	556	569	582	595	608	621	5	6.5
336	634	647	660	673	686	699	711	724	737	750	6	7.8
337	763	776	789	802	815	827	840	853	866	879	7	9.1
338	892	905	917	930	943	956	969	982	994	53 007	8	10.4
339	53 020	53 033	53 046	53 058	53 071	53 084	53 097	53 110	53 122	135	9	11.7
340	53 148	53 161	53 173	53 186	53 199	53 212	53 224	53 237	53 250	53 263		**12**
341	275	288	301	314	326	339	352	364	377	390	1	1.2
342	403	415	428	441	453	466	479	491	504	517	2	2.4
343	529	542	555	567	580	593	605	618	631	643	3	3.6
344	656	668	681	694	706	719	732	744	757	769	4	4.8
345	782	794	807	820	832	845	857	870	882	895	5	6.0
346	908	920	933	945	958	970	983	995	54 008	54 020	6	7.2
347	54 033	54 045	54 058	54 070	54 083	54 095	54 108	54 120	133	145	7	8.4
348	158	170	183	195	208	220	233	245	258	270	8	9.6
349	283	295	307	320	332	345	357	370	382	394	9	10.8
350	54 407	54 419	54 432	54 444	54 456	54 469	54 481	54 494	54 506	54 518		
N	**0**	**1**	**2**	**3**	**4**	**5**	**6**	**7**	**8**	**9**		

52. Antilogarithms.—A number is called the **antilogarithm** (written antilog) of its logarithm.

Thus, if $a = \log N$, then $N = $ antilog a.

If the given mantissa occurs exactly in the table, then the corresponding number (the antilog) can be found at once.

Thus, if the given mantissa is 68538 we find at once that the significant part of the required number is 4846.

When the mantissa does not occur exactly in the table the process of finding the number is shown in the following example.

Example. Find antilog 1.66413.
Solution: We first find the significant part of the number. For this purpose the characteristic is disregarded. From the first column of logarithms we see that the given mantissa lies between the mantissas of 461 and 462. Hence, we write 461 as the first part of the required number. Passing along the line of 461, we see that the given mantissa lies between the mantissas of 4614 and 4615. Hence we annex the number 4 to 461, obtaining 4614. The tabular difference at this point $(417 - 408)$ is 9 and the given mantissa is 5 greater than the mantissa of 4614. Looking in the table of proportional parts under 9, we find that a tabular difference of 5 corresponds most nearly to the extra digit 6. Hence we annex 6 to 4614, obtaining 46,146 as the significant part of the required number.
Hence, by §48, antilog 1.66413 = 46.146.
NOTE.—In the above example the given mantissa, 66413, lies 5/9 or .556 of the way from 66408 to 66417 (the mantissas of 4614 and 4615, respectively). Hence, if conditions warranted and required that degree of accuracy, 556 should be annexed to 4614. However, a five-place table admits of error even in the fifth place. Moreover, the data in any ordinary practical problem will contain errors which make it useless to attempt a higher degree of accuracy in computation.

EXERCISES

Find the antilogs of the following.

1. 1.65427.	11. 1.66902.	21. 2.68013.
2. 2.66671.	12. 0.67207.	22. $\bar{1}$.69004.
3. 3.67779.	13. 0.69100.	23. $\bar{2}$.65940.
4. 0.68314.	14. $\bar{2}$.68002.	24. $\bar{3}$.67894.
5. $\bar{1}$.69179.	15. $\bar{3}$.65490.	25. $\bar{1}$.67932.
6. 1.65394.	16. 0.69012.	26. 2.68003.
7. 2.67194.	17. $\bar{4}$.67204.	27. 4.67046.
8. $\bar{1}$.68034.	18. $\bar{2}$.68300.	28. 3.69040.
9. $\bar{2}$.69137.	19. $\bar{2}$.67094.	29. $\bar{2}$.67893.
10. 0.66491.	20. $\bar{1}$.66714.	30. 0.69216.

Logarithms 450–500

N	0	1	2	3	4	5	6	7	8	9
						Numbers 450–500			Logs 65321–69975	
450	65 321	65 331	65 341	65 350	65 360	65 369	65 379	65 389	65 398	65 408
451	418	427	437	447	456	466	475	485	495̄	504
452	514	523	533	543	552	562	571	581	591	600
453	610	619	629	639	648	658	667	677	686	696
454	706	715	725̄	734	744	753	763	772	782	792
455	801	811	820	830	839	849	858	868	877	887
456	896	906	916	925	935̄	944	954	963	973	982
457	992	66 001	66 011	66 020	66 030	66 039	66 049	66 058	66 068	66 077
458	66 087	096	106	115̄	124	134	143	153	162	172
459	181	191	200	210	219	229	238	247	257	266
460	66 276	66 285	66 295̄	66 304	66 314	66 323	66 332	66 342	66 351	66 361
461	370	380	389	398	408	417	427	436	445	455̄
462	464	474	483	492	502	511̲	521	530	539	549
463	558	567	577	586	596	605̄	614	624	633	642
464	652	661	671	680	689	699	708	717	727	736
465	745	755̄	764	773	783	792	801	811	820	829
466	839	848	857	867	876	885	894	904	913	922
467	932	941	950	960	969	978	987	997	67 006	67 015
468	67 025̄	67 034	67 043	67 052	67 062	67 071	67 080	67 089	099	108
469	117	127	136	145	154	164	173	182	191	201
470	67 210	67 219	67 228	67 237	67 247	67 256	67 265	67 274	67 284	67 293
471	302	311	321	330	339	348	357	367	376	385̄
472	394	403	413	422	431	440	449	459	468	477
473	486	495	504	514	523	532	541	550	560	569
474	578	587	596	605	614	624	633	642	651	660
475	669	679	688	697	706	715	724	733	742	752
476	761	770	779	788	797	806	815	825̄	834	843
477	852	861	870	879	888	897	906	916	925̄	934
478	943	952	961	970	979	988	997	68 006	68 015	68 024
479	68 034	68 043	68 052	68 061	68 070	68 079	68 088	097	106	115
480	68 124	68 133	68 142	68 151	68 160	68 169	68 178	68 187	68 196	68 205
481	215̄	224	233	242	251	260	269	278	287	296
482	305̄	314	323	332	341	350	359	368	377	386
483	395̄	404	413	422	431	440	449	458	467	476
484	485̄	494	502	511	520	529	538	547	556	565
485	574	583	592	601	610	619	628	637	646	655̄
486	664	673	681	690	699	708	717	726	735	744
487	753	762	771	780	789	797	806	815	824	833
488	842	851	860	869	878	886	895	904	913	922
489	931	940	949	958	966	975	984	993	69 002	69 011
490	69 020	69 028	69 037	69 046	69 055	69 064	69 073	69 082	69 090	69 099
491	108	117	126	135̄	144	152	161	170	179	188
492	197	205̄	214	223	232	241	249	258	267	276
493	285̄	294	302	311	320	329	338	346	355	364
494	373	381	390	399	408	417	425	434	443	452
495	461	469	478	487	496	504	513	522	531	539
496	548	557	566	574	583	592	601	609	618	627
497	636	644	653	662	671	679	688	697	705	714
498	723	732	740	749	758	767	775	784	793	801
499	810	819	827	836	845̄	854	862	871	880	888
500	69 897	69 906	69 914	69 923	69 932	69 940	69 949	69 958	69 966	69 975
N	0	1	2	3	4	5	6	7	8	9

P.P.

10

1	1.0
2	2.0
3	3.0
4	4.0
5	5.0
6	6.0
7	7.0
8	8.0
9	9.0

9

1	0.9
2	1.8
3	2.7
4	3.6
5	4.5
6	5.4
7	6.3
8	7.2
9	8.1

8

1	0.8
2	1.6
3	2.4
4	3.2
5	4.0
6	4.8
7	5.6
8	6.4
9	7.2

53. Interpolation in logarithms.—The process is exactly like that described in §32 for natural functions. In finding numbers whose logarithms are given, interpolation must be used very frequently, since only in exceptional cases does a given mantissa occur in the table. (See §52.)

The process of interpolation must also be used in finding the logarithms of given numbers when these contain more than four significant figures, since in this case the logarithms cannot be read directly from the table.

Example. Find log 32,714.

Solution: Using the table on page 39 we find
$$\log 32710 = 4.51468$$
and $\qquad\qquad\qquad$ $\log 32720 = 4.51481.$

The number 32,714 lies four-tenths of the way from 32,710 to 32,720. A reasonable approximation to its logarithm is the number four-tenths of the way from 4.51468 to 4.51481. The difference of these logarithms is 13 (hundred-thousandths); four-tenths of 13 is 5.2; hence we add 5 to the mantissa 51468 and have log 32714 = 4.51473.

In the column at the right of the table we find that for a tabular difference of 13, an extra digit of 4 corresponds to 5.2. Use of the tabular difference lists (called table of proportional parts) often shortens this work.

In working with a five-place table do not extend the figures in the mantissa beyond that number.

SIGHT WORK

Find the logarithms of the following.

1. 325.47	2. 47323	3. 3.2001	4. 309.84
5. 4985.3	6. 336.38	7. 4897.4	8. 3016.3
9. 31.715	10. 4895.4	11. 32247	12. 4.5956
13. 4.6324	14. 30.059	15. 456.91	16. 34.752

54. Errors in interpolation.—Using a six-place table, we find that the logarithm of 32,714 is 4.514734. Hence whatever error may be due to interpolation, it does not in this case affect the mantissa in the last place when working with a five-place table. With unimportant exceptions, it is true that when interpolating between any two consecutive mantissas given in a table, the result will be correct to the number of places of that table.

However, if we attempt to find the logarithm of a number by interpolation between two mantissas that are far apart there will be serious error. Thus, suppose we interpolate between log 200 = 2.30103 and log 300 = 2.47712 to find log 250, we shall have log 250 = 2.38908, whereas in reality log 250 = 2.39794.

55. Operations on logarithms.—Any computation by means of logarithms consists essentially of three steps:

(1) Finding logarithms of numbers given in the problem.

(2) Combining these logarithms by means of addition, subtraction, multiplication, and division, thus obtaining the logarithm of the desired result.

(3) Finding the number corresponding to this final logarithm.

Steps (1) and (3) have already been studied in §§50–54. The only difficulty in step (2) arises from the fact that the mantissa is *always* positive, while the characteristic may be positive or negative, but must *always* be an integer.

Thus, it is not so clear how $\bar{2}.79426$ may be divided by 3 in such a way as to make the characteristic of the result an integer and the mantissa positive.

In the following paragraphs we shall study the operations on logarithms and the various devices used to adapt them to the requirements of practical computation.

56. Adding logarithms.—Adding logarithms when the characteristics are positive is exactly the same as adding ordinary decimals. When one or more characteristics are negative the process is shown by the following examples.

Example 1. Add 2.47162 and $\bar{2}.86473$.

Solution: Rewriting the second logarithm by adding and subtracting 10, we have $8.86473 - 10$.

$$2.47162$$
$$8.86473 - 10$$

The addition is now performed as in algebra. The characteristic is $11 - 10$, or $+1$. The result may then be written 1.33635.

$$\overline{11.33635 - 10}$$
$$\text{or } 1.33635$$

Example 2. Add 1.40198, 0.16432 and $\bar{3}.66219$.

Solution: After rewriting the third logarithm we have the example in addition shown at the right.

$$1.40198$$
$$0.16432$$
$$7.66219 - 10$$
$$\overline{9.22849 - 10}$$

The characteristic in the result is $9 - 10$, or -1, and the result may therefore be written $\bar{1}.22849$. However, this change is not necessary.

57. Subtracting logarithms.—The following examples show the various combinations that arise in subtracting logarithms.

Example 1. Subtract 2.34718 from 4.16782.

In this case the subtraction differs in no respect from the subtraction of ordinary decimals.

$$4.16782$$
$$2.34718$$
$$\overline{1.82064}$$

Example 2. Subtract 2.17142 from 1.29476.

Solution: In place of 1.29476 write 11.29476 − 10. We then have the operation shown at the right.

$$11.29476 - 10$$
$$\underline{2.17142}$$
$$9.12334 - 10$$

For use in finding the antilogarithm it is to be noted that the characteristic is −1, but no change in the written form is required.

Example 3. Subtract $\overline{2}.14762$ from 1.98764.

Solution: Rewriting both in the form suggested above, we have

$$11.98764 - 10$$
$$\underline{8.14762 - 10}$$
$$3.84002$$

Example 4. Subtract $\overline{1}.62387$ from $\overline{2}.27941$.

Solution: Proceed exactly as in the preceding, except that in the minuend 18 − 20 instead of 8 − 10 should be used.

$$18.27941 - 20$$
$$\underline{9.62387 - 10}$$
$$8.65554 - 10$$

58. Multiplying logarithms.—This presents no difficulty when the characteristic is positive. If the characteristic is negative, it may be expressed as some number less 10, and then the multiplying is done as in algebra.

Example: Multiply $\overline{3}.84361$ by 3.

The solution is shown at the right.

$$7.84361 - 10$$
$$\underline{3}$$
$$23.53083 - 30$$
$$= 3.53083 - 10$$
$$= \overline{7}.53083$$

59. Dividing a logarithm.—Difficulty arises when the characteristic is negative. To the characteristic should be added and subtracted some number which is exactly divisible by the number by which the logarithm is to be divided.

Example. Divide $\overline{1}.84762$ by 3.

Solution (1): Add and subtract 30. We then have 29.84762 − 30 to be divided by 3. The quotient is 9.94921 − 10, or $\overline{1}.94921$.

Solution (2): Add and subtract 3. Then 2.84762 − 3 divided by 3 gives .94921 − 1 or $\overline{1}.94921$, as before.

SIGHT WORK

Add and also subtract:

1. 4.19178	3. 2.62191	5. 1.61241	7. $\overline{3}.45264$
1.47214	3.45231	$\overline{3}.71592$	2.89317
2. 3.86421	4. 1.97162	6. $\overline{4}.64825$	8. 3.91724
$\overline{1}.93261$	2.14645	$\overline{1}.91476$	$\overline{5}.61987$

Multiply and also divide:

9. 3.48265 by 3.	12. $\overline{4}.82671$ by 2.	15. $\overline{1}.81437$ by 3.
10. 2.78436 by 3.	13. 3.61938 by 3.	16. 2.85723 by 4.
11. $\overline{1}.18136$ by 4.	14. $\overline{3}.19641$ by 2.	17. $\overline{5}.17143$ by 2.

60. Practice in using logarithms.—The Examples on this page illustrate the uses of logarithms and the forms into which the work should be put. The table at the end of the book, or a separate table, is now used. We note that since there are no logarithms of negative numbers, products (and quotients) of negative numbers are obtained as if they were all positive; the proper sign is then prefixed in the result.

Example 1. Find the product of 49.6×82.7
Solution:

$$
\begin{array}{rl}
\log 49.6 = & 1.69548 \\
\log 82.7 = & 1.91751 \\
\hline
& 3.61299 = \log 4101.9.
\end{array}
$$

Hence the product is 4101.9.

Example 2. Find the value of $\dfrac{14.64 \times 811.2}{61.34}$
Solution:

$$
\begin{array}{rl}
\log \ 14.64 \ = & 1.16554 \\
\log \ 811.2 \ = & 2.90913 \\
\hline
& 4.07467 \\
\log \ 61.34 \ = & 1.78774 \\
\hline
& 2.28693 = \log 193.61.
\end{array}
$$

Example 3. Find the value of $9.47^2 \times 1.19^2$.
Solution:

$$
\begin{array}{rl}
\log \ \ 9.47^2 = & 1.95270 \\
\log \ \ 1.19^2 = & .15110 \\
\hline
& 2.10380 = \log 127.00.
\end{array}
$$

Writing down $\log 9.47^2 = 1.95270$ involves multiplying the logarithm of 9.47 by 2. This should be done mentally and no numbers should be written down, except those shown here. Log 1.19^2 is found in the same manner.

Example 4. Find the value of

$$\frac{21.3^2 \times 64.7^3}{34.1^4}$$

Solution:

$$
\begin{array}{rl}
\log 21.3^2 = & 2.65676 \\
\log 64.7^3 = & 5.43270 \\
\hline
& 8.08946 \\
\log 34.1^4 = & 6.13100 \\
\hline
& 1.95846 \\
= & \log 90.878
\end{array}
$$

Example 5. Find the value of

$$\sqrt{\frac{17.4 \times 81.6}{24.3^2}}$$

Solution:

$$
\begin{array}{rl}
\log 17.4 \ = & 1.24055 \\
\log 81.6 \ = & 1.91169 \\
\hline
& 3.15224 \\
\log 24.3^2 = & 2.77122 \\
\hline
2|\ & .38102 \\
\hline
& .19051 \\
= & \log 1.5506
\end{array}
$$

EXERCISES

Find the values of the following correct to five significant figures.

1. 71.23×4.26
2. $8.6^2 \times 2.91^3$
3. $51.4 \times 63.1 \times 2.91$
4. $\dfrac{82.3 \times 61.7}{41.2^2}$

5. $126 \times 3.7^4 \times 38$
6. $.98^2 \times 6.1^3 \times 12$
7. $440 \times .034^2 \times 6$
8. $\dfrac{53 \times 262 \times 18}{26.4^3}$

9. $7.14 \times 29.8 \times \sqrt{69.3}$
10. $\sqrt[3]{845} \times 79.3 \times \sqrt{29.6}$
11. $31.6 \times \sqrt[4]{76.8} \times \sqrt{69.2}$
12. $\dfrac{93^2 \times \sqrt[3]{806} \times 41}{31.2^4}$

61. Logarithm of a reciprocal.—Since the logarithm of 1 is 0, the logarithm of a fraction whose numerator is unity may be obtained by subtracting the logarithm of the denominator from zero. Thus log $1/384$ = log 1 − log 384 = 0 − 2.58433 = 7.41567 − 10. In this manner the logarithm of the reciprocal of a number may be written down directly from the logarithm of the number itself. The result must be written from right to left as the subtraction proceeds.

62. Multiplying by a reciprocal.—Instead of dividing by a number, one may multiply by its reciprocal. Thus, instead of dividing by 384 one may multiply by $1/384$. Hence, instead of subtracting log 384 (2.58433) we may add log $1/384$ (7.41567 − 10).

63. Cologarithms.—The logarithm of the reciprocal of a number is called the **cologarithm** (written colog) of the number itself. The use of cologarithms is suggested above and is shown in the following Examples.

Example 1. Find the value of
$$\frac{8.19 \times 7.48}{36.7}$$

Solution:
log	8.19 =	0.91328
log	7.48 =	0.87390
colog	36.7 =	8.43533 − 10
		10.22251 − 10
		= log 1.6692

Example 2. Find the value of
$$\frac{18.3^4}{17 \times 8.92 \times 4.26}$$

Solution:
log	18.3^4 =	5.04980
colog	17 =	8.76955 − 10
colog	8.92 =	9.04964 − 10
colog	4.26 =	9.37059 − 10
		32.23958 − 30
		= log 173.61

To find the colog of a number such as 384, we may write log 384 on a separate slip of paper and then subtract from 0, or colog 384 may be written down directly as suggested above. Only colog 384 should appear in the computation.

64. The advantage of using cologarithms.—The chief advantage in the use of cologarithms appears when we attempt to compute by subtracting logarithms (as was done on page 45) instead of adding cologarithms.

In Example 1 above, we should have to add the first two logarithms and then subtract the last. This would necessitate the writing of one extra line of figures.

In Example 2 we should have to add the last three logarithms and then subtract this sum from the first. This, however, is balanced in part by the greater difficulty of finding cologarithms. The chief advantage in the use of cologarithms arises when the divisor or dividend is expressed as the product of two or more factors. In such cases the work is made more compact and intelligible by their use.

EXERCISES

GROUP A

Use cologarithms for all divisions.

1. $\dfrac{89.6}{39 \times 43.7}$

2. $\dfrac{683}{13.4 \times 3.71^2}$

3. $\dfrac{16.5 \times 76.4}{19.7 \times 14.8}$

4. $\dfrac{89.47 \times 7.8}{5.4 \times 7.34^2}$

5. $\dfrac{3.7 \times 4.9 \times 8.7}{7.3 \times 9.4 \times 7.8}$

6. $\dfrac{10.4 \times 39.7}{27.3 \times 19.8^2}$

7. $\dfrac{37.2 \times 8.91}{73.9 \times 40.1}$

8. $\dfrac{98.46 \times 71.42}{42 \times 67 \times 81}$

9. $\dfrac{\sqrt{37.8} \times \sqrt{95.7}}{74.6 \times 46.7}$

10. $\sqrt{\dfrac{45.6 \times 29}{77.6 \times 84}}$

11. $\dfrac{12.9 \times 9.78}{7.19 \times \sqrt{764}}$

12. $\dfrac{41.64 \times 71.8}{\sqrt{241} \times \sqrt{874}}$

13. $\sqrt{\dfrac{14.82 \times 39.2}{41.28 \times 29.3}}$

14. $\dfrac{71.92 \times 28.4}{19.27 \times 48.2}$

15. $\dfrac{71.4 \times 82.6}{41.7 \times 28.6}$

16. $\dfrac{79.4 \times 9.26}{94.7 \times 69.2}$

17. $\dfrac{35.7 \times 98.2}{.048 \times 9426}$

18. $\dfrac{49.3 \times 176.8}{.471 \times 9840}$

GROUP B

1. $\sqrt{\dfrac{31.9 \times 7.3}{6.4 \times 3.9^3}}$

2. $\dfrac{5.7 \times \sqrt{4.7}}{9.8 \times 5.3}$

3. $\dfrac{6.8 \times \sqrt{8.9}}{\sqrt{4.7} \times 37}$

4. $\sqrt{\dfrac{65.4 \times 37.8}{4.56 \times 78.3}}$

5. $\dfrac{\sqrt[3]{6.54} \times 38.7}{54.6 \times 84.7}$

6. $\dfrac{\sqrt{6.58} \times \sqrt{41.7}}{\sqrt{81.7} \times \sqrt{8.7}}$

7. $\dfrac{\sqrt{12.3 \times 45.6}}{1.28 \times 7.41}$

8. $\dfrac{92.7 \times 34.1}{16.4 \times 27 \times 8}$

9. $\sqrt{\dfrac{64.1 \times 72 \times 6}{13 \times 47 \times 61}}$

10. $\dfrac{31 \times 74 \times 16.9}{14.6 \times 27 \times 12}$

11. $\dfrac{19.8 \times 72.4 \times 31.7}{98.1 \times 24.7 \times 17.3}$

12. $\dfrac{640 \times .0139}{.024 \times 71.6 \times .028}$

13. $\sqrt{\dfrac{46 \times 319 \times 47}{71.6 \times 34.7 \times 21}}$

14. $\dfrac{87.8 \times 93.2 \times 17}{14 \times 12 \times 8 \times 94}$

15. $\dfrac{37.8 \times 78.3}{83.7 \times 7.38}$

16. $\dfrac{34.6 \times 27.8}{45.3 \times 78.2}$

17. $\sqrt{\dfrac{49.8 \times 26.4 \times 17}{34.2 \times 71.5 \times 19}}$

18. $\sqrt{\dfrac{31.6 \times 71.7 \times 24}{4.82 \times 92.7 \times 84}}$

GROUP C

1. $\dfrac{38.42 \times 6.54}{74.78 \times 913}$

2. $\dfrac{7.76 \times 67.8}{\sqrt{89.3} \times \sqrt{874}}$

3. $\dfrac{38.62 \times 29.42}{73 \times .191 \times 871}$

4. $\dfrac{49.3 \times 34.8}{84.8 \times 2.64}$

5. $\sqrt[3]{\dfrac{13.4 \times 6.43}{3.41 \times 26.4}}$

6. $\dfrac{62.8 \times 26.8}{39 \times 76 \times 84}$

7. $\sqrt{\dfrac{78.2 \times 34.6}{86.4 \times 2.64}}$

8. $\dfrac{7.31 \times 49.6}{81 \times 42 \times 73}$

9. $\sqrt{\dfrac{67.72 \times 84.9}{7.14 \times 27 \times 43}}$

10. $\dfrac{\sqrt{71.4 \times 26.8}}{\sqrt[3]{93.8 \times 176}}$

11. $\dfrac{3876}{\sqrt{2} \times \sqrt[3]{3} \times \sqrt[4]{8760}}$

12. $\dfrac{61.9 \times 847}{39 \times 8.7 \times 64.8}$

13. $\dfrac{74.8 \times 48.7}{32.1 \times 13.2}$

14. $\dfrac{\sqrt{89.4} \times \sqrt[3]{74.8}}{\sqrt{1240} \times \sqrt[3]{942}}$

15. $\dfrac{37.62 \times 47.8}{27.3 \times 14 \times 89}$

16. $\dfrac{.450 \times .0174}{.045 \times 87 \times .0072}$

17. $\dfrac{19.84 \times 64.7}{34.7 \times 26 \times 92}$

18. $\sqrt[3]{\dfrac{74.3 \times 29.17}{62.8 \times 47.6}}$

65. Logarithms of trigonometric functions.—Tables giving the logarithms of trigonometric functions are in general use. The opposite page gives log sin, log cos, log tan, log cot, for every minute of angle from 18° to 19° and also from 71° to 72°. In the table use is made of the fact that cofunctions of complementary angles are equal.

Thus, the columns read downward give the functions of the angles from 18° to 19°, while read upward they give the functions from 71° to 72°.

Since the sine and cosine of an angle are never greater than unity, characteristics of their logarithms are negative. In the table opposite they are in reality −1. Instead 9 − 10 is used, the −10 being omitted in printing.

Since the tangent of an angle greater than 45° and the cotangent of an angle less than 45° are greater than unity, the characteristic is zero, or a positive integer.

Remember that a five-place table corresponds to angle-accuracy of 5 seconds.

66. Use of tabular differences in interpolating.—The use of the table of proportional parts is best understood from examples.

Example 1. Find log sin 18° 17′ 18″.

Solution: From the table find log sin 18° 17′ and note that log sin 18° 18′ is 38 greater. We then add the differences corresponding to 10″ and 8″. In no case should more than five figures be used.

log sin 18° 17′ = 9.49654 − 10
Diff. for 10″ = .00006
Diff. for 8″ = .00005
log sin 18° 17′ 18″ = 9.49665 − 10

To find the difference corresponding to 10″, 20″ up to 50″, take 10 times the difference for 1″, 2″, etc.

Example 2. Find the angle A if log tan A = 0.47456.

Solution: From the table we find log tan 71° 27′ = 0.47422, with a tabular difference of 42; while the given logarithm shows a difference of 34. From the table of proportional parts the difference 34 corresponds to 49″ (28 corresponds to 40″ and 6.3 to 9″). Hence A = 71° 27′ 49″.

EXERCISES

In Examples 1–12 find the logarithms and in Examples 13–18 find A.

1. log sin 18° 35′.
2. log cos 18° 52′.
3. log tan 18° 39′.
4. log cot 18° 7′.
5. log sin 71° 14′.
6. log cos 71° 38′.

7. log tan 71° 52′.
8. log cot 71° 1′.
9. log sin 71° 13′ 25″.
10. log cos 18° 7′ 15″.
11. log tan 18° 45′ 20″.
12. log cot 18° 57′ 10″.

13. log sin A = 9.50389.
14. log tan A = 9.51863.
15. log cos A = 9.97744.
16. log cot A = 9.53216.
17. log sin A = 9.97612.
18. log cos A = 9.49971.

′	L. Sin.	d.	L. Tang.	c. d.	L. Cotg.	L. Cos.	d.	′
0	9.48 998	39	9.51 178	43	0.48 822	9.97 821	4	60
1	9.49 037	39	221	43	779	817	5	59
2	076	39	264	42	736	812	4	58
3	115	38	306	43	694	808	4	57
4	153	39	349	43	651	804	4	56
5	192	39	392	43	608	800	4	55
6	231	38	435	43	565	796	4	54
7	269	39	478	42	522	792	4	53
8	308	39	520	43	480	788	4	52
9	347	38	563	43	437	784	5	51
10	9.49 385	39	9.51 606	42	0.48 394	9.97 779	4	50
11	424	38	648	43	352	775	4	49
12	462	38	691	43	309	771	4	48
13	500	39	734	42	266	767	4	47
14	539	38	776	43	224	763	4	46
15	577	38	819	42	181	759	5	45
16	615	39	861	42	139	754	4	44
17	654	38	903	43	097	750	4	43
18	692	38	946	42	054	746	4	42
19	730	38	988	43	012	742	4	41
20	9.49 768	38	9.52 031	42	0.47 969	9.97 738	4	40
21	806	38	073	42	927	734	5	39
22	844	38	115	42	885	729	4	38
23	882	38	157	43	843	725	4	37
24	920	38	200	42	800	721	4	36
25	958	38	242	42	758	717	4	35
26	996	38	284	42	716	713	5	34
27	9.50 034	38	326	42	674	708	4	33
28	072	38	368	42	632	704	4	32
29	110	38	410	42	590	700	4	31
30	9.50 148	37	9.52 452	42	0.47 548	9.97 696	5	30
31	185	38	494	42	506	691	4	29
32	223	38	536	42	464	687	4	28
33	261	37	578	42	422	683	4	27
34	298	38	620	41	380	679	5	26
35	336	38	661	42	339	674	4	25
36	374	37	703	42	297	670	4	24
37	411	38	745	42	255	666	4	23
38	449	37	787	42	213	662	5	22
39	486	37	829	41	171	657	4	21
40	9.50 523	38	9.52 870	42	0.47 130	9.97 653	4	20
41	561	37	912	41	088	649	4	19
42	598	37	953	42	047	645	5	18
43	635	38	995	42	005	640	4	17
44	673	37	9.53 037	41	0.46 963	636	4	16
45	710	37	078	42	922	632	4	15
46	747	37	120	41	880	628	5	14
47	784	37	161	41	839	623	4	13
48	821	37	202	42	798	619	4	12
49	858	38	244	41	756	615	5	11
50	9.50 896	37	9.53 285	42	0.46 715	9.97 610	4	10
51	933	37	327	41	673	606	4	9
52	970	37	368	41	632	602	5	8
53	9.51 007	36	409	41	591	597	4	7
54	043	37	450	42	550	593	4	6
55	080	37	492	41	508	589	4	5
56	117	37	533	41	467	584	5	4
57	154	37	574	41	426	580	4	3
58	191	36	615	41	385	576	5	2
59	227	37	656	41	344	571	4	1
60	9.51 264		9.53 697		0.46 303	9.97 567		0

′	L. Cos.	d.	L. Cotg.	c. d.	L. Tang.	L. Sin.	d.	′

P. P.

1′	43	42
1″	0.7	0.7
2″	1.4	1.4
3″	2.2	2.1
4″	2.9	2.8
5″	3.6	3.5
6″	4.3	4.2
7″	5.0	4.9
8″	5.7	5.6
9″	6.5	6.3

1′	41	39
1″	0.7	0.7
2″	1.4	1.3
3″	2.1	2.0
4″	2.7	2.6
5″	3.4	3.3
6″	4.1	3.9
7″	4.8	4.6
8″	5.5	5.2
9″	6.2	5.9

1′	38
1″	0.6
2″	1.3
3″	1.9
4″	2.5
5″	3.2
6″	3.8
7″	4.4
8″	5.1
9″	5.7

1′	37
1″	0.6
2″	1.2
3″	1.9
4″	2.5
5″	3.1
6″	3.7
7″	4.3
8″	4.9
9″	5.6

1′	36
1″	0.6
2″	1.2
3″	1.8
4″	2.4
5″	3.0
6″	3.6
7″	4.2
8″	4.8
9″	5.4

1′	4	5
1″	0.07	0.08
2″	0.13	0.17
3″	0.20	0.25
4″	0.27	0.33
5″	0.33	0.42
6″	0.40	0.50
7″	0.47	0.58
8″	0.53	0.67
9″	0.60	0.75

71°

EXERCISES IN THE USE OF TABLES

GROUP A

Find each of the following:

1. $84 \sin 54° 18'$
2. $173 \cos 53° 35'$
3. $264 \tan 31° 17'$
4. $528 \cot 61° 24'$
5. $\sin 35° 17' \times$ $\cos 18° 40'$
6. $\sin 62° 48' \times$ $\tan 37° 18'$
7. $\sin 13° 41' \times$ $\cos 73° 14'$
8. $36 \times 84 \times$ $\sin 31° 36'$
9. $12 \times 48.9 \times$ $\cos 37° 14'$

10. $\dfrac{\sqrt{81} \times \sqrt[3]{3.9}}{3.7 \times 8.5}$

11. $\dfrac{\sqrt[3]{6.4} \times \sqrt{3.2}}{8.7 \times 93.4}$

12. $\sqrt[3]{17.4 \times 81.7 \times 26}$

13. $\dfrac{6.24 \times .83 \times 6.4}{31.9 \times 7.6}$

14. $\dfrac{19.3 \times 6.7}{3.12 \times .38 \times 4.6}$

15. $\sqrt{1.94 \times 0.78 \times .06}$

16. $\dfrac{9.41^2 \times 7.3^2}{5.28^2 \times 1.74^2}$

17. $\dfrac{17.4^2 \times \sqrt[3]{1.89}}{41.7 \times 9.18}$

18. $\dfrac{7.52 \times 3 \sqrt{85}}{16 \times 8 \times 53^2}$

19. $\sqrt[4]{2.81 \times 1.82 \times 9.12}$

20. $\dfrac{4.71 \times 28.4}{19 \times 37 \times 64}$

21. $\dfrac{4.56^2 \times 3.76^2}{2.4^3 \times 3.2^2 \times 6.1^2}$

22. $\sqrt{\dfrac{9.8 \times 34 \times 63}{9.1 \times 43 \times 37}}$

23. $\dfrac{5.91 \times 8.37}{9.25 \times 17 \times 91}$

GROUP B

1. $89 \sin 38° 15'$
2. $76 \cos 65° 47'$
3. $142 \tan 13° 12'$
4. $31 \cot 71° 19'$
5. $45 \sin 17° \tan 48°$
6. $\sin 81° 12' \times$ $\cos 17° 13'$
7. $\sin 37° \tan 48°$
8. $\sqrt{7} \cot 37° 14'$
9. $\sqrt{19.2} \tan 51° 13'$
10. 24×73 $\sin 38° 51'$

11. $\dfrac{64 \times \sqrt[3]{81}}{93 \times 87 \times 67}$

12. $\sqrt{39.1 \times 78.2 \times 32.6}$

13. $\dfrac{191.6 \times 831.5}{\sqrt{39} \times \sqrt{79.4}}$

14. $\sqrt[3]{1246 \times .0938}$

15. $\dfrac{93.7 \times 37.9}{84.2 \times 24.8}$

16. $\sqrt{293 \times 13.78 \times .042}$

17. $\dfrac{174.2 \times 49.3 \times 14}{61.6 \times 45 \times 71 \times 21}$

18. $\sqrt{34.8 \times 67 \times 93 \times 12}$

19. $\sqrt{29.2 \times .117 \times .087}$

20. $\dfrac{67 \times 82 \times 93}{\sqrt{8760 \times 4982}}$

21. $\sqrt{\dfrac{30 \times 28 \times 67 \times 42}{17 \times 13 \times 41 \times 11}}$

22. $\sqrt[3]{67.1 \times 92.3 \times .074}$

GROUP C

1. $74 \sin 67° 38'$
2. $95 \cos 49° 23'$
3. $84 \tan 76° 13'$
4. $104 \cot 18° 47'$
5. $\sin 38° \cos 57°$
6. $\sin 59° \tan 28°$
7. $\cos 74° \cot 37°$
8. $\sin 15° 12' \times$ $\cos 37° 14'$
9. $\sqrt{41} \sin 42° 18'$
10. $\sqrt[3]{149} \cos 13° 49'$
11. $\sqrt[4]{85} \cot 39°$

12. $\dfrac{65.9}{\tan 18° 42'}$

13. $\dfrac{35.4 \times 81.7}{\sin 62° 48'}$

14. $\sqrt{167.1 \times 76.11 \times 71.6}$

15. $\sqrt{\sin 41° 40' \times \cos 19°}$

16. $\sqrt{\dfrac{51.4 \times 7.35}{145 \times 37.5 \times 15.7}}$

17. $\dfrac{87.6 \times 75.8 \times 67.2}{7.92 \times 27.9 \times 92.7}$

18. $\dfrac{45.6 \times 167.8 \times 9.12}{22.8 \times 8.39 \times 4.56}$

19. $\sqrt{8.49 \times 58.9 \times 32.4}$

20. $\dfrac{47.6 \times 64.7 \times 32.9}{31.7 \times 50.4 \times 24.9}$

21. $\dfrac{13.7 \times 42.7 \times 3146}{41.2 \times 5.46 \times 19.8}$

22. $\sqrt[3]{8.52 \times 7.94 \times 50.7}$

23. $\dfrac{6.71 \times 3.45 \times .0107}{.14 \times 1.82 \times 2.417}$

CHAPTER IV

SOLUTION OF RIGHT TRIANGLES USING LOGARITHMS

WHEN one of the acute angles of a right triangle is known, the other acute angle may be found from the fact that these angles are complementary.

Thus, if in the right triangle, ABC, angle B is known, then angle A is found from the relation $\angle A = 90° - \angle B$.

It follows from this that in solving a right triangle, as ABC, only four parts, namely, a, b, c, and one acute angle as A, need be considered. Of these four parts, two must be given to make it possible to find the others.

67. The six problems in solving right triangles.—This gives rise to six problems, namely: find the remaining parts of the right triangle ABC, when any one of the following pairs of parts is given: $\angle A, a; \angle A, b; \angle A, c; a, b; a, c; b, c$. (See page 20.)

Problem I. In a right triangle ABC, given $\angle A$ and side a, to find the remaining parts.

Formulas:
$$\begin{cases} \sin A = \dfrac{a}{c} \text{ and hence } c = \dfrac{a}{\sin A}. \\ \tan A = \dfrac{a}{b} \text{ and hence } b = \dfrac{a}{\tan A} = a \cot A. \end{cases}$$

Problem II. In a right triangle ABC, given $\angle A$ and side b, to find the remaining parts.

Formulas:
$$\begin{cases} \cos A = \dfrac{b}{c} \text{ and hence } c = \dfrac{b}{\cos A}. \\ \tan A = \dfrac{a}{b} \text{ and hence } a = b \tan A. \end{cases}$$

Problem III. Given $\angle A$ and side c, to find the remaining parts

Formulas: $a = c \sin A$ and $b = c \cos A$.

Problem IV. Given sides a, b, to find the remaining parts.

Formulas: $\tan A = \dfrac{a}{b}$ and $c = \dfrac{a}{\sin A}$

In solving this problem $\angle A$ is found first, and then $\sin A$ is found and substituted in the second formula.

The other two problems: *viz.*, when a, c or b, c are given, are solved in the same manner.

68. Logarithmic solutions.—The formulas used in the logarithmic solution of right triangles are exactly those used in solving by natural functions. The difference arises from the fact that logarithms are used in the computations. Proper arrangement of work is important in such computations, and the forms used in the solutions given below should be studied.

Example 1. In the right triangle, ABC, $\angle C = 90°$, $\angle A = 42° \ 23'$; $a = 18.3$. Find b and c.

Formulas:
$$b = \frac{a}{\tan A}, \qquad c = \frac{a}{\sin A}.$$
$$\log b = \log a - \log \tan A, \qquad \log c = \log a - \log \sin A.$$

Forms:

$\log 18.3 =$	$\log 18.3 =$
$\log \tan 42° \ 23' =$	$\log \sin \ 42° \ 23' =$
$\log b =$	$\log c =$
$b =$	$c =$

To facilitate the computation first write down the forms as shown above. Notice that 18.3 occurs in both forms and be sure to fill in both places at the same time. Similarly, $\tan 42° \ 23'$ and $\sin 42° \ 23'$ should be found at the same time, since this saves turning to this angle again.

When finished, the above forms are as follows.

$\log 18.3 = 11.26245 - 10$	$\log 18.3 = 11.26245 - 10$
$\log \tan 42° \ 23' = \ \ 9.96028 - 10$	$\log \sin 42° \ 23' = \ \ 9.82872 - 10$
$\log b = \ \ 1.30217$	$\log c = \ \ 1.43373$
$b = 20.053$	$c = 27.148$

Example 2. Given $A = 56° \ 14'$, $c = 23.76$, find a and b.

Solution:

$a = c \sin A$	$b = c \cos A$
$\log a = \log c + \log \sin A$	$\log b = \log c + \log \cos A$
$\log 23.76 = \ \ 1.37585$	$\log 23.76 = \ \ 1.37585$
$\log \sin 56° \ 14' = \ \ 9.91976 - 10$	$\log \cos 56° \ 14' = \ \ 9.74493 - 10$
$\log a = \ \ 1.29561$	$\log b = \ \ 1.12078$
$a = 19.752$	$b = 13.206$

Notice that $\log 23.76$ occurs in both solutions. Also when finding $\log \sin A$ for the form to the left fill in $\log \cos A$ in the form to the right.

Example 3. Given $a = 31.62$, $b = 28.37$, find A, c.

Solution:

$\tan A = a/b$	$c = a/\sin A$
$\log \tan A = \log a - \log b$	$\log c = \log a - \log \sin A$
$\log 31.62 = 1.49996$	$\log 31.62 = 11.49996 - 10$
$\log 28.37 = 1.45286$	$\log \sin A = \ \ 9.87175 - 10$
$\log \tan A = \ \ .04710$	$\log c = \ \ 1.62821$
$A = 48° \ 6' \ 2''$	$c = 42.483.$

Example 4. Given $a = 51.39$, and $c = 69.22$, find $\angle A$ and b.

Solution:

$$\sin A = a/c$$
$$\log \sin A = \log a - \log c$$
$$\log 51.39 = 11.71088 - 10$$
$$\log 69.22 = \underline{1.84023}$$
$$\log \sin A = 9.87065 - 10$$
$$A = 47° 56' 16''$$

$$b = c \cos A$$
$$\log b = \log c + \log \cos A$$
$$\log 69.22 = 1.84023$$
$$\log \cos A = \underline{9.82603 - 10}$$
$$\log b = 1.66626$$
$$b = 46.372$$

EXERCISES

Solve the right triangles ABC, in which C is $90°$, and the given parts are as follows.

GROUP A

1. $A =$	$35° 13'$,	$a =$	51.67	10. $a =$	86.35,	$b = 13.75$
2. $A =$	$63° 47'$,	$b =$	15.64	11. $a =$	162.20,	$c = 175.31$
3. $A =$	$74° 29'$,	$c =$	36.45	12. $b =$	71.16,	$c = 153.17$
4. $a =$	68.27,	$b =$	46.73	13. $A =$	$71° 16'$,	$a = 27.64$
5. $a =$	86.21,	$c =$	108.41	14. $A =$	$39° 18'$,	$b = 42.67$
6. $c =$	45.73,	$b =$	24.81	15. $A =$	$83° 24'$,	$c = 62.74$
7. $A =$	$22° 49'$,	$a =$	42.18	16. $a =$	34.18,	$b = 47.26$
8. $A =$	$74° 36'$,	$b =$	12.84	17. $a =$	18.24,	$c = 27.46$
9. $A =$	$37° 27'$,	$c =$	47.65	18. $b =$	80.25,	$c = 97.34$

GROUP B

1. $A =$	$41° 25'$,	$a =$	17.56	10. $a =$	69.35,	$b = 91.62$
2. $A =$	$62° 45'$,	$b =$	75.61	11. $a =$	92.48,	$c = 173.46$
3. $A =$	$29° 50'$,	$c =$	97.17	12. $b =$	65.67,	$c = 107.89$
4. $a =$	83.85,	$b =$	49.83	13. $A =$	$77° 12'$,	$a = 47.64$
5. $a =$	257.25,	$c =$	342.14	14. $A =$	$81° 48'$,	$b = 136.47$
6. $b =$	708.15,	$c =$	980.17	15. $A =$	$65° 55'$,	$c = 337.94$
7. $A =$	$8° 20'$,	$a =$	27.42	16. $a =$	148.85,	$b = 55.60$
8. $A =$	$29° 30'$,	$b =$	93.86	17. $a =$	417.18,	$c = 640.80$
9. $A =$	$37° 48'$,	$c =$	392.81	18. $b =$	375.24,	$c = 467.59$

GROUP C

1. $A =$	$42° 54'$,	$a =$	24.80	10. $a =$	55.35,	$b = 53.49$
2. $A =$	$57° 18'$,	$b =$	482.61	11. $a =$	65.48,	$c = 94.13$
3. $A =$	$71° 12'$,	$c =$	284.16	12. $b =$	70.90,	$c = 101.54$
4. $a =$	78.80,	$b =$	48.62	13. $A =$	$23° 16'$,	$a = 41.51$
5. $a =$	90.75,	$c =$	142.63	14. $A =$	$37° 48'$,	$b = 54.11$
6. $b =$	250.70,	$c =$	514.21	15. $A =$	$73° 55'$,	$c = 85.83$
7. $A =$	$76° 27'$,	$a =$	154.12	16. $a =$	87.35,	$b = 57.38$
8. $A =$	$79° 30'$,	$b =$	241.36	17. $a =$	191.60,	$c = 275.83$
9. $A =$	$53° 50'$,	$c =$	286.45	18. $b =$	82.37,	$c = 221.40$

69. Projection of one line on another.—Let two lines OM and ON meet in a point O, making an angle A. Let P and Q be two points on ON and let PP_1 and QQ_1 be perpendicular to OM. Then P_1Q_1 is called the **projection** of the line-segment PQ on the line OM. If PQ' is drawn parallel to OM, then $PQ' = P_1Q_1$ and $\angle Q'PQ = \angle A$. Since $PQ' = PQ \cos \angle Q'PQ$, it follows that $P_1Q_1 = PQ \cos A$.

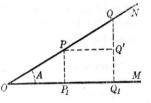

That is, *the projection upon a line of a segment lying in another line is equal to the projected segment multiplied by the cosine of the angle between the lines.*

70. Projection of a segment upon two perpendicular lines.—Let OX and OY be two lines at right angles to each other and P_1Q_1 and P_2Q_2 be the projections of PQ upon these two lines. Let A be the angle which the line PQ makes with OX. Then as above, $P_1Q_1 = PQ \cos A$. Since $Q'Q = P_2Q_2$, it follows that $P_2Q_2 = PQ \sin A$. Hence we have the two equations,

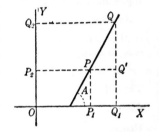

$$P_1Q_1 = PQ \cos A, \quad P_2Q_2 = PQ \sin A$$

These equations are used frequently in applications to physics. If the line PQ represents the magnitude and direction of a force, then P_1Q_1 and P_2Q_2 are said to represent respectively the x-component and the y-component of this force.

Example 1. Find the length of a segment if the projections on two perpendicular lines are a and b, respectively.

Note that the projections P_1Q_1 and P_2Q_2 are equal to the sides PQ' and $Q'Q$ of the right triangle $PQ'Q$. Hence the problem is the same as the second part of Example 3 page 52. We may also use $PQ = \sqrt{a^2 + b^2}$.

Example 2. A ship sails at a rate of 17.4 knots (nautical miles per hour) along a straight course, making an angle A with an east-and-west line. At what rate is the ship going eastward and at what rate is it going northward?

Solution: If OP represents the distance the ship goes in one hour along its course, then OP_1 represents the distance it goes eastward and OP_2 the distance it goes northward. Hence its eastward speed is 17.4 cos A and its northward speed is 17.4 sin A.

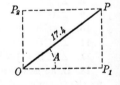

71. Solution of isosceles triangles.—Since an isosceles triangle may be divided into two right triangles by drawing the median upon its base, it follows that problems on isosceles triangles may be solved by means of the formulas already found.

Problem 1. Given one of the equal sides of an isosceles triangle and a base angle, to find the base and the altitude of the triangle.

Solution: Let ABC be the given triangle and CD the median upon the base. Then AD is half the base, and $CD =$ $AC \sin A$, and $AD = AC \cos A$. Hence the altitude $= AC \sin A$ and the base $= 2\,AC \cos A$. Thus, if $AC = 17.8$ and $A = 37° 30'$, then, $\qquad CD = 17.8 \sin 37° 30'$ and $\qquad AB = 2 \times 17.8 \cos 37° 30'$.

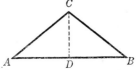

Problem 2. Given the three sides of an isosceles triangle, to find its angles and the altitude on the base.

Solution: Using the figure of Problem 1, we have $\cos A = \dfrac{AD}{AC}$. Since AD (half of AB) and AC are given, $\cos A$ may be found, and hence angle A may be found.

From the equation $DC = AC \sin A$ the altitude may then be found.

Thus, if $\qquad\qquad AC = 49.36$ and $AB = 43.64$

then, $\qquad\qquad \cos A = \dfrac{21.82}{49.36}$ and $\angle A = 63° 46'$.

Hence, $\qquad\qquad DC = 49.36 \times \sin 63° 46'$

EXERCISES

Using the same figure as in Problem 1 above, find the required parts in each of the following isosceles triangles.

Given	Required	
1. $AC = 14.97$, $\angle A = 43°21'$	AB,	CD
2. $AB = 43.12$, $CD = 17.38$	AC,	$\angle A$
3. $\angle A = 27° 34'$, $CD = 23.86$	AB,	AC
4. $\angle A = 35° 57'$, $AB = 188.8$	AC,	CD
5. $AC = 98.24$, $AB = 160.50$	$\angle A$,	CD
6. $\angle ACD = 49° 42'$, $AC = 221.5$	AD,	DC
7. $\angle ACD = 61° 34'$, $AD = 48.92$	AC,	DC
8. $\angle ACD = 58° 49'$, $CD = 76.37$	AD,	AC
9. $\angle ACB = 84° 40'$, $AD = 852.1$	AC,	DC
10. $\angle ACB = 92° 38'$, $CD = 73.86$	AD,	AC
11. $\angle ACB = 106° 46'$, $AC = 97.42$	AD,	DC
12. $\angle ACB = 128° 32'$, $AB = 75.84$	AC,	DC

13. In an isosceles triangle ABC, $AC = BC$, what parts may be given to fix the triangle and thus make its solution possible?

72. Solution of regular polygons.—Since a regular polygon may be divided into isosceles triangles by drawing lines from its center to its vertices, it follows that many problems on regular polygons may be solved by means of the formulas already found.

If a regular polygon has n sides, then the vertex angles of the isosceles triangles into which it is divided are all $360° \div n$.

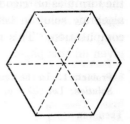

Problem 1. Given the number of sides of a regular polygon and the length of each side, to find the radius of the circumscribed circle.

Solution: Let the number of sides be n. Let a be the length of each side, and r the radius of the circumscribed circle.

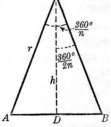

Then, $\quad \sin \dfrac{360°}{2n} = \sin \dfrac{180°}{n} = \dfrac{a}{2} \div r = \dfrac{a}{2r}$

and $\quad\quad\quad r = \dfrac{a}{2 \sin \dfrac{180°}{n}}.$

Problem 2. A regular polygon of n sides is inscribed in a circle of radius r; find the length of each side (AB) of the polygon.

Solution: Using the same notation as in Problem 1,

$$r = \frac{a}{2 \sin \dfrac{180°}{n}}, \quad \text{and hence } a = 2r \sin \frac{180°}{n}$$

Thus, if r equals unity, and $n = 16$, then $a = 2 \sin 11° 15'$.

Problem 3. Given the number of sides of a regular polygon and the length of each side, to find the area of the polygon.

Solution: Using the notation of Problem 1, let $OD = h$

Then, $\quad\quad \dfrac{h}{a/2} = \dfrac{2h}{a} = \cot \dfrac{180°}{n} \text{ and } h = \dfrac{a}{2} \cot \dfrac{180°}{n}.$

Hence, $\quad\quad \text{area} = n \times \dfrac{a}{2} \times \dfrac{a}{2} \cot \dfrac{180°}{n} = n \dfrac{a^2}{4} \cot \dfrac{180°}{n}.$

Thus, if $n = 12$, and $a = 20$, then area $= 12 \cdot \dfrac{400}{4} \cot \dfrac{180°}{12} = 1200 \cot 15°.$

EXERCISES

Using the notation of the above Problems, find the required parts in each of the following.

Given	Required	Given	Required
1. $a = 6, n = 10$	r, h	4. $r = 8, n = 12$	a, area
2. $a = 15, n = 7$	r, h	5. $r = 20, n = 32$	a, area
3. $r = 10, n = 9$	a, h	6. $a = 2, n = 24$	r, area

73. The solution of problems.—In solving problems by using the formulas of trigonometry it is important to obtain a general algebraic solution before doing any of the work of numerical computation. This is illustrated in the solutions of Problems given on this page.

Problem 1. In the figure find the line x (DB) in terms[1] of α, β, and b.
Solution: Let $CD = a$.

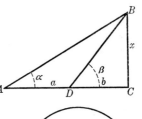

Then, $\tan \alpha = \dfrac{a}{b}$

and $\tan \beta = \dfrac{a + x}{b}$.

Hence, $\tan \beta - \tan \alpha = \dfrac{a + x}{b} - \dfrac{a}{b} = \dfrac{x}{b}$

and $\qquad x = b (\tan \beta - \tan \alpha)$.

Thus, if
$\beta = 37° 20'$, $\alpha = 21° 40'$, and $b = 140$,
then,
$b (\tan \beta - \tan \alpha) = 140 (.7627 - .3973) = 51.156 = x$.

In this case the table of natural functions should be used to find $\tan \beta$ and $\tan \alpha$.

Problem 2. In the figure find x in terms of a, α, and β.
Solution: Let $DC = b$.

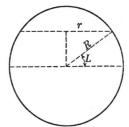

Then, $\qquad \cot \beta = \dfrac{b}{x}$ and $\cot \alpha = \dfrac{b + a}{x}$.

Hence, $\qquad \cot \alpha - \cot \beta = \dfrac{b + a}{x} - \dfrac{b}{x} = \dfrac{a}{x}$

and $\qquad x = \dfrac{a}{\cot \alpha - \cot \beta}$.

Thus, if $\alpha = 14° 50'$, $\beta = 31° 30'$, and $a = 500$,

then, $x = \dfrac{500}{3.7760 - 1.6319} = \dfrac{500}{2.1441} = 233.20$.

Problem 3. Find the length of a degree of longitude on the earth when the latitude and the radius of the earth are given.

Solution: Let L = latitude in degrees, R the radius of the earth (it is assumed that the earth is spherical in shape), and r the radius of the circle of latitude. Then, $r = R \cos L$.

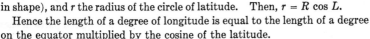

Hence the length of a degree of longitude is equal to the length of a degree on the equator multiplied by the cosine of the latitude.

Thus the length of a degree of longitude on the 42d parallel is $\cos 42°$ multiplied by the length of one degree at the equator.

---

[1] Greek letters, such as α (alpha), β (beta), γ (gamma), θ (theta), etc., are often used to designate angles.

74. Simple surveying using right triangles.—The first step in surveying a straight line A_1B_1 is to determine its direction, which is called its **bearing.** The surveyor stands at the point A_1 and faces north (in the first figure).[1] He then turns eastward through an angle of 37° and says that the bearing of A_1B_1 is N. 37° E. (read "north 37° east"). In the second figure the bearing of A_2B_2 is N. 69° W. (north 69° west); in the third it is S. 28° W.; and the fourth, S. 43° E.

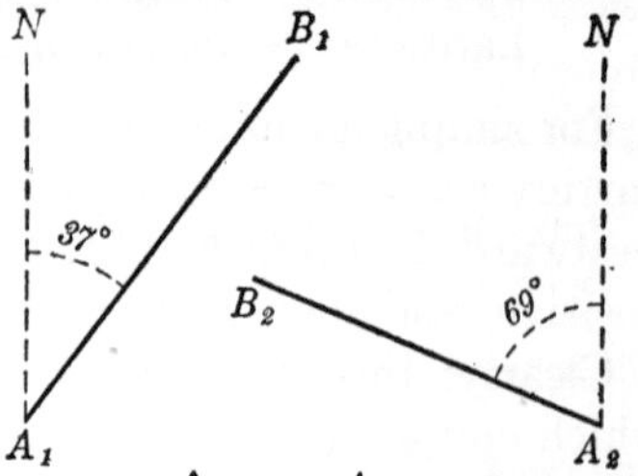

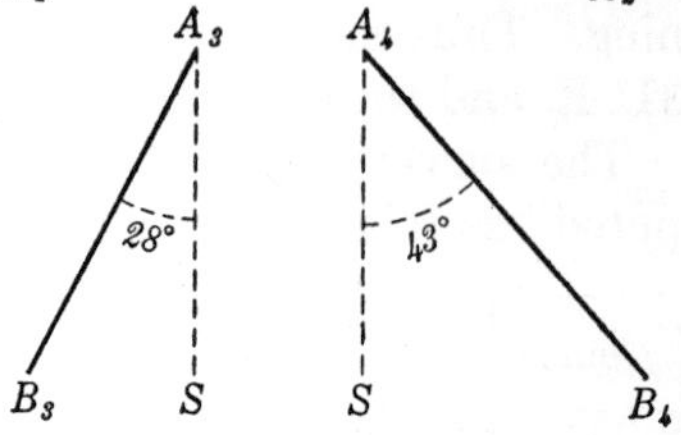

For the present we will assume that the survey is on a level plane. The length of the line AB is then called the **course** AB. The surveyor's work then consists in finding the bearing and length of each course in his survey. In the survey sketched at the right the surveyor obtains the following data.

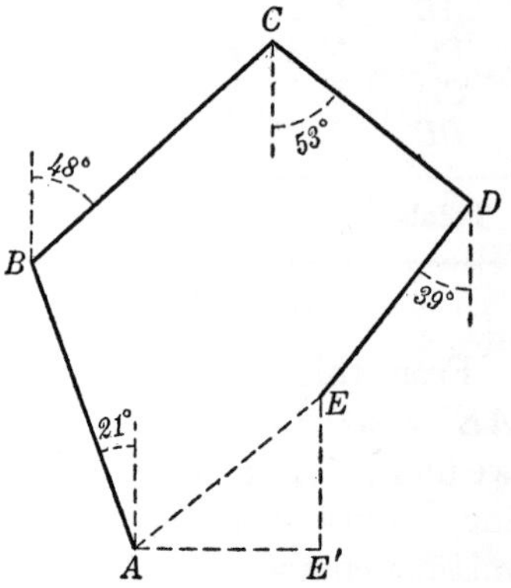

Course	Bearing	Length
AB	N. 21° W.	387.4
BC	N. 48° E.	432.5
CD	S. 53° E.	291.6
DE	S. 39° W.	214.8

In going from A to B in this figure one goes north (or south) a distance AC. This is called the **latitude** of the course AB. The eastward (or westward) component, CB, is the **departure** of the course.

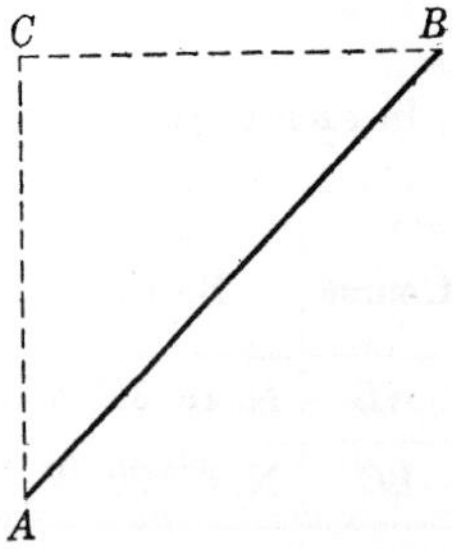

---

[1] In practice the line A_1N does not point exactly north, since the direction is read from the compass, but in a small survey the compass needle points nearly enough in the same direction so that the dotted lines shown in the figures will be "sensibly" parallel, and this is really what is needed.

The following formulas are now obvious

Departure = length of course × sine of bearing.   [13]
Latitude   = length of course × cosine of bearing.   [14]

For simplicity in arranging the computing, departure eastward is called positive and departure westward is negative. Latitude northward is positive, and southward negative.

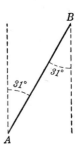

Clearly, the direction of these depends upon which end of the course is regarded as its beginning. Thus the bearing of AB in the figure is N. 31° E. and the bearing of BA is S. 31° W.

The survey noted on page 58 is then "computed" as follows.

Course	Bearing	Length	Dept.+	Dept.−	Lat.+	Lat.−
AB	N. 21° W.	387.4		138.8	361.7	
BC	N. 48° E.	432.5	321.4		289.4	
CD	S. 53° E.	291.6	232.9			175.5
DE	S. 39° W.	214.8		135.2		166.9
Totals			554.3	274.0	651.1	342.4

Net Dept. = 280.3+   Net Lat. = 308.7+

From this computation we know that in the figure (page 58) $AE' = 280.3$ and $E'E = 308.7$. Computing the right $\triangle AE'E$ we find $\angle E'EA$, which gives the bearing of the missing, or "closing," course EA, and the length EA, which is the length of the missing course.

EXERCISES

In each of the following find the missing data.

1.

Course	Bearing	Length of Course
AB	N. 49° 30′ W.	493.7
BC	N. 67° 20′ W.	2067.0
CD	S. 12° 20′ W.	964.2
DA	?	?

2.

Course	Bearing	Length of Course
AB	S. 17° E.	837.6
BC	S. 81° 30′ E.	928.2
CD	N. 16° W.	727.9
DA	?	?

PROBLEMS

For the sake of practice, by interpolating, compute angles to the nearest second and distances to five significant digits.

GROUP A

1. A hole is bored through a six-inch timber making an angle of 68° 30′ with the face of the timber. Find the length of the hole.

2. The cross section of a cement block is a right triangle. The hypotenuse measures 37.8 inches, one side 22.5 inches. Find the angle between these.

3. An upright pole is broken off in such a way that the top end touches the ground 12 feet 6 inches from the foot, and makes an angle of 72° with the ground. Find the original height of the pole.

4. A tree stands on a level plot of ground. The line of sight from the top of the tree to a point on the ground 125 feet from the foot of the tree makes an angle of 53° 20′ with the horizontal. Find the height of the tree.

5. A straightedge 7.632 inches long cuts off a corner of a square, 5.016 inches from one corner. Find the angles which it makes with the sides of the square.

6. A guy wire 50 feet long makes an angle of 64° 30′ with the horizontal and touches the ground in the same horizontal plane with the base of the pole which it supports. Find the height from the ground to the point at which it is attached to the pole.

7. From one corner of a square field whose side is 360 feet long, a line is run to the middle of an opposite side. Find the angles which the line makes with the three sides which it meets.

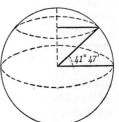

8. Find the length of a degree of longitude at latitude 41° 47′, the radius of the earth being 3956 miles.

9. Find the angles of an isosceles triangle whose sides are 16, 16, and 21.

10. Find the length of a side of a regular polygon of 12 sides inscribed in a circle with radius 9.45 inches.

GROUP B

1. The top of a vertical cliff is known to be 227 feet above the level of a lake. The angle of elevation of the top of the cliff as viewed from a boat on the lake is 20° 20′. Find the horizontal distance from the boat to the face of the cliff.

2. A river flows directly southward at the rate of 4.5 miles an hour. A boat pointed directly westward moves at the rate of 10.5 miles an hour. Find the direction in which the boat actually moves.

3. The ridge pole of a roof is 6 feet 4 inches above the eaves, and the rafters are 9 feet 6 inches long. Find the angle the rafter makes with the horizontal.

4. A rectangular field is 635 feet long and 217 feet wide. Find the angle that a line connecting opposite corners makes with the longer sides.

5. Find the angles of an isosceles triangle whose sides are 16, 21, and 21.

6. Find the length of a degree of longitude at latitude 58° 15′, the earth's radius being 3956 miles. (See figure for problem 8, group A, page 60.)

7. The legs of a carpenter's horse are 26 inches long. At the top they are 7 inches apart, at the base 18 inches apart. Find the angle which each makes with the vertical.

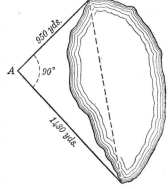

8. A straight level tunnel runs through an embankment. The surface of this embankment makes an angle of 41° 50′ with the horizontal on one side, of 48° 10′ on the other. The former slope measures 580 feet from the opening of the tunnel to the ridge. Find the length of the tunnel.

9. Find the length of a side of a regular polygon of 10 sides inscribed in a circle whose radius is 8.65 inches.

10. Two sides of a triangle are 18.64 and 13.45. The angle between them is 48° 15′. Find the projection of the shorter upon the longer.

GROUP C

1. The angle of elevation of the top of a tower from a point in the same horizontal plane as its base is 39° 10′. If the point of observation is 212 feet from the base, what is the height of the tower?

2. A brace between two shelves one foot apart is 13.87 inches long. Find the acute angle between the brace and one of the shelves.

3. From a point A, 950 yards from one end of a lake and 1430 yards from the other extremity, the lake subtends an angle of 90°. Find the length of the lake.

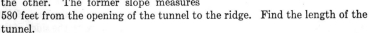

4. Find the angles which the diagonal of a rectangle makes with the longer side if the sides are 7.37 and 5.19.

5. Find the length of one of the two equal sides of an isosceles triangle if the base is 18.25 and the angle opposite the base is 70° 25′.

6. A ship travels N. 24° 37′ E. with a speed of 18 miles per hour. Find its northward speed.

7. A stretched string 24 feet long reaches from a window sill to a point on a level ground 11 feet 4 inches from the base of the building. Find the angle between the string and the horizontal.

8. Find the length of a degree of longitude at latitude 35° 14', the radius of the earth being 3956.   (See figure for problem 8, Group A, page 60.)

9. The roof of a garage slopes at an angle of 38° 30' with the horizontal for a distance of 9 feet 8 inches.   If the eaves are 12 feet 5 inches above the ground, find the height of the ridge pole.

10. Find the length of the side of a regular polygon of 16 sides inscribed in a circle whose radius is 5.42 inches.

MISCELLANEOUS PROBLEMS

For computations which cannot be made by the use of logarithms, use natural functions from the Table, pages 74–91.

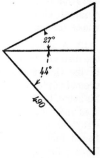

1. A regular octagonal nut measures $1\frac{15}{16}$ inches from A to B.   Find the distance from C to D.

2. The beam of a hoisting crane is 36 feet long. The crane is supported on a surface which dips 12° from the horizontal.   Find the vertical distance from the top of the beam to the sloping surface when the beam makes an angle of 47° with the horizontal.

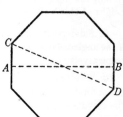

3. In the side of a hill which slopes upward at an angle of 27° a tunnel is bored, sloping downward at an angle of 44° with the horizontal.   What is the vertical distance to the surface of the hill from a point 490 feet down the tunnel?

4. The shadow of a post is 5 feet longer when the sun's altitude is 30° than when it is 45°.   Find the height of the post.   See figure below.

5. A ship sailing on a straight course observes a lighthouse at an angle of 27° 10' to the left of its course.   After sailing 4 miles this angle is 38° 40'.   What is the shortest distance from the lighthouse to the course of the ship?

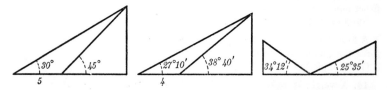

6. Two pillars of equal height stand on opposite sides of a roadway which is 100 feet wide.   At a point in the road between the pillars, the angles of elevation of their tops are 25° 35' and 34° 12', respectively.   Find the height of the pillars and the position of the point of observation.

7. Solve problem 6 if the width of the roadway is a, and the angles of elevation are α and β. Show that the height of the pillars and the distances from the sides of the roadway to the point of observation are

$$\frac{a \tan \alpha \tan \beta}{\tan \alpha + \tan \beta}, \quad \frac{a \tan \alpha}{\tan \alpha + \tan \beta}, \quad \frac{a \tan \beta}{\tan \alpha + \tan \beta}$$

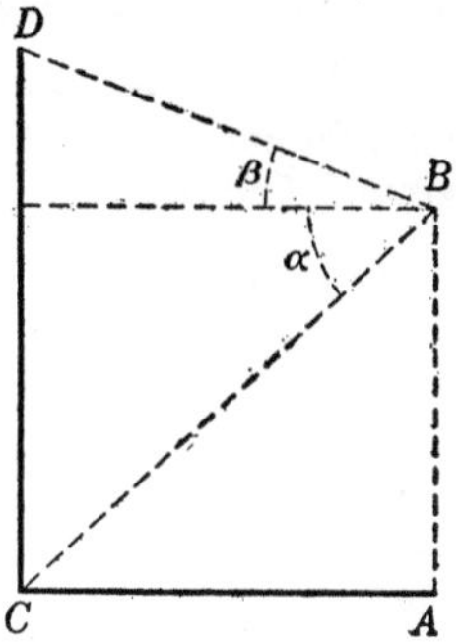

8. From a window 36 feet above a street the angle of depression of the bottom of a building on the opposite side is 24° 45′ and the angle of elevation of the top of this building is 37° 20′. Find the height of this building.

9. Solve problem 8 if in the figure $AB = a$, and if the angles of depression and elevation are α and β, respectively.

10. Two towers are 75 and 180 feet high, respectively. From the foot of the second, the elevation of the top of the first is found to be 58° 11′. Find the elevation of the top of the second from the foot of the first.

11. Solve problem 10 if the heights of the towers are a and b and the elevation of the first tower from the foot of the second is α. Show that the required elevation is the angle whose tangent is $(b \tan \alpha)/a$.

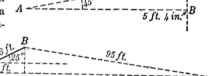

12. A surveyor wants to find the distance from A to B across a ravine that makes direct measurement difficult. He sends his helper to B with a graduated rod. Leveling his instrument at A he reads 5 feet 4 inches on the rod.

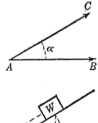

Then pointing the instrument to the point marked 14 feet on the rod he reads a vertical angle of 45′. What is the distance from A to B?

13. A fishing pole 16 feet long is held 5 feet above the surface of the lake and at an angle of 25°. If the length of the line is 95 feet, how far from his position can the fisherman cast his bait?

Suggestion: First find DB in the figure above.

A force f acting in the direction AB has a component force along a line AC, which is equal to $f \cos \alpha$ where α is the angle between AB and AC.

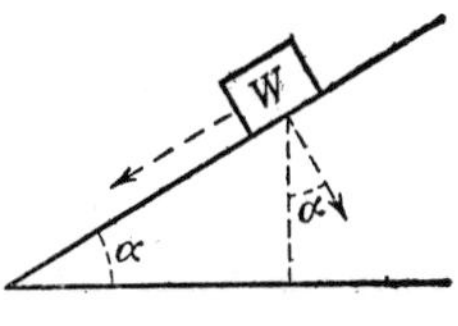

14. A weight W rests on an inclined plank making an angle α with the horizontal. Find formulas giving the components of this weight acting at right angles to the plank (tending to bend it) and the component tending to make the weight slide down the plank.

15. In the figure, $ABCD$ is a parallelogram, in which AB represents a force acting in the direction AB, and AD represents a force acting in the direction AD. The lengths of these lines represent the magnitude of the forces. Show that the length of the line AC represents the sum of the components of these forces acting in the direction AC.

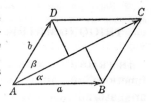

16. If in the figure $AC = 6$, and $CE = 3.5$, find the area of that part of the circle which is above the line AB.

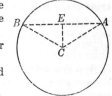

Suggestion: (1) Find $\angle ACB$, (2) find area of sector ACB, (3) find area of triangle ACB.

17. Find the angle between a diagonal of a cube and an edge of the cube which meets it.

18. A right pyramid whose base is a square with sides 16 has an altitude 9. Find the angle between an edge and a side of the base meeting it.

19. The base of the Great Pyramid is a square whose sides are 756 feet. The edge from a corner to the apex is 699 feet. Find the altitude of the pyramid and the angle with the plane of the base made by the edge. That is, in the figure find VE and $\angle VBE$. Also find $\angle VFE$, F being the middle point of BC. This angle is the inclination of the sides of the pyramid.

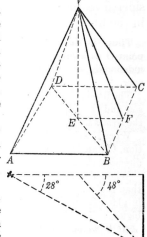

20. An airplane is flying at the rate of 150 miles per hour. The pilot observes a town directly under his path with angle of depression of $28°$. One minute later this angle is $48°$. At what elevation is he flying?

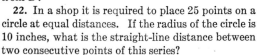

21. In the figure below, $\angle B$ is a right angle. At A is a tower which seen from B has an angle of elevation of $58°$ and from C has an elevation of $31°$. If D is the middle point of CB, what is the angle of elevation of the tower when seen from D?

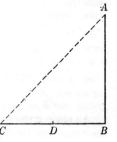

22. In a shop it is required to place 25 points on a circle at equal distances. If the radius of the circle is 10 inches, what is the straight-line distance between two consecutive points of this series?

23. A mountain observed from a point B directly south of it has an elevation of $8° 40'$. The survey then goes 2 miles on a horizontal line directly west of B and finds that the elevation is $6° 20'$. What is the height of the mountain above the plane and what is the horizontal distance from B to the mountain?

CHAPTER V

TRIGONOMETRIC FUNCTIONS OF ANY ANGLE

IN PRACTICAL work in solving triangles the "trigonometric functions" are always used. For acute angles these functions are naturally and easily defined in terms of the sides of a right triangle. But in dealing with obtuse angles it is most natural to define them in a way that applies without change when "angle" is considered from a more general point of view. In this chapter we will therefore define any "angle" and then define the trigonometric functions of such angles.

75. A general definition of angle.—An angle may be regarded as *generated* by making one of its sides rotate about the vertex while the other side remains fixed. The angle may be considered as the amount of rotation of a line about a fixed point in the line.

Thus, the side *OA* may be regarded as fixed, while *OB* rotates about the point *O* as a pivot. In this manner the side *OB* may continue to rotate indefinitely, sweeping out any number of degrees whatever.

The fixed side *OA* of the angle *AOB* is called the *initial side* and the side *OB*, which generates the angle, is called the *terminal side*.

When the side *OB* swings in the counterclockwise direction, the angle is regarded as *positive*, and when *OB* swings in the clockwise direction the angle is *negative*.

When dealing with angles greater than 180°, the notation for angles used in plane geometry often leads to ambiguity. Thus in the first figure below ∠*AOB* would naturally indicate an ordinary obtuse angle, or possibly a

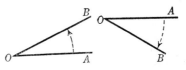

negative angle. If we wish to refer to the angle generated when the terminal side *OB* swings through 225°, it becomes necessary to use some other notation. We may, as in the figure, use an arc with the number of degrees. Or we may use a single letter with the arc.

An angle greater than 360° may be represented as in the third figure.

76. A system of coordinates.—Before defining the "functions" of general angles, it is necessary to describe a special method of locating points in a plane.

Two fixed lines at right angles to each other are taken as reference lines and the distances and directions from these lines to a point serve to locate the point. The fixed lines are called the **coordinate axes,** the horizontal axis being called the **x-axis,** and the vertical axis the **y-axis.**

The distances AP and BP from the x-axis and y-axis, respectively, to the point P are called the **coordinates** of the point P. The distance BP from the y-axis (parallel to the x-axis) is called the **abscissa** of P, and the distance AP from the x-axis is the **ordinate** of P.

In giving the coordinates of a point the abscissa is always given first. Thus, the point (3, 2) is the point whose abscissa is 3 and whose ordinate is 2. The abscissa is often denoted by x and the ordinate by y. The point (3, 2) is the point $x = 3, y = 2$.

If the point P (or S) is to the right of the y-axis, its abscissa is positive, and if Q (or R) is to the left of the y-axis, the abscissa is negative. If P (or Q) is above the x-axis, its ordinate is positive, and if R (or S) is below the x-axis, its ordinate is negative.

This method of locating a point in a plane is closely analogous to the method used in geography for locating a point on the earth's surface. The latitude is the distance in degrees north or south of the equator and the longitude is the distance east or west of the prime meridian (the meridian of Greenwich).

The horizontal axis then corresponds to the equator and the vertical axis to the prime meridian. Instead of *north* and *south, east* and *west* used in geography to indicate direction from the reference lines, the signs + and − are used.

Hence, both in geography and in mathematics, two numbers giving the distances and directions from two fundamental lines serve to locate a point.

In the United States land survey the description of location of townships also uses this method. Principal meridians are established and also parallels of latitude. A township is then said to be so far east or west of a particular principal meridian, and so far north or south of a certain parallel.

In this case the parallel of latitude corresponds to the x-axis and the principal meridian corresponds to the y-axis.

77. Angles in various quadrants.—The coordinate axes divide the plane into four parts called **quadrants.** These quadrants are called the first, second, third, and fourth quadrants, as indicated in the figure.

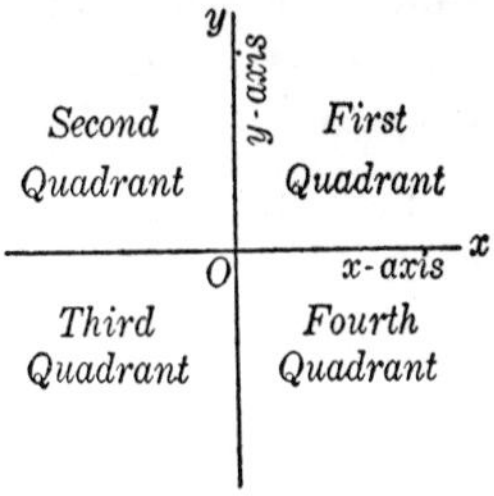

In studying angles, the vertex is placed at the intersection point O of a pair of coordinate axes, with the initial side extending to the right along the x-axis.

If the terminal side of an angle so placed falls within the first quadrant the angle is said to be in the first quadrant. That is, an angle between 0° and 90° is in the first quadrant.

If the terminal side of the angle lies within the second quadrant, the angle is in the second quadrant. That is, angles between 90° and 180° are in the second quadrant. Thus AOB is in the first quadrant and AOB' is in the second.

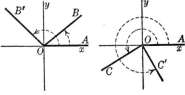

Similarly, the angles AOC and AOC' in the second figure are said to be in the third and fourth quadrants, respectively.

That is, angles between 180° and 270° are in the third quadrant and angles between 270° and 360° are in the fourth quadrant.

In general, any angle is said to be in the quadrant in which its terminal side lies.

This statement applies also to negative angles. Thus, an angle between −270° and −360° is in the first quadrant, an angle between −180° and −270° is in the second quadrant, and so on.

78. Positive and negative line segments.—A line segment on the x-axis is positive if read from left to right, no matter whether the segment lies to the right or the left of the origin.

Thus, OA and MO are positive segments, while AO and OM are negative. Similarly, segments read upward are positive and those read downward are negative.

Any segment read in the direction away from the origin on the terminal side of an angle is positive, while it is negative if on a prolongation of the terminal side backward through the origin.

79. Definitions of functions of any angle.—Consider a given angle A of any size and quality. Place the angle upon a set of coordinate axes XOY (any one of the four figures below), with its vertex at O and its initial side along OX. On its terminal side select any point P. From P drop a perpendicular QP to the x-axis.

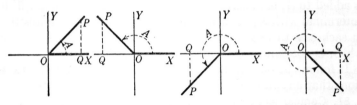

We have the following definitions applicable to all four figures.

$$\sin A = \frac{QP}{OP} = \frac{\text{ordinate}}{\text{distance}} \qquad \csc A = \frac{OP}{QP} = \frac{\text{distance}}{\text{ordinate}}$$

$$\cos A = \frac{OQ}{OP} = \frac{\text{abscissa}}{\text{distance}} \qquad \sec A = \frac{OP}{OQ} = \frac{\text{distance}}{\text{abscissa}}$$

$$\tan A = \frac{QP}{OQ} = \frac{\text{ordinate}}{\text{abscissa}} \qquad \cot A = \frac{OQ}{QP} = \frac{\text{abscissa}}{\text{ordinate}}$$

SIGHT WORK

1. In which quadrants is the ordinate of a point positive? In which quadrants is it negative?

2. The distance OP on the terminal side of the angle has which sign, positive or negative?

3. In which quadrants is the sine of an angle positive? In which quadrants is it negative?

4. In which quadrants is the abscissa of a point positive? In which quadrants is it negative?

5. In which quadrants is the cosine of an angle positive? In which quadrants is it negative?

6. In which quadrants is the tangent of an angle positive? In which quadrants is it negative?

7. Answer questions like those in problem 6 for cotangents, secants, cosecants.

8. Which functions of $67°$ are positive? Which ones, if any, are negative?

9. Which functions if any of $135°$ are positive? Which ones, if any, are negative?

10. Which functions of $225°$, if any, are positive? Which ones are negative?

11. Which functions of $330°$, if any, are positive? Which ones are negative?

80. Coterminal angles and their functions.—Angles whose initial and terminal sides coincide are said to be **coterminal**. It is clear that if 360° is added to the angle A in the figures on page 68, or subtracted from it, the resulting angle will be coterminal with A. Similarly, if twice 360° $(2 \cdot 360°)$, $3 \cdot 360°$, etc., is added to A, or subtracted from it, the resulting angle will be coterminal with A. It is apparent directly from the figures that in each case there is a negative angle numerically less than 360° which is coterminal with A.

It follows at once from the definitions of trigonometric functions that any function is the same for all *coterminal angles*.

81. Comparison of definitions.—In the first figure on page 68 the triangle OQP is an ordinary right triangle. Using this figure we may write the definitions

$$\sin A = \frac{QP}{OP} = \frac{\text{side opposite}}{\text{hypotenuse}} \qquad \csc A = \frac{OP}{QP} = \frac{\text{hypotenuse}}{\text{side opposite}}$$

$$\cos A = \frac{OQ}{OP} = \frac{\text{side adjacent}}{\text{hypotenuse}} \qquad \sec A = \frac{OP}{OQ} = \frac{\text{hypotenuse}}{\text{side adjacent}}$$

$$\tan A = \frac{QP}{OQ} = \frac{\text{side opposite}}{\text{side adjacent}} \qquad \cot A = \frac{OQ}{QP} = \frac{\text{side adjacent}}{\text{side opposite}}$$

These definitions, which are those given on page 11 for acute angles, are therefore identical with those on page 68 when the latter are made to apply to acute angles.

From the purely logical point of view definitions in mathematics are entirely arbitrary. We can define a word any way we like, the only restriction being that, the definition once made, we *must* adhere to it throughout. That is, we must use the word with precisely the meaning we have given it in our definition.

For practical purposes there are restrictions, however. For one thing we must fix our schemes and definitions so that the resulting theory will flow smoothly, with few if any exceptions to our general statements, and so that the statements will be as precise and brief as possible.

Another restriction on us is that we must use words with the meaning that others attach to them in case the words are in general use. The language of mathematics is exceptionally fixed in this respect. It is in fact international. Wherever trigonometry, for example, is studied, the words we have defined have exactly the meaning that we have given them.

82. Functions of supplementary angles.—Two angles whose sum is 180° (two rt $\angle s$) are said to be **supplementary.** In the figure let $\angle AOB$ and $\angle AOB'$ be supplementary. Lay off $OP = OP'$, and construct PQ and $P'Q'$ perpendicular to the x-axis. It is clear that $\angle AOB = \angle COB'$, and hence that $QP = Q'P'$ and $OQ = -OQ'$. It follows at once that,

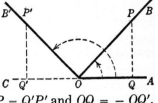

(1) $\sin AOB = \sin AOB'$,
(2) $\cos AOB = -\cos AOB'$,
(3) $\tan AOB = -\tan AOB'$,

(4) $\cot AOB = -\cot AOB'$,
(5) $\sec AOB = -\sec AOB'$,
(6) $\csc AOB = \csc AOB'$.

These propositions hold also for positive and negative angles of any size. This subject is considered further in Chapter VIII. Stated in words, these formulas are:

If two angles are supplementary their sines are equal, and also their cosecants. The cosines, tangents, cotangents, and secants of these angles are equal numerically, but opposite in sign.

Since A and $180° - A$ are supplementary angles, this rule may be stated as follows:

$\sin A = \sin (180° - A)$ [15] $\cos A = -\cos (180° - A)$ [16]
$\tan A = -\tan (180° - A)$ [17] $\cot A = -\cot (180° - A)$ [18]
$\sec A = -\sec (180° - A)$ [19] $\csc A = \csc (180° - A)$ [20]

From the formula $\sin A = \sin (180° - A)$ we know that in order to find the sine of an angle between 90° and 180° we subtract the angle from 180° and then find the sine of the remainder.

Thus $\sin 147° = \sin (180° - 147°) = \sin 33°$.

Note that 147° and 33° have the same sine. Hence if the sine of an angle of a triangle is given we do not know whether the angle is acute or obtuse.

Make similar statements for finding the other five functions of an angle between 90° and 180°.

EXERCISES

Find the following, using the table of natural functions. Also find the "logarithmic functions" of these angles.

1. $\sin 127° 18'$
2. $\sin 104° 54' 15''$
3. $\cos 157° 40'$
4. $\cos 131° 12' 45''$

5. $\tan 112° 18' 30''$
6. $\cot 98° 35' 15''$
7. $\sin 161° 12' 20''$
8. $\cos 91° 0' 36''$

9. $\cot 131° 12' 45''$
10. $\cos 150° 15' 30''$
11. $\sin 95° 26' 18''$
12. $\tan 167° 4' 40''$

CHAPTER VI

SOLUTION OF OBLIQUE TRIANGLES

A TRIANGLE which is not right angled is said to be **oblique**. We will now proceed to solve such triangles. As has already been noted, a triangle is completely determined if there are given:

(a) two angles and any side; (b) two sides and the included angle; (c) three sides.

If two sides and the angle opposite one of them are given, it is sometimes possible to construct two different triangles fulfilling the conditions. Again, there may be only one such triangle, or possibly none. This case requires special discussion, but is naturally connected with (a), and is given as our Case II.

It is evident, therefore, that the problem of solving oblique triangles falls under four essentially different cases:

Case   I. Given two angles and any side.
Case   II. Given two sides and the angle opposite one of them.
Case III. Given two sides and the included angle.
Case IV. Given three sides.

For the purpose of this chapter we will use the notation shown in the figure for the parts of a triangle. In terms of this notation Cases I, II, III, IV may be stated as follows.

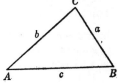

Case   I. Given A, B, c; find C, a, b. Given A, B, a; find C, b, c.

Case   II. Given a, b, A; find c, B, C.
Case III. Given b, c, A; find a, B, C.
Case IV. Given a, b, c; find A, B, C.

We shall also solve the problem of finding the area of a triangle when parts sufficient to determine it are given.

83. Solution of oblique triangles using right triangles.—That oblique triangles may be solved by dividing them into right triangles is easily shown. We will solve in order the four problems enumerated on page 71.

Case I. Since any angle of a triangle may be found when two angles are given ($C = 180 - \overline{A + B}$), we find C at once. The angle C may be acute or obtuse as indicated in the figures.

> Given A, B, c;
> find C, a, b.

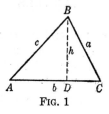 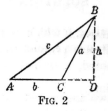

FIG. 1   FIG. 2

In both figures $BD = h$ is perpendicular to the line AC. In Fig. 1, $b = AD + DC$ and in Fig. 2, $b = AD - CD$. In both figures $AD = c \cos A$ and $h = c \sin A$.

In both figures, in the right triangle CBD, h and an acute angle are now known. (Note that in Fig. 2, $\angle DCB = 180° - \angle ACB$.) Hence a and DC can be found and then b can be found for both triangles, and our problem is solved completely.

Case II. Since A, c, a are given, it is clear that a must be long enough to reach from B to the line AC. If a is exactly equal to h in the figure the right-angled triangle ABD is the required triangle.

> Given A, c, a;
> find B, C, b.

If a is greater than h but less than c we have the two triangles ABC and ABC'. In the right triangle ABD, $h = c \sin A$ and $AD = c \cos A$. In the right triangle CBD we now know h and a and hence we can find angle C and the side DC. But $AC = AD + DC$ and $AC' = AD - CD$. Since $\angle AC'B = 180° - \angle C$ we find the required parts in the two triangles ABC and ABC'.

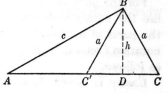

Each of these triangles is a correct answer to our problem. If a is equal to, or greater than, c, there is obviously only one correct answer.

Cases III and IV. These cases are solved by finding a formula involving three sides and one angle of a triangle. In the first figure (an acute angled triangle)

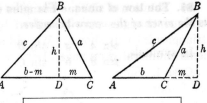

Given a, b, C; find A, B, c.
Given a, b, c; find A, B, C.

$$h^2 = a^2 - m^2 \text{ and}$$
$$c^2 = h^2 + (b - m)^2 = h^2 + b^2 - 2bm + m^2$$

Substituting for h^2, $c^2 = a^2 + b^2 - 2bm$
But $m = a \cos c$, and hence,

$$c^2 = a^2 + b^2 - 2ab \cos C \qquad [21]$$

Similarly, $\quad b^2 = a^2 + c^2 - 2ac \cos B,$
and $\quad c^2 = b^2 + c^2 - 2bc \cos A.$

In the second figure, $c^2 = h^2 + (b + m)^2 = h^2 + b^2 + 2bm + m^2$.
But in this figure $\cos C = -m/a$, or $m = -a \cos C$.
Hence in this figure also $c^2 = a^2 + b^2 - 2ab \cos C$.

These formulas are stated in words as follows:

In any triangle, the square of one side is equal to the sum of the squares of the other sides minus twice their product multiplied by the cosine of the included angle.

This theorem is called the **law of cosines.**

Solving the above formula for $\cos C$, we have

$\cos C = \dfrac{a^2 + b^2 - c^2}{2ab}$, and similarly for $\cos A$ and $\cos B$.

By means of these formulas the angles of a triangle may be found when its sides are given.

EXERCISES

Solve the following triangles.

1. $A = 47° 30'$
   $B = 32° 15'$
   $c = 87.6$

2. $A = 61° 20'$
   $b = 36.4$
   $a = 41.8$

3. $a = 8$
   $b = 9$
   $c = 10$

4. $a = 12$
   $b = 16$
   $C = 51° 41'$

The work on pages 72 and 73 is intended primarily to show that oblique triangles may be solved by means of right triangles. But these methods are not adapted to the use of logarithms, and we will now proceed to develop formulas that will simplify greatly the work of computing.

84. The law of sines.—*The sides of a triangle are proportional to the sines of the opposite angles.*

In symbols, $\dfrac{\sin A}{\sin B} = \dfrac{a}{b}$, $\dfrac{\sin B}{\sin C} = \dfrac{b}{c}$, $\dfrac{\sin C}{\sin A} = \dfrac{c}{a}$. [22]

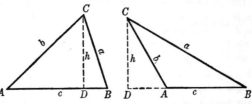

Proof: In the triangle ABC (either figure), drop the perpendicular h from the vertex C to the side AB (extended if necessary).

Then, $\sin A = \dfrac{h}{b}$ and $\sin B = \dfrac{h}{a}$

Dividing, $\sin A/\sin B = \dfrac{h/b}{h/a} = \dfrac{a}{b}$

Similarly we may prove

$\sin B/\sin C = b/c$ and $\sin C/\sin A = c/a$

85. Solution of triangles.—**Case I.** When two angles and a side of a triangle are given, the law of sines is used in solving the triangle.

Suppose the given parts are A, B, and side b. The first step is to find C by means of the formula $C = 180° - (A + B)$.

From $\sin A/\sin B = a/b$ we obtain $a = b \sin A/\sin B$.

Similarly, from $\sin C/\sin B = c/b$ we obtain $c = b \sin C/\sin B$.

Check: To check these values of a and c, use the formula

$\sin A/\sin C = a/c$ or $\sin C/\sin A = c/a$

If this relation holds, the values are *very likely* correct. If the relation does not hold, the values cannot be correct. These quotients should be found by long division using the natural functions from the table, for if they are found by using the same logarithms that were used in solving the problem, an error in finding a logarithm or an antilogarithm may not be disclosed. For another check, see page 185.

86. Computation.—The actual work of computing by logarithms in Case I is shown in the following.

Example. Given, $\angle A = 68° 30'$, $\angle B = 53° 18'$, $a = 58$. Find $\angle C$, and sides b and c.

First, $\angle C = 180° - (\angle A + \angle B) = 58° 12'$.

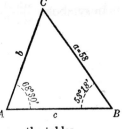

From $\dfrac{b}{a} = \dfrac{\sin B}{\sin A}$ and $\dfrac{c}{a} = \dfrac{\sin C}{\sin A}$ we have

$$b = a\,\frac{\sin B}{\sin A}, \quad c = a\,\frac{\sin C}{\sin A}.$$

Hence $\log b = \log a + \log \sin B - \log \sin A$,

and $\log c = \log a + \log \sin C - \log \sin A$.

Arrange all the work as follows before beginning to use the tables.

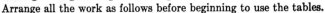

log 58 =	log 58 =
log sin 53° 18' = _____	log sin 58° 12' = _____
log sin 68° 30' =	log sin 68° 30' =
log b =	log c =
b =	c =

This skeleton should then be filled in as follows.

log 58 =	1.76343	log 58 =	1.76343
log sin 53° 18' =	9.90405	log sin 58° 12' =	9.92936
	11.66748		11.69279
log sin 68° 30' =	9.96868	log sin 68° 30' =	9.96868
log b =	1.69880	log c =	1.72411
b =	49.980	c =	52.980

Check: Use $\dfrac{b}{\sin B} = \dfrac{c}{\sin C}$, or better $\dfrac{\sin B}{b} = \dfrac{\sin C}{c}$.

From the table of natural functions, $\sin B = .80178$, $\sin C = .84989$.

```
           .01604 +                      .01604 +
    49.98)80178                   52.98)84989
          4998                          5298
         30198                         32009
         29988                         31788
          21000                         22100
          19992                         21192
```

EXERCISES

1. Using the figure of §84, draw the altitude on the side AC and prove that $\sin A / \sin C = a/c$.

Find the elements not given in the following:

2. $\begin{cases} \angle A = 52° 23' \\ \angle B = 73° 12' \\ a = 181.8 \end{cases}$ **3.** $\begin{cases} \angle A = 58° 28' \\ \angle B = 24° 19' \\ b = 381.6 \end{cases}$ **4.** $\begin{cases} \angle A = 81° 7' \\ \angle B = 23° 58' \\ c = 94.36 \end{cases}$

87. Solution of triangles.—Case II (the ambiguous case).
If it is required to solve a triangle having two given sides a and b and a given acute angle, as A, opposite one of them, then a number of possibilities arise, as indicated by the figures:

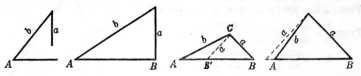

(1) If $a < b \sin A$, then there is no solution of the problem.

(2) If $a = b \sin A$, then there is only one solution, and the triangle is right angled at B.

(3) If $a < b$ and also $a > b \sin A$, then there are two triangles possessing the given properties.

That is, there are two solutions of the problem. In this case the angles opposite the side b ($\angle ABC$ and $\angle AB'C$) are supplementary. Hence, angle B or angle B' of the figure must be obtuse.

(4) If $a = b$ or $a > b$, there is only one solution, since in that case the angle opposite b is equal to or less than the angle opposite a. That is, angle B cannot be obtuse.

88. Computation.—The various possibilities just stated will appear when the attempt is made to compute the triangle. This is shown in the following examples.

Example 1. Compute the triangle if $a = 28$, $b = 46$, and $\angle A = 71° 43'$.

Solution: From $\dfrac{a}{\sin A} = \dfrac{b}{\sin B}$, we find

$$\sin B = \frac{b \sin A}{a},$$

and $\log \sin B = \log b + \log \sin A - \log a$.

$\log 46 =$	1.66276
$\log \sin 71° 43' =$	9.97750
	1.64026
$\log 28 =$	1.44716
$\log \sin B =$	$10.19310 - 10$

But $\log \sin B = 0.19310$ is at once seen to be impossible, for this would make $\sin B$ greater than 1. Hence in this case there is no solution.

Example 2. Compute the triangle if $a = 12$, $b = 24$, and $\angle A = 30°$.

Solution: Use $\sin B = \dfrac{b \sin A}{a}$

$\log 24 =$	1.38021
$\log \sin 30° =$	9.69897
	11.07918
$\log 12 =$	1.07918
$\log \sin B =$	0.00000

Since $\log \sin B = O$, we know that $\sin B = 1$, and hence $B = 90$. That is, the triangle ABC is right angled at B. In this case $a = b \sin A$.

Example 3. Solve the triangle if $a = 37.8$, $b = 43.2$ and $\angle A = 57°\ 45'$.

Solution: Use formula $\sin B = \dfrac{b \sin A}{a}$.

Then $\log \sin B = \log b + \log \sin A - \log a$.

$\log 43.2 = 1.63548$

$\log \sin 57°\ 45' = 9.92723$

$\overline{\ 11.56271}$

$\log 37.8 = 1.57749$

$\overline{\log \sin B = \ 9.98522}$

However, since $\sin x = \sin (180° - x)$ the angle B may also be $180° - 75°\ 8'$ $= 104°\ 52'$.

$B = 75°\ 8'\ 15''$, or $75°\ 8'$ to the nearest minute.

Then, $C = 180° - (57°\ 45' + 75°\ 8') = 47°\ 7'$ or
$C = 180° - (57°\ 45' + 104°\ 52') = 17°\ 23'$.

Using the sine formula, we now find the two possible values of the side c by using in succession these two values of angle C.

89. Ambiguity of Case II as shown in the computation. In all the examples given in §88 the formula $\sin B = \dfrac{b \sin A}{a}$ is used for the purpose of finding the angle B. From this formula the various possible cases are at once apparent.

(1) If $\sin B > 1$, i.e., $a < b \sin A$, the problem is obviously impossible, since a sine cannot be greater than unity.

(2) If $\sin B = 1$, i.e., $a = b \sin A$, then the only possible angle is a right angle, since $\sin 90° = 1$.

(3) If $\sin B < 1$, i.e., $a > b \sin A$, then there are two angles, each less than 180°, which have the required sine. Both of these are possible unless $a \lessgtr b$, in which case only the smaller may be used.

Problem: Study the case when $\angle A$, opposite a given side, is obtuse. Construct the figure and show that there is only one solution.

EXERCISES

In the following give all possible solutions:

1. $A = 47°\ 53'$	5. $C = 112°\ 21'$	9. $B = 58°\ 39'$
$a = 127.3$	$c = 855.5$	$C = 77°\ 12'$
$b = 148.2$	$b = 583.7$	$b = 563.0$
2. $A = 19°\ 38'$	6. $A = 18°\ 28'$	10. $C = 43°\ 41'$
$a = 10.92$	$C = 81°\ 19'$	$b = 104.21$
$b = 32.50$	$b = 7.562$	$c = 86.19$
3. $A = 68°\ 12'$	7. $B = 51°\ 12'$	11. $A = 96°\ 50'$
$a = 139.3$	$a = 357.2$	$a = 71.84$
$b = 151.7$	$b = 312.7$	$b = 75.60$
4. $B = 63°\ 28'$	8. $C = 18°\ 33'$	12. $A = 16°\ 18'$
$a = 722.8$	$a = 2.803$	$B = 58°\ 30'$
$b = 688.1$	$c = 2.001$	$c = 29.35$

90. The law of tangents.—When two sides and the included angle of a triangle are given, the remaining parts cannot be found by means of the sine formula. It is therefore necessary to develop another formula for this purpose. One such formula is the *tangent formula* or the *law of tangents.*

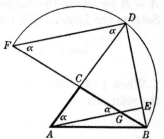

In the figure, ABC is any triangle in which BC is greater than AC. That is, $a > b$. With C as center and radius CB, construct a semicircle and extend the sides AC and BC to meet it in D and F as shown in the figure. Draw FD and BD, and then draw AE parallel to FD and meeting BC in G and BD in E. Since $\angle FDB$ is inscribed in a semicircle, it is a right angle, and hence AE is perpendicular to BD.

Since $\triangle CDF$ is isosceles, and AG and DF are parallel, it follows that the four angles marked α are equal. Hence $GC = AC = b$. Also $CF = a$. Hence $BG = a - b$ and $GF = a + b$.

In the triangles ABC and DFC, the angles at C are equal, and hence $2\alpha = A + B$, and $\alpha = \frac{1}{2}(A + B)$. Again $\angle BAE = \angle A - \angle \alpha = \angle A - \frac{1}{2}(A + B) = \frac{1}{2}(A - B)$.

In the two right triangles, BAE and DAE, $\tan BAE = BE/AE$ and $\tan DAE = ED/AE$.

Since $\angle BAE = \frac{1}{2}(A - B)$ and $\angle DAE = \alpha = \frac{1}{2}(A + B)$, we have

$$\frac{\tan \frac{1}{2}(A - B)}{\tan \frac{1}{2}(A + B)} = \frac{BE}{AE} \div \frac{ED}{AE} = \frac{BE}{ED}$$

In the triangle BDF, GE is parallel to FD and hence

$$\frac{BE}{ED} = \frac{BG}{GF} = \frac{a - b}{a + b}$$

Therefore

$$\frac{\tan \frac{1}{2}(A - B)}{\tan \frac{1}{2}(A + B)} = \frac{a - b}{a + b} \qquad [23]$$

Similarly

$$\frac{\tan \frac{1}{2}(B - C)}{\tan \frac{1}{2}(B + C)} = \frac{b - c}{b + c}, \quad \text{and} \quad \frac{\tan \frac{1}{2}(C - A)}{\tan \frac{1}{2}(C + A)} = \frac{c - a}{c + a}$$

These formulas are referred to as the **law of tangents.**

91. Solution of triangles: Case III.—If we have given two sides a and b and the included angle C, the first step is to find $A - B$ by using the tangent formula.
Solving the formula [23] for $\tan \frac{1}{2} (A - B)$, we have

$$\tan \tfrac{1}{2} (A - B) = \frac{a - b}{a + b} \tan \tfrac{1}{2} (A + B).$$

When $\frac{1}{2} (A - B)$ has been found, A and B are obtained from the relations:

$$A = \tfrac{1}{2} (A + B) + \tfrac{1}{2} (A - B)$$
$$B = \tfrac{1}{2} (A + B) - \tfrac{1}{2} (A - B).$$

The remaining side c may then be found by using the law of sines as in case I.   (Use $c = a \sin C / \sin A$.)

Check: To check see whether the relation $c = \dfrac{b \sin C}{\sin B}$ is satisfied.
If a as given is less than b, then $A < B$ and the formula becomes

$$\tan \tfrac{1}{2} (B - A) = \frac{b - a}{b + a} \tan \tfrac{1}{2} (B + A)$$

Computation.   Example: Given $A = 83°\ 44'$, $b = 78.4$, and $c = 61.3$.   Find angles B and C and side a.

The solution may be arranged thus:
Since $A + B + C = 180°$, $\frac{1}{2} (B + C) = 90° - \frac{1}{2} A = 90° - 41° 52' = 48° 8'$.

$$\tan \tfrac{1}{2} (B - C) = \frac{b - c}{b + c} \tan \tfrac{1}{2}(B + C), \quad a = \frac{b \sin A}{\sin B} = \frac{c \sin A}{\sin C}$$

$\log \tan \frac{1}{2} (B - C) = \log (b - c) + \log \tan \frac{1}{2} (B + C) + \text{colog} (b + c)$.
$\log a = \log b + \log \sin A + \text{colog} \sin B = \log c + \log \sin A + \text{colog} \sin C$

$b = \quad 78.4$	$\log b = 1.89432$
$c = \quad 61.3$	$\log \sin A = 9.99740$
$b + c = \overline{139.7}$	$\text{colog} \sin B = 0.08188$
$b - c = \quad 17.1$	$\log a = \overline{1.97360}$

$\log (b - c) = 1.23300$	$\log c = 1.78746$
$\log \tan \frac{1}{2} (B + C) = 0.04760$	$\log \sin A = 9.99740$
$\text{colog} (b + c) = 7.85480$	$\text{colog} \sin C = 0.18874$
$\log \tan \frac{1}{2} (B - C) = \overline{9.13540}$	$\log a = \overline{1.97360}$
$\frac{1}{2} (B - C) = \quad 7° 46' 39''$	
$\frac{1}{2} (B + C) = 48° 8'$	$a = 94.102$

$$B = 55° 54' 39''$$
$$C = 40° 21' 21''$$

This agreement furnishes a check on the work.

EXERCISES

Solve the following triangles.

1. $A = 61°34'$ 2. $B = 17°57'$ 3. $C = 73°29'$
   $b = 31.4$ $a = 416.3$ $a = 2894$
   $c = 47.1$ $c = 372.5$ $b = 3562$

92. Area of a triangle.—The area of a triangle may be found in terms of any set of elements that are sufficient to determine the triangle. We therefore have three cases to consider:

Case   I. Given two sides and the included angle.
Case II. Given two angles and any side.
Case III. Given three sides.

Case I. Given b, c, A.

In the triangle ABC, let h be the altitude upon the side c.

Denoting the area by S we have
$$S = \tfrac{1}{2} ch$$
But $h = b \sin A$
Hence, $S = \tfrac{1}{2} bc \sin A$ [24]
Similarly, $S = \tfrac{1}{2} ac \sin B = \tfrac{1}{2} ab \sin C$.

Case II. Let the given parts be a, B, C. Then A can be found at once. From the law of sines,

$$c = \frac{a \sin C}{\sin A} \quad \text{and from Case I,} \quad S = \tfrac{1}{2} ac \sin B.$$

Hence, $$S = \frac{a^2 \sin B \sin C}{2 \sin A}$$ [25]

Case III. Let the given parts be a, b, c.

It is necessary to express h, the altitude, in terms of the sides of the triangle. Denote AD by m.

In ADC, $h^2 = b^2 - m^2$, and in BDC, $h^2 = a^2 - (c - m)^2$

Hence, $b^2 - m^2 = a^2 - c^2 + 2cm - m^2$,   or $m = \dfrac{b^2 + c^2 - a^2}{2c}$

Then $h^2 = b^2 - \left(\dfrac{b^2 + c^2 - a^2}{2c}\right)^2 = \dfrac{4b^2c^2 - (b^2 + c^2 - a^2)^2}{4c^2}$

$= \dfrac{1}{4c^2} (2bc + b^2 + c^2 - a^2)(2bc - b^2 - c^2 + a^2)$

$= \dfrac{1}{4c^2} (b + c + a)(b + c - a)(a + c - b)(a + b - c)$

(Note that $2bc + b^2 + c^2 - a^2 = (b + c)^2 - a^2$ and
$2bc - b^2 - c^2 + a^2 = a^2 - (b - c)^2$.)

Let s equal one-half the perimeter of the triangle; that is, let $a + b + c = 2s$.

Subtracting $2a$, $2b$, $2c$, from both members, we obtain

$$b + c - a = 2s - 2a = 2(s - a)$$
$$a + c - b = 2s - 2b = 2(s - b)$$
$$a + b - c = 2s - 2c = 2(s - c)$$

Then

$$h = \frac{1}{2c}\sqrt{16s(s - a)(s - b)(s - c)}$$

$$= \frac{2}{c}\sqrt{s(s - a)(s - b)(s - c)}$$

Hence, $S = \frac{1}{2} ch = \sqrt{s(s - a)(s - b)(s - c)}$ [26]

This is known as **Heron's formula.**

93. Radius of an inscribed circle.—If r is the radius of the circle inscribed in a triangle whose sides are a, b, c, then the area S of the triangle is

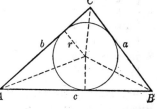

$$S = \tfrac{1}{2} ar + \tfrac{1}{2} br + \tfrac{1}{2} cr = \tfrac{1}{2} r (a + b + c) = \tfrac{1}{2} r \cdot 2s = rs.$$

But by [26], $S = \sqrt{s(s - a)(s - b)(s - c)} = rs.$

Hence, $r = \dfrac{1}{s}\sqrt{s (s - a) (s - b) (s - c)}$ [27]

$$= \sqrt{\frac{(s - a) (s - b) (s - c)}{s}}$$

94. Radius of a circumscribed circle.—In the figure let O be the center of the circumscribed circle, with radius R, and let OD be the perpendicular bisector of the side AC. Then $\angle AOC$ is measured by the arc AC, while $\angle ABC$ or $\angle B$ is measured by half of this arc. Hence,

$$\angle AOC = 2 \angle B \text{ and } \angle AOD = \angle B.$$

But $AO = R$ and $AD = b/2$.

Then, $R \sin AOD = R \sin B = b/2$, and $R = \dfrac{b}{2 \sin B}$.

Since $S = \frac{1}{2} ac \sin B$, we have $\sin B = 2S/ac$.

Hence, $R = b \div 2 \cdot \dfrac{2S}{ac} = \dfrac{abc}{4S}$,

and we have, $R = \dfrac{abc}{4\sqrt{s(s - a) (s - b) (s - c)}}$ [28]

EXERCISES

Find the radii of the inscribed and circumscribed circles for the following triangles.

1. $\begin{cases} a = 12 \\ b = 14 \\ c = 16 \end{cases}$ 2. $\begin{cases} a = 25.6 \\ b = 30.4 \\ c = 35.8 \end{cases}$ 3. $\begin{cases} a = 40 \\ b = 42 \\ c = 44 \end{cases}$ 4. $\begin{cases} a = 55 \\ b = 60 \\ c = 65 \end{cases}$

5. $\begin{cases} \angle A = 71° 50' \\ b = 28 \\ c = 30 \end{cases}$ In Exercise 5 find the unknown side before finding the required radius.

Find the areas of the following triangles.

6. $\begin{cases} a = 134.5 \\ b = 241.7 \\ \angle C = 54° 47' \end{cases}$ 8. $\begin{cases} \angle A = 41° 56' \\ \angle B = 67° 49' \\ c = 210.6 \end{cases}$ 10. $\begin{cases} a = 62.7 \\ b = 78.4 \\ c = 93.6 \end{cases}$

7. $\begin{cases} \angle A = 73° 42' \\ b = 37.5 \\ c = 47.8 \end{cases}$ 9. $\begin{cases} \angle A = 57° 32' \\ \angle B = 81° 27' \\ a = 397.4 \end{cases}$ 11. $\begin{cases} a = 386.7 \\ b = 296.4 \\ c = 487.6 \end{cases}$

95. Half-angle formulas.—We shall now derive formulas by means of which we can find the angles of a triangle when the sides are given. That is, we shall solve Case IV as given on page 71.

Let r be the radius of the circle inscribed in the triangle ABC whose sides a, b, and c are given. Since tangents from an external point to a circle are equal, we have

$$2AD + 2BD + 2CE = a + b + c = 2s,$$

where

$$s = \frac{a + b + c}{2}.$$

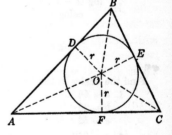

Then

$$AD + BD + CE = s, \quad AD = s - a,$$
$$BD = s - b, \quad CE = s - c.$$

(Note that $BD + CE = BE + CE = a$.)

From the above figure,

$$\tan \tfrac{1}{2}A = \frac{r}{AD} = \frac{r}{s - a} \qquad [29]$$

$$\tan \tfrac{1}{2}B = \frac{r}{BD} = \frac{r}{s - b}, \quad \text{and} \quad \tan \tfrac{1}{2}C = \frac{r}{CE} = \frac{r}{s - c},$$

which are called the half-angle formulas.

96. Solution of triangles.—Case IV. If we have given the three sides of a triangle, the angles may be found independently by means of the formulas for the tangents of the half angles. The results may be checked by adding the angles. The work is well adapted to logarithmic computation.

Example: Find the angles of a triangle ABC, given the sides a, b, and c.

Formulas: $r = \sqrt{\dfrac{(s-a)\,(s-b)\,(s-c)}{s}}$

and, $\tan \dfrac{A}{2} = \dfrac{r}{s-a}$, $\tan \dfrac{B}{2} = \dfrac{r}{s-b}$, $\tan \dfrac{C}{2} = \dfrac{r}{s-c}$

$\log r = \frac{1}{2}[\log (s-a) + \log (s-b) + \log (s-c) - \log s]$ and $\log \tan \frac{1}{2}A = \log r - \log (s-a)$, etc.

We may arrange the following skeleton solution.

$a =$	$\log r =$
$b =$	$\log (s-a) =$
$c =$	$\log \tan \frac{1}{2}A =$
$2s =$	$\frac{1}{2}A =$
$s =$	$\log r =$
$s - a =$	$\log (s-b) =$
$s - b =$	$\log \tan \frac{1}{2}B =$
$s - c =$	$\frac{1}{2}B =$
$\log (s-a) =$	$\log r =$
$\log (s-b) =$	$\log (s-c) =$
$\log (s-c) =$	$\log \tan \frac{1}{2}C =$
$\operatorname{colog} s =$	$\frac{1}{2}C =$
$2)$	
$\log r =$	

EXERCISES

Find the angles in the following triangles.

1. $a = 56$
   $b = 25$
   $c = 52$

2. $a = 297$
   $b = 410$
   $c = 337$

3. $a = 18.32$
   $b = 12.85$
   $c = 16.77$

4. $a = .951$
   $b = 1.833$
   $c = 1.527$

5. $a = 128.3$
   $b = 271.1$
   $c = 183.8$

6. $a = 0.0311$
   $b = 0.0822$
   $c = 0.0752$

7. $a = 2.1683$
   $b = 1.7831$
   $c = 1.5792$

8. $a = 84.85$
   $b = 103.25$
   $c = 99.83$

9. $a = 4257$
   $b = 4873$
   $c = 7582$

10. $a = 173.2$
    $b = 271.5$
    $c = 307.5$

11. $a = 0.8931$
    $b = 0.9621$
    $c = 1.0754$

12. $a = 1516.3$
    $b = 1295.5$
    $c = 976.4$

97. Résumé of solution of triangles.—In practical work in computing triangles the two formulas used are

$$\frac{\sin A}{\sin B} = \frac{a}{b} \quad \text{and} \quad \frac{\tan \frac{1}{2}(A - B)}{\tan \frac{1}{2}(A + B)} = \frac{a - b}{a + b}$$

when the parts that are given include at least one angle. These are the *law of sines* and the *law of tangents*.

The law of sines is used when the parts that are given contain one pair of opposite elements; that is, when an angle and the side opposite are given either directly or by implication. When two angles of a triangle are given, the third angle is given by implication since it is found at once by using the fact that the sum of the angles of a triangle is two right angles.

When one angle and the sides adjacent to it are given, the law of tangents must be used. In this case the sum of the unknown angles is found at once. When the difference between these angles is found, each angle is easily found. The law of tangents is used to find the difference between the unknown angles. In fact it is one-half this difference that is found, and this with one-half the sum serves to find both angles.

When the three sides of a triangle are given, the problem is to find its angles. This may be done by using the formula

$$\tan \tfrac{1}{2}A = \frac{r}{s - a}, \text{ where } r = \sqrt{\frac{(s - a)\ (s - b)\ (s - c)}{s}},$$

and similarly for $\tan \frac{1}{2}B$ and $\tan \frac{1}{2}C$.

In practice the angles of a triangle are seldom found this way since measuring an angle is much easier than measuring a side. Also, in such indirect measuring as is done in surveying, what is wanted is more often a distance than an angle.

The problems of finding the radii of inscribed and circumscribed circles when the sides of the triangle are given are also solved in this chapter.

The area of a triangle in terms of its sides is found in plane geometry and does not essentially involve trigonometric functions. This is also true of the radius of the inscribed circle. The radius of the circumscribed circle may also be found without using the sine of an angle as is the case in the development given on page 81. However, the work is then a little more complicated.

EXERCISES IN SOLVING TRIANGLES
GROUP A

1. $A = 108° 35' 15''$
   $B = 33° 40' 10''$
   $c = 256.35$

2. $A = 59° 21' 40''$
   $b = 178.42$
   $c = 258.84$

3. $A = 65° 45' 5''$
   $a = 109.57$
   $b = 118.71$

4. $a = 120.33$
   $b = 213.75$
   $c = 125.88$

5. $B = 27° 18' 5''$
   $b = 0.4623$
   $c = 1.0133$

6. $a = 1.1702$
   $b = 3.0986$
   $c = 2.1280$

7. $A = 128° 26' 15''$
   $C = 37° 18' 40''$
   $a = 22.183$

8. $B = 101° 19' 25''$
   $a = 18.173$
   $c = 25.217$

9. $a = 847.2$
   $b = 983.89$
   $c = 1077.2$

10. $B = 76° 41' 5''$
    $C = 38° 52' 35''$
    $b = 176.34$

11. $B = 22° 42' 40''$
    $a = 12.853$
    $b = 17.189$

12. $C = 14° 52' 50''$
    $a = 1284.2$
    $b = 1591.7$

GROUP B

1. $A = 71'' 50' 30''$
   $b = 273.84$
   $c = 181.73$

2. $A = 71° 9' 20''$
   $a = 1181.2$
   $b = 1217.4$

3. $a = 22.184$
   $b = 73.381$
   $c = 64.130$

4. $C = 81° 12' 55''$
   $a = 683.21$
   $c = 637.73$

5. $B = 49'' 48' 30''$
   $a = 439.83$
   $b = 330.16$

6. $B = 38° 28' 55''$
   $C = 41° 12' 15''$
   $a = 217.12$

7. $C = 38° 12' 40''$
   $a = 76.213$
   $b = 101.504$

8. $a = 25.178$
   $b = 48.217$
   $c = 37.111$

9. $A = 52° 29' 15''$
   $B = 67° 12' 25''$
   $c = 0.18125$

10. $a = 13.132$
    $b = 12.855$
    $c = 19.213$

11. $A = 85° 22' 30''$
    $c = 1027.3$
    $b = 9212$

12. $A = 52° 58' 5''$
    $C = 68° 24' 55''$
    $c = 216.3$

GROUP C

1. $a = 227.83$
   $b = 321.19$
   $c = 418.24$

2. $A = 47° 5' 25''$
   $C = 67° 35' 5''$
   $b = 31.011$

3. $A = 107° 10' 20''$
   $a = 174.43$
   $b = 162.81$

4. $A = 78° 51' 45''$
   $b = 375.82$
   $c = 438.17$

5. $B = 11° 45' 5''$
   $C = 63° 11' 35''$
   $c = 833.39$

6. $C = 19° 37' 20''$
   $a = 10.376$
   $b = 17.853$

7. $C = 55° 40' 30''$
   $b = 10564$
   $c = 86226$

8. $a = 21121$
   $b = 19334$
   $c = 26477$

9. $C = 40° 13' 15''$
   $a = 728.51$
   $c = 458.18$

10. $a = 283.74$
    $b = 356.15$
    $c = 101.57$

11. $A = 31° 54' 40''$
    $B = 101° 41' 25''$
    $b = 247.36$

12. $B = 19° 5' 20''$
    $a = 181.54$
    $c = 273.78$

98. A simple survey.—The data shown in this figure were obtained by a class in surveying near the city of Missoula, Montana. The line AB was measured along a paved road running east and west near the city. The points marked C, D, E, F, G, H, I represent hills and mountains surrounding the level plane. From the data thus found in the field, distances such as AC, BC, CD, CE, etc., were computed as was also the height of these points above the plane on which the city is situated.

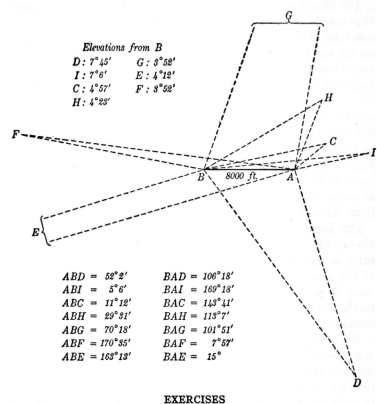

Elevations from B

D : 7° 45'	G : 3° 52'
I : 7° 6'	E : 4° 12'
C : 4° 57'	F : 3° 52'
H : 4° 23'	

ABD = 52° 2'	BAD = 106° 18'
ABI = 5° 6'	BAI = 169° 18'
ABC = 11° 12'	BAC = 143° 41'
ABH = 29° 31'	BAH = 113° 7'
ABG = 70° 18'	BAG = 101° 51'
ABF = 170° 35'	BAF = 7° 57'
ABE = 163° 13'	BAE = 15°

EXERCISES

1. From the given data find AG, BG, AH, BH, GH.
2. Find the height of G and H above the point B.

99. Finding the scale of the solar system.—From certain known laws of the motion of the planets around the sun it is possible to find the relative distances of the planets from the sun. That is, we can find that Jupiter is about five times as

far from the sun as is the earth, without knowing anything
about how many miles distant either of them is. However, if
we can find the distance in miles from the earth to any one of
the planets, in any definite position in the orbits, we shall be
able to find the "scale" of the whole solar system. And this is
exactly what we can do by using the distance between two points
on the earth's surface, then measuring two angles, and using
elementary trigonometry.

For this purpose we naturally select that one of the planets
that comes nearest the earth. This happens to be a very small
one (one of the asteroids) called Eros. At two points A and B
on the earth's surface, it is
contrived to measure the
angles ABC and BAC at
the same time. Since the
size of the earth is known
in miles, it is also contrived
to find the distance AB in

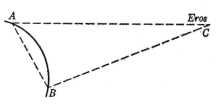

miles. By computing the triangle ABC, the distance from the
earth to Eros is thus found in miles. Thus by a method hinted
at above, the distances to all the planets (including the earth's)
from the sun are found in miles.

100. Distances to the fixed stars.—By a process similar to the
above, but using two points on opposite sides of the earth's
orbit as our points A and B, we can find the distances to many
of the stars nearer to us. Measuring the angles at A and B
must now be done indi-
rectly. The method is as
follows.

We select a star S that
is supposed to be within a
distance than can be measured by this method. Near

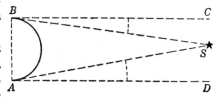

to it we select a small star that we have reason to believe is very
far away. We see it from A in the direction AD, and measure
the angle DAS. Then six months later, when the earth has
gone halfway round its orbit to the point B, we see the small
star in the direction BC. Its distance is so great that AD and
BC are "sensibly" parallel. But S now appears in a direction
that is a little different. We then measure the angle SBC. It

is obvious that we can now find the angle ASB. Knowing this angle and the length of the line AB we can compute the distance of the star S. Half of the angle ASB is called the *parallax* of the star. For the star nearest the sun this angle is $0.76''$. For our brightest star, Sirius, this angle is $.37''$, and for the Polar Star it is $0.01''$. So you see these angles are very small, so small that ordinary methods cannot be used in measuring them. Astronomers have developed means for measuring angles far more effective than those used by any surveyor.

It is interesting to note that when the parallax of a star is known its distance is found without using any formula from trigonometry. Suppose we want to find the distance of Sirius whose parallax is $0.37''$. The distance in miles is then found as shown at the right. In practice the distances to the stars are given in light-years. That is, the unit of

> Arc of $0.37'' = 93{,}000{,}000$ miles.
> Arc $0.37''$ is contained $3{,}500{,}000$ times in $360°$
>
> $$\text{Distance} = \frac{3{,}500{,}000 \times 93{,}000{,}000}{2\pi}$$
>
> $= 50{,}000{,}000{,}000{,}000$ miles, approximately.

distance is the distance that light travels in one year, going as it does at the rate of about $186{,}000$ miles a second. So it turns out that Sirius is about 9 light years away. A star whose parallax is not measurable is at least 500 light years away. By very complicated means it is known that some of the outlying galaxies are many millions of light years away. Our own galaxy containing some billions of stars is in the shape of a disk about 30,000 light years thick and about 300,000 in its greatest diameter.

PROBLEMS

GROUP A

1. Three intersecting streets form a plot of ground whose sides are 516.7 feet, 621.9 feet, and 672.3 feet. Find the angles of this piece and also its area.

2. A telephone wire is to be strung up a hill of uniform slope from A to B. A distance $AC = 350$ feet is measured on level ground directly away from the hill, and the angles ACB and CAB are found to be $19°\ 40'$ and $153°$, respectively. Find the length of the line from A to B.

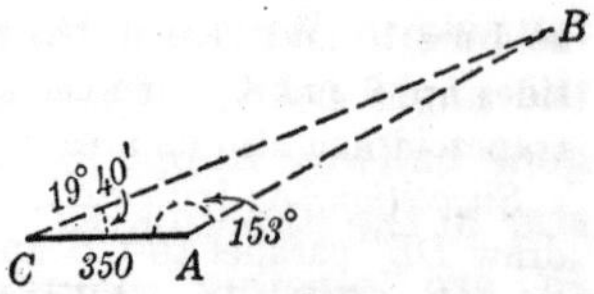

3. In making a survey it becomes necessary to find the distance from A to B which are located on opposite sides of a steep hill. Instead of measuring directly across the hill, the lines AC and CB and the angle C are measured and found to be 391 feet, 475 feet, and 76° 20′, respectively. Compute the distance from A to B.

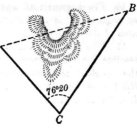

4. It is desired to find the shortest distance from a point A on the bank of a river to a straight road on the opposite side. On this road two points, B and C, are located 560 feet apart and the angles ABC and BCA are found to be 43° 20′ and 109° 50′, respectively. From these data compute the required distance.

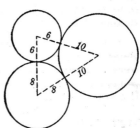

5. The diagonals of a parallelogram are 227.2 and 201.7 feet and meet in an angle of 114° 30′. Find the sides of the parallelogram and also its area.

6. From a point of observation, A, two batteries at B and C subtend an angle of 71° 15′. The sound from the battery at B reaches the observer 3½ seconds after the flash and the report from that at C reaches him 7 seconds after the flash. If sound travels 1,090 feet per second, how far apart are the batteries?

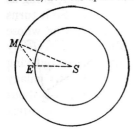

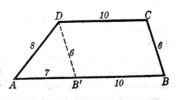

7. The distances in miles from the earth and Mars to the sun are about 93,000,000 and 141,000,000, respectively. How far is Mars from us when it appears at an angular distance of 144° from the sun?

8. Three circles whose radii are 6, 8, 10 are tangent externally as shown in the figure. Find the angles between the lines of centers.

9. The two parallel sides of a trapezoid are 10 and 17, and the non-parallel sides are 6 and 8. Find the angles of the trapezoid and also its area.

Suggestion: As indicated in the figure, draw DB′ parallel to CB and solve the triangle AB′D. Is ∠AB′D acute or obtuse?

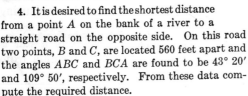

10. The diagonals AC and BD of a quadrilateral meet in a point O, making an angle of 67° 30'. If $AO = 12$, $OC = 17$, $BO = 14$, and $OD = 19$, find the area of the quadrilateral.

11. Two points A and B (see figure) are inaccessible but visible from C and D. At C and D the angles are measured. $CDA = 42° 12'$, $BDA = 38° 30'$, $DCA = 12° 10'$, $BCA = 19° 30'$. If $CD = 5280$ ft., find AB.

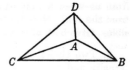

GROUP B

1. To find the angle at which the side of a railway embankment is inclined to the horizontal, a distance $BC = 28.2$ feet is measured up the embankment, a distance $BA = 41.15$ feet on the level ground and directly away from it, and then a surveyor's chain is stretched from A to C, finding this distance to be 62.5 feet. Using these data, find the angle DBC in the figure.

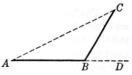

Question: Could the angle ABC be measured easily by means of a surveyor's transit?

2. To find the distance from the point A on one side of a river to the point B on the other side, a line AC 285 feet long is measured and the angles A and C are found to be 56° 15' and 116° 45', respectively. Compute AB.

3. In surveying a straight line, an obstacle is encountered so it becomes necessary to make a detour from B to C (see figure), returning to the line at D. If $\angle ABC = 147° 10'$, $\angle C = 69° 50'$, and $BC = 647.3$ feet, what must be the length of CD? of BD?

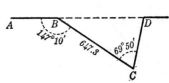

4. From a ship sailing in a straight course a lighthouse is observed to be 17° 35' to the left of the course. After sailing $11\frac{1}{2}$ miles the lighthouse is 43° 20' to the left of the course. What is the shortest distance from the lighthouse to the course of the ship?

5. The diagonals of a parallelogram are 17.46 feet and 21.62 feet long and meet in an angle of 53° 18'. Find the sides of the parallelogram and also its area.

6. Two warships are observed to fire simultaneously, the reports reaching the observer in 6 seconds and 9 seconds, respectively. How far apart are the ships if they subtend an angle of 59° 40' from the position of the observer and if sound is traveling at the rate of 1100 feet per second?

7. The distances in miles from the earth and Mercury to the sun are about 93,000,000 and 36,000,000, respectively. How far is Mercury from us when it appears at a distance of 15° from the sun? Note that two answers are possible. Give both of them.

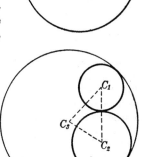

8. Two circles, C_1 and C_2, are tangent externally and each is tangent internally to the circle C_3. If the radii of the circles are 4, 6, and 12, find the angles made by their lines of centers.

9. The two parallel sides of a trapezoid are 12 and 16 and the non-parallel sides are 8 and 10. Find the angles of the trapezoid and also its area.

Suggestion: Draw DB' parallel to CB and study $AB'D$. Why is the angle $AB'B$ obtuse? (See figure for problem 9, page 89.)

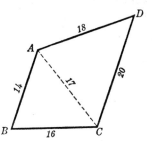

10. In a quadrilateral $ABCD$, $AB = 14$, $BC = 16$, $CD = 20$, $DA = 18$, and the diagonal $AC = 17$. Find the angles of the quadrilateral and also its area.

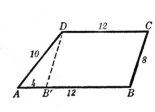

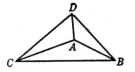

11. Two points A and B (see figure) are inaccessible but are visible from C and D. $CDA = 31° 15'$, $BDA = 18° 10'$, $DCA = 29° 5'$, $BCA = 33° 40'$. If $CD = 2000$ ft., find AB.

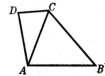

GROUP C

1. A surveyor wishing to measure a four-sided plot of ground and having no surveying instrument with him except a tape for measuring distances, measured the four sides and a diagonal and found these to be $AB = 213.2$ feet, $BC = 251.1$ feet, $CD = 107.8$ feet, $DA = 208.3$ feet, and $AC = 212.6$ feet. Find the four angles of the plot $ABCD$. What is the length of the diagonal BD?

2. A road runs from A to B and from B to C, making an angle of 162° at B. If $AB =$ 1860 feet and $BC = 2142$ feet, find the length of a straight road from A to C.

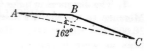

3. To find the distance across a pond from A to B the straight lines AC and BC are measured and found to be 492.2 and 581.7 feet, respectively, and the angle C is 73° 10′. Compute the length of AB.

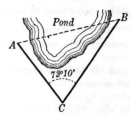

4. In running a straight line in a survey a point is observed to be 21° 30′ to the right of the line, and after going 392.5 feet farther along this line the point is 67° 30′ to the right of it. Find the shortest distance from this point to the line.

5. The diagonals of a parallelogram are 38.55 feet and 52.75 feet and meet in an angle of 77° 50′. Find the length of the sides of the parallelogram and also its area.

6. Two stations connected by a straight railway are known to be $2\frac{1}{8}$ miles apart. From a farmhouse it is observed that the sound of the whistle from one station reaches it in 8 seconds and from the other in 14 seconds. What is the shortest distance from the farmhouse to the railway line?

7. The distances in miles from the earth and Venus to the sun are about 93,000,000 and 67,000,000. How far is Venus from us when it appears at a distance of 32° from the sun? Note that two answers are possible. Give both of them.

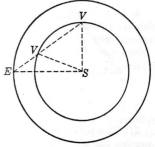

8. The sides of a triangle ABC are AB = 13, $BC = 14$, $CA = 16$. The line AD bisects the side BC at D. Find the angles of the triangle ABD.

9. In the triangle ABC, $AB = 31$, $AC = 42$, and $A = 51°\ 15′$. Find the length of the median from B upon the side AC.

10. A tree stands at a distance from straight road. At a point A in the road the line to the tree makes an angle of 21° with the line of the road, and at a point B the line to the tree makes an angle of 51° with the line of the road. If $AB = 3400$ feet, find the shortest distance from the tree to the road.

Suggestion: Show that as stated this problem has two correct answers, and find both.

MISCELLANEOUS PROBLEMS

1. Three circles with radii 5, 6, and 8 are tangent externally as shown in the figure. Find the area (shaded in the figure) inclosed by them.

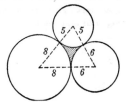

2. In the triangle ABC, $\angle A$, $\angle B$, and side c are given. Show how to solve this triangle completely by means of the formulas on right triangles. In what ways is this solution inferior to the solution by means of the sine formula?

Suggestion: In the figure $\dfrac{c - x}{h} = \cot A$,

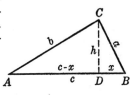

$\dfrac{x}{h} = \cot B$.

3. In the triangle ABC, $\angle A$, and sides b and c are given. Solve the triangle completely by means of formulas on right triangles. In what ways is this solution inferior to the solution by means of the tangent formula?

Suggestion: Using the figure of problem 2, $\triangle ADC$ can be solved at once and this gives the values of h and x.

4. In a circle with radius 10, a chord AB is a distance 4 from the center. Find the area of the segment inclosed by this chord and the arc ACB.

Suggestion: Find (a) $\angle AOB$, (b) area $AOBC$, (c) area $\triangle AOB$.

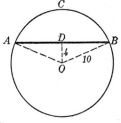

5. It is desired to keep a "gauge" on a large cylindrical tank to show the amount of liquid in it when it is filled to various heights. The gauge consists of a series of horizontal lines on one end of the tank, with figures on each line showing how many gallons it contains when filled up to this line. In a tank 8 feet in diameter and 32 feet long how many gallons are contained below a line AB which is 2 feet from the lower edge? One gallon contains 231 cubic inches. Note that the tank is in the horizontal position.

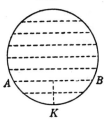

Suggestion: Find the area of the segment AKB and multiply by the length of the tank.

6. Make a table for the gauge for the tank in problem 5, the distance between the lines being 12 inches. After completing the lower half of the scale, devise a simple plan for making the upper half of it.

7. Two mountain peaks, C and D, are visible from the campus of a university. It is desired to find the distance from a point A to each of the peaks and also the distance between the peaks. A line AB is measured and found to be 6840 feet. Further, $\angle BAC = 27°\ 40'$; $\angle ABC = 149°\ 50'$; $\angle BAD = 46°\ 30'$; and $\angle ABD = 131°\ 10'$. Find AC, AD, and CD. To check the solution find BC, BD, and CD.

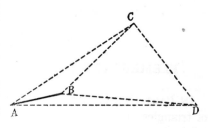

NOTE. While the points C and D are above the level of the horizontal line AB, the surveying is done as if they were in the same horizontal plane with it. The angles that are measured lie in this horizontal plane, and the distances found in the computation are horizontal distances. What is wanted in land surveying and in geographical surveying is horizontal distances. A map shows distances between points as if they were all on the same level.

8. Viewed from a point directly south of it, the top of a hill shows an elevation of $27°\ 40'$. After going along a horizontal road in a due westerly direction for a distance of 1000 feet the top of the hill shows an elevation of $21°\ 10'$. Find height of the hill above the road.

9. A bridge across a deep ravine has its ends at the points A and B. At a point C in the bottom of the ravine it is desired to build a pier to support the bridge. Find the height of this pier if the elevations of A and B as seen from C are $49°$ and $57°$, respectively, and if the length of the bridge (AB) is 567 feet.

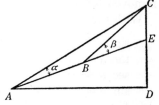

10. In surveying for a road the following problem occurs. In the figure the line AD is horizontal and the line DC is vertical. The surveyor measures the angle of elevation of C as seen from A (DAC), the angles α and β, and the length of the line AB. The problem is to compute the line EC. Give the series of steps required in this computation.

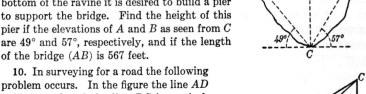

11. If in problem 10, $DAC = 14°\ 45'$, $\alpha = 4°\ 25'$, $\beta = 7°\ 30'$, and $AB = 1586$ feet, what is the length of EC?

NOTE. Exercises on surveying, page 175 may be taken at this time if desired.

CHAPTER VII

ELEMENTARY TRIGONOMETRIC IDENTITIES

In Part One of this book we have dealt with the solution of triangles, developing only so much of the general theory of trigonometry as is necessary for this purpose. The only point at which this limit has been exceeded is in the definitions of the trigonometric functions, which have been so stated that they apply to any angle whatever. However, trigonometric functions are of great importance in problems other than the solution of triangles, and many properties of these functions, and many relations among them, are required besides those studied thus far. In Part Two we will develop our subject further so as to make it more adequate for these purposes.

101. Identities.—We have seen that $\sin \alpha = \cos (90° - \alpha)$ (§17) for all values of α[1] between 0° and 90°. Later we shall prove that this equation holds for any value whatever of α. Since the equation holds for all values of α, we call it an identity in α, or simply an **identity**. In this chapter we shall develop a large number of trigonometric identities, but the proofs will be made in most cases only for positive angles that do not exceed 180°. In Chapter XII all restrictions on the angles will be removed for all these identities.

With the above restrictions we have thus far established:

$$\sin \alpha = \cos (90° - \alpha) \qquad \cos \alpha = \sin (90° - \alpha)$$
$$\tan \alpha = \cot (90° - \alpha) \qquad \cot \alpha = \tan (90° - \alpha)$$
$$\sec \alpha = \csc (90° - \alpha) \qquad \csc \alpha = \sec (90° - \alpha)$$
$$\sin \alpha = \sin (180° - \alpha) \qquad \cos \alpha = - \cos (180° - \alpha)$$
$$\tan \alpha = - \tan (180° - \alpha) \qquad \cot \alpha = - \cot (180° - \alpha)$$
$$\sec \alpha = - \sec (180° - \alpha) \qquad \csc \alpha = \csc (180° - \alpha)$$

Since the members of an equation may be interchanged, the above equations may be read so as to give the functions of $(90° - \alpha)$ in terms of α. That is, $\sin (90° - \alpha) = \cos \alpha$, $\cos (90° - \alpha) = \sin \alpha$, and so on.

[1] From now on we will represent angles by capital letters, by "small" letters, or by Greek letters, as may be convenient.

102. Reciprocal relations.—The six trigonometric functions are reciprocal in pairs.

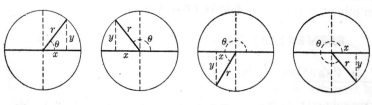

From $\sin \theta = y/r$, $\csc \theta = r/y$, it follows that

$$\sin \theta = 1/\csc \theta, \qquad \csc \theta = 1/\sin \theta \qquad [30]$$

(Note that the definitions used apply to any angle.)

Again, from $\cos \theta = x/r$ and $\sec \theta = r/x$, it follows that

$$\cos \theta = 1/\sec \theta, \qquad \sec \theta = 1/\cos \theta \qquad [31]$$

Since $\tan \theta = y/x$ and $\cot \theta = x/y$, it follows that

$$\tan \theta = 1/\cot \theta, \qquad \cot \theta = 1/\tan \theta \qquad [32]$$

These identities may also be stated in the following form.

$$\sin \theta \csc \theta = 1, \qquad \cos \theta \sec \theta = 1, \qquad \tan \theta \cot \theta = 1$$

103. Trigonometric functions expressed in terms of sines and cosines.—In §102 we have seen that the secant may be expressed in terms of cosine, and cosecant in terms of sine. The tangent and cotangent may be expressed in terms of sine and cosine. Thus,

$$\tan \theta = \frac{y}{x} = \frac{y/r}{x/r} = \frac{\sin \theta}{\cos \theta} \qquad [33]$$

$$\cot \theta = \frac{x}{y} = \frac{x/r}{y/r} = \frac{\cos \theta}{\sin \theta} \qquad [34]$$

It follows from these and from [30], [31] above and [35] on page 97 that in any expression containing trigonometric functions these may all be expressed in terms of sines and cosines, or in terms of either of these.

Thus, for example, using $\cos \theta = \sqrt{1 - \sin^2 \theta}$, we have $\tan \theta = \dfrac{\sin \theta}{\sqrt{1 - \sin^2 \theta}}$, and $\cot \theta = \dfrac{\sqrt{1 - \sin^2 \theta}}{\sin \theta}$. See page 99.

104. Relations derived from the Pythagorean proposition.— While x and y are positive in some of these figures and negative in others, it is evident that in all of them

$$x^2 + y^2 = r^2$$

since $(-x)^2 = x^2$ and $(-y)^2 = y^2$.

Dividing these equals successively by r^2, x^2, and y^2, we have

$$
\begin{aligned}
x^2/r^2 + y^2/r^2 &= r^2/r^2, &&\text{or}&& \sin^2\theta + \cos^2\theta = 1 && [35]\\
x^2/x^2 + y^2/x^2 &= r^2/x^2, &&\text{or}&& \tan^2\theta + 1 \;\;\;\;\;= \sec^2\theta && [36]\\
x^2/y^2 + y^2/y^2 &= r^2/y^2, &&\text{or}&& \cot^2\theta + 1 \;\;\;\;\;= \csc^2\theta && [37]
\end{aligned}
$$

105. List of formulas.— The following list contains the most important elementary formulas on the relations among the functions of an angle.

(1) $\sin\ \theta = 1/\csc\theta$ (2) $\cos\ \theta = 1/\sec\theta$

(3) $\tan\ \theta = 1/\cot\theta$ (4) $\tan\theta = \sin\theta/\cos\theta$

(5) $\cot\ \theta = \cos\theta/\sin\theta$ (6) $\sin^2\theta + \cos^2\theta = 1$

(7) $\tan^2\theta + 1 = \sec^2\theta$ (8) $\cot^2\theta + 1 = \csc^2\theta$

Since these identities are obtained directly from the general definitions of the trigonometric functions it follows that they have been proved for any angle whatever.

Note that (3), (4), (5) have no meaning when $\cot\ \theta = 0$, $\cos\ \theta = 0$, or $\sin\ \theta = 0$. These cases will be considered later.

SIGHT WORK

1. From $\sin^2\theta + \cos^2\theta = 1$ show that $\sin^2\theta = 1 - \cos^2\theta$ and hence that $\sin\theta = \pm\sqrt{1 - \cos^2\theta}$.

2. From $\sin^2\theta + \cos^2\theta = 1$ show that $\cos\theta = \pm\sqrt{1 - \sin^2\theta}$.

Remark. The two formulas $\sin\theta = \pm\sqrt{1 - \cos^2\theta}$ and $\cos\theta = \pm\sqrt{1 - \sin^2\theta}$ are used very frequently in solving problems.

3. From $\tan^2\theta + 1 = \sec^2\theta$ show that $\tan\theta = \pm\sqrt{\sec^2\theta - 1}$.

4. From $\cot^2\theta + 1 = \csc^2\theta$ show that $\cot\theta = \pm\sqrt{\csc^2\theta - 1}$.

5. From $\tan\theta = \sin\theta/\cos\theta$ and $\cot\theta = \cos\theta/\sin\theta$, show that $\tan\theta \cdot \cot\theta = 1$.

106. Finding all the functions of an acute angle when one function is given.—When one function of an acute angle is given, the other functions may be found by constructing a right triangle one of whose acute angles has the given function. The other functions may then be read directly from the triangle.

Example 1. Find the functions of an acute angle whose sine is 2/3.

Solution: Construct a right triangle ABC such that CB is two units long and AB is three units.

Then $\sin A = CB/AB = 2/3$.

From the theorem of Pythagoras we have,

$$3^2 = 2^2 + \overline{AC}^2 \text{ or } \overline{AC}^2 = 3^2 - 2^2 = 5.$$

Hence,

$$AC = \sqrt{5}.$$

We now read at once,

$$\cos A = \sqrt{5}/3, \tan A = 2/\sqrt{5}, \cot A = \sqrt{5}/2,$$
$$\sec A = 3/\sqrt{5}, \text{ and } \csc A = 3/2.$$

From these values verify (1) that $\sin A = 1/\csc A$, (2) $\cos A = 1/\sec A$, (3) $\tan A = 1/\cot A$, (4) $\tan A = \sin A/\cos A$, (5) $\cot A = \cos A/\sin A$, (6) $\sin^2 A + \cos^2 A = 1$, (7) $\tan^2 A + 1 = \sec^2 A$, (8) $\cot^2 A + 1 = \csc^2 A$.

Example 2. Find the functions of an acute angle whose secant is 5/3.

Solution: Construct a right triangle ABC with AB five units and AC three units. Then CB is four units.

Then, $\sec A = 5/3$, $\sin A = 4/5$, $\cos A = 3/5$,
$\tan A = 4/3$, $\cot A = 3/4$, $\csc A = 5/4$.

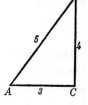

From these values of the functions verify as in Example 1 formulas (1)–(8) §105.

Since all functions of an acute angle are positive, only the positive square roots are used in the answers.

EXERCISES

1. Construct an angle whose cosine is 3/7, and find all its other functions. From these values of the functions verify statements (1)–(8) in §105.

2. Construct an angle whose tangent is 5/7 and find all its other functions. Verify formulas as in example 1.

3. Construct an angle whose cotangent is 7/8 and find its other functions. Verify formulas as in example 1.

4. Construct an angle whose cosecant is 8/5 and find its other functions. Verify formulas as in example 1.

107. Expressing trigonometric functions of any angle in terms of one function.—All functions of an angle may be expressed in terms of any one function. For this purpose the eight formulas collected in §105 are used. The general method is shown in the following examples.

Example 1. Express all trigonometric functions in terms of the sine.

Solution: From $\sin^2 \theta + \cos^2 \theta = 1$ we have $\cos^2 \theta = 1 - \sin^2 \theta$ or $\cos \theta = \pm \sqrt{1 - \sin^2 \theta}$.

Also $\tan \theta = \dfrac{\sin \theta}{\cos \theta} = \dfrac{\sin \theta}{\pm \sqrt{1 - \sin^2 \theta}}$,

$\cot \theta = \dfrac{\cos \theta}{\sin \theta} = \dfrac{\pm \sqrt{1 - \sin^2 \theta}}{\sin \theta}$,

$\sec \theta = \dfrac{1}{\cos \theta} = \dfrac{1}{\pm \sqrt{1 - \sin^2 \theta}}$.

Example 2. Express all trigonometric functions in terms of the tangent.

Solution: Since $\tan \theta \cot \theta = 1$, $\cot \theta = \dfrac{1}{\tan \theta}$.

Since $\sec^2 \theta = 1 + \tan^2 \theta$, $\sec \theta = \pm \sqrt{1 + \tan^2 \theta}$,

and $\cos \theta = \dfrac{1}{\sec \theta} = \dfrac{1}{\pm \sqrt{1 + \tan^2 \theta}}$.

Now, $\csc^2 \theta = 1 + \cot^2 \theta = 1 + \dfrac{1}{\tan^2 \theta} = \dfrac{\tan^2 \theta + 1}{\tan^2 \theta}$.

Hence, $\csc \theta = \dfrac{\pm \sqrt{1 + \tan^2 \theta}}{\tan \theta}$ and $\sin \theta = \dfrac{\tan \theta}{\pm \sqrt{1 + \tan^2 \theta}}$.

EXERCISES

Derive the values given in the following table from the fundamental identities of §105.

$\sin \theta =$	$\sin \theta$	$\pm\sqrt{1-\cos^2\theta}$	$\dfrac{\tan\theta}{\pm\sqrt{1+\tan^2\theta}}$	$\dfrac{1}{\pm\sqrt{1+\cot^2\theta}}$	$\dfrac{\pm\sqrt{\sec^2\theta-1}}{\sec\theta}$	$\dfrac{1}{\csc\theta}$
$\cos \theta=$	$\pm\sqrt{1-\sin^2\theta}$	$\cos\theta$	$\dfrac{1}{\pm\sqrt{1+\tan^2\theta}}$	$\dfrac{\cot\theta}{\pm\sqrt{1+\cot^2\theta}}$	$\dfrac{1}{\sec\theta}$	$\dfrac{\pm\sqrt{\csc^2\theta-1}}{\csc\theta}$
$\tan \theta=$	$\dfrac{\sin\theta}{\pm\sqrt{1-\sin^2\theta}}$	$\dfrac{\pm\sqrt{1-\cos^2\theta}}{\cos\theta}$	$\tan\theta$	$\dfrac{1}{\cot\theta}$	$\pm\sqrt{\sec^2\theta-1}$	$\dfrac{1}{\pm\sqrt{\csc^2\theta-1}}$
$\cot \theta=$	$\dfrac{\pm\sqrt{1-\sin^2\theta}}{\sin\theta}$	$\dfrac{\cos\theta}{\pm\sqrt{1-\cos^2\theta}}$	$\dfrac{1}{\tan\theta}$	$\cot\theta$	$\dfrac{1}{\pm\sqrt{\sec^2\theta-1}}$	$\pm\sqrt{\csc^2\theta-1}$
$\sec \theta=$	$\dfrac{1}{\pm\sqrt{1-\sin^2\theta}}$	$\dfrac{1}{\cos\theta}$	$\pm\sqrt{1+\tan^2\theta}$	$\dfrac{\pm\sqrt{1+\cot^2\theta}}{\cot\theta}$	$\sec\theta$	$\dfrac{\csc\theta}{\pm\sqrt{\csc^2\theta-1}}$
$\csc \theta=$	$\dfrac{1}{\sin\theta}$	$\dfrac{1}{\pm\sqrt{1-\cos^2\theta}}$	$\dfrac{\pm\sqrt{1+\tan^2\theta}}{\tan\theta}$	$\pm\sqrt{1+\cot^2\theta}$	$\dfrac{\sec\theta}{\pm\sqrt{\sec^2\theta-1}}$	$\csc\theta$

108. Sign before radical in expressing trigonometric functions in terms of sines, cosines, etc.—As we have seen, page 68, the sign of a trigonometric function depends upon the quadrant in which the angle lies. The distribution of these signs is shown in the following scheme.

Sine		Cosine		Tangent		Cotangent		Secant		Cosecant	
+	+	−	+	−	+	−	+	−	+	+	+
−	−	−	+	+	−	+	−	−	+	−	−

That is, the sine is positive in the first and second quadrants and negative in the third and fourth; the cosine is positive in the first and fourth quadrants, and negative in the second and third, and so on.

In the equation $\cos \theta = \pm \sqrt{1 - \sin^2 \theta}$ we must know the quadrant of θ before we can decide which sign is to be used. If θ is in the first quadrant, the positive sign must be used; if it is in the second quadrant, the negative sign must be used, and so on. In $\sin \theta = \pm \sqrt{1 - \sin^2 \theta}$, the positive sign must be used for θ in the first and second quadrants and the negative sign for θ in the third and fourth quadrants.

In general, if a square root occurs in the result when a problem is solved, one cannot decide which sign is to be used without examining the problem itself. In some problems both signs give correct answers. That is, there are two answers, equally good. Again either the positive or negative sign, but not both, may give the correct answer. Finally neither sign may give a correct answer, in which case there is no correct answer to the problem. Thus, in $\tan \theta = \pm \sqrt{1 - \cos^2 \theta}/\cos \theta$, if θ is in the third quadrant, we know that the tangent is positive while the cosine is negative. Hence the negative sign must be used before the radical.

EXERCISES

1. If θ is in the first quadrant, decide what sign is to be used before each radical sign in the table on page 99.

2. Decide on the signs required in example 1, if θ is in the second quadrant.

3. Decide on the signs to be used if θ is in the third quadrant; in the fourth quadrant.

109. Algebraic operations on trigonometric expressions.— From the definitions of the various functions of an angle it is evident that each function of a given angle is a number. Thus sin α and cos α stand for numbers, just as in algebra the letters a and x stand for numbers. It follows that algebraic operations, such as addition, subtraction, multiplication, division, involution, and evolution, may be performed upon these functions. In general, these are done in the same manner as in algebra. Certain forms, however, should be noted.

The product of sin α and cos α is sin α cos α, and the sum of sin α and sin β is sin α + sin β. The product of sin α multiplied by itself is (sin α)^2. It is usual, however, to write instead $\sin^2\alpha$, and this expression is read "sine squared of α," or more briefly "sine square α." Similarly we have $\cos^2\alpha$, $\tan^2\alpha$, $\cot^2\alpha$, etc.

The expression sin ($\alpha + \beta$) stands for the sine of the angle obtained by adding the angles α and β. It is natural to inquire whether sin α + sin β is equal to sin ($\alpha + \beta$). We certainly have no reason to believe that such is the case, and shall find later that in general the two expressions are not equal.

The expression sin 4α stands for the sine of the angle 4α. Again, sin 4α is not in general equal to 4 sin α.

A few problems will illustrate the use of trigonometric expressions in algebraic processes:

Example 1. Find the product of (cos α + sin α) (cos α − sin α).
Solution: Since this is the product of the sum and difference of two terms, the result is the difference of their squares. That is,

$$(\cos \alpha + \sin \alpha) (\cos \alpha - \sin \alpha) = \cos^2 \alpha - \sin^2 \alpha.$$

Example 2. Perform the indicated addition:

$$\frac{\sin \alpha}{\cos \beta} + \frac{\sin \beta}{\cos \alpha}.$$

Solution: Evidently cos β cos α is the common denominator. Then

$$\frac{\sin \alpha}{\cos \beta} + \frac{\sin \beta}{\cos \alpha} = \frac{\sin \alpha \cos \alpha}{\cos \beta \cos \alpha} + \frac{\sin \beta \cos \beta}{\cos \beta \cos \alpha}$$
$$= \frac{\sin \alpha \cos \alpha + \sin \beta \cos \beta}{\cos \beta \cos \alpha}.$$

Example 3. Factor tan α sin α − $\sin^2 \alpha$.
Solution: sin α is a factor common to both terms. Hence

$$\tan \alpha \sin \alpha - \sin^2 \alpha = \sin \alpha (\tan \alpha - \sin \alpha).$$

EXERCISES

Group A

Perform the following indicated operations.

1. $(\sin \alpha + \cos \beta)^2 = ?$

2. $\dfrac{\tan \alpha}{\cos \beta} - \dfrac{\sin \beta}{\tan \beta \cos \beta} = ?$

3. $\sqrt{\sin^4 \alpha \cos^2 \beta} = ?$

4. $1 + \dfrac{\cos^2 \alpha}{\sin^2 \alpha} = ?$

5. $\left(\sin \alpha + \dfrac{\sqrt{2}}{2}\right)\left(\sin \alpha - \dfrac{\sqrt{2}}{2}\right) = ?$

Factor the following expressions:

6. $\cos^2 \alpha - \sin \alpha \cos \alpha.$

7. $\cos^4 \alpha - \cos^2 \beta.$

8. $\sin^4 \alpha - \cos^4 \alpha.$

9. $\tan^2 \alpha - 2 \tan \alpha \cot \alpha + \cot^2 \alpha.$

10. $\sin^2 \alpha - \sin^2 \alpha \cos^2 \alpha.$

11. $\sin^2 \alpha - \sin \alpha \sec \alpha - 6 \sec^2 \alpha.$

Simplify the following expressions:

12. $\dfrac{\dfrac{\sin \alpha}{\cos \alpha}}{\dfrac{\cos \alpha}{\sin^2 \alpha}}.$

13. $\dfrac{\dfrac{\sin \alpha}{\cos \beta} + \dfrac{\cos \alpha}{\sin \beta}}{\sin \beta \cos \beta}.$

Group B

1. $(\sin \alpha + \sin \beta)(\cos \alpha + \sin \beta) = ?$

2. $\sqrt{\tan^2 \beta \cos^6 \alpha} = ?$

3. $\dfrac{\cos \alpha}{\tan \beta} + \dfrac{\cot \beta}{\cos \alpha \tan \beta} = ?$

4. $\dfrac{\sin^2 \alpha}{\cos^2 \alpha} + 1 = ?$

5. $(\tan \alpha + \tfrac{1}{3} \sqrt{3})(\tan \alpha - \tfrac{1}{3} \sqrt{3}) = ?$

Factor the following expressions:

6. $\sin^2 \alpha + \sin \alpha \tan \alpha.$

7. $\sin^2 \alpha \cos \alpha - \sin \alpha \cos^2 \alpha.$

8. $\sin^2 \alpha \cos^3 \alpha + \sin^3 \alpha \cos^2 \alpha.$

9. $\sin^2 \alpha + 2 \sin \alpha \cos \alpha + \cos^2 \alpha.$

10. $\tan^3 \alpha \cos^2 \alpha - \tan^2\alpha \cos^3 \alpha + \tan \alpha \cos \alpha.$

11. $\cos^2 \alpha + \sin^2 \alpha \cos \alpha - 2 \sin^4 \alpha.$

Simplify:

12. $\dfrac{1 + \dfrac{\sin^2 \alpha}{\cos^2 \alpha}}{1 - \dfrac{\sin^2 \alpha}{\cos^2 \alpha}}.$

13. $\dfrac{\dfrac{\tan \alpha}{\cot \alpha} - \dfrac{\cot \alpha}{\tan \alpha}}{\dfrac{\tan \alpha}{\cot \alpha} + \dfrac{\cot \alpha}{\tan \alpha}}.$

110. Proving trigonometric identities.—By means of the fundamental identities given on page 97, a large number of identities may be proved. The method of making such proofs is best understood from examples:

Example 1. Prove that $\sin^2 \alpha \cos^2 \alpha + \cos^4 \alpha = 1 - \sin^2 \alpha$ is an identity.

Proof: $\sin^2 \alpha \cos^2 \alpha + \cos^4 \alpha = \cos^2 \alpha (\sin^2 \alpha + \cos^2 \alpha) = \cos^2 \alpha,$

$$\text{since} \quad \sin^2 \alpha + \cos^2 \alpha = 1.$$

From this last identity we also have $\cos^2 \alpha = 1 - \sin^2 \alpha.$
Hence the given statement is proved.

Example 2. Prove that $\dfrac{1}{\tan \alpha + \cot \alpha} = \sin \alpha \cos \alpha$ is an identity.   (1)

Proof: Clearing (1) of fractions,

$$1 = \tan \alpha \sin \alpha \cos \alpha + \cot \alpha \sin \alpha \cos \alpha. \tag{2}$$

Substituting $\tan \alpha = \dfrac{\sin \alpha}{\cos \alpha}$ and $\cot \alpha = \dfrac{\cos \alpha}{\sin \alpha}$ in (2),

$$1 = \frac{\sin \alpha}{\cos \alpha} \sin \alpha \cos \alpha + \frac{\cos \alpha}{\sin \alpha} \sin \alpha \cos \alpha, \tag{3}$$

or $1 = \sin^2 \alpha + \cos^2 \alpha,$ (4)

which is a known identity.

In this proof each of the equalities (2), (3), (4) is obtained from the one preceding it by an algebraic transformation or by substitution from one of the fundamental identities. Hence we have proved that (2) follows from (1), (3) follows from (2), and (4) follows from (3). But (4) is known to be an identity. We now notice that each of these steps may be reversed. That is, (3) may be proved from (4), (2) from (3), and (1) from (2). Hence (1) has been proved to be a true identity. The general method is to begin with the proposed identity and obtain from it a known identity. This proves the proposed identity, since each step is reversible.

Such proofs apply only to those values of the angle which do not make a multiplier or a divisor zero. This is not a valid objection, however, since an identity that holds for all other values will hold for these also in case the expressions have a meaning. Note, for example, that $\cos \theta / \sin \theta$ has no meaning for $\theta = 0$ since that reduces the expression to $1/0$. Division by zero is not possible in mathematics.

SIGHT WORK

Prove that each of the following is an identity.

1. $\sin \alpha \cot \alpha = \cos \alpha.$
2. $\cos \alpha \tan \alpha = \sin \alpha.$
3. $\sec \alpha \cot \alpha = \csc \alpha.$
4. $\csc \alpha \tan \alpha = \sec \alpha.$
5. $\sec \alpha \sin \alpha = \tan \alpha.$
6. $\cos \alpha \csc \alpha = \cot \alpha.$
7. $\sin \alpha / \csc \alpha = \sin^2 \alpha.$
8. $\cos \alpha / \sec \alpha = \cos^2 \alpha.$
9. $\sin^2 \alpha / \csc^2 \alpha = \sin^4 \alpha.$
10. $\cos^2 \alpha / \sec^2 \alpha = \cos^4 \alpha.$
11. $\sin^2 \alpha / \cot^2 \alpha = \sin^4 \alpha \sec^2 \alpha.$
12. $\cot \alpha / \csc \alpha = \cos \alpha.$
13. $\sin \alpha \sec \alpha \cot \alpha = 1.$
14. $\cos \alpha \csc \alpha \tan \alpha = 1.$
15. $\sin^2 \alpha / \cos^2 \alpha = \sec^2 \alpha - 1.$
16. $\cos^2 \alpha / \sin^2 \alpha = \csc^2 \alpha - 1.$
17. $\sin^2 \alpha \cot \alpha = \sin \alpha \cos \alpha.$
18. $(\sin \alpha + \cos \alpha)^2 = 1 + 2 \sin \alpha \cos \alpha.$
19. $\sin^2 \alpha - \cos^2 \alpha = 1 - 2 \cos^2 \alpha.$
20. $\sin^4 \alpha - \cos^4 \alpha = \sin^2 \alpha - \cos^2 \alpha.$

WRITTEN EXERCISES
GROUP A

Prove that each of the following is an identity.

1. $\cot \alpha \cos \alpha + \sin \alpha = \csc \alpha$.

2. $\cot \alpha + \tan \alpha = \sec \alpha \csc \alpha$.

3. $\tan^2 \alpha - \sin^2 \alpha = \sin^2 \alpha \tan^2 \alpha$.

4. $\tan^2 \alpha - \cot^2 \alpha = \sec^2 \alpha - \csc^2 \alpha$.

5. $\csc^4 \alpha - \cot^4 \alpha = \csc^2 \alpha + \cot^2 \alpha$.

6. $\sec^2 \alpha + \csc^2 \alpha = \tan^2 \alpha + \cot^2 \alpha + 2$.

7. $\dfrac{\cos \alpha + \sin \alpha}{\sec \alpha + \csc \alpha} = \cos \alpha \sin \alpha$.

8. $\dfrac{\cot \alpha \cos \alpha}{\cot \alpha - \cos \alpha} = \dfrac{\cos \alpha}{1 - \sin \alpha}$.

9. $\dfrac{\sin \alpha + \tan \alpha}{\csc \alpha + \cot \alpha} = \sin \alpha \tan \alpha$.

10. $\dfrac{\tan \alpha - \sin \alpha}{\sin^3 \alpha} = \dfrac{1 - \cos \alpha}{\sin^2 \alpha \cos \alpha}$.

11. $\dfrac{\cot \alpha + 1}{\sin \alpha + \cos \alpha} = \csc \alpha$.

12. $\dfrac{1}{1 + \sin \alpha} + \dfrac{1}{1 - \sin \alpha} = 2 \sec^2 \alpha$.

13. $\dfrac{\sec \alpha + 1}{\tan \alpha} = \dfrac{\tan \alpha}{\sec \alpha - 1}$.

14. $\dfrac{1}{\sec \alpha + \tan \alpha} = \sec \alpha - \tan \alpha$.

15. $(\tan \alpha + \cot \alpha) \sin \alpha \cos \alpha = 1$.

16. $\cot \alpha - \sec \alpha \csc \alpha (1 - 2 \sin^2 \alpha) = \tan \alpha$.

GROUP B

Prove that each of the following is an identity.

1. $1 + \cot^2 \alpha = \cot^2 \alpha \sec^2 \alpha$

2. $\tan \alpha \sin \alpha + \cos \alpha = \sec \alpha$

3. $\sin^2 \alpha \cos^2 \alpha + \cos^4 \alpha = 1 - \sin^2 \alpha$

4. $\cot^2 \alpha - \cos^2 \alpha = \cot^2 \alpha \cos^2 \alpha$

5. $\dfrac{\cos \alpha + \cot \alpha}{\sec \alpha + \tan \alpha} = \cos \alpha \cot \alpha$

6. $\tan^4 \alpha + \tan^2 \alpha = \sec^4 \alpha - \sec^2 \alpha$

7. $\dfrac{\cos^2 \alpha}{1 + \sin \alpha} = 1 - \sin \alpha$

8. $\dfrac{\cot \alpha - \cos \alpha}{\cot \alpha} = 1 - \sin \alpha$

9. $\dfrac{\csc \alpha}{\cot \alpha + \tan \alpha} = \cos \alpha$

10. $\dfrac{\tan \alpha - \cot \alpha}{\tan \alpha + \cot \alpha} = 2 \sin^2 \alpha - 1$

11. $\dfrac{\sec^2 \alpha + \csc^2 \alpha}{\sec \alpha \csc \alpha} = \tan \alpha + \cot \alpha$

12. $\dfrac{1 + \tan^2 \alpha}{1 + \cot^2 \alpha} = \dfrac{\sin^2 \alpha}{\cos^2 \alpha}$

13. $\dfrac{\sec \alpha}{\cot \alpha + \tan \alpha} = \sin \alpha$

14. $\sec^4 \alpha - 1 = 2 \tan^2 \alpha + \tan^4 \alpha$

15. $(\tan \alpha - \cot \alpha) \sin \alpha \cos \alpha = \sin^2 \alpha - \cos^2 \alpha$

16. If $x = r \cdot \cos \alpha$ and $y = r \cdot \sin \alpha$, prove $x^2 + y^2 = r^2$

111. Addition formulas for trigonometric functions.—From the tables of natural functions it is apparent that a change in a function of an angle is not proportional to the change in the angle. Thus doubling an angle does not double any one of its functions. In general, $\sin \alpha + \sin \beta$ is not equal to $\sin (\alpha + \beta)$, and so for the other functions.

Thus $\sin 20° = .34202$ and $\sin 40° = .64279$
and hence $\sin 20° + \sin 40° = .98481$, while
               $\sin (20° + 40°) = \sin 60° = .86603$

Again $\cos 20° = .93969$ and $\cos 40° = .76604$
and hence $\cos 20° + \cos 40° = 1.70573$, while
               $\cos (20° + 40°) = \cos 60° = .50000$

We now proceed to develop formulas giving the functions of the sum or difference of two angles in terms of the functions of the angles themselves. As will be seen, $\sin (A + B)$, for example, is expressed in terms of $\sin A$, $\sin B$, $\cos A$, $\cos B$, not merely in terms of $\sin A$ and $\sin B$. The fundamental formulas are:

$$\sin (A + B) = \sin A \cos B + \cos A \sin B \qquad [38]$$
$$\sin (A - B) = \sin A \cos B - \cos A \sin B \qquad [39]$$
$$\cos (A + B) = \cos A \cos B - \sin A \sin B \qquad [40]$$
$$\cos (A - B) = \cos A \cos B + \sin A \sin B \qquad [41]$$

From these, other formulas will be derived giving the tangent and cotangent of the sum and of the difference of two angles.

112. Formulas used in this chapter.—In deriving these formulas use will be made of some that have already been developed. Among these the more important are:

(1) Using the usual notation for the parts of a right triangle, $a = c \sin A$, $b = c \cos A$ (§26).

(2) If two angles A and B are supplementary, then we have $\sin A = \sin B$ and $\cos A = - \cos B$ (§82).

We notice that the sum of any two angles of a triangle is less than 180°, and that if one such angle is obtuse, the other is acute. We also recall from plane geometry that if the sides of $\angle A$ are perpendicular, respectively, to the sides of $\angle B$, then angles A and B are equal or supplementary.

For the present we will confine ourselves to positive angles and hence the difference of two angles will be taken in such a way as to make it positive.

113. Formula for the sine of the sum of two angles.—For the present we will consider the case of two angles, A and B, each of which is positive and whose sum is less than 180°. In each of the three figures, let $\angle XOC$ be the angle A, and $\angle COP$ be the angle B.

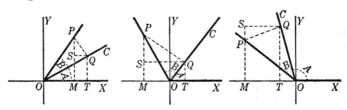

Notice that the initial side of angle B coincides with the terminal side of angle A. Then $\angle XOP$ is the angle $A + B$.

From P, a point in the terminal side of $A + B$, draw $MP \perp OX$ and $PQ \perp OC$. From Q draw $TQ \perp OX$ and $QS \perp MP$ (extended if necessary, as in the third figure).

In the $\triangle SPQ$, $SP \perp OX$, $PQ \perp OC$, and hence $\angle SPQ = \angle A$ or $\angle SPQ$ and $\angle A$ are supplementary.

Then for either of the first two figures, we have:

$$TQ = OQ \sin A \qquad SP = QP \cos A$$
$$OT = OQ \cos A \qquad QP = OP \sin B$$
$$SQ = QP \sin A \qquad OQ = OP \cos B.$$

Hence,

$$\sin (A + B) = \frac{MP}{OP} = \frac{TQ + SP}{OP} = \frac{OQ \sin A + QP \cos A}{OP}$$
$$= \frac{OP \cos B \sin A + OP \sin B \cos A}{OP}$$
$$= \cos B \sin A + \sin B \cos A.$$

That is,

$$\sin (A + B) = \sin A \cos B + \cos A \sin B.$$

In applying this proof to the third figure notice that $MP = TQ - SP$ and also that $\angle SPQ$ and $\angle A$ are supplementary.

Stated in words this formula is: *the sine of the sum of two angles is equal to the sine of the first times the cosine of the second plus the cosine of the first times the sine of the second.*

114. The cosine of the sum of two angles.—From the figures of §113 and the values of the line segments given there we have

$$\cos (A + B) = \frac{OM}{OP} = \frac{OT - SQ}{OP} = \frac{OQ \cos A - QP \sin A}{OP}$$

$$= \frac{OP \cos B \cos A - OP \sin B \sin A}{OP}.$$

That is, $\cos (A + B) = \cos A \cos B - \sin A \sin B$.

115. The sine of the difference of two angles.—In the case when $\angle A$ is acute (the first figure) we have

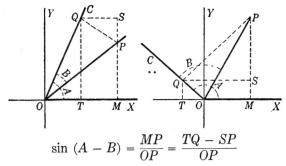

$$\sin (A - B) = \frac{MP}{OP} = \frac{TQ - SP}{OP}$$

Using the values of TQ, OT, SQ, SP, QP, OQ given in §113, we have $\sin (A - B) = \sin A \cos B - \cos A \sin B$.

In the case when A is obtuse (the second figure) we have

$$\sin (A - B) = \frac{MP}{OP} = \frac{TQ + SP}{OP}.$$

Using the same substitutions as in the first case and noting that $\angle A$ and $\angle SPQ$ are supplementary and that therefore $\cos \angle SPQ = - \cos A$, we obtain the same formula.

116. The cosine of the difference of two angles.—In the case when $\angle A$ is acute (the first figure in §115), we have

$$\cos (A - B) = \frac{OM}{OP} = \frac{OT + QS}{OP}.$$

Making the same substitution as above we have

$$\cos (A - B) = \cos A \cos B + \sin A \sin B.$$

In the case when $\angle A$ is obtuse (the second figure in §115) we have

$$\cos (A - B) = \frac{OM}{OP} = \frac{QS - TO}{OP}.$$

Using the same substitution as above, except that $TO = - OQ \cos A$ (TO is positive while $\cos A$ is negative), we have the same formula.

117. The sine and cosine of double-angles and half-angles.—
By letting $B = A$ in the formulas for $\sin (A + B)$ and cos $(A + B)$ we have

$$\sin 2A = 2 \sin A \cos A \qquad [42]$$

and

$$\cos 2A = \cos^2 A - \sin^2 A \qquad [43]$$

If in these formulas $2A$ is replaced by P, we have

$$\sin P = 2 \sin \frac{P}{2} \cos \frac{P}{2} \text{ and } \cos P = \cos^2 \frac{P}{2} - \sin^2 \frac{P}{2}.$$

Using [35] we have,

$$\cos P = \cos^2 \frac{P}{2} - \sin^2 \frac{P}{2} = 2 \cos^2 \frac{P}{2} - 1 = 1 - 2 \sin^2 \frac{P}{2},$$

and hence

$$\sin^2 \frac{P}{2} = \frac{1 - \cos P}{2} \text{ or } \sin \frac{P}{2} = \pm \sqrt{\frac{1 - \cos P}{2}} \qquad [44]$$

and

$$\cos^2 \frac{P}{2} = \frac{1 + \cos P}{2} \text{ or } \cos \frac{P}{2} = \pm \sqrt{\frac{1 + \cos P}{2}} \qquad [45]$$

EXERCISES

1. Using the formula for $\sin (A + B)$ find $\sin 75°$ ($75° = 45° + 30°$).

2. By means of the formula for $\cos (A - B)$ and using the combination $30° - 30° = 0$ verify that $\cos 0° = 1$.

3. If $\sin A = \frac{3}{4}$ and $\sin B = \frac{1}{3}$, find $\sin (A + B)$ and also $\sin (A - B)$.
Suggestion: First find $\cos A$ and $\cos B$.

4. If $\cos A = \frac{1}{3}$, $\cos B = \frac{2}{3}$, find $\cos (A + B)$ and also $\cos (A - B)$.

5. If $\sin A = \frac{1}{2}$ and $\cos B = \frac{1}{3}$, find $\sin (A + B)$.

6. If $\cos A = \frac{1}{3}$ and $\sin B = \frac{3}{4}$, find $\cos (A - B)$.

Prove the following.

7. $\sin (45° - A) \cos (45° - B) - \cos (45° - A) \sin (45° - B) = \sin (B - A)$.
Suggestion: What is the sine of the difference of the two angles $45° - A$ and $45° - B$?

8. $\cos A \cos (B - A) - \sin A \sin (B - A) = \cos B$.

9. $\sin (m + 1) A \cos (m - 1) A - \cos (m + 1) A \sin (m - 1) A = \sin 2A$.

10. $\cos (m + 1) A \cos (m - 1) A + \sin (m + 1) A \sin (m - 1) A = \cos 2A$.

11. $\sin (60° - A) \cos (60° - B) - \cos (60° - A) \sin (60° - B) = \sin (B - A)$.
Suggestion: What is the difference of the angles $60° - A$ and $60° - B$?

12. $\cos (B - A) \cos B + \sin (B - A) \sin B = \cos (-A)$.

13. $\sin (m + 2) A \cos (m - 2) A - \cos (m + 2) A \sin (m - 2) A = \sin 4A$.

118. Formula for tan $(A + B)$.—Since $\tan A = \sin A/\cos A$, it follows that

$$\tan (A + B) = \frac{\sin (A + B)}{\cos (A + B)}.$$

Substituting from §§113, 114 we have

$$\tan (A + B) = \frac{\sin A \cos B + \cos A \sin B}{\cos A \cos B - \sin A \sin B}.$$

Dividing each term of both numerator and denominator by $\cos A \cos B$, we have

$$\tan (A + B) = \frac{\dfrac{\sin A}{\cos A} + \dfrac{\sin B}{\cos B}}{1 - \dfrac{\sin A \sin B}{\cos A \cos B}} = \frac{\dfrac{\sin A}{\cos A} + \dfrac{\sin B}{\cos B}}{1 - \dfrac{\sin A}{\cos A} \times \dfrac{\sin B}{\cos B}}.$$

But

$$\frac{\sin A}{\cos A} = \tan A \text{ and } \frac{\sin B}{\cos B} = \tan B.$$

Substituting, we have

$$\tan (A + B) = \frac{\tan A + \tan B}{1 - \tan A \tan B} \qquad [46]$$

119. Formula for tan $(A - B)$.—Substituting from §§115, 116 in

$$\tan (A - B) = \frac{\sin (A - B)}{\cos (A - B)}$$

and proceeding as above, we have

$$\tan (A - B) = \frac{\tan A - \tan B}{1 + \tan A \tan B} \qquad [47]$$

120. Formulas for cot $(A + B)$ and cot $(A - B)$.—By a process similar to that used in §§118, 119 we find

$$\cot (A + B) = \frac{\cot A \cot B - 1}{\cot A + \cot B} \qquad [48]$$

and

$$\cot (A - B) = \frac{\cot A \cot B + 1}{\cot B - \cot A} \qquad [49]$$

121. Formulas for tan $2A$ and cot $2A$.—Letting $B = A$ in the formulas for $\tan (A + B)$ and $\cot (A + B)$, (§§118, 120) we have

$$\tan 2A = \frac{2 \tan A}{1 - \tan^2 A} \qquad [50]$$

and

$$\cot 2A = \frac{\cot^2 A - 1}{2 \cot A} \qquad [51]$$

It should be noted that the formulas in §§117–121 have been proved under the same limitations on the angles A and B that were imposed in proving the corresponding formulas in §§113–116. When the formulas on sines and cosines are proved for all angles, the formulas on tangents and cotangents will follow for all angles by the argument used above.

EXERCISES

GROUP A

1. If $\sin A = \frac{3}{5}$, find $\sin 2A$ and $\cos 2A$.
2. If $\cos A = \frac{1}{2}$, find $\sin \frac{1}{2}A$ and $\cos \frac{1}{2}A$.
3. Using the formula for $\tan (45° + 30°)$, find $\tan 75°$.

Suggestion: For values of $\tan 45°$ and $\tan 30°$ see §19.

4. Using the formula for $\tan (45° - 30°)$, find $\tan 15°$.
5. Using the formula for $\cot (45° + 30°)$, find $\cot 75°$.

Suggestion: Note that $\cot A = 1/\tan A$. For values of $\tan 45°$ and $\tan 30°$ see §19.

6. Using the formula for $\cot (45° - 30°)$ find $\cot 15°$. Compare $\tan 75°$ and $\cot 15°$, also $\cot 75°$ and $\tan 15°$.
7. If $\tan A = \frac{1}{2}$ and $\tan B = \frac{1}{3}$, find $\tan (A + B)$, also $\tan (A - B)$.
8. Prove that $\tan (A + 45°) \tan (A - 45°) = -1$.

Suggestion: Note that $\tan 45° = 1$.

9. Prove that $\tan (A + B) \tan (A - B) = \dfrac{\sin^2 A - \sin^2 B}{\cos^2 A - \sin^2 B}$.

10. Prove that $\dfrac{\cot (A + B)}{\cot (A - B)} = \dfrac{\sin A \cos A - \sin B \cos B}{\sin A \cos A + \sin B \cos B}$.

GROUP B

1. If $\cos A = \frac{2}{3}$, find $\sin 2A$ and $\cos 2A$.
2. If $\sin A = \frac{2}{5}$, find $\sin \frac{1}{2}A$ and $\cos \frac{1}{2}A$.
3. Using the formula for $\tan (60° + 45°)$, find $\tan 105°$.

Suggestion: For values of $\tan 45°$ and $\tan 60°$, see §19.

4. Using the formula for $\tan (60° + 60°)$ (or $\tan 2 \cdot 60°$) find $\tan 120°$. Compare this value with $\tan 60°$.
5. Using the formula for $\cot (60° + 45°)$, find $\cot 105°$. Compare this in value with $\tan 105°$.
6. Using the formula for $\cot (60° + 60°)$ (or $\cot 2 \cdot 60°$), find $\cot 120°$. Compare this value with $\cot 60°$.
7. If $\tan A = 3$ and $\tan B = 1$, find $\tan (A + B)$, also $\tan (A - B)$.
8. Prove that $\cot (A + 45°) \cot (A - 45°) = -1$.

9. Prove that $\cot (A + B) \cot (A - B) = \dfrac{\cos^2 A - \sin^2 B}{\sin^2 A - \sin^2 B}$.

10. Prove that $\dfrac{\tan (A + B)}{\tan (A - B)} = \dfrac{\sin A \cos A + \sin B \cos B}{\sin A \cos A - \sin B \cos B}$.

122. The sum and difference of sines and cosines of two angles.—We have already developed the following four formulas.

$$\sin (A + B) = \sin A \cos B + \cos A \sin B$$
$$\sin (A - B) = \sin A \cos B - \cos A \sin B$$
$$\cos (A + B) = \cos A \cos B - \sin A \sin B$$
$$\cos (A - B) = \cos A \cos B + \sin A \sin B.$$

Adding and subtracting the first two, we have,

$$\sin (A + B) + \sin (A - B) = 2 \sin A \cos B \qquad (1)$$
$$\sin (A + B) - \sin (A - B) = 2 \cos A \sin B. \qquad (2)$$

Similarly, from the last two we have,

$$\cos (A + B) + \cos (A - B) = 2 \cos A \cos B \qquad (3)$$
$$\cos (A + B) - \cos (A - B) = - 2 \sin A \sin B. \qquad (4)$$

If we let $A + B = P$, and $A - B = Q$, then we have $A = \dfrac{P + Q}{2}$, $B = \dfrac{P - Q}{2}$.

Substituting these values in (1) $-$ (4) we obtain

$$\sin P + \sin Q = 2 \sin \frac{P + Q}{2} \cos \frac{P - Q}{2} \qquad [52]$$

$$\sin P - \sin Q = 2 \cos \frac{P + Q}{2} \sin \frac{P - Q}{2} \qquad [53]$$

$$\cos P + \cos Q = 2 \cos \frac{P + Q}{2} \cos \frac{P - Q}{2} \qquad [54]$$

$$\cos P - \cos Q = - 2 \sin \frac{P + Q}{2} \sin \frac{P - Q}{2} \qquad [55]$$

A formula that leads easily to the law of tangents for solving triangles is obtained from the first two of these formulas. Dividing [53] by [52]

$$\frac{\sin P - \sin Q}{\sin P + \sin Q} = \frac{\cos \frac{1}{2} (P + Q) \sin \frac{1}{2} (P - Q)}{\sin \frac{1}{2} (P + Q) \cos \frac{1}{2} (P - Q)}$$
$$= \tan \tfrac{1}{2} (P - Q) \cot \tfrac{1}{2} (P + Q)$$

or, since $\cot \tfrac{1}{2} (P + Q) = \dfrac{1}{\tan \frac{1}{2} (P + Q)}$,

$$\frac{\sin P - \sin Q}{\sin P + \sin Q} = \frac{\tan \frac{1}{2} (P - Q)}{\tan \frac{1}{2} (P + Q)}.$$

NOTE.—Formulas [52]—[55] make possible many useful reductions. Many of the exercises on the next page may be solved by means of these formulas.

123. Product of sines and cosines of two angles.—From the relations sin $(A + B)$ + sin $(A - B)$ = 2 sin A cos B, etc. (see page 111), we have:

$$\sin A \cos B = \tfrac{1}{2} \sin (A + B) + \tfrac{1}{2} \sin (A - B) \qquad [56]$$
$$\cos A \sin B = \tfrac{1}{2} \sin (A + B) - \tfrac{1}{2} \sin (A - B) \qquad [57]$$
$$\cos A \cos B = \tfrac{1}{2} \cos (A + B) + \tfrac{1}{2} \cos (A - B) \qquad [58]$$
$$\sin A \sin B = - \tfrac{1}{2} \cos (A + B) + \tfrac{1}{2} \cos (A - B) \qquad [59]$$

These formulas enable us to express a product of sines and cosines as a sum.

EXERCISES

Prove:

1. sin 40° + sin 20° = cos 10°.

Suggestion: sin 30° = $\tfrac{1}{2}$.

2. sin 60° + sin 30° = $\sqrt{2}$ cos 15°.

3. sin 50° − sin 10° = $\sqrt{3}$ sin 20°.

Suggestion: cos 30° = $\tfrac{1}{2} \sqrt{3}$.

4. sin 70° − sin 50° = sin 10°.

5. cos 25° + cos 35° = $\sqrt{3}$ cos 5°.

6. cos 75° + cos 15° = $\sqrt{2}$ cos 30°.

7. cos 85° − cos 35° = $- \sqrt{3}$ sin 25°.

8. cos 87° − cos 27° = $-$ sin 57°.

9. sin 6x + sin 4x = 2 sin 5x cos x.

10. sin 6x − sin 2x = 2 cos 4x sin 2x.

11. cos 5x + cos 3x = 2 cos 4x cos x.

12. cos 7x − cos 3x = $-$ 2 sin 5x sin 2x.

13. 2 sin 3A cos A = sin 4A + sin 2A.

14. 2 cos 5A sin 3A = sin 8A − sin 2A.

15. 2 cos 4x cos 2x = cos 6x + cos 2x.

16. 2 sin 3x sin 2x = $-$ cos 5x + cos x.

17. 2 sin $(3x + 2y)$ cos $(3x - 2y)$ = sin 6x + sin 4y.

18. 2 cos $(3x + 2y)$ cos $(3x - 2y)$ = cos 6x + cos 4y.

19. $\dfrac{\cos x + \cos y}{\cos x - \cos y} = - \cot \tfrac{1}{2} (x + y) \cot \tfrac{1}{2} (x - y).$

Compare the formula for $\dfrac{\sin P - \sin Q}{\sin P + \sin Q}$ developed in §122.

20. $\dfrac{\sin A + \sin B}{\cos A + \cos B} = \tan \dfrac{A + B}{2}.$

21. $\dfrac{\sin 3A + \sin A}{\cos 3A + \cos A} = \tan 2A.$

22. $\dfrac{\sin 2A + \sin 2B}{\sin 2A - \sin 2B} = \tan (A + B) \cot (A - B).$

23. $\dfrac{\sin 3A + \sin A}{\sin 6A - \sin 2A} = \cos A \sec 4A.$

124. The half-angle formulas.—By formulas [44] and [45] §117 we have

$$\sin^2 \tfrac{1}{2} A = \frac{1 - \cos A}{2}, \qquad \cos^2 \tfrac{1}{2} A = \frac{1 + \cos A}{2}.$$

By means of these formulas and the law of cosines we are enabled to express the functions of the half-angles in terms of the sides of the triangle.

Let s equal one-half the perimeter of the triangle; that is, let $a + b + c = 2s$.

Subtracting successively $2a$, $2b$, $2c$, from both sides of this equality, we obtain

$$b + c - a = 2s - 2a = 2 (s - a)$$
$$a + c - b = 2s - 2b = 2 (s - b)$$
$$a + b - c = 2s - 2c = 2 (s - c).$$

By the law of cosines, $\cos A = \dfrac{b^2 + c^2 - a^2}{2bc}$.

Hence,
$$1 - \cos A = 1 - \frac{b^2 + c^2 - a^2}{2bc} = \frac{2bc - b^2 - c^2 + a^2}{2bc}$$
$$= \frac{a^2 - (b - c)^2}{2bc} = \frac{(a + b - c)(a - b + c)}{2bc}$$
$$= \frac{2 (s - c)(s - b)}{bc}.$$

Similarly, $1 + \cos A = \dfrac{2s (s - a)}{bc}$.

Therefore, $\sin^2 \tfrac{1}{2} A = \dfrac{(s - b)(s - c)}{bc}$ and $\cos^2 \tfrac{1}{2} A = \dfrac{s (s - a)}{bc}$.

Hence,
$$\sin \frac{A}{2} = \sqrt{\frac{(s - b)(s - c)}{bc}} \qquad [60]$$

and
$$\cos \frac{A}{2} = \sqrt{\frac{s (s - a)}{bc}} \qquad [61]$$

Then by division, $\tan \dfrac{A}{2} = \sqrt{\dfrac{(s - b)(s - c)}{s (s - a)}}$ $\qquad$ [62]

Since $\sqrt{\dfrac{(s - b)(s - c)}{s (s - a)}} = \sqrt{\dfrac{(s - a)(s - b)(s - c)}{s (s - a)^2}}.$

we have $\quad \tan A/2 = \dfrac{1}{s - a} \sqrt{\dfrac{(s - a)(s - b)(s - c)}{s}} = \dfrac{r}{s - a},$

which is formula [29] of §95.

EXERCISES

1. Express sin $\frac{1}{2}B$ and sin $\frac{1}{2}C$ in terms of the sides a, b, c of the triangle ABC.

2. Express cos $\frac{1}{2}B$ and cos $\frac{1}{2}C$ in terms of the sides a, b, c of the triangle ABC.

3. Express tan $\frac{1}{2}B$ and tan $\frac{1}{2}C$ in terms of the sides a, b, c of the triangle ABC.

Find the angles in the following triangles and check by adding the angles.

4. $a = 27$	**5.** $a = 1.94$	**6.** $a = 317.3$
$b = 28$	$b = 2.13$	$b = 214.8$
$c = 29$	$c = 1.64$	$c = 391.6$

Prove:

7. $\tan \theta + \tan \phi = \dfrac{\sin (\theta + \phi)}{\cos \theta \cos \phi}$

8. $\tan \dfrac{(A + B)}{2} - \dfrac{\tan (A - B)}{2} = \dfrac{2 \sin B}{\cos A + \cos B}$

9. $\cos^2 3\theta - \sin^2 3\theta = \cos 6\theta$.

10. $\cos^4 6x + 2\sin^2 6x \cos^2 6x + \sin^4 6x = 1$.

If A, B, C, a, b, c are parts of a right triangle in the usual notation, prove:

11. $\tan 2A = \dfrac{2ab}{b^2 - a^2}$

12. $\tan A/2 = \dfrac{a}{b + c}$

13. $\sin 2A + \sin 2B = 2 \cos (A - B)$

14. $\sin 2A = \sin 2B$

15. $\sin 2A = \cos (A - B)$

16. From the sine formula and the formula at the bottom of page 111, derive the law of tangents formula,

$$\frac{a - b}{a + b} = \frac{\tan \frac{1}{2} (A - B)}{\tan \frac{1}{2} (A + B)}$$

Suggestion: Since

$$\frac{a}{b} = \frac{\sin A}{\sin B}, \qquad \frac{a - b}{a + b} = \frac{\sin A - \sin B}{\sin A + \sin B} \quad \text{(Why?)}$$

From the formula at the bottom of page 111, what is the value of the expression

$$\frac{\sin A - \sin B}{\sin A + \sin B} \, ?$$

CHAPTER VIII

VARIATION OF TRIGONOMETRIC FUNCTIONS; GRAPHS

BY USING circles of unit radius we construct figures in which all the trigonometric ratios (functions) are represented by straight line segments. For the sine and cosine this construction is very obvious since the ordinate of the point P (in all the figures) is the sine and the abscissa is the cosine.

125. The remaining line functions.—The remaining functions may also be represented by lines though not quite so naturally. In the left figure below, tan $\theta = QP/OQ = MN/OM$. Since $OM = 1$, tan $\theta = MN$.

It is easily seen that the triangles OQP and SRO are similar. Hence cot $\theta = OQ/QP = RS/OR = RS$.

Again, sec $\theta = OP/OQ = ON/OM = ON$ and csc $\theta = OP/QP = OS/OR = OS$.

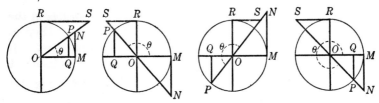

Noting that in the second figure MN, RS, and ON are negative, while OS is positive, we see that these line segments represent these functions for θ in the second quadrant.

In these figures the notation is arranged so that the proofs are exactly the same.

EXERCISES

Using the third and fourth figures above show that tan $\theta = MN$, cot $\theta = RS$, sec $\theta = ON$, csc $\theta = OS$.

Notice how the points M and R are placed in all the figures on this page. Note how the tangents and secants are found by means of the intersection of the terminal side of the angle with the tangent at the point M, while the cotangent and cosecant are found by means of the tangents at R. Note also the cases in which the tangents and cotangents point in the positive directions. Finally, note that the secant is positive when read along the terminal side of the angle, and negative when read along this side extended backward.

115

126. The variation of sine and cosine.—In these figures the circles are drawn with radius unity. Hence in each figure the sine of the angle θ is QP and its cosine is OQ.

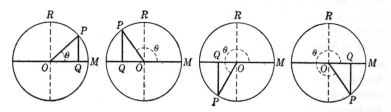

It is now obvious that as OP swings from the position OM to OR (as θ increases from 0° to 90°), the sine, QP, increases from 0 to 1, and also that as θ increases from 90° to 180° the sine decreases from 1 to 0. Again as θ increases from 180° to 270° the sine, QP, changes from 0 to -1. We say the sine *decreases* from 0 to -1 (as we also say that the temperature *decreases*, falls, from 0° to $-10°$). Finally, as θ increases from 270° to 360°, the sine *increases* from -1 to 0.

Now let us suppose that OP starts at OM and swings in the clockwise direction so as to develop negative angles. Then as θ decreases from 0° to $-90°$, sin θ decreases from 0 to -1, as θ decreases from $-90°$ to $-180°$, sin θ increases from -1 to 0, and so on as the change of the angle continues.

SIGHT WORK

Supply the words and numbers that are missing in the following.

1. As the angle θ increases from 0 to 90°, cos θ —— from —— to ——.

2. As θ increases from 90° to 180°, cos θ —— —— —— ——.

3. As θ increases from 180° to 270°, cos θ —— —— —— —— ——.

4. As θ increases from 270° to 360°, cos θ —— —— —— —— ——.

5. As θ decreases from $-90°$ to $-180°$, sin θ —— —— —— —— ——.

6. As θ decreases from $-180°$ to $-270°$, sin θ —— —— —— —— ——.

7. As θ decreases from $-270°$ to $-360°$, sin θ —— —— —— —— ——.

8. Make similar statements for cos θ as θ decreases successively from 0° to $-90°$, from $-90°$ to $-180°$, from $-180°$ to $-270°$, and from $-270°$ to $-360°$.

9. Describe the variation of sine and cosine as θ increases from 360° to $2 \cdot 360°$, from $2 \cdot 360°$ to $3 \cdot 360°$, etc.

10. Describe the variation of sine and cosine as θ decreases from $-360°$ to $-2 \cdot 360°$, from $-2 \cdot 360°$ to $-3 \cdot 360°$, and so on.

127. The variation of tan θ in the first quadrant.—If in this figure the radius OM is unity, then (see §125) tan $\theta = MN$. Consider the variation of tan θ (MN) as ON revolves about the fixed point O, beginning at the position OM. Clearly the initial value is zero. As ON swings so as to approach the direction OR, the line ON becomes more and more nearly parallel to MN and the intersection point N moves indefinitely far out along the

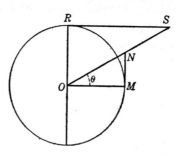

fixed tangent line. That is, the length of MN increases without limit. All this is expressed by saying:

As θ increases from 0° to 90° the tangent increases from 0 to infinity.[1]

This means that no matter what fixed point K we take on the tangent line, we can take the angle θ so near 90° that the point N will be beyond K. When $\theta = 90°$ the terminal line of the angle will be parallel to the line tangent to the circle at M, and the lines will not meet. That is, in this case there will be no intersection point N. Hence we see that an angle of 90°, strictly speaking, has no tangent.

The symbol ∞ is used instead of the word infinity. Using this symbol we say that the tangent increases from 0 to ∞. It is sometimes said that tan 90° = ∞. This must be taken to mean that as θ approaches 90° the tangent increases without any fixed limit.

128. The variation of cot θ in the first quadrant.—We know (see §125) that in the above figure cot $\theta = RS$. Hence we see that for $\theta = 90°$ the cotangent is 0, but that when the angle is made very small the cotangent becomes large without limit.

That the angle 0° has no cotangent is now clear for exactly the same reason that the angle 90° has no tangent. Clearly, as the angle increases from zero toward 90° the cotangent decreases from indefinitely large values toward zero. All this is expressed by saying:

As θ increases from 0 to 90°, cot θ decreases from ∞ to 0.

[1] The word infinity really means without limit or boundary.

129. The variation of sec θ in the first quadrant.—From §125 we know that in the figure sec $\theta = ON$. Clearly, when θ is very small the secant ON is very nearly equal to the radius OM, or unity, and when θ is made equal to 0 the secant is unity. Compare this with sec $0 = \dfrac{1}{\cos 0} = \dfrac{1}{1} = 1.$

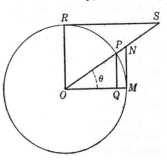

When θ approaches 90° the secant ON grows large beyond any fixed limit exactly the same way as the tangent. Hence we see that:

As θ varies from 0 to 90°, the secant varies from 1 to ∞.

130. The variation of csc θ in the first quadrant.—From §125 we know that csc $\theta = OS$ as shown in the figure. It is now evident that for $\theta = 90°$, csc $\theta = OR$ or unity. Now let θ decrease from 90° toward 0. Then the line OS becomes more and more nearly parallel to RS and the intersection point S moves out indefinitely along the fixed tangent at R. Hence we see that as the angle approaches zero in value the cosecant OS grows large in the positive direction beyond any fixed limit. The meaning of the following statement will now be evident.

As θ varies from 0 to 90°, csc θ varies from ∞ to 1.

131. The variation of tan θ as θ varies from 90° to 180°.—From §125 we know that in this figure tan $\theta = MN$. Since MN is now negative the tangent of θ in the second quadrant is negative. Let us think of θ as decreasing from 180° toward 90°. Clearly tan 180° = 0. Then as the angle decreases the tangent increases in absolute value but in the negative direction. As the angle is made to decrease toward 90° the point N

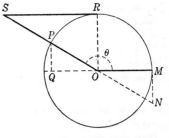

passes along the tangent at M beyond any fixed limit. Since MN grows beyond any fixed limit in the negative direction we say that it becomes $-\infty$. Hence we have the statement:

As θ increases from 90° to 180°, tan θ increases from $-\infty$ to 0.

SIGHT WORK

1. Using the fact that in the last figure on page 118, cot θ = RS, decide whether in the second quadrant cot θ is positive or negative.

2. As θ varies from 90° to 180° how does cot θ vary?

3. In the figure in §131 sec θ = ON (see §125). How does sec θ vary as θ varies from 90° to 180°?

Note that ON is on the terminal side of the angle when extended backward. Hence ON is negative.

4. In the figure in §125, csc θ = OS (see §131). How does csc θ vary as θ varies from 90° to 180°?

5. In this figure tan θ = MN (see §127). How does tan θ vary as θ varies from 180° to 270°?

6. In the same figure cot θ = RS (see §128). How does cot θ vary as θ varies from 180° to 270°?

7. Using sec θ = ON (see §129), how does sec θ vary as θ varies from 180° to 270°? Note that ON is laid off on the terminal side of the angle extended backward.

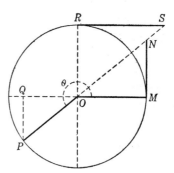

8. Using csc θ = OQ (see §130), how does csc θ vary when θ varies from 180° to 270°? Is csc θ positive or negative in this quadrant? Why?

9. In this figure tan θ = MN (see §127). Is MN positive or negative? How does tan θ vary as θ varies from 270° to 360°?

10. What line in this figure represents cot θ? Is cot θ positive or negative? How does cot θ vary as θ varies from 270° to 360°?

11. What line in the figure represents sec θ? Is sec θ positive or negative? Why? How does sec θ vary as θ varies from 270° to 360°?

12. What line in this figure represents csc θ? Is csc θ positive or negative? Why? How does csc θ vary as θ varies from 270° to 360°?

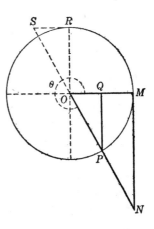

13. For what values of θ does tan θ approach either ∞ or − ∞?

14. Answer questions like the preceding for cot θ, sec θ, and csc θ.

132. Résumé of variation of functions.—We have already seen (§126) that as the angle varies through the four quadrants, the sine varies from 0 to 1 in the first quadrant, then from 1 to − 1 in the second and third quadrants, and finally from − 1 to 0 in the fourth quadrant.

Similarly, we have seen (§126) that for the same variation of the angle the cosine varies from 1 to − 1 in the first and second quadrants and from − 1 to + 1 in the third and fourth quadrants. In the first quadrant the tangent varies from 0 to + ∞, in the second quadrant from − ∞ to 0, in the third from 0 to + ∞, and in the fourth from − ∞ to 0; while the cotangent varies from + ∞ to 0 in the first quadrant, from 0 to − ∞ in the second, from + ∞ to 0 in the third, and from 0 to − ∞ in the fourth.

Again, in the first quadrant the secant varies from 1 to ∞, in the second quadrant from − ∞ to − 1, in the third quadrant from − 1 to − ∞, and in the fourth quadrant from + ∞ to 1.

Finally, the cosecant varies from + ∞ to 1 in the first quadrant, from 1 to + ∞ in the second quadrant, from − ∞ to − 1 in the third quadrant, and from − 1 to − ∞ in the fourth quadrant.

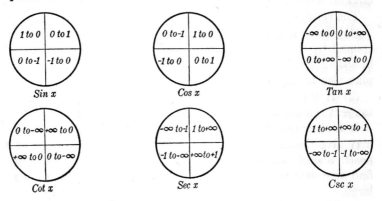

| | | |
| Sin x | Cos x | Tan x |

| | | |
| Cot x | Sec x | Csc x |

SIGHT WORK

1. Using tan θ = sin θ / cos θ and the known variations of sin θ and cos θ, discuss the variation of tan θ as θ varies from 0 to 360°.

2. Using cot θ = cos θ / sin θ, discuss the variation of cot θ as θ varies from 0 to 360°.

3. Using sec θ = 1/cos θ and csc θ = 1/sin θ, discuss the variation of sec θ and csc θ as θ varies from 0 to 360°.

133. Functions of $\theta + 180°$ in terms of functions of θ.—In each of these figures it is obvious that

$$\sin (\theta + 180°) = - \sin \theta \ [63] \text{ and } \cos (\theta + 180°) = - \cos \theta \ [64]$$

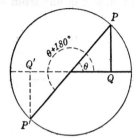 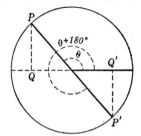

From the values in terms of sine and cosine of the remaining functions we then have

$$\tan (\theta + 180°) = \tan \theta \quad [65] \qquad \cot (\theta° + 180°) = \cot \theta \quad [66]$$
$$\sec (\theta + 180°) = - \sec \theta \ [67] \qquad \csc (\theta + 180°) = - \csc \theta \ [68]$$

The best way to remember these relations is to fix in mind the figures just given and the relations for sine and cosine that they show. The relations for the remaining functions are then obvious when we recall their values in terms of sine and cosine.

The results just obtained may also be stated as follows.

(1) If the angle is changed by 180° (either increased or decreased by this amount) the sine and cosine remain unchanged in absolute value, but are changed in sign. Obviously this applies also to the secant and cosecant.

(2) If the angle is changed by 180°, the tangent and cotangent remain unchanged in all respects.

It is clear that by repeated application of these formulas we may give the functions of *any* angle in terms of functions of a positive angle less than 180°. But in the next section we shall find more effective means of doing this when the angles are very large.

SIGHT WORK

Give the value of each of the following in terms of a function of a positive angle not greater than 45°.

1. sin 240°, cos 324°, tan 196°, cot 230°, sec 187°, csc 328°.
2. sin (−48°), cos (−147°), tan (−70°), cot (−160°).
3. sec (−112°), csc (−54°), tan (−280°), cot (−290°).

134. Periodicity of functions.—It is at once obvious from the definitions of the trigonometric functions that adding 360° to an angle or subtracting 360° from it does not change the value of any of its functions. It follows that the variation of each

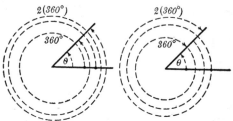

function is exactly the same when the angle varies from 360° to 2 (360°) as it is when the angle varies from 0 to 360°, and that the variation is also the same when the angle varies from − 360° to 0.

It is evident that the same variation is repeated as the angle varies from 2 (360°) to 3 (360°), from 3 (360°) to 4 (360°), etc., and also as it varies from − 2 (360°) to − 360°, from − 3 (360°) to − 2 (360°), etc. More generally, if we start with any angle θ and then consider the angle as varying between θ and $\theta + 360°$, any one of the functions will undergo a certain variation. Then if the angle varies between $\theta + 360°$ and $\theta + 2$ (360°), this function will undergo exactly the same variation. This is indicated in mathematical language by saying that these functions have a **period** 360°.

By looking ahead at the graphs on pages 126 and 127, it is evident that these show this periodicity for the sine and cosine. So we conclude that the sine and the cosine have a period 360°.

Since $\sec \theta = 1/\cos \theta$ and $\csc \theta = 1/\sin \theta$, it follows that these functions have the same period as the sine and cosine, namely, 360°.

Since $\tan (\theta + 180°) = \tan \theta$ and $\cot (\theta + 180°) = \cot \theta$, it follows that the tangent and cotangent have a period 180°. This is also evident from the graphs on page 129. That is, the tangent, for instance, goes through a certain variation from θ to $180° + \theta$, and then repeats exactly the same variation as the angle varies from $180° + \theta$ to $360° + \theta$, from $360° + \theta$ to $540° + \theta$, and so on, and also as the angle varies from − 180° + θ to 0 + θ, from − 360° + θ to − 180° + θ, and so on.

Similar remarks apply to the cotangent. Hence both tangent and cotangent have a smallest period 180°. It is clear that this does not contradict the statement above that these functions also have a period 360°. For the sine, cosine, secant, and cosecant, the smallest period is 360°.

135. Reducing a function of any angle to a function of a positive angle less than, or equal to, 45°.—It follows at once from the discussion on page 122 that any function of any angle may be reduced to the same function of a positive angle less than 360°. If the angle is negative, or positive and greater than 360°, we simply add or subtract a multiple of 360°.

Thus tan 974° = tan (974° − 720°) = tan 254°

That is, we subtract 360° twice, or 2 × 360° = 720°.

Again, tan (− 164°) = tan (− 164° + 360°) = tan 196°, and similarly for any angle and any function.

On page 121 we found the following formulas

$$\sin (\theta + 180°) = - \sin \theta \qquad \cos (\theta + 180°) = - \cos \theta$$
$$\tan (\theta + 180°) = \quad \tan \theta \qquad \cot (\theta + 180°) = \quad \cot \theta$$
$$\sec (\theta + 180°) = - \sec \theta \qquad \csc (\theta + 180°) = - \csc \theta$$

If $\theta + 180°$ is between 180° and 360°, then θ is between 0° and 180°. Hence the angle has now been reduced to a positive angle less than 180°.

Using the formulas on the sine and cosine of supplementary angles (page 70) and formulas following immediately from them by representing tangent, cotangent, secant and cosecant in terms of sine and cosine, we have:

$$\sin (180° − \theta) = \sin \theta \quad [69] \qquad \cos (180° − \theta) = - \cos \theta \quad [70]$$
$$\tan (180° − \theta) = - \tan \theta \quad [71] \qquad \cot (180° − \theta) = - \cot \theta \quad [72]$$
$$\sec (180° − \theta) = - \sec \theta \quad [73] \qquad \csc (180° − \theta) = \csc \theta \quad [74]$$

If $180° − \theta$ is between 90° and 180°, then θ is an acute angle.

Using the theorem on cofunctions of complementary angles, we can now reduce the angle to an angle between 0° and 45°.

We may note that the period of 180° for tangent and cotangent enables us to reduce the angle at once to one between 0 and 180° by subtracting or adding some multiple of 360° and then subtracting 180°. In the cases of sine, cosine, secant, and cosecant this last subtraction requires a change of sign of the functions.

EXERCISES

1. Prove that sin $(-1145°) = -\cos 25°$.

Solution: sin $(-1145°) = \sin (-1145 + 4 \cdot 360°)$
$$= \sin 295° \text{ (by §134)}$$

$$\sin 295° = -\sin 115° \text{ (by [63])}$$
$$-\sin 115° = -\sin 65° \text{ (suppl. } \angle s)$$
$$-\sin 65° = -\cos 25° \text{ (comp. } \angle s)$$

2. Express each of the following as a function of an angle between 0 and 45°.

(a) cos 173°	(e) cos $(-1027°)$	(i) sin 2028°
(b) tan 127°	(f) cot 1831	(j) csc $(-1550°)$
(c) cos $(-73°)$	(g) sin $(-784°)$	(k) cot 783°
(d) sin 853°	(h) sec 1020°	(l) cos 527°

3. Construct the angle 1650° on a set of coordinate axes. From the figure determine the six trigonometric functions of 1650°.

4. Prove that

$$\sin (\theta + n \cdot 180°) = -\sin \theta$$
$$\cos (\theta + n \cdot 180°) = -\cos \theta$$

when n is odd.

5. State and prove formulas similar to those in example 4 when n is even.

6. State formulas for secant and cosecant similar to those in example 4. Use both odd and even values of n.

7. State formulas for tangent and cotangent similar to those in example 4. Use both odd and even values of n.

8. If θ is an angle between 0 and 90°, express sin $(-\theta)$ as a function of θ.

Solution: Adding 180° to the angle, we have

$$\sin (-\theta) = -\sin (-\theta + 180°)$$

The supplement of $-\theta + 180°$ is

$$180° - (-\theta + 180°) = 180° + \theta - 180° = \theta$$
$$-\sin (-\theta + 180°) = -\sin \theta$$

Hence sin $(-\theta) = -\sin \theta$.

9. Prove cos $(-\theta) = \cos \theta$.

10. Prove sin $(90° + \phi) = \cos \phi$.

Hint: sin $\theta = \cos (90° - \theta)$. Let $\theta = 90° - \phi$.

11. Prove cos $(90° + \phi) = -\sin \phi$.

12. Express each of the following as a function of θ.

(a) sec $(-\theta)$	(c) cos $(\theta - 270°)$	(e) tan $(-\theta)$
(b) sin $(\theta + 270°)$	(d) tan $(270° - \theta)$	(f) cot $(\theta - 540°)$

136. Radian measure.—Up to this point the degree, minute, and second have been used as units of measure of angles. These units are used in nearly all tables of trigonometric functions. For certain purposes however another unit of angle, called the radian, is used exclusively.

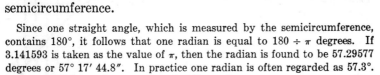

If the vertex of the angle AOB is the center of a circle and if the length of the arc AB is equal to the radius of the circle, then the angle AOB is one **radian.** That is,

A radian is a central angle whose intercepted arc is equal in length to the radius of the circle.

From geometry we know that the circumference of a circle is equal to the diameter multiplied by π where $\pi = 3.1416$ (approximately), or, what is the same thing, that the radius multiplied by π is equal to the semicircumference.

Since one straight angle, which is measured by the semicircumference, contains 180°, it follows that one radian is equal to $180 \div \pi$ degrees. If 3.141593 is taken as the value of π, then the radian is found to be 57.29577 degrees or 57° 17′ 44.8″. In practice one radian is often regarded as 57.3°.

Since 180° is equal to π radians it follows that

$$90° = \frac{\pi}{2}, \ 60° = \frac{\pi}{3}, \ 30° = \frac{\pi}{6}, \ 120° = \frac{2}{3}\pi, \ 135° = \frac{3}{4}\pi, \ 150° = \frac{5}{6}\pi.$$

The second member in each of these equations is expressed in radians. From now on either the radian or the degree will be used as a unit of angle as convenience requires.

137. Rule for converting radians into degrees and degrees into radians.—Since one radian contains $\dfrac{180}{\pi}$ degrees, it follows that an angle of x radians contains $\dfrac{180}{\pi} \cdot x$ degrees, and an angle of y degrees contains $y \div \dfrac{180}{\pi}$, or $\dfrac{\pi}{180} \cdot y$, radians.

Hence we have the rule:

To convert radians into degrees multiply by 180/π and to convert degrees into radians multiply by π/180.

EXERCISES

1. How many radians are there in 75°? in 84°? in 97°? in 114° 30′? Give each result correct to three decimals.

2. How many degrees, minutes, and seconds are there in ½ radian? in 1⅓ radians? in 2 radians? in 2.7 radians?

138. Graphic representation of the variation of the sine.—
For the purpose of constructing graphs representing the variation of trigonometric functions the radian is used as the unit of
angle.

We note that

$$15° = \frac{1}{12}\,\pi,\ 30° = \frac{1}{6}\,\pi,\ 45° = \frac{1}{4}\,\pi,\ 60° = \frac{1}{3}\,\pi,\ 75° = \frac{5}{12}\,\pi,\ 90° = \frac{1}{2}\,\pi,$$

$$105° = \frac{7}{12}\,\pi,\ 120° = \frac{2}{3}\,\pi,\ 135° = \frac{3}{4}\,\pi,\ 150° = \frac{5}{6}\,\pi,\ 165° = \frac{11}{12}\,\pi,\ 180° = \pi$$

Reducing these values to decimals correct to two places we have,

15° = 0.26 (radians)	60° = 1.05	105° = 1.83	150° = 2.62
30° = 0.52	75° = 1.31	120° = 2.09	165° = 2.88
45° = 0.79	90° = 1.57	135° = 2.36	180° = 3.14

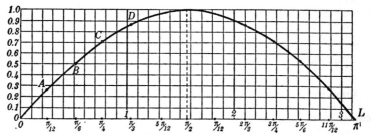

If we plot the points whose abscissas represent angles and whose ordinates
represent the corresponding values of the sine, we have the points O, A, B,
. . . L, as shown in the figure. The coordinates of these points are O
$(0, 0)$, A $(.26, .26)$, B $(.52, .50)$, C $(.79, .71)$, . . . L $(3.14, 0)$. If a smooth
curve is drawn through these points, we have the *sine curve* from 0 to π.

If this curve is continued from π to 2π it will have exactly the same shape
as the arc shown above, but will lie below the x-axis. Similarly, from 0 to
$-\pi$ it will lie below the x-axis, while from $-\pi$ to -2π it will be above
the x-axis. The general shape of this curve is shown below.

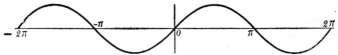

In this graph the arcs 0 to π, π to 2π, 0 to $-\pi$ and $-\pi$ to -2π have
exactly the same shape.

EXERCISES

1. From the first figure find sin 10°, sin 40°, sin 70° correct to two decimals
and compare with the values given on page 25.

Suggestion: $10° = \frac{\pi}{18} = .17$ (to the nearest hundredth).

2. From the second figure verify that sin $x = -\sin(-x)$. In particular
what are the values of sin $\frac{\pi}{2}$ and sin $\left(-\frac{\pi}{2}\right)$? of sin $\frac{3\pi}{2}$ and sin $\left(-\frac{3\pi}{2}\right)$?

139. Graphic representation of the variation of the cosine.— Starting at the point $-\frac{\pi}{2}$ (-1.57) on the x-axis, we mark the points -1.31, -1.05, -0.79, -0.52, -0.26, 0, 0.26, 0.52, 0.79, 1.05, 1.31, 1.57, which represent the angles $-90°$, $-75°$, $-60°$, $-45°$, $-30°$, $-15°$, 0, $15°$, $30°$, $45°$, $60°$, $75°$, $90°$. At these points we erect perpendiculars equal to the cosines of these angles and mark the ends of these A, B, C, . . . , L.

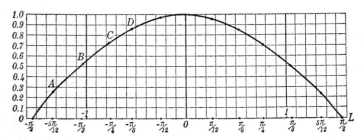

Drawing a smooth curve through these points, we have the *cosine curve* from $-\frac{\pi}{2}$ to $\frac{\pi}{2}$.

If this curve is continued from $\frac{\pi}{2}$ to $\frac{3\pi}{2}$ it will have exactly the same shape as the arc just shown, but will be below the x-axis, while from $\frac{3\pi}{2}$ to $\frac{5\pi}{2}$ it will be above the axis. Similarly from $-\frac{\pi}{2}$ to $-\frac{3\pi}{2}$ it will be below the axis and from $-\frac{3\pi}{2}$ to $-\frac{5\pi}{2}$ it will be above the axis.

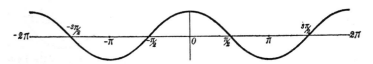

From this curve we may verify that $\cos(-x) = \cos x$.

SIGHT WORK

1. From the first figure find the values of $\cos 10°$, $\cos 40°$, $\cos 70°$, to the nearest hundredth, and compare with results from the tables.

2. From the second figure give a series of angles (eight or more) for which the cosine is zero.

140. Comparison of the sine curve and the cosine curve.—By placing the two graphs on the same axes their relation becomes apparent.

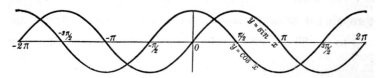

These curves have exactly the same shape, and if the cosine curve is moved a distance $\frac{\pi}{2}$ to the right (or the sine curve a distance $\frac{\pi}{2}$ to the left) the curves will coincide completely.

From this graph, formulas [89], . . . [92] (page 160) may now be verified. Thus $\sin (x + 90°) = \cos x$ is verified by the fact that if the sine curve is moved a distance $\frac{\pi}{2}$, or 90°, to the left it will coincide with the cosine curve.

EXERCISES

1. Using the sine curve, verify that $\sin (\pi - x) = \sin x$. (See § 82.)

2. Using the cosine curve, verify that $\cos (\pi - x) = -\cos x$. (See § 82.)

3. Using the sine and cosine curves, verify that if two angles are complementary the sine of either is equal to the cosine of the other.

4. Express each of the following as a function of an angle from 0° to 45°.

(*a*) $\sin 68°$
(*b*) $\cos 79°$
(*c*) $\sin 100°$
(*d*) $\cos 100°$
(*e*) $\sin 135°$
(*f*) $\cos 169°$

(*g*) $\sin (-30°)$
(*h*) $\cos (-30°)$
(*i*) $\sin (-82°)$
(*j*) $\cos (-76°)$
(*k*) $\sin (-120°)$
(*l*) $\cos (-150°)$

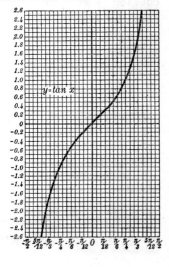

141. Variation of the tangent.— Study the graph of the tangent as shown at the right. Recall (see page 117) the variation of the tangent as the angle moves from 0 to $\pi/2$ (90°) and also from $-\pi/2$ (— 90°) to 0. Tell how the graph represents this variation.

Since by [65], tan $(180° + x) = $ tan x, or, stated in more usual language, tan $(\pi + x) = $ tan x, for any value of x, it follows that as x varies from $\frac{\pi}{2}$ to $\frac{3\pi}{2}$ or from $- \frac{3\pi}{2}$ to $- \frac{\pi}{2}$ the tangent passes through the same variation that it does when x varies from $- \frac{\pi}{2}$ to $\frac{\pi}{2}$. This relation may be verified from the graph below, in which the solid curves represent tan x and the dotted curves represent cot x.

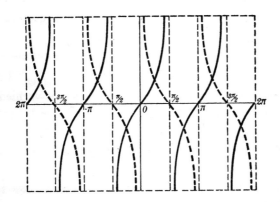

142. Variation of the cotangent.—By using the relation cot $(180° + x) = $ cot x [66], or, stated in the form, cot $(\pi + x) = $ cot x, for any value of x, we can compare the variation of the cotangent as x varies from π to 2π or from $- \pi$ to 0 with its variation as x varies from 0 to π.

This relation may be verified from the graph above.

EXERCISES

1. Using the tangent curve, verify that tan $(\pi - x) = -$ tan x.
2. Using the cotangent curve, verify that cot $(\pi - x) = -$ cot x.
3. Using the tangent and cotangent curves, verify tan $x = $ tan $(x \pm \pi)$ and cot $x = $ cot $(x \pm \pi)$.
4. Express each of the following as a function of an angle between $0°$ and $45°$.

(a) tan $69°$ (d) cot $112°$ (g) cot $(- 60°)$ (j) tan $(- 145°)$
(b) cot $74°$ (e) tan $172°$ (h) cot $(- 84°)$ (k) cot $(- 160°)$
(c) tan $98°$ (f) tan $(- 40°)$ (i) tan $(- 94°)$ (l) cot $(- 174°)$

MISCELLANEOUS EXERCISES

1. Construct a table showing the number of radians in angles of 10°, 20°, 30°, 40°, 50°, 60°, 70°, 80°, 90°, each expressed in decimal notation correct to three places.

2. Construct similarly a three-place table showing the radian measure for 10°, 11°, 12°, 13°, 14°, 15°, 16°, 17°, 18°, 19°, 20°.

3. Construct similarly a three-place table showing the radian measure for 1°, 2°, 3°, . . . up to 9°.

4. Using the results obtained in examples 2 and 3, and two-place values of the sines of these angles, construct the graph of $\sin x$ from $x = 0$ to $x = 20°$. Use a scale in which one horizontal unit represents 1° of angle and one vertical unit represents one-tenth. Compare this graph with a straight line.

5. Find the radian measure correct to two decimals for each of the following: (a) 36°; (b) 63°; (c) 24° 30'; (d) 74° 15'; (e) 112° 45'.

6. Find the number of degrees, minutes, and seconds in the angle whose radian measure is (a) 2; (b) .6; (c) .375; (d) 1.05; (e) 8.125.

7. A wheel 60 inches in diameter spins at such a speed that one of its spokes generates an angle of 360π per minute. Find the linear speed in feet per second of a point upon its periphery.

8. Find the linear speed in feet per second of a particle on the periphery of a wheel one foot in diameter if the wheel is making 3600 revolutions per minute.

9. Fill in a table similar to that shown below, with decimal values correct to two decimal places, and from the table construct the corresponding parts of the graphs of

$$(a) \ y = 1 + \sin x$$
$$(b) \ y = x + \sin x$$

x	0	$\pi/6$	$\pi/4$	$\pi/3$	$\pi/2$	$2\pi/3$	$3\pi/4$	$5\pi/6$	2π
$1 + \sin x$									
$x + \sin x$									

Prove:

10. $\sin (x + \pi/4) + \sin (x + 3\pi/4) = \sqrt{2} \cos x.$

11. $(1 + \tan \theta) \tan (\pi/4 - \theta) = 1 - \tan \theta.$

12. $\tan (\pi/4 - \alpha) = \dfrac{1 - \tan \alpha}{1 + \tan \alpha}.$

13. $\cos \pi/6 - \cos (-\pi/3) = \dfrac{\sqrt{3} - 1}{2}.$

Expand and simplify by substituting numerical values for functions of known angles:

14. $\sin (\pi/4 - \theta)$

15. $\cos (\pi/3 - \theta)$

16. $\tan (\pi/6 - \theta)$

17. $\sin (\pi/6 - \theta)$

CHAPTER IX

INVERSE FUNCTIONS AND TRIGONOMETRIC EQUATIONS

IN THE courses in mathematics which precede trigonometry there occur several cases of what are called inverse operations. Thus subtraction is the inverse operation of addition, division is the inverse of multiplication, and finding a root is the inverse of raising to a power. In the course in trigonometry we have already encountered pairs of operations in which each one is the inverse of the other.

Thus the two operations—(1) finding the sine of a given angle and (2) finding an angle whose sine is given—are inverse, each of the other. Such operations lead to what are called inverse trigonometric functions which we now proceed to study.

143. Inverse trigonometric functions and their notation.— The sine, cosine, tangent, cotangent, secant, and cosecant of an angle are all definitely fixed when the angle is given, and it is for this reason that they are called functions of the angle.

If an angle is known to be acute and if one of its functions is given, then the angle is definitely fixed. For this reason an angle is said to be a function of its sine, of its cosine, of its tangent, etc.

Thus "the angle whose sine is y" is a function of y. This function of y is designated by the symbol $\sin^{-1} y$, which is read "the angle whose sine is y," or "the inverse sine y," or "arc sine y."

Similarly "the angle whose cosine is y" is designated by the symbol $\cos^{-1} y$, which is also read "the inverse cosine y," or "arc cosine y." The symbols $\tan^{-1} y$, $\cot^{-1} y$, $\sec^{-1} y$, and $\csc^{-1} y$ are used to designate, respectively, "the angle whose tangent is y," "the angle whose cotangent is y," "the angle whose secant is y," and "the angle whose cosecant is y."

The six functions, $\sin^{-1} y$, $\cos^{-1} y$, $\tan^{-1} y$, $\cot^{-1} y$, $\sec^{-1} y$, $\csc^{-1} y$, are **inverse trigonometric functions** of y.

It should be noted with care that each of these symbols represents an *angle*. Thus the whole expression "$\sin^{-1}y$" represents an angle, and it gives the information that the sine of the angle is y. That is, $y = \sin x$ and $x = \sin^{-1}y$ represent the same fact.

In expressions like $\sin^{-1}y$ the $^{-1}$ is in no sense a negative exponent, but indicates simply an *inverse function.* Thus $(\sin y)^{-1}$ means $\dfrac{1}{\sin y}$ (one divided by the sine of the angle y), while $\sin^{-1}y$ means the angle whose sine is y.[1]

144. Simple examples involving inverse functions.

—As was suggested on the preceding page, many of the examples already solved in this course really involve the use of inverse functions. We will now restate some of these, using the inverse notation.

Example 1. Find $\sin^{-1}\frac{1}{2}$, if it is given that the angle is acute.

Solution: Since it is known that $\sin 30° = \frac{1}{2}$, it follows that $30° = \sin^{-1}\frac{1}{2}$. This result may also be given in radians, namely, $\dfrac{\pi}{6} = \sin^{-1}\frac{1}{2}$.

Example 2. Find $\cos^{-1}\dfrac{\sqrt{3}}{3}$, if it is given that the angle is acute.

Solution: $\dfrac{\sqrt{3}}{3} = .57735$. From the table of natural functions we find that the angle whose cosine is 0.57735 is $54° \, 44'$.

Hence

$$\cos^{-1}\frac{\sqrt{3}}{3} = 54° \, 44'.$$

Example 3. Find the value of $\tan\left(\sin^{-1}\dfrac{2}{3}\right)$, if it is given that the angle is acute.

Solution: This example was solved on page 98, where it was required to find the functions (among them the tangent) of an angle whose sine is $\dfrac{2}{3}$. We may now carry out the solution as follows:

Let $x = \sin^{-1}\frac{2}{3}$. Then $\sin x = \frac{2}{3}$.

Hence,

$$\cos x = \sqrt{1 - \frac{4}{9}} = \frac{1}{3}\sqrt{5}$$

Therefore,

$$\tan x = \frac{\frac{2}{3}}{\frac{1}{3}\sqrt{5}} = \frac{2}{\sqrt{5}}, \text{ or } \tan\left(\sin^{-1}\frac{2}{3}\right) = \frac{2}{\sqrt{5}}.$$

It should be understood clearly that the only new element introduced here in this problem is the inverse notation.

Example 4. Express each of the other five functions of $\sin^{-1}u$ in terms of u.

This example is solved completely on page 99. The results are given in the first column of the table at the bottom of that page, $\sin A$ being used instead of u.

[1] The symbol $^{-1}$ is used for *any* inverse function out of analogy to the particular case of division where this symbol is a negative exponent as well as an inverse symbol.

EXERCISES

Find the value of x in each of the following, the angle being acute.

1. $x = \sin^{-1}\frac{1}{2} \sqrt{2}$.

2. $x = \tan^{-1} \sqrt{3}$.

3. $x = \cos^{-1}\frac{\sqrt{2}}{2}$.

4. $x = \sin^{-1}\frac{\sqrt{3}}{2}$.

5. $x = \tan^{-1}\frac{\sqrt{3}}{3}$.

6. $x = \cos^{-1}\frac{3}{4}$.

Find the values of the following, the angles being acute.

7. $\sin\left(\cos^{-1}\frac{1}{2}\right)$

8. $\cos\left(\sin^{-1}\frac{3}{4}\right)$

9. $\tan\left(\sin^{-1}\frac{3}{5}\right)$

10. $\tan\left(\cot^{-1}1\right)$

11. $\sin\left(\cot^{-1}\frac{4}{3}\right)$

12. $\cos\left(\tan^{-1}\frac{7}{24}\right)$

13. $\tan\left(\cot^{-1}x\right)$

14. $\sin\left(\csc^{-1}x\right)$

15. $\cos\left(\sec^{-1}x\right)$

145. Multiple values of inverse functions.—For any definite value of x there is one and only one value of $\sin x$. This is expressed by saying that $\sin x$ is a **single-valued function** of x. In the examples on finding the values of inverse functions that have been solved in this chapter it has been given that the angles are acute. With this restriction each inverse function is single-valued; but with the restriction removed inverse trigonometric functions have an unlimited number of values.

Thus $\sin^{-1}\frac{1}{2}$ has the value $\frac{\pi}{6}$, or 30°, if the angle is to be acute. Otherwise there is an unlimited number of angles whose sine is $\frac{1}{2}$.

From [15], $\sin\frac{\pi}{6} = \sin\left(\pi - \frac{\pi}{6}\right) = \sin\frac{5\pi}{6}$.
That is,

$$\sin^{-1}\frac{1}{2} = \frac{5\pi}{6} \text{ as well as } \frac{\pi}{6}.$$

Again from § 134, $\sin(x + 2n\pi) = \sin x$ for all integral values of n (positive or negative).

Hence if $\sin x = \frac{1}{2}$, then x may have any of the values $\frac{\pi}{6} + 2n\pi$ and also any of the values $\frac{5\pi}{6} + 2n\pi$, for all integral values of n. These are all values of $\sin^{-1}\frac{1}{2}$.

In a similar manner it may be shown that each of the other inverse functions has an unlimited number of values.

Hence inverse trigonometric functions are said to be **multiple-valued**. On the following pages we will study the problem of finding all angles which have a given value of one of its functions.

146. The principal value of inverse functions.—The angle that has the smallest absolute value is the principal value of an inverse function. If a positive and a negative angle of the same absolute value result, the positive angle is used.

Thus $\pi/6$, or $30°$, is the principal value of $\sin^{-1} \frac{1}{2}$, since this is the angle with the smallest absolute value whose sine is $\frac{1}{2}$. Again $-\pi/2$, or $-90°$, is the angle with smallest absolute value whose sine is -1.

EXERCISES

Find the principal value of each of the following, and also two other values.

1. $\sin^{-1} \frac{1}{2}$.

2. $\sin^{-1} (-\frac{1}{2})$.

3. $\sin^{-1} \frac{\sqrt{2}}{2}$.

4. $\sin^{-1} \left(-\frac{\sqrt{2}}{2}\right)$.

5. $\sin^{-1} 1$.

6. $\sin^{-1} (1-1)$.

7. $\cos^{-1} \frac{1}{2}$.

8. $\cos^{-1} (-\frac{1}{2})$.

9. $\cos^{-1} \frac{\sqrt{2}}{2}$.

10. $\cos^{-1} \left(-\frac{\sqrt{2}}{2}\right)$.

11. $\cos^{-1} 1$.

12. $\tan^{-1} 1$.

13. $\tan^{-1} (-1)$.

14. $\tan^{-1} \sqrt{3}$.

15. $\tan^{-1} (-\sqrt{3})$.

16. $\tan^{-1} \frac{\sqrt{3}}{3}$.

17. $\tan^{-1} \left(-\frac{\sqrt{3}}{3}\right)$.

18. $\tan^{-1} \frac{\sqrt{2}}{2}$.

19. $\tan^{-1} \left(-\frac{\sqrt{2}}{2}\right)$.

20. $\cot^{-1} 1$.

21. $\cot^{-1} (-1)$.

22. $\cot^{-1} \frac{\sqrt{3}}{3}$.

23. $\cot^{-1} \left(-\frac{\sqrt{3}}{3}\right)$.

24. $\cot^{-1} (-\sqrt{3})$.

25. $\sec^{-1} 1$.

26. $\sec^{-1} (-1)$.

27. $\sec^{-1} \sqrt{2}$.

28. $\sec^{-1} \sqrt{3}$.

29. $\sec (-\sqrt{2})$.

30. $\csc^{-1} 1$.

31. $\csc^{-1} (-1)$.

32. $\csc^{-1} \sqrt{3}$.

33. $\csc^{-1} \sqrt{5}$.

147. Angles having the same sine.—Let c be a number between -1 and $+1$ (or possibly equal to -1 or to $+1$).

If c is positive there is an angle A in the first quadrant such that $\sin A = c$. If c is negative there is a negative angle in the fourth quadrant such that $\sin A = c$.

In either case A is the principal value of $\sin^{-1} c$ and by [15] $\sin A = \sin (\pi - A)$ for all values of A.

Note that if A is negative, then $\pi - A$ is in the third quadrant.

By §134

$$\sin A = \sin (A + 2n\pi) \qquad (1)$$

and

$$\sin (\pi - A) = \sin (\pi - A + 2n\pi) = \sin [(2n + 1)\,\pi - A], \quad (2)$$

for all integral values of n. These may be written

$$\sin A = \sin (n\pi + A) \ (3) \text{ and } \sin A = \sin (n\pi - A) \quad (4)$$

with the provision that n shall be even in (3) and odd in (4).

The expression $\sin [n\pi + (- 1)^n A]$ includes both of these, since $(- 1)^n = 1$ for even values of n and $(- 1)^n = - 1$ for odd values of n. Hence we know that $n\pi + (- 1)^n A$ includes all angles whose sines are equal to $\sin A$.

That is, if $\sin x = \sin A$, then $x = n\pi + (- 1)^n A$.

Hence,

$$\sin A = \sin [n\pi + (- 1)^n A] \qquad [75]$$

SIGHT WORK

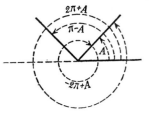

1. Find the values of $n\pi + (- 1)^n A$ for $A = 60°$ and $n = 0$, $n = 1$, $n = 2$, $n = 3$, $n = - 1$, $n = - 2$, $n = - 3$.

2. Using the figure in the margin, point out the angles A, $\pi - A$, $2\pi + A$, $-2\pi + A$ and show why their sines are equal.

3. Construct a similar figure making $A = 215°$ and show why the general formula gives angles whose sines are equal to $\sin 215°$.

148. **Angles having the same cosine.**—By a study similar to that just made for the sine we find that

$$\cos A = \cos (2n\pi \pm A) \qquad [76]$$

for all integral values of n.

That is, if $\cos x = \cos A$, then, $x = 2n\pi \pm A$.

149. **Angles having the same secant and cosecant.**—From the relations

$$\sec A = \frac{1}{\cos A} \text{ and } \csc A = \frac{1}{\sin A}$$

it follows that

$$\sec A = \sec (2\,n\pi \pm A) \qquad [77]$$

and

$$\csc A = \csc [n\pi + (- 1)^n A] \qquad [78]$$

150. Angles having the same tangent and cotangent.—The tangent is positive in the first and third quadrants, and negative in the second and fourth.

Hence, if $\tan x = \tan A$, then x terminates either in the same quadrant as A (is coterminal with A), or it terminates in the opposite quadrant from A. This is a direct consequence of the formula [65].

$$\tan x = \tan (x \pm \pi).$$

From this formula it also follows that

$$\tan A = \tan (n\pi + A) \qquad [79]$$

where n takes all integral values, both positive and negative.

Hence, if $\tan x = \tan A,$

then, $x = n\pi + A.$

In exactly the same manner we obtain

$$\cot A = \cot (n\pi + A). \qquad [80]$$

Hence, if $\cot x = \cot A,$

then, $x = n\pi + A.$

Formulas [75] . . . [80] may be verified readily from the graphs of the trigonometric functions.

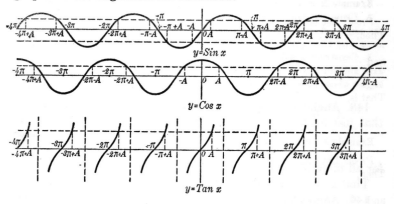

EXERCISES

1. From the first graph find a series of angles whose sines are $\frac{3}{4}$, and also a series whose sines are $-\frac{3}{4}$. How would you find from the graph a series whose sines are 4/7? whose sines are 1? whose sines are -1?

2. From the second graph find a series of angles whose cosines are $\frac{1}{2}$. How would you find a series of angles whose cosines are $-\frac{1}{2}$?

3. From the third graph find a series of angles whose tangents are 1. How would you find a series of angles whose tangents are $-5/6$?

151. Identities involving inverse functions.—From the converse of the statement in §17 it follows that

$$\sin^{-1} x + \cos^{-1} x = \frac{\pi}{2}.$$

In this equation it is understood that x is positive and that $\sin^{-1} x$ and $\cos^{-1} x$ both represent principal values.

Similarly, under the same restrictions, we have

$$\tan^{-1} y + \cot^{-1} y = \frac{\pi}{2}$$

and

$$\sec^{-1} y + \csc^{-1} y = \frac{\pi}{2}.$$

Example 1. Prove, $\sin(\cos^{-1} u) = \sqrt{1 - u^2}$.

Proof: Let $\cos^{-1} u = A$.

Then,

$$\cos A = u$$

and

$$\sin A = \sqrt{1 - u^2}.$$

That is,

$$\sin(\cos^{-1} u) = \sqrt{1 - u^2}.$$

Example 2. Prove, $\tan^{-1} u + \tan^{-1} v = \tan^{-1} \dfrac{u + v}{1 - uv}$.

Proof: Let $\tan^{-1} u = A$ and $\tan^{-1} v = B$.

Then,

$$\tan A = u \text{ and } \tan B = v$$

and

$$\tan(A + B) = \frac{u + v}{1 - uv}.$$

That is,

$$A + B = \tan^{-1} \frac{u + v}{1 - uv} \text{ or } \tan^{-1} u + \tan^{-1} v = \tan^{-1} \frac{u + v}{1 - uv}.$$

Example 3. Prove, $\tan^{-1} u + \tan^{-1} v + \tan^{-1} w = \tan^{-1} \dfrac{u + v + w - uvw}{1 - uv - vw - wu}$.

Proof: Let $\tan^{-1} u = A$, $\tan^{-1} v = B$, $\tan^{-1} w = C$.

Then,

$$\tan A = u, \tan B = v, \tan C = w,$$

and

$$\tan(A + B + C) = \tan(A + \overline{B + C}) = \frac{\tan A + \tan(B + C)}{1 - \tan A \tan(B + C)}$$

$$= \frac{u + \dfrac{v + w}{1 - vw}}{1 - u \dfrac{v + w}{1 - vw}} = \frac{u + v + w - uvw}{1 - uv - vw - wu}.$$

Hence,

$$\tan^{-1} u + \tan^{-1} v + \tan^{-1} w = \tan^{-1} \frac{u + v + w - uvw}{1 - uv - vw - wu}.$$

SIGHT WORK

Prove the following.

1. $\sin(\tan^{-1}u) = \dfrac{u}{\sqrt{u^2 - 1}}$

2. $\cot(\cot^{-1}1 + \cot^{-1}2) = \frac{1}{3}$

3. $\tan(2\tan^{-1}x) = \dfrac{2x}{1 - x^2}$

4. $\tan(\tan^{-1}x - \tan^{-1}y) = \dfrac{x - y}{1 + xy}$

EXERCISES

Prove the following.

1. $\sin(\sin^{-1}x + \sin^{-1}y) = x\sqrt{1 - y^2} + y\sqrt{1 - x^2}$.

2. $\tan(\tan^{-1}\frac{1}{2} + \tan^{-1}\frac{1}{3}) = 1$.

3. $\tan(\tan^{-1}1 + \tan^{-1}2 + \tan^{-1}3) = 0$.

4. $\tan^{-1}\dfrac{x}{\sqrt{1 - x^2}} = \sin^{-1}x$.

5. $\tan^{-1}x + \cot^{-1}(x + 1) = \tan^{-1}(x^2 + x + 1)$.

6. $\tan\left[\tan^{-1}\dfrac{a - b}{1 + ab} + \tan^{-1}\dfrac{b - c}{1 + bc} + \tan^{-1}\dfrac{c - a}{1 + ac}\right] = 0$.

7. $\sin(\sin^{-1} + \cos^{-1}y) = xy + \sqrt{1 - x^2}\cdot\sqrt{1 - y^2}$.

8. $\tan(\tan^{-1}\frac{1}{2} + \tan^{-1}\frac{1}{3} + \tan^{-1}\frac{1}{4}) = 1\frac{2}{3}$.

9. $\tan\left[\tan^{-1}\dfrac{x}{x - 1} - \tan^{-1}\dfrac{x - 1}{x}\right] = \dfrac{2x - 1}{2x(x - 1)}$.

10. $\tan\left[\tan^{-1}\dfrac{x - 1}{x + 2} + \tan^{-1}\dfrac{x + 1}{x + 2}\right] = \dfrac{2x(x + 2)}{4x + 5}$.

Find the values of the following:

11. $\tan(\tan^{-1}\frac{2}{3} + \tan^{-1}\frac{1}{2} + \tan^{-1}\frac{1}{4})$.

12. $\tan(\tan^{-1}\frac{1}{2} + \tan^{-1}\frac{1}{4} + \tan^{-1}\frac{1}{8})$.

13. $\tan\left(\tan^{-1}\frac{1}{3} + \tan^{-1}\dfrac{1}{5} + \tan^{-1}\dfrac{1}{7} + \tan^{-1}\dfrac{1}{9}\right)$.

14. $\tan\left[\tan^{-1}\dfrac{x + 1}{x - 1} + \tan^{-1}\dfrac{x - 1}{x}\right]$.

15. $\sin(\sin^{-1}x + \sin^{-1}2x)$.

16. $\sin(\sin^{-1}\frac{1}{2} + \sin^{-1}\frac{1}{3} + \sin^{-1}\frac{1}{4})$.

17. $\sin\left(\tan^{-1}\frac{1}{3} + \tan^{-1}\frac{1}{4} + \tan^{-1}\dfrac{1}{6}\right)$.

18. $\cos\left(\sin^{-1}\frac{1}{3} + \sin^{-1}\frac{1}{6} + \sin^{-1}\dfrac{1}{12}\right)$.

19. $\tan\left(\cos^{-1}\frac{1}{2} + \cos^{-1}\frac{1}{4} + \cos^{-1}\dfrac{1}{8}\right)$.

20. $\cos\left(\tan^{-1}\dfrac{1}{5} + \tan^{-1}\dfrac{1}{10} + \tan^{-1}\dfrac{1}{20}\right)$.

21. $\sin(\cot^{-1}\frac{1}{2} + \cot^{-1}\frac{1}{3} + \cot^{-1}\frac{1}{4})$.

152. Trigonometric equations.—A number of simple trigonometric equations have already been solved (pages 132–136).

Thus it was found that if $\sin x = \sin A$, then $x = n\pi + (-1)^n A$.

If the equation is given in the form $\sin x = c$ and if $\sin^{-1} c$ is taken to represent only the principal value, then one value of x is $x = \sin^{-1} c$, and all the values of x which satisfy the equation $\sin x = c$ are given by

$$x = n\pi + (-1)^n \sin^{-1} c.$$

We will now consider the relation

$$\sin^2 x - \sqrt{2} \sin x + \tfrac{1}{2} = 0. \tag{1}$$

This equality is certainly not an identity, since it is not satisfied for all values of x. It does not hold, for instance, for $x = 0$.

Solving this equation for $\sin x$ we find

$$\sin x = \tfrac{1}{2} \sqrt{2} \tag{2}$$

Hence equation (1) is satisfied by $x = \dfrac{\pi}{4}$.

By [75], the set of all values of x which satisfy (2) is given by the expression

$$x = n\pi + (-1)^n \frac{\pi}{4}.$$

Therefore this expression gives all values of x which satisfy (1).

153. Solving trigonometric equations.—Solving a trigonometric equation consists in finding all values of the unknown angle (or angles) which satisfy the equation.

Example 1. Solve $4 \sin x = \csc x$.
Solution: We have

$$4 \sin x = \frac{1}{\sin x} \text{ or } 4 \sin^2 x = 1.$$

Hence, $\sin x = \pm \tfrac{1}{2}$,
and by [75],

$$x = n\pi + (-1)^n \frac{\pi}{6}, \text{ and } x = n\pi - (-1)^n \frac{\pi}{6}.$$

Example 2. Solve $2 \cos^2 x + 7 \sin x - 5 = 0$.
Solution: We have

$$2 (1 - \sin^2 x) + 7 \sin x - 5 = 0,$$
$$2 \sin^2 x - 7 \sin x + 3 = 0,$$
$$\sin x = \frac{7 \pm \sqrt{49 - 24}}{4} = 3, \tfrac{1}{2}.$$

Since 3 cannot be the value of the sine of an angle, it follows that $\frac{1}{2}$ is the only value of the sine which satisfies this equation.
Hence by [75],

$$x = n\pi + (-1)^n \frac{\pi}{6}.$$

Example 3. Solve, $\tan x - 6 \cot x + 1 = 0$.
Solution: We have

$$\tan x - \frac{6}{\tan x} + 1 = 0,$$
$$\tan^2 x - 6 + \tan x = 0.$$

Hence

$$\tan x = 2 \text{ or } -3,$$

and by [79],

$$x = n\pi + \tan^{-1} 2, \quad x = n\pi + \tan^{-1} (-3),$$

$\tan^{-1} 2$ and $\tan^{-1} (-3)$ being understood to represent principal values only.

Example 4. Solve, $\cos 2x \sec x + \sec x + 1 = 0$.
Solution: We have

$$\frac{(\cos^2 x - \sin^2 x)}{\cos x} + \frac{1}{\cos x} + 1 = 0,$$
$$\cos^2 x - \sin^2 x + 1 + \cos x = 0,$$
$$2 \cos^2 x + \cos x = 0,$$
$$\cos x (2 \cos x + 1) = 0.$$

Hence

$$\cos x = 0 \text{ and } \cos x = -\tfrac{1}{2}.$$

But $\cos x = 0$ does not satisfy the given equation, since this makes $x = \frac{\pi}{2}$, and for this value of x the secant is not defined. From $\cos x = -\frac{1}{2}, x = 2n\pi \pm \frac{2\pi}{3}$.

No general rule can be given for solving trigonometric equations. It is usually convenient, however, first to reduce the equation so it will contain only one function of the same angle.

EXERCISES

Solve the following equations.

1. $\cos x = \cot^2 x$.
2. $\cos 2x = 2 \sin x$.
3. $\sin 2x = 2 \cos x$.
4. $\sin x = \cos 2x$.
5. $\sec x = 2 \csc x$.
6. $\cos 2x = -\cos x$.
7. $2 \sin^2 x + 3 \cos x = 0$.
8. $\sin x + \cos x = \sqrt{2}$.
9. $\cos 2x + \cos x = -1$.
10. $\cos 2x = \cos^2 x$.
11. $\sin^2 x - 2 \cos x + \frac{1}{4} = 0$.
12. $\cos 2x + \sin x = 1$.
13. $\tan 2x + 2 \sin x = 0$.

14. $3 \cos x + 5 \sin x = 4$.
15. $\sin x + 2 \cos x = 1$.
16. $\sec 2x = 2 \cos x - 1$.
17. $2 \sin^2 x + \sin^2 2x = 2$.
18. $\sin x \sec 2x = 1$.
19. $\tan 2x \tan x = 1$.
20. $\sin^2 x - \cos^2 x = 0$.
21. $\cos x \cos 3x = -\frac{1}{2}$.
22. $\cos 2x = \sin 4x$.
23. $\tan^2 x + \cot^2 x = 2$.
24. $\sec^2 x + 3 \tan^2 x = 5$.
25. $\cos 3x + \sin x = \cos x$.
26. $\sin x + \sin 2x + \sin 3x = 0$.

154. Simultaneous trigonometric equations.—The examples given below illustrate the more important types of simultaneous trigonometric equations.

Example 1.   Solve for x and y the equations:

$$\begin{cases} \sin x + \sin y = a & (1) \\ \cos x + \cos y = b & (2) \end{cases}$$

Solution: By [52],

$$\sin x + \sin y = 2 \sin \tfrac{1}{2}(x+y) \cos \tfrac{1}{2}(x-y) = a, \qquad (3)$$

and by [54],

$$\cos x + \cos y = 2 \cos \tfrac{1}{2}(x+y) \cos \tfrac{1}{2}(x-y) = b. \qquad (4)$$

Dividing (3) by (4),

$$\tan \tfrac{1}{2}(x+y) = \frac{a}{b}. \qquad (5)$$

Therefore,

$$\sin \tfrac{1}{2}(x+y) = \pm \frac{a}{\sqrt{a^2+b^2}}. \qquad (6)$$

Substituting (6) in (3),

$$\cos \tfrac{1}{2}(x-y) = \pm \tfrac{1}{2}\sqrt{a^2+b^2}. \qquad (7)$$

From (5),

$$\frac{x+y}{2} = k_1\pi + \tan^{-1}\frac{a}{b}.$$

From (7),

$$\frac{x-y}{2} = 2k_2\pi \pm \cos^{-1}(\pm \tfrac{1}{2}\sqrt{a^2+b^2}).$$

Hence,

$$x = (k_1 + 2k_2)\pi + \tan^{-1}\frac{a}{b} \pm \cos^{-1}(\pm \tfrac{1}{2}\sqrt{a^2+b^2}),$$

$$y = (k_1 - 2k_2)\pi + \tan^{-1}\frac{a}{b} \mp \cos^{-1}(\pm \tfrac{1}{2}\sqrt{a^2+b^2}).$$

Thus the general solution is:

$$x = n_1\pi + \tan^{-1}\frac{a}{b} + \cos^{-1}(\pm \tfrac{1}{2}\sqrt{a^2+b^2}),$$

$$y = n_2\pi + \tan^{-1}\frac{a}{b} - \cos^{-1}(\pm \tfrac{1}{2}\sqrt{a^2+b^2})$$

where the inverse functions represent principal values.

Thus, if it is given that

$$\begin{cases} \sin x + \sin y = \dfrac{1}{2}, \\ \cos x + \cos y = \dfrac{3}{2}, \end{cases}$$

then,

$$x = n_1\pi + \tan^{-1}\frac{1}{3} \pm \cos^{-1}\left(\pm \frac{1}{4}\sqrt{10}\right),$$

$$y = n_2\pi + \tan^{-1}\frac{1}{3} \mp \cos^{-1}\left(\pm \frac{1}{4}\sqrt{10}\right).$$

Example 2. Solve for r and x the system

$$\begin{cases} r \sin x = a, & \text{(1)} \\ r \cos x = b. & \text{(2)} \end{cases}$$

Solution: Squaring both members of (1) and (2) and adding,

$$r^2 (\sin^2 x + \cos^2 x) = a^2 + b^2, \text{ or } r = \pm \sqrt{a^2 + b^2}.$$

Dividing (1) by (2),

$$\tan x = \frac{a}{b},$$

and

$$x = \tan^{-1} \frac{a}{b}.$$

The sign of $\sqrt{a^2 + b^2}$ must be so chosen that (1) and (2) will be satisfied. Thus, if

$$r \sin x = 4,$$
$$r \cos x = 6,$$

Then,

$$r = \pm 2 \sqrt{13} \quad \text{and } x = \tan^{-1} \frac{2}{3}.$$

If the principal value of $\tan^{-1} \frac{2}{3}$ is taken, r must be positive. That is, in this case $r = 2 \sqrt{13}$.

Example 3. Solve for r, x, y the system

$$\begin{cases} r \sin x \cos y = a, & \text{(1)} \\ r \sin x \sin y = b, & \text{(2)} \\ r \cos x = c. & \text{(3)} \end{cases}$$

Solution: Dividing (2) by (1),

$$\tan y = \frac{b}{a} \text{ and } y = \tan^{-1} \frac{b}{a}.$$

Squaring (1), (2), (3) and adding

$$\begin{aligned} r^2 (\sin^2 x \cos^2 y + \sin^2 x \sin^2 y + \cos^2 x) &= a^2 + b^2 + c^2 \\ &= r^2 [\sin^2 x (\cos^2 y + \sin^2 y) + \cos^2 x] \\ &= r^2 (\sin^2 x + \cos^2 x) = r^2. \end{aligned}$$

Hence,

$$r^2 = a^2 + b^2 + c^2 \quad \text{or} \quad r = \pm \sqrt{a^2 + b^2 + c^2}.$$

From (3)

$$\cos x = \pm \frac{c}{\sqrt{a^2 + b^2 + c^2}}$$

or

$$x = \cos^{-1} \left(\pm \frac{c}{\sqrt{a^2 + b^2 + c^2}} \right).$$

Hence the complete solution is

$$r = \pm \sqrt{a^2 + b^2 + c^2}$$

$$x = 2n\pi \pm \cos^{-1}\left(\pm \frac{c}{\sqrt{a^2 + b^2 + c^2}} \right)$$

$$y = n\pi + \tan^{-1} \frac{b}{a}$$

The signs of $\frac{1}{2}\sqrt{a^2 + b^2}$ and of $\sqrt{a^2 + b^2 + c^2}$ in Exs. 1 and 3 must be taken so that original equations will be satisfied.

EXERCISES

Solve the following systems of equations.

1. $\begin{cases} \sin x + \sin y = \dfrac{1}{3} \\ \cos x + \cos y = \dfrac{5}{4}. \end{cases}$

6. $\begin{cases} r \sin x = 4 \\ r \cos x = 2. \end{cases}$

2. $\begin{cases} \sin x - \sin y = \dfrac{1}{4} \\ \cos x - \cos y = \dfrac{1}{3}. \end{cases}$

7. $\begin{cases} r \sin x = 2\sqrt{5} \\ r \cos x = -3\sqrt{3}. \end{cases}$

3. $\begin{cases} \cos x + \cos y = a \\ \cos 2x + \cos 2y = b. \end{cases}$

8. $\begin{cases} r \sin x = -3\sqrt{2} \\ r \cos x = -4\sqrt{5}. \end{cases}$

4. $\begin{cases} r \sin x \cos y = 2 \\ r \sin x \sin y = 3 \\ r \cos y = 4. \end{cases}$

9. $\begin{cases} r \sin x \cos y = \sqrt{5} \\ r \sin x \sin y = \sqrt{7} \\ r \cos y = \sqrt{10}. \end{cases}$

5. $\begin{cases} r \sin x \cos y = 8 \\ r \sin x \sin y = 10 \\ r \cos y = 12. \end{cases}$

10. $\begin{cases} r \sin x \cos y = 2 \\ r \sin x \sin y = \sqrt{5} \\ r \cos y = \sqrt{7}. \end{cases}$

155. Equations stated in terms of inverse functions.—An equality of the form

$$\cos^{-1} x + \cos^{-1} 2x = \cos^{-1} \tfrac{1}{2}$$

is not an identity and hence presents a problem for solution.

Example 1. Solve for x, $\cos^{-1} x + \cos^{-1} 2x = \cos^{-1} \frac{1}{2}$.
Solution: Let $\cos^{-1} x = A$ and $\cos^{-1} 2x = B$.
Then,

$$\cos A = x \text{ and } \cos B = 2x.$$

Hence,

$$\sin A = \sqrt{1 - x^2}, \ \sin B = \sqrt{1 - 4x^2}$$

and

$$\cos (A + B) = \cos A \cos B - \sin A \sin B$$
$$= x \cdot 2x - \sqrt{1 - x^2} \cdot \sqrt{1 - 4x^2}.$$

That is,

$$2x^2 - \sqrt{1 - x^2} \cdot \sqrt{1 - 4x^2} = \tfrac{1}{2}.$$

Then,

$$(2x^2 - \tfrac{1}{2})^2 = (1 - x^2)(1 - 4x^2)$$

or

$$4x^4 - 2x^2 + \tfrac{1}{4} = 1 - 5x^2 + 4x^4,$$

or

$$3x^2 = \tfrac{3}{4} \text{ and } x = \pm \tfrac{1}{2}.$$

If $\cos A = \tfrac{1}{2}$, then $A = \dfrac{\pi}{3}$ and if $\cos B = 1$, then $B = 0$.

Since in this case $A + B = \dfrac{\pi}{3}$, and since $\cos \dfrac{\pi}{3} = \tfrac{1}{2}$, the given equation is satisfied.

If $\cos A = -\tfrac{1}{2}$, then $A = \dfrac{2\pi}{3}$, and if $\cos B = -1$, then $B = \pi$, and $A + B = \pi + \dfrac{2\pi}{3}$.

Since $\cos \left(\pi + \dfrac{2\pi}{3} \right) = \cos \dfrac{5\pi}{3} = \tfrac{1}{2}$, the given equation is satisfied.

Hence $x = \tfrac{1}{2}$ and $x = -\tfrac{1}{2}$ both satisfy the given equation.

Example 2. $\tan^{-1}(x + 1) + \tan^{-1}(x - 1) = \tan^{-1} \tfrac{1}{4}$.

Solution: Let $\tan^{-1}(x + 1) = A$ and $\tan^{-1}(x - 1) = B$.

Then,

$$\tan A = x + 1 \text{ and } \tan B = x - 1$$

and

$$\tan (A + B) = \frac{\tan A + \tan B}{1 - \tan A \tan B} = \frac{x + 1 + x - 1}{1 - (x + 1)(x - 1)}.$$
$$= \frac{2x}{2 - x^2}$$

Hence,

$$\frac{2x}{2 - x^2} = \frac{1}{4} \text{ and } x = -4 \pm 3\sqrt{2}.$$

EXERCISES

Solve the following equations.

1. $\sin^{-1} x = \cos^{-1} x$.

2. $2 \sin^{-1} x = 3 \cos^{-1} x$.

3. $\tan^{-1} x = \cot^{-1} x$.

4. $\sin^{-1} \dfrac{5}{x} + \sin^{-1} \dfrac{12}{x} = \dfrac{\pi}{2}$.

5. $\sin^{-1} x + \sin^{-1} 2x = \dfrac{\pi}{3}$.

6. $\tan^{-1} x + 2 \cot^{-1} x = \dfrac{3\pi}{4}$.

7. $\sin^{-1} x + 3 \cos^{-1} x = \dfrac{7\pi}{6}$.

8. $\cot^{-1} x + \cot^{-1} 2x = \dfrac{3\pi}{4}$.

9. $\cos^{-1} x + \cos^{-1} \sqrt{1 - x^2} = \cos^{-1} x\sqrt{3}$.

10. $\tan^{-1} \dfrac{x - 1}{x + 2} + \tan^{-1} \dfrac{x + 1}{x + 2} = \dfrac{\pi}{4}$.

11. $2 \tan^{-1} \tfrac{1}{2} + \sin^{-1} \dfrac{4}{5} = \sin^{-1} \dfrac{1}{x}$.

12. $\tan^{-1} \dfrac{x + 1}{x - 1} + \tan^{-1} \dfrac{x - 1}{x} = \tan^{-1}(-7)$.

CHAPTER X

DE MOIVRE'S THEOREM

THIS chapter contains the beginnings of a theory which uses trigonometric functions in the study of complex numbers. While at the outset this theory appears to be purely abstract and of no practical value, it eventually leads to important applications in various branches of mathematics and also in physics, mechanics, and in practical engineering.

156. Real numbers.—The ordinary numbers of arithmetic indicate magnitude only, while the *real number system* of algebra includes both positive and negative numbers, and hence the numbers of algebra represent both magnitude and quality.

The numerals $+1$ and -1 may be regarded as quality units, and any real number may be regarded as a multiple of one of these. Thus $+5$ may be regarded as $5(+1)$ and -5 as $5(-1)$. The multiplier 5 is a number which represents magnitude only, and is the kind of number which is used in elementary arithmetic. A real number therefore is the product of an arithmetic number and a quality unit. The arithmetic multiplier is called the **arithmetic value** or the **absolute value** of the real number.

157. Imaginary numbers.—Since the square of any real number is positive whether the number itself is positive or negative, it follows that in the real number system there is no square root of a negative number. Thus there is no real number which is the root of an equation like $x^2 = -1$, $x^2 = -2$, or $x^2 = -25$.

Imaginary numbers were deliberately invented so that every algebraic equation might have a root. The essential element of this system is the **imaginary unit**, $\sqrt{-1}$, also designated by i, which has the property that $i^2 = -1$, or $(\sqrt{-1})^2 = -1$.

An imaginary number is a product of a real number and the imaginary unit. Thus $6i$, $-3i$, etc., are imaginary numbers.

The square of an imaginary number is always a negative real number. Thus $(6i)^2 = 6^2 i^2 = 36(-1) = -36$,

$$\text{and } (-3i)^2 = (-3)^2 (i)^2 = 9(-1) = -9.$$

Both imaginary and real numbers may be considered as special cases of the complex number which we now proceed to study.

145

158. Complex numbers.—A number expressed in the form $a + bi$, where a and b are real numbers, is a **complex number.** Thus $2 + 3i$, $\sqrt{2} - 2i$, and $-6 + \sqrt{3}i$ are complex numbers.

The complex number $a + bi$ is thus seen to be the "sum" of a real number a and an imaginary number bi (or ib). The a is called the *real* part of the number and bi the imaginary part.

159. Graphical representation of complex numbers.—Complex numbers admit of a convenient geometric representation by what is known as the Argand diagram. Use is made of ordinary square-ruled paper with a pair of mutually perpendicular axes. Real numbers are represented by line-segments extending from the origin to points on the horizontal axis, or **axis of reals.** As in the figures studied earlier in this course (see page 66 *et seq.*), distances to the right of the origin represent positive numbers and distances to the left represent negative numbers.

Imaginary numbers are represented on the vertical axis, or the axis of imaginaries. Thus $2i$ is represented by a point on this axis two units above the origin, and $-3i$ is represented by a point three units below the origin.

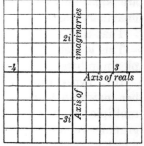

Since the origin lies on both axes, the number zero belongs to the system of real numbers and also to the system of imaginary numbers, and is the only number that has this property.

To represent a complex number $a + bi$ graphically, lay off a along the axis of reals beginning at the origin as described above, and from the extremity of this segment lay off b in the vertical direction, reaching the point P in the figure. The line-segment from the origin to P is a graphic representation of the complex number $a + bi$. The point P itself may also be regarded as a representation of this number.

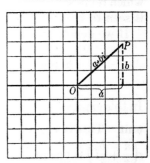

In this manner every point in the plane is made to represent a complex number, and conversely, every complex number is represented by such a point.

It should·be noted that in $a + bi$, the real numbers a and b may have any values whatever including zero. It follows that real numbers and also pure imaginaries are special cases of the complex number. If $b = 0$, $a + bi$ reduces to $a + 0 \cdot i = a$, and the corresponding point lies on the axis of reals. If $a = 0$, $a + bi = 0 + bi = bi$, which is a pure imaginary, and the corresponding point lies on the axis of imaginaries. If $a = 0$ and $b = 0$, the corresponding point is the origin.

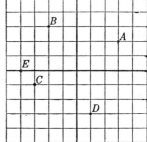

SIGHT WORK

1. What numbers are represented by the points A, B, C, D, E, in the figure?

2. On a graph mark the points corresponding to $1 + 2i$, $3 - 2i$, $-2 - 2i$, $-2 + 2i$, $2 - i$.

160. Equality of complex numbers.—Two complex numbers are equal only when their real parts are equal and also their imaginary parts.

That is, $a + bi = c + di$ if, and only if, $a = c$ and $b = d$.

This is seen at once from the graphic representation of complex numbers.

161. Type-forms of the complex number.—A complex number may also be regarded as an arithmetic multiple of a *complex unit*. From the graphic representation, the line segment which represents the complex number $a + bi$ is seen to be $\sqrt{a^2 + b^2}$ in length.

If we denote this quantity by r, we have

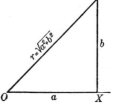

$$a + bi = r\left(\frac{a}{r} + \frac{b}{r}i\right)$$

In this expression r is called the **modulus** and $\frac{a}{r} + i\frac{b}{r}$ the **complex unit.** This is one of the type forms of the complex unit and $r\left(\frac{a}{r} + \frac{b}{r}i\right)$ is one of the type forms of the general complex number. Denoting by φ the angle XOP, we have

$$\frac{a}{r} = \cos\,\varphi \text{ and } \frac{b}{r} = \sin\,\varphi.$$

Substituting

$$\frac{a}{r} = \cos \varphi \text{ and } \frac{b}{r} = \sin \varphi \text{ in the type forms on page 147 gives}$$

$$\cos \varphi + i \sin \varphi \text{ and } r (\cos \varphi + i \sin \varphi)$$

which are the respective trigonometric type forms of the complex unit and of the general complex number. The angle φ is called the **amplitude** of the complex number.

Notice that a line segment representing a complex unit is always of unit length, and that hence a point P representing a complex unit lies on a circle with radius unity and center at the origin.

Since coterminal angles have equal functions it follows that

$$\cos \varphi + i \sin \varphi = \cos (2n\pi + \varphi) + i \sin (2n\pi + \varphi).$$

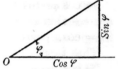

This latter form may be designated as the general trigonometric type form of the complex unit.

It should be noted that while the modulus of the complex unit is always equal to unity, the amplitude may be any angle whatever. That is, complex units are not equal in the ordinary sense.

SIGHT WORK

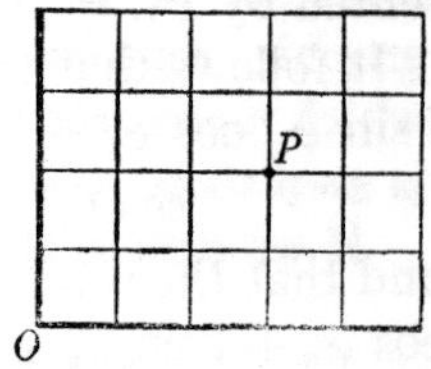

1. Show why the modulus of the number represented by P in the figure is $\sqrt{13}$.

2. Find the sine and the cosine of the amplitude of the number represented by the point marked P in the figure.

3. Find the modulus of the number $3 + 4i$. Also find the sine and cosine of its amplitude.

4. Find the modulus of each of the following numbers: $1 - 7i$, $-5 + 4i$, $5 - 4i$, $-2 - 7i$, $3 - 5i$, $-7 + 3i$.

5. Find the sine and the cosine of the amplitude of each of the complex numbers in example 4.

162. Arithmetic operations on complex numbers.—Two complex numbers such as $a + bi$ and $c + di$ are added by adding the real parts and also the complex parts. Thus,

$$(a + bi) + (c + di) = a + c + (b + d)i.$$

The product of two complex numbers is found exactly in the same manner as the product of two ordinary binomials, remembering that $(i)^2 = -1$. Thus,

$$(a + bi)(c + di) = ac + adi + bci + bd(i)^2$$
$$= ac - bd + (ad + bc)i.$$

Sight Work

Find the products of **1.** $(3 + 2i)(1 - 2i)$, **2.** $(1 - 3i)(2 - i)$, **3.** $(2 - 7i)(-1 + i)$, **4.** $(-4 + 2i)(3 - 2i)$, **5.** $(-1 + i)(1 - i)$, **6.** $(2 - i)(2 + i)$, **7.** $(-4 + 7i)(-4 - 7i)$.

163. Multiplication of complex units.—We shall now consider more in detail the products of complex numbers, and in particular of complex units.

Putting two complex units into the trigonometric type form and multiplying as above, we have:

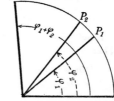

$(\cos \varphi_1 + i \sin \varphi_1)(\cos \varphi_2 + i \sin \varphi_2)$
$= \cos \varphi_1 \cdot \cos \varphi_2 + i^2 \sin \varphi_1 \sin \varphi_2$
$\quad + i \sin \varphi_1 \cos \varphi_2 + i \sin \varphi_2 \cos \varphi_1$
$= \cos \varphi_1 \cdot \cos \varphi_2 - \sin \varphi_1 \sin \varphi_2$
$\quad + i (\sin \varphi_1 \cos \varphi_2 + \sin \varphi_2 \cos \varphi_1)$
$= \cos (\varphi_1 + \varphi_2) + i \sin (\varphi_1 + \varphi_2).$

Thus it is seen that the product of two complex units is another complex unit whose amplitude is the sum of the amplitudes of the given units. In the figure these three numbers are represented by P_1, P_2, and P_3.

It follows that the product of three complex units $\cos \varphi_1 + i \sin \varphi_1$, $\cos \varphi_2 + i \sin \varphi_2$, $\cos \varphi_3 + i \sin \varphi_3$ is

$$\cos (\varphi_1 + \varphi_2 + \varphi_3) + i \sin (\varphi_1 + \varphi_2 + \varphi_3)$$

and that the product of n complex units $\cos \varphi_1 + i \sin \varphi_1$, ..., $\cos \varphi_n + i \sin \varphi_n$, is $\cos (\varphi_1 + \varphi_2 + ... + \varphi_n) + i \sin (\varphi_1 + \varphi_2 + ... + \varphi_n).$

Sight Work

1. If it is given that $\sin 30° = \frac{1}{2}$, $\cos 30° = \frac{1}{2} \sqrt{3}$, $\sin 45° = \frac{1}{2} \sqrt{2}$, $\cos 45° = \frac{1}{2} \sqrt{2}$, find $\sin 75°$ and $\cos 75°$.

Suggestion: $(\cos 30° + i \sin 30°)(\cos 45° + i \sin 45°) = \cos 75° + i \sin 75°$. Substitute the given values in the first member and multiply.

2. If it is given that $\sin (-30°) = -\frac{1}{2}$ and $\cos (-30°) = \frac{1}{2} \sqrt{3}$, find $\sin (-60°)$ and $\cos (-60°)$.

3. If it is given that $\sin 30° = \frac{1}{2}$, $\cos 30° = \frac{1}{2} \sqrt{3}$, $\sin 60° = \frac{1}{2} \sqrt{3}$, and $\cos 60° = \frac{1}{2}$, show by the method suggested above that $\sin 90° = 1$ and $\cos 90° = 0$.

164. De Moivre's theorem.—If a complex unit is multiplied by itself by the method of §163, we find that a complex unit may be squared by simply doubling its amplitude.

That is,

$$(\cos \varphi + i \sin \varphi)^2 = (\cos \varphi + i \sin \varphi)(\cos \varphi + i \sin \varphi)$$
$$= \cos (\varphi + \varphi) + i \sin (\varphi + \varphi) = \cos 2\varphi + i \sin 2\varphi.$$

Similarly, a complex unit may be cubed by multiplying its amplitude by 3, may be raised to the fourth power by multiplying its amplitude by 4, and so on.

These are special cases of the theorem known as De Moivre's theorem:

The n*th power*[1] *of a complex unit is a complex unit whose amplitude is* n *times the amplitude of the base.*

In symbols,

$$(\cos \varphi + i \sin \varphi)^n = \cos n\varphi + i \sin n\varphi \qquad [81]$$

Proof: Case I. Let n be a positive integer k.

Then

$$(\cos \varphi + i \sin \varphi)^k = (\cos \varphi + i \sin \varphi)(\cos \varphi + i \sin \varphi) \ldots \text{to } k \text{ factors.}$$
$$= \cos (\varphi + \varphi + \text{to } k \text{ terms}) + i \sin (\varphi + \varphi + \text{to } k \text{ terms})$$
$$= \cos k \varphi + i \sin k \varphi.$$

Case II. Let n be the fraction $\dfrac{r}{s}$, r and s being positive integers, and $\dfrac{r}{s}$ being in its lowest terms.

By Case I it follows that

$$\left(\cos \frac{\varphi}{s} + i \sin \frac{\varphi}{s}\right)^s = \cos \varphi + i \sin \varphi.$$

Taking the sth root of each side,

$$\cos \frac{\varphi}{s} + i \sin \frac{\varphi}{s} = (\cos \varphi + i \sin \varphi)^{\frac{1}{s}}$$

Raising each member to the rth power,

$$\cos \frac{r}{s} \varphi + i \sin \frac{r}{s} \varphi = (\cos \varphi + i \sin \varphi)^{\frac{r}{s}}.$$

Case III. Let n be any negative number $- p$. By actual multiplication

$$[\cos \varphi + i \sin \varphi][\cos (-\varphi) + i \sin (-\varphi)] = \cos 0 + i \sin 0 = 1.$$

Hence,

$$\cos (-\varphi) + i \sin (-\varphi) = \frac{1}{\cos \varphi + i \sin \varphi} = (\cos \varphi + i \sin \varphi)^{-1}.$$

That is,

$$(\cos \varphi + i \sin \varphi)^{-1} = \cos (-\varphi) + i \sin (-\varphi).$$

[1] The word "power" is used here to denote the result of affecting the number by an exponent n, whether n is integral or fractional, positive or negative.

Raising both members to the power p, by Cases I and II,

$$(\cos \varphi + i \sin \varphi)^{-p} = [\cos (-\varphi) + i \sin (-\varphi)]^p.$$
$$= \cos (-p\,\varphi) + i \sin (-p\,\varphi).$$

This proves the theorem for any rational exponents. It may be extended to the case of irrational exponents by an argument involving the method of limits.

165. Roots of complex units.—Since the square of a complex unit expressed in the form $\cos \varphi + i \sin \varphi$ may be found by doubling its amplitude, it follows that a square root of such a unit may be found by dividing the amplitude by 2.

That is, from $(\cos \varphi + i \sin \varphi)^2 = \cos 2\varphi + i \sin 2\varphi$

it follows that $\sqrt{\cos \varphi + i \sin \varphi} = \cos \dfrac{\varphi}{2} + i \sin \dfrac{\varphi}{2}.$

Similarly, it follows that

$$\sqrt[3]{\cos \varphi + i \sin \varphi} = \cos \frac{\varphi}{3} + i \sin \frac{\varphi}{3}$$

$$\sqrt[4]{\cos \varphi + i \sin \varphi} = \cos \frac{\varphi}{4} + i \sin \frac{\varphi}{4}$$

and in general

$$\sqrt[n]{\cos \varphi + i \sin \varphi} = \cos \frac{\varphi}{n} + i \sin \frac{\varphi}{n}.$$

We have seen (§161) that

$$\cos \varphi + i \sin \varphi = \cos (2k\,\pi + \varphi) + i \sin (2k\,\pi + \varphi)$$

for all integral values of k.
Hence we have,

$$\sqrt[n]{\cos \varphi + i \sin \varphi} = \cos \frac{2k\,\pi + \varphi}{n} + i \sin \frac{2k\,\pi + \varphi}{n}$$

for all integral values of k.

This means, for instance, that each of the expressions

$$\cos \frac{\varphi}{3} + i \sin \frac{\varphi}{3},\; \cos \frac{2\pi + \varphi}{3} + i \sin \frac{2\pi + \varphi}{3},$$

$$\cos \frac{4\pi + \varphi}{3} + i \sin \frac{4\pi + \varphi}{3},\; \cos \frac{6\pi + \varphi}{3} + i \sin \frac{6\pi + \varphi}{3}, \;\ldots$$

is a cube root of $\cos \varphi + i \sin \varphi.$

However, this process gives only three distinct cube roots of a complex unit, since

$$\cos \frac{6\pi + \varphi}{3} + i \sin \frac{6\pi + \varphi}{3} = \cos \frac{\varphi}{3} + i \sin \frac{\varphi}{3},$$

$$\cos \frac{8\pi + \varphi}{3} + i \sin \frac{8\pi + \varphi}{3} = \cos \frac{2\pi + \varphi}{3} + i \sin \frac{2\pi + \varphi}{3},$$

$$\cos \frac{10\pi + \varphi}{3} + i \sin \frac{10\pi + \varphi}{3} = \cos \frac{4\pi + \varphi}{3} + i \sin \frac{4\pi + \varphi}{3}, \text{ etc.}$$

Hence,

$$\cos \frac{\varphi}{3} + i \sin \frac{\varphi}{3}, \cos \frac{2\pi + \varphi}{3} + i \sin \frac{2\pi + \varphi}{3},$$

$$\cos \frac{4\pi + \varphi}{3} + i \sin \frac{4\pi + \varphi}{3}$$ are the cube roots of $\cos \varphi + i \sin \varphi$ obtained by this process.

In the same manner we find four fourth roots of $\cos \varphi + i \sin \varphi$, and, if n is a positive integer, n nth roots of $\cos \varphi + i \sin \varphi$.

EXERCISES

1. Show fully how to find the four fourth roots of $\cos \varphi + i \sin \varphi$, and show why there are not more than four distinct fourth roots.

2. In a similar manner show that $\cos \varphi + i \sin \varphi$ has exactly five distinct fifth roots and exactly six sixth roots.

3. Find the eight distinct eighth roots of unity.

166. The roots of any number.—Since any complex number may be expressed in the form $r (\cos \varphi + i \sin \varphi)$, where r and φ are positive real numbers, and since we have seen that there are n nth roots of $\cos \varphi + i \sin \varphi$, and since the positive real number r has one arithmetic nth root, it follows that $r (\cos \varphi + i \sin \varphi)$ has n distinct nth roots. That is,

$$\sqrt[n]{r (\cos \varphi + i \sin \varphi)} = r^{\frac{1}{n}} \left(\cos \frac{2k\,\pi + \varphi}{n} + i \sin \frac{2k + \varphi}{n} \right) \quad [82]$$

for all integral values of k. As shown in §165 this gives rise to exactly n distinct roots.

But any number, real or complex, may be expressed in the form $r (\cos \varphi + i \sin \varphi)$.

Thus,

$$2 = 2 (\cos 0 + i \sin 0), 3i = 3 \left(\cos \frac{\pi}{2} + i \sin \frac{\pi}{2} \right)$$

and

$$3 + 5i = \sqrt{34}\left[\cos \left(\tan^{-1} \frac{5}{3} \right) + i \sin \left(\tan^{-1} \frac{5}{3} \right) \right].$$

If $\varphi = \tan^{-1}\dfrac{5}{3}$, then $3 + 5i = \sqrt{34}\,(\cos \varphi + i \sin \varphi)$.

Hence it follows that every number (real, purely imaginary, or complex) has n distinct nth roots.

Example. Find the six sixth roots of $1 + 3\,i$.
Solution: $r = \sqrt{1 + 9} = \sqrt{10}$, and $\varphi = \tan^{-1} 3 = 71° 33' 54''$.
Hence,

$$\sqrt[6]{1 + 3\,i} = (\sqrt{10})^{\frac{1}{6}}\left(\cos \frac{71° 33' 54''}{6} + i \sin \frac{71° 33' 54''}{6}\right)$$

$$= (10)^{\frac{1}{12}}\,(\cos 11° 55' 39'' + i \sin 11° 55' 39'')$$

$$= 10^{\frac{1}{12}}\,[.9784 + i\,(.2066)], \text{ is one of the sixth roots of } 1 + 3i.$$

From

$$10^{\frac{1}{12}}\left(\cos \frac{360° + 71° 33' 54''}{6} + i \sin \frac{360° + 71° 33' 54''}{6}\right)$$

we obtain another sixth root, and so on. If it is desired to find a decimal approximation of $(10)^{\frac{1}{12}}$, logarithms should be used.

Hence, the n nth roots of a number, n being a positive integer, may be obtained through the following steps.

(a) *Put the number into the general trigonometric type form of a complex number.*

(b) *Apply De Moivre's theorem.*

(c) *Assign to k the values $0, 1, 2, \ldots, n - 1$.*

EXERCISES

1. Find the five fifth roots of $1 + i$.
Suggestion:

$$1 + i = \sqrt{2}\left(\cos \frac{\pi}{4} + i \sin \frac{\pi}{4}\right).$$

Hence,

$$\sqrt[5]{1 + i} = 2^{\frac{1}{10}}\left(\cos \frac{2k\pi + \frac{\pi}{4}}{5} + i \sin \frac{2k\pi + \frac{\pi}{4}}{5}\right).$$

Assign the values $0, 1, 2, 3, 4$ to k and find the roots.

2. Find the three cube roots of unity and compare with the roots of $x^3 - 1 = 0$.

3. Find the three cube roots of i and check by raising each to the third power.

4. Find the four fourth roots of i and check by raising each to the fourth power.

167. Formulas for sine and cosine of multiple angles.—By using De Moivre's theorem, formulas for the sine and cosine of multiple angles may be obtained as follows:

$$(\cos \varphi + i \sin \varphi)^n = \cos n\varphi + i \sin n\varphi.$$

Expanding the left member by the Binomial Theorem, we have

$$\cos n\varphi + i \sin n\varphi = \cos^n \varphi + n \cos^{n-1} \varphi \, (i \sin \varphi) +$$
$$\frac{n\,(n-1)}{2} \cos^{n-2} \varphi \, (i \sin \varphi)^2 +$$
$$\frac{n\,(n-1)\,(n-2)}{2\cdot3} \cos^{n-3} \varphi \, (i \sin \varphi)^3 + \cdots$$

Noting that $i^2 = -1$, $i^3 = -i$, $i^4 = 1$, etc., and collecting real and imaginary terms, we have

$$\cos n\varphi + i \sin n\varphi = \cos^n \varphi - \frac{n\,(n-1)}{2} \cos^{n-2} \varphi \sin^2 \varphi$$
$$+ \frac{n\,(n-1)\,(n-2)\,(n-3)}{2\cdot3\cdot4} \cos^{n-4} \varphi \sin^4 \varphi \cdots$$
$$+ i \left[n \cos^{n-1} \varphi \sin \varphi - \frac{n\,(n-1)\,(n-2)}{2\cdot3} \cos^{n-3} \varphi \sin^3 \varphi + \right.$$
$$\left. \frac{n\,(n-1)\,(n-2)\,(n-3)\,(n-4)}{2\cdot3\cdot4\cdot5} \cos^{n-5} \varphi \sin^5 \varphi \cdots \right]$$

Then by §160,

$$\cos n\varphi = \cos^n \varphi - \frac{n\,(n-1)}{2} \cos^{n-2} \varphi \sin^2 \varphi +$$
$$\frac{n\,(n-1)\,(n-2)\,(n-3)}{2\cdot3\cdot4} \cos^{n-4} \varphi \sin^4 \varphi - \cdots \quad [83]$$

$$\sin n\varphi = n \cos^{n-1} \varphi \sin \varphi - \frac{n\,(n-1)\,(n-2)}{2\cdot3} \cos^{n-3} \varphi \sin^3 \varphi +$$
$$\frac{n\,(n-1)\,(n-2)\,(n-3)\,(n-4)}{2\cdot3\cdot4\cdot5} \cos^{n-5} \varphi \sin^5 \varphi - \cdots \quad [84]$$

EXERCISES

Using formulas [83] and [84], prove the following.

1. $\cos 2\theta = \cos^2\theta - \sin^2\theta$ 2. $\sin 2\theta = 2 \cos \theta \sin \theta$
3. $\sin 3\theta = 3 \sin \theta - r \sin^3 \theta$ 4. $\cos 3\theta = 4 \cos^3 \theta - 3 \cos \theta$

5. Express $\cos 3\theta$ in the form of a product of $\cos \theta$ multiplied by an expression containing powers of $\cos \theta$.

6. Express $\sin 4\theta$ and $\sin 5\theta$ in the form of a product of $\sin \theta$ multiplied by an expression containing powers of $\cos \theta$.

7. Express $\cos 5\theta$ in terms of a product of $\cos \theta$ multiplied by an expression containing powers of $\cos \theta$.

CHAPTER XI

EXPONENTIAL AND HYPERBOLIC FUNCTIONS

IN THE calculus the following series are developed.

$$\sin x = x - \frac{x^3}{3!} + \frac{x^5}{5!} - \frac{x^7}{7!} + \cdots \tag{A}$$

$$\cos x = 1 - \frac{x^2}{2!} + \frac{x^4}{4!} - \frac{x^6}{6!} + \cdots \tag{B}$$

$$e^x = 1 + \frac{x}{1} + \frac{x^2}{2!} + \frac{x^3}{3!} + \cdots \tag{C}$$

These are known as the sine, cosine, and exponential series, respectively. In series (A) and (B), x denotes the radian measure of the angle. In (C), the symbol e denotes the base of the Naperian logarithms. The notation $n!$, read "factorial n," denotes the product of all the integers from 1 to n, inclusive.

168. Exponential form of the complex unit.—We now define $\sin(a + bi)$, $\cos(a + bi)$, $e^{(a+bi)}$, by replacing x by $a + bi$ in (A), (B), (C).

Then,

$$\sin(a + bi) = a + bi - \frac{(a + bi)^3}{3!} + \frac{(a + bi)^5}{5!} - \frac{(a + bi)^7}{7!} + \cdots$$

$$\cos(a + bi) = 1 - \frac{(a + bi)^2}{2!} + \frac{(a + bi)^4}{4!} - \frac{(a + bi)^6}{6!} + \cdots$$

$$e^{(a+bi)} = 1 + \frac{(a + bi)}{1} + \frac{(a + bi)^2}{2!} + \frac{(a + bi)^3}{3!} + \cdots$$

If in (C) x is replaced by xi, we have

$$e^{xi} = 1 + xi + \frac{(xi)^2}{2!} + \frac{(xi)^3}{3!} + \frac{(xi)^4}{4!} + \cdots$$

$$= \left(1 - \frac{x^2}{2!} + \frac{x^4}{4!} - \frac{x^6}{6!} + \cdots\right) + i\left(x - \frac{x^3}{3!} + \frac{x^5}{5!} - \frac{x^7}{7!} + \cdots\right).$$

The first parenthesis is exactly the right member of (B) and the second parenthesis is the right member of (A).

Hence we have the equality

$$e^{xi} = \cos x + i \sin x.$$

In other words, e^{xi} is a complex unit whose amplitude is x.

155

169. Exponential form of the sine and cosine.—If in the identity

$$e^{xi} = \cos x + i \sin x \tag{1}$$

x is replaced by $-x$ we have

$$e^{-xi} = \cos x - i \sin x \tag{2}$$

Subtracting (2) from (1) and dividing by $2i$,

$$\sin x = \frac{e^{xi} - e^{-xi}}{2i} \tag{85}$$

Similarly, adding (1) and (2) and dividing by 2,

$$\cos x = \frac{e^{xi} + e^{-xi}}{2} \tag{86}$$

These are known as Euler's exponential values of $\sin x$ and $\cos x$.

170. Hyperbolic functions.—Closely allied to Euler's exponential values of $\sin x$ and $\cos x$ are the functions

$$\frac{e^x - e^{-x}}{2} \quad \text{and} \quad \frac{e^x + e^{-x}}{2}$$

which are called the **hyperbolic sine** of x and the **hyperbolic cosine** of x, respectively. These functions are denoted by $\sinh x$ and $\cosh x$.

That is,

$$\sinh x = \frac{e^x - e^{-x}}{2}, \qquad \cosh x = \frac{e^x + e^{-x}}{2}.$$

The hyperbolic tangent (tanh), cotangent (coth), secant (sech), and cosecant (csch) are defined by the relations,

$$\tanh x = \frac{\sinh x}{\cosh x}, \qquad \coth x = \frac{\cosh x}{\sinh x}$$

$$\mathrm{sech}\ x = \frac{1}{\cosh x}, \qquad \mathrm{csch}\ x = \frac{1}{\sinh x}.$$

From

$$\sin x = \frac{e^{xi} - e^{-xi}}{2i} \quad \text{and} \quad \sinh x = \frac{e^x - e^{-x}}{2}$$

it follows that

$$\sin xi = \frac{e^{ixi} - e^{-ixi}}{2i} = \frac{e^{-x} - e^{x}}{2i}$$

$$= \frac{i\,(e^{-x} - e^{x})}{2\,(i)^2} = \frac{i\,(e^{x} - e^{-x})}{2},$$

and hence,

$$\sin xi = i \sinh x.$$

EXERCISES

Show that $\cos xi = \cosh x$, $\tan xi = i \tanh x$, $\cot xi = -i \coth x$, $\sec xi = \mathrm{sech}\ x$, $\csc xi = -i\ \mathrm{csch}\ x$.

171. Relations among hyperbolic functions.—From the definitions given in §170, tanh x, coth x, sech x, and csch x may be expressed in forms analogous to those given for sinh x and cosh x.

Thus,

$$\tanh x = \frac{\sinh x}{\cosh x} = \frac{\dfrac{e^x - e^{-x}}{2}}{\dfrac{e^x + e^{-x}}{2}} = \frac{e^x - e^{-x}}{e^x + e^{-x}}.$$

Similarly,

$$\coth x = \frac{e^x + e^{-x}}{e^x - e^{-x}}, \ \text{sech} \ x = \frac{2}{e^x + e^{-x}}, \ \text{and}$$

$$\text{csch} \ x = \frac{2}{e^x - e^{-x}}.$$

Identities similar to those found for trigonometric functions may now be found for hyperbolic functions.

Example 1. Prove, $\cosh^2 x - \sinh^2 x = 1$.

Proof:

$$\cosh^2 x - \sinh^2 x = \left(\frac{e^x + e^{-x}}{2}\right)^2 - \left(\frac{e^x - e^{-x}}{2}\right)^2$$

$$= \frac{e^{2x} + 2 + e^{-2x}}{4} - \frac{e^{2x} - 2 + e^{-2x}}{4} = 1.$$

Example 2. Prove $\sinh 2x = 2 \sinh x \cosh x$.

Proof:

$$\sinh 2x = \frac{e^{2x} - e^{-2x}}{2} = 2 \ \frac{e^x - e^{-x}}{2} \cdot \frac{e^x + e^{-x}}{2}$$

$$= 2 \sinh x \cosh x.$$

EXERCISES

Show that the following identities hold.

1. $\sinh (- x) = - \sinh x.$
2. $\cosh (- x) = \cosh x.$
3. $\cosh 2x = \cosh^2 x + \sinh^2 x.$
4. $\text{sech}^2 x + \tanh^2 x = 1.$
5. $\coth^2 x - \text{csch}^2 x = 1.$

6. $e^x = \cosh x + \sinh x.$
7. $\tanh 2x = \dfrac{2 \tanh x}{1 + \tanh^2 x}.$
8. $\coth 2x = \dfrac{\coth^2 x + 1}{2 \coth x}.$

9. $\sinh (x \pm y) = \sinh x \cosh y \pm \cosh x \sinh y.$
10. $\cosh (x \pm y) = \cosh x \cosh y \pm \sinh x \sinh y.$

11. $\sinh x + \sinh y = 2 \sinh \dfrac{x + y}{2} \cosh \dfrac{x - y}{2}.$

12. $\sinh x - \sinh y = 2 \cosh \dfrac{x + y}{2} \sinh \dfrac{x - y}{2}.$

13. $\cosh x + \cosh y = 2 \cosh \dfrac{x + y}{2} \cosh \dfrac{x - y}{2}.$

14. $\cosh x - \cosh y = 2 \sinh \dfrac{x + y}{2} \sinh \dfrac{x - y}{2}.$

172. Inverse hyperbolic functions.—Functions similar to the inverse trigonometric functions (see Chapter IX) are obtained for hyperbolic functions.

If

$$y = \sinh x = \frac{e^x - e^{-x}}{2} = \frac{e^x - \dfrac{1}{e^x}}{2} = \frac{e^{2x} - 1}{2e^x},$$

then

$$2\,ye^x = e^{2x} - 1.$$

Solving the quadratic in e^x we have,

$$e^x = y \pm \sqrt{y^2 + 1}.$$

Since e^x is positive, the negative sign is excluded. Hence,

$$x = \log_e (y + \sqrt{y^2 + 1}).$$

In general mathematical discussions logarithms are always taken to the base e. Hence in practice this base is frequently omitted and the above equation written

$$x = \log (y + \sqrt{y^2 + 1}).$$

In $x = \sinh^{-1} y$, the notation $\sinh^{-1} y$ is used to indicate the inverse function, as is the case in trigonometric functions. That is,

$$\sinh^{-1} y = \log (y + \sqrt{y^2 + 1}).$$

EXERCISES

Prove the following identities.

1. $\cosh^{-1} x = \log (x + \sqrt{x^2 - 1}).$

2. $\tanh^{-1} x = \frac{1}{2} \log \dfrac{1 + x}{1 - x}.$

3. $\coth^{-1} x = \tanh^{-1} \dfrac{1}{x} = \frac{1}{2} \log \dfrac{x + 1}{x - 1}.$

4. $\operatorname{sech}^{-1} x = \cosh^{-1} \dfrac{1}{x} = \log \dfrac{1 + \sqrt{1 - x^2}}{x}.$

5. $\operatorname{csch}^{-1} x = \sinh^{-1} \dfrac{1}{x} = \log \dfrac{1 + \sqrt{1 + x^2}}{x}.$

6. $\tanh^{-1} x + \tanh^{-1} y = \tanh^{-1} \dfrac{x + y}{1 + xy}.$

7. $\sinh^{-1} x = \tanh^{-1} \dfrac{x}{\sqrt{1 + x^2}}.$

8. $\tanh^{-1} \dfrac{2x}{1 + x^2} = 2 \tanh^{-1} x.$

CHAPTER XII

MISCELLANEOUS WORK ON TRIGONOMETRIC IDENTITIES

IN THIS chapter we will make a further study of trigonometric identities. For the sake of completeness we shall extend the proofs of the addition formulas [sin $(A + B)$, etc.] so as to make them apply to any angles whatever. We shall also study certain more complicated identities that are important in applications in physics and in more advanced courses in mathematics. We shall begin with some very simple identities.

173. Relations of functions of positive and negative angles.— To study the relations of the sine and cosine of positive and negative angles, construct the figures below. In these figures

$$XOB_1 = - XOB_1', \quad XOB_2 = - XOB_2', \text{ and so on.}$$

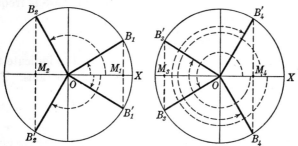

From the figures it is evident that

$$\sin XOB_1 = - \sin XOB_1', \quad \sin XOB_2 = - \sin XOB_2', \text{ etc.}$$

Hence for all values of A less than 2π

$$\sin A = - \sin (- A) \qquad [87]$$

Since by §134 for any angle A, $\sin A = \sin (A \pm 2n\pi)$ it follows that [87] holds for any angle whatever.

From the figures it is also evident that

$$\cos XOB_1 = \cos XOB_1', \quad \cos XOB_2 = \cos XOB_2', \text{ etc.}$$

Hence we have, by proceeding as above, that for any angle A

$$\cos A = \cos (- A) \qquad [88]$$

159

174. Sin $(A \pm 90°)$, cos $(A \pm 90°)$.—In extending the proof of the addition formulas the following formulas will be used.

$$\sin (A + 90°) = \cos A \quad [89] \qquad \cos (A + 90°) = - \sin A \quad [91]$$
$$\sin (A - 90°) = - \cos A \quad [90] \qquad \cos (A - 90°) = \sin A \quad [92]$$

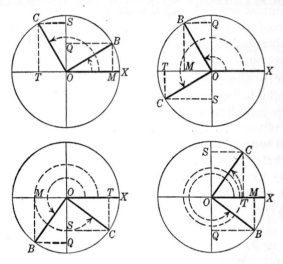

In each of the four figures, XOB represents an angle A, and XOC represents $A + 90°$.

Since in each figure $TC = QB$ and $SC = - MB$, we have

$$\sin (A + 90°) = \cos A \text{ and } \cos (A + 90°) = - \sin A.$$

Since by §134, $\sin A = \sin (A + 360°)$ and $\cos A = \cos (A + 360°)$, [89] and [91] are proved for any positive angle A.

Since the angle is coterminal with a negative angle, it follows that these formulas hold also for negative angles.

Formula [89] may be read: "The sine of an angle is equal to the cosine of an angle which is 90° smaller." If this angle is represented by B, then $\sin B = \cos (B - 90°)$ which is [92].

In a similar manner [91] follows from [90].

175. Extension of proof of identities.—In §§113–116 the following formulas were proved.

$$\sin (A + B) = \sin A \cos B + \cos A \sin B$$
$$\sin (A - B) = \sin A \cos B - \cos A \sin B$$
$$\cos (A + B) = \cos A \cos B - \sin A \sin B$$
$$\cos (A - B) = \cos A \cos B + \sin A \sin B$$

These proofs were made under the restriction that all angles involved were positive and that the sum of two angles involved should be less than 180°. That is, the formulas were proved for such angles as occur in triangles. It now remains to prove these formulas when A and B represent any angles whatever.

The proof will be made by showing that these formulas hold when either angle is increased or decreased by 90°. If this is proved we shall find that the formulas hold when the given angles are increased or decreased by 90° any number of times and hence for any angles whatever. In the proof we need to make use of formulas [89]–[92] which have been proved for all values of A.

(1) Assuming $\sin (A + B) = \sin A \cos B + \cos A \sin B$, which is known for positive acute angles A and B, we will show that

$$\sin (A + 90° + B) = \sin (A + 90°) \cos B + \cos (A + 90°) \sin B. \qquad \text{I}$$

Using [89], we have $\sin (\overline{A + 90°} + B) = \sin (A + B + 90°) = \cos (A + B)$. Hence the first member of equation I has been reduced to $\cos (A + B)$. Using [89] and [91] we have,

$\sin (A + 90°) \cos B + \cos (A + 90°) \sin B = \cos A \cos B - \sin A \sin B$, which by [40] is equal to $\cos (A + B)$.

Hence each member of I has reduced to $\cos (A + B)$, and the identity is proved provided A and B are subject to the restrictions imposed in §113.

That is, we have shown that the formula for the sine of the sum of two angles holds when either angle is increased by 90°.

(2) Assuming $\sin (A + B) = \sin A \cos B + \cos A \sin B$, we will prove that

$$\sin (A - 90° + B) = \sin (A - 90°) \cos B + \cos (A - 90°) \sin B. \qquad \text{II}$$

Using [90],

$$\sin (A - 90° + B) = \sin (\overline{A + B} - 90°) = - \cos (A + B).$$

Using [90] and [92], the second member of II reduces to

$$- \cos A \cos B + \sin A \sin B = - \cos (A + B).$$

It follows as under (1) that the formula for $\sin (A + B)$ has been proved when either A or B is decreased by 90°.

Hence we know that

$$\sin (A_1 + B_1) = \sin A_1 \cos B_1 + \cos A_1 \sin B_1$$

where A_1 and B_1 may be either 90° larger or smaller than A and B.

Since 90° may be added or subtracted in this manner as often as we wish, it follows that this formula holds for any angles whatever.

It may be proved in exactly the same manner that the other three formulas hold for any angles whatever.

For convenience we repeat these formulas:

$$\sin (A + 90°) = \cos A \quad [89] \qquad \cos (A + 90°) = - \sin A \quad [91]$$
$$\sin (A - 90°) = - \cos A \quad [90] \qquad \cos (A - 90°) = \sin A \quad [92]$$

EXERCISES

Using these formulas, and proceeding as on page 161, prove the following identities.

1. $\sin (\overline{A + 90°} - B) = \sin (A + 90°) \cos B - \cos (A + 90°) \sin B$.
2. $\sin (A - \overline{B + 90°}) = \sin A \cos (B + 90°) - \cos A \sin (B + 90°)$.
3. $\sin (A - \overline{B - 90°}) = \sin A \cos (B - 90°) - \cos A \sin (B - 90°)$.
4. $\cos (\overline{A + 90°} + B) = \cos (A + 90°) \cos B - \sin (A + 90°) \sin B$.
5. $\cos (\overline{A - 90°} + B) = \cos (A - 90°) \cos B - \sin (A - 90°) \sin B$.
6. $\cos (A - \overline{B + 90°}) = \cos A \cos (B + 90°) + \sin A \sin (B + 90°)$.

7. Show how the identities just proved may be used to prove that all identities in §175 may be extended for all values of A and B.

8. Show how the proof of

$$\tan (A + B) = \frac{\tan A + \tan B}{1 - \tan A \tan B}, \qquad \tan (A - B) = \frac{\tan A - \tan B}{1 + \tan A \tan B}$$

may be extended to apply to all values of A and B.

9. Show how the proof of the formulas giving $\cot (A + B)$ and $\cot (A - B)$ may be extended to apply to all values of A and B.

10. Can it be shown that the proof of the formulas for $\sin A + \sin B$, $\sin A - \sin B$, $\cos A + \cos B$, $\cos A - \cos B$ has now been extended to cover all values of A and B?

11. Discuss the same question for the formulas giving $\sin A \sin B$, $\sin A \cos B$, $\cos A \cos B$.

12. Using the formulas $\sin (A + 90°) = \cos A$, $\cos (A + 90°) = - \sin A$, show that $\tan (A + 90°) = - 1/\tan A$.

13. If two angles differ by 90°, how are their tangents related?

176. Miscellaneous examples.—On this page and the one following are shown additional trigonometric identities. In Example 1 the angles are restricted to positive angles whose sum is 180°. That is, the angles are the angles of a triangle.

Example 1. If $A + B + C = 180°$, prove $\sin A + \sin B + \sin C = 4 \cos \frac{1}{2} A \cos \frac{1}{2} B \cos \frac{1}{2} C$.

Proof: By [15], since $C = 180° - (A + B)$, $\sin C = \sin (A + B)$, and by [42]

$$\sin (A + B) = 2 \sin \frac{1}{2} (A + B) \cos \frac{1}{2} (A + B).$$

By [52]

$$\sin A + \sin B = 2 \sin \frac{1}{2} (A + B) \cos \frac{1}{2} (A - B).$$

Hence,

$$\sin A + \sin B + \sin C = 2 \sin \tfrac{1}{2} (A + B) [\cos \tfrac{1}{2} (A - B) + \cos \tfrac{1}{2} (A + B)]$$
$$= 4 \sin \tfrac{1}{2} (A + B) \cos \tfrac{1}{2} A \cos (- \tfrac{1}{2} B).$$

Since

$$\tfrac{1}{2}(A + B) + \tfrac{1}{2} C = 90°, \ \sin \tfrac{1}{2}(A + B) = \cos \tfrac{1}{2} C.$$

Using $\cos(-\tfrac{1}{2} B) = \cos \tfrac{1}{2} B$ [88], we have

$$\sin A + \sin B + \sin C = 4 \cos \tfrac{1}{2} A \cos \tfrac{1}{2} B \cos \tfrac{1}{2} C.$$

Example 2. Express as a product the sum of the series
$$S_n = \sin A + \sin(A + B) + \sin(A + 2B) + \ldots + \sin[A + (n-1)B].$$
Solution: Multiply each term of the series by $\sin \tfrac{1}{2} B$.
Then

$$S_n \sin \tfrac{1}{2} B = \sin A \sin \tfrac{1}{2} B + \ldots + \sin[A + (n-1)B] \sin \tfrac{1}{2} B.$$
by [59]

$$\sin A \sin \tfrac{1}{2} B = \tfrac{1}{2} \cos(A - \tfrac{1}{2} B) - \tfrac{1}{2} \cos(A + \tfrac{1}{2} B),$$
$$\sin(A + B) \sin \tfrac{1}{2} B = \tfrac{1}{2} \cos(A + \tfrac{1}{2} B) - \tfrac{1}{2} \cos(A + \tfrac{3}{2} B),$$

$$\cdots \cdots \cdots \cdots \cdots \cdots \cdots$$

$$\sin[A + (n-1)B] \sin \tfrac{1}{2} B$$
$$= \tfrac{1}{2} \cos[A + \tfrac{1}{2}(2n-3)B] - \tfrac{1}{2} \cos[A + \tfrac{1}{2}(2n-1)B].$$

Adding, we have,

$$S_n \sin \tfrac{1}{2} B = \tfrac{1}{2} \cos(A - \tfrac{1}{2} B) - \tfrac{1}{2} \cos[A + \tfrac{1}{2}(2n-1)B].$$

Applying [55] to the second member and dividing by $\sin \tfrac{1}{2} B$, we have

$$S_n = \frac{\sin[A + \tfrac{1}{2}(n-1)B] \sin \dfrac{n}{2} B}{\sin \tfrac{1}{2} B}$$

Example 3. Express as a product the sum of the series
$$S_n = \cos A + \cos(A + B) + \cos(A + 2B) + \ldots + \cos[A + (n-1)B]$$
Solution: Multiply each term of the series by $\sin \tfrac{1}{2} B$.
Then,

$$S_n \sin \tfrac{1}{2} B = \cos A \sin \tfrac{1}{2} B + \ldots + \cos[A + (n-1)B] \sin \tfrac{1}{2} B.$$

Using [57] and proceeding as in Example 4, we have

$$\cos A \sin \tfrac{1}{2} B = \tfrac{1}{2} \sin(A + \tfrac{1}{2} B) - \tfrac{1}{2} \sin(A - \tfrac{1}{2} B)$$
$$\cos(A + B) \sin \tfrac{1}{2} B = \tfrac{1}{2} \sin(A + \tfrac{3}{2} B) - \tfrac{1}{2} \sin(A + \tfrac{1}{2} B)$$

$$\cdots \cdots \cdots \cdots \cdots \cdots \cdots$$

$$\cos[A + (n-1)B] \sin \tfrac{1}{2} B = \tfrac{1}{2} \sin\left(A + \frac{2n-1}{2}B\right) - \tfrac{1}{2} \sin\left(A + \frac{2n-3}{2}B\right).$$

Adding and using [53],

$$S_n \sin \tfrac{1}{2} B = -\tfrac{1}{2} \sin(A - \tfrac{1}{2} B) + \tfrac{1}{2} \sin[A + \tfrac{1}{2}(2n-1)B]$$
$$= \cos[A + \tfrac{1}{2}(n-1)B] \sin \frac{n}{2} B$$

Hence,

$$S_n = \frac{\cos[A + \tfrac{1}{2}(n-1)B] \sin \dfrac{n}{2} B}{\sin \tfrac{1}{2} B}.$$

EXERCISES

Prove the following identities.

1. $\sin (A + B) + \sin (A - B) = 2 \sin A \cos B$
2. $\sin (A + B) - \sin (A - B) = 2 \sin B \cos A$
3. $\cos (A + B) + \cos (A - B) = 2 \cos A \cos B$
4. $\cos (A + B) - \cos (A - B) = -2 \sin A \sin B$
5. $\cot 3A = \dfrac{\cot^3 A - 3 \cot A}{3 \cot^2 A - 1}$
6. $\sin 4A = 4 \sin A \cos^3 A - 4 \cos A \sin^3 A$
7. $\cos 4A = 1 - 8 \cos^2 A + 8 \cos^4 A$
8. $\tan (A + B + C) = \dfrac{\tan A + \tan B + \tan C - \tan A \tan B \tan C}{1 - \tan A \tan B - \tan B \tan C - \tan C \tan A}$
9. $\cot (A + B + C) = \dfrac{\cot A \cot B \cot C - \cot A - \cot B - \cot C}{\cot A \cot B + \cot B \cot C + \cot C \cot A - 1}$
10. $\dfrac{1}{1 + \sin^2 A} + \dfrac{1}{1 + \cos^2 A} + \dfrac{1}{1 + \sec^2 A} + \dfrac{1}{1 + \csc^2 A} = 2$
11. $\cos 3A \csc A + \sin 3A \sec A = 2 \cos 2A \csc 2A$
12. $\sin 5A = 16 \sin^5 A - 20 \sin^3 A + 5 \sin A$
13. $\cos 5A = 16 \cos^5 A - 20 \cos^3 A + 5 \cos A$
14. $\tan 4A = \dfrac{4 \tan A (1 - \tan^2 A)}{1 - 6 \tan^2 A + \tan^4 A}$

By substituting in the series in examples 2 and 3 on page 163 find the sums of the following series.

15. $\sin A + \sin 2A + \sin 3A + \ldots + \sin (n\,A)$
16. $\cos A + \cos 2A + \cos 3A + \ldots + \cos (n\,A)$
17. $\sin A + \sin 3A + \sin 5A + \ldots + \sin (2n - 1) A$
18. $\cos A + \cos 3A + \cos 5A + \ldots + \cos (2n - 1) A$

If A, B, C are angles of a triangle, prove each of the following.

Suggestion: Since $A + B + C = 180°$, we have, $\sin (A + B) = \sin C$ [15], $\cos (A + B) = - \cos C$ [16], and also $\sin \frac{1}{2} (A + B) = \cos \frac{1}{2} C$ [7].

19. $\sin A + \sin B - \sin C = 4 \sin \frac{1}{2} A \sin \frac{1}{2} B \cos \frac{1}{2} C$
20. $\cos A + \cos B + \cos C = 1 + 4 \sin \frac{1}{2} A \sin \frac{1}{2} B \sin \frac{1}{2} C$
21. $\cos A + \cos B - \cos C = -1 + 4 \cos \frac{1}{2} A \cos \frac{1}{2} B \sin \frac{1}{2} C$
22. $\sin 2A + \sin 2B + \sin 2C = 4 \sin A \sin B \sin C$
23. $\sin^2 A + \sin^2 B + \sin^2 C = 2 (1 + \cos A \cos B \cos C)$
24. $\sin^2 A + \sin^2 B - \sin^2 C = 2 \sin A \sin B \cos C$
25. $\cos^2 A + \cos^2 B + \cos^2 C = 1 - 2 \cos A \cos B \cos C$
26. $\cos^2 A + \cos^2 B - \cos^2 C = 1 - 2 \sin A \sin B \cos C$
27. $\tan A + \tan B + \tan C = \tan A \tan B \tan C$

CHAPTER XIII

MISCELLANEOUS SUPPLEMENTARY MATERIAL

IN THIS chapter is given certain material that does not find a natural place at any point in the main body of the text. Some of this material, such as the cumulative reviews, should be used in an ordinary course in trigonometry. Other parts, such as "the slide rule," "topics from physics," and the more difficult problems on pages 182–185, will be omitted by many.

177. Sources of errors in computation.—The practical surveyor, engineer, or scientific worker must check his results so that he *knows* they are correct to the required degree of accuracy. To check intelligently so as to discover not only incorrect results but also the errors which led to them, it is necessary to know the principal sources of errors.

Gross errors in trigonometric computation are likely to be due to one of the following.

(1) Use of wrong formulas in solving the problem.

(2) Misplacement of the decimal point or, what results in the same error, use of a wrong characteristic.

(3) Wrong operation on logarithms, such as adding instead of subtracting.

(4) Using a wrong column of trigonometric functions, as, for instance, using sines instead of cosines or tangents.

(5) Reading a table of trigonometric functions from the top of the page instead of from the bottom or *vice versa*.

(6) Incorrect addition or subtraction of logarithms near the left end of the numbers.

If a check such as those suggested on pages 75, 79, shows a slight error, then the error is likely to be one of the following:

(1) Incorrect interpolation.

(2) Adding instead of subtracting *in interpolation* or vice versa.

(3) Incorrect addition or subtraction of logarithms in the higher decimals.

178. Checking gross errors by geometric construction.— Suppose it is given that in a right triangle ABC, $\angle A = 42° 23'$, $a = 18.3$ and it is required to find b and c.

Construction: Make construction on a large piece of paper. Construct a right angle C. Lay off $CB = 18.3$, using a quarter-inch as a unit. With a protractor lay off an angle nearly $42° 23'$ (about $42\frac{1}{2}°$) and complete the triangle. On measuring, it should then be found that AB is about 27 units (27.148) and AC is about 20 units (20.05).

Again, suppose it is given that $\angle A = 68° 30'$, $\angle B = 53° 18'$, $a = 58$. First find $\angle C = 180° - (A + B) = 58° 12'$.

Construction: Using a convenient unit, possibly one-eighth of an inch, lay off $BC = 58$. At the ends of BC lay off angles as nearly as may be equal to $53° 18'$ ($53°$) and $58° 12'$ ($58°$), and complete the triangle. On measuring, it should then be found that AB and AC are 53 units (52.98) and 50 units (49.98), respectively.

If this check is used, the construction should be made before the work of computing is begun.

179. Finding small angles in exceptional cases.— From the table we find that log cos $0°$ to log cos $0° 16'$ are all given as 0.00000, log cos $0° 17'$ to log cos $0° 28'$ are all given as 9.99999, log cos $0° 29'$ to log cos $0° 36'$ are all given as 9.99998, etc. It thus appears that the cosines of very small angles are not well adapted for computation. This applies for the same reason to the sines of angles near $90°$. For this reason the cosines of small angles should be avoided, and also the sines of angles near $90°$. It may occur, however, that the data given (or obtained from measurement) are such as to lead to the cosine of a small angle.

Suppose that in the right triangle ABC, b and c are given and it is required to find the angle A. We then proceed as follows: Construct the bisector of $\angle A$ and draw BE perpendicular to it.

Then $AE = c$, $CE = c - b$, $\angle EAD = \angle CBE$, and

$$\tan CBE = \frac{CE}{BC} = \frac{c - b}{BC} = \frac{c - b}{\sqrt{c^2 - b^2}} = \sqrt{\frac{c - b}{c + b}}.$$

That is,

$$\tan \frac{A}{2} = \sqrt{\frac{c - b}{c + b}}$$

This equation should be used to find $\angle A$.

For angles near $90°$ a similar formula involving the cotangent should be used.

180. The slide rule.—*The slide rule* is a device by means of which products, quotients, and roots are read off directly to a very considerable degree of accuracy. The principles involved are the same as in logarithms, and the device consists of an adaptation of what is called the *logarithmic scale*.

From a table of logarithms we find that

log 1 = 0.00	log 2 = 0.30	log 3 = 0.48
log 4 = 0.60	log 5 = 0.70	log 6 = 0.78
log 7 = 0.85	log 8 = 0.90	log 9 = 0.95
log 10 = 1.00		

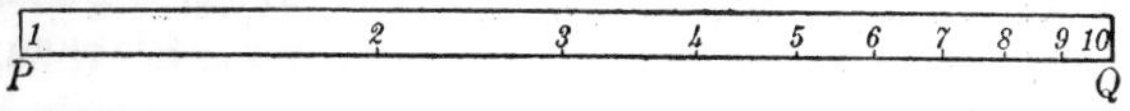

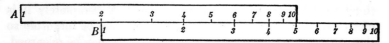

From these numbers a logarithmic scale is constructed by taking a convenient segment PQ as a unit and laying off on it from the left end segments whose lengths are equal to the logarithms of the numbers written above the line.

Thus the left end of the line is marked 1 because log 1 = 0. The distance from P to the point marked 2 is 0.30 because log 2 = 0.30, the distance from P to the point marked 3 is 0.48 because log 3 = 0.48, etc. This scale represents the logarithms of numbers from 0 to 10.

For practical use the scale is extended to twice this length, so as to give the logarithms of numbers from 1 to 100, but the principle used is the same as that of the scale given here.

Suppose we have two logarithmic scales, exactly alike, and that they are placed side by side as shown in the figure, so that the numeral 1 in the lower scale B is exactly opposite the numeral 2 in the upper scale A. Then 2 on

scale B is opposite 4 on scale A, 3 on scale B is opposite 6 on scale A, etc. This is due to the fact that placing 1 on scale B opposite 2 on scale A, moves scale B a distance to the right equal to log 2. By the theory of logarithms we know that adding log 2 to the logarithm of a number gives the logarithm of the product when that number is multiplied by 2.

If 1 on scale B is placed opposite 3 on scale A, then 2 on B will be opposite 6 on A and 3 on B will be opposite to 9 on A.

To divide 6 by 2 place 2 on scale B opposite 6 on A. Then 1 on B will be opposite 3 on A, and this is the required quotient.

The slide rule consists of a rule carrying two scales usually marked A and D and a slide carrying two scales marked B and C. Scales A and B are exactly alike and are used for finding products and quotients.

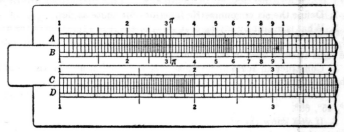

The two scales C and D are also just alike, but the distance from the end point to each number is twice as great as in scales A and B. It follows that on scale C each numeral falls exactly opposite its square on scale B. These two scales may therefore be used to find squares and square roots.

Scales A and B are in direct contact and may be read easily. To compare scales B and C a device called a *runner*, is useful.

Since scales C and D are alike, they may be used exactly the same as A and B to find products and quotients when the numbers involved are small.

The slide may be pulled out entirely and inserted so as to show its reverse side, on which it carries a scale of logarithmic sines marked S, and a scale of logarithmic tangents marked T. These are used with scales A or D to find products and quotients when sines and tangents are involved.

Effective use of the slide rule involves many details which cannot be given here. But mastery of the simple principles just stated will make the rest comparatively easy. Detailed rules for using this instrument are usually compiled by the manufacturers and presented to each purchaser.

The results obtained from the ordinary slide rule are sufficiently accurate for many purposes and in all cases they constitute effective checks except for slight errors. Simple inexpensive rules, called students' slide rules, may be obtained. These are useful in learning to use the instrument and for checking.

181. Cumulative reviews.—It is a well-known fact that anything that has been learned, no matter how completely it is mastered at the time of first learning, will soon be forgotten so that complete reproduction is impossible. It may be relearned, however, with less effort than was required for the original learning. To secure comparatively permanent lodgment in the memory, a series of relearnings of considerable length is necessary. To meet this requirement a series of cumulative reviews is here provided. In these reviews the principal formulas of trigonometry are made to appear so that each one will be reviewed in accordance with the latest information about the best spacing of such reviews.

CUMULATIVE REVIEW I

(May be used after page 32 of text)

1. Define the six trigonometric functions for acute angles.

2. What is meant by saying that sin A or cos A is a function of the angle A? Prove that cos A depends upon the size of $\angle A$ and not upon the size of the right triangle used in the definition.

3. Construct an acute angle whose sine is $\frac{3}{4}$. What are the values of the other five functions of this angle?

4. Find the values of the six trigonometric functions of each of the angles 30°, 45°, 60°.

5. If you know the value of sin 37°, how do you find the cosine of 53°? State a theorem involving complementary angles and their cofunctions.

6. "Round" the number 14278306 to seven figures, to six figures, to five figures, to four figures, to three figures.

7. What is meant by three-place accuracy? by four-place accuracy? by five-place accuracy? State the accuracy of angle that can be obtained by using each of these.

8. Discuss the variation of sin A, cos A, and tan A as the angle A varies from 0° to 90°. What is meant by the statement tan 90° = ∞?

9. Find sin 42° 50′ by interpolating between sin 42° and 43°. Also find tan 42° 50′ and cos 42° 50′ by interpolating. Use the table on page 25.

10. What is meant by "angle of elevation" and by "angle of depression"? Give examples.

CUMULATIVE REVIEW II

(May be used after page 50 of text)

1. If cos $x = 4/9$, find the values of the other six functions of x, it being given that $\angle x$ is acute.

2. If in a right triangle ABC (C being the right angle) c and $\angle A$ are given, how may a and b be found?

3. If in Example 2, $\angle A$ and a are known, how may b and c be found?

4. Define logarithm, characteristic, mantissa, base.

5. Give rules for finding the logarithm of a product, of a quotient, of a power, of a root. State the laws of exponents upon which these rules are based.

6. Multiply and also divide $\bar{2}.84678$ by 3. Find the sum of $\bar{1}.81906$ $\bar{3}.65270$, $\bar{1}.91645$.

7. Give the rule for finding the characteristic of the logarithm of a number.

8. Give a list of the laws of exponents. Then give the corresponding list of rules for using logarithms.

9. Express each of the following as a function of an angle between 0° and 45°: sec 78°, csc 49°, sin 56°, cos 83°, tan 64°, cot 69°.

10. In the right triangle ABC, $\angle C = 90°$, and the sides are a, b, c. Give formulas for finding the remaining parts when the following parts are given: a, b; a, c; b, c; A, a; A, b; A, c.

Find the values of the following.

11. $\dfrac{79.4 \times 1.27 \times 0.079}{5.37 \times 0.787}.$

12. $\dfrac{(0.592)^2 \times (0.0276)^3}{8.15 \times (0.917)^4}.$

13. $\dfrac{\sqrt[3]{1.917} \times \sqrt[4]{0.986} \times \sqrt[2]{2.46}}{3.59 \times (0.426)^3}.$

14. $\dfrac{3.4 \times \tan\,(62°\,41') \cos\,(39°\,25')}{9 \sin\,(42°\,16'\,20'')}.$

In each of the following find A.

15. $\log \sin A = 9.81426.$

16. $\log \tan A = 0.81914.$

17. $\cos A = \dfrac{19 \sin 41°\,47' \times \cos 13°\,51'}{24 \cos 51°\,32'}.$

18. $\tan A = \dfrac{164 \sin 61°\,27' \cot 19°\,12'}{37 \tan 39°\,37'\,40''}.$

CUMULATIVE REVIEW III

(May be used after page 70 of text)

1. Define the projection of a segment upon a line; give formulas for finding the projections of a segment AB upon each of the mutually perpendicular axes OX and OY.

2. Express each of the following as a function of an angle between $0°$ and $45°$: $\sin 49°$, $\cos 56°$, $\tan 62°$, $\cot 57°$, $\sec 74°$, $\csc 46°$.

3. Express each of the following as a function of an angle between $0°$ and $90°$: $\sin 98°$, $\cos 174°$, $\tan 135°$, $\cot 127°$, $\sec 149°$, $\csc 164°$.

4. Express each of the following as a function of an angle between $0°$ and $45°$: $\sin 147°$, $\cos 122°$, $\tan 94°$, $\cot 108°$, $\sec 167°$, $\csc 151°$.

5. Find the area of a regular twelve-sided polygon inscribed in a circle whose radius is 12 inches; also find the area of such a polygon circumscribed about such a circle.

6. If x and y are the coordinates of a point P on the terminal side of an angle which is placed as in §82, and if r is the distance from O to P, give the definitions of the six functions in terms of x, y, and r.

Find the values of the following.

7. $\dfrac{31.6 \cos 52°\,18' \times \sin 41°\,12'}{\sqrt[3]{9.16 \sin 67°\,47' \times \tan 62°\,45'}}.$

8. $\dfrac{(0.462)^3 \times (1.94)^2 \times (0.067)^4}{486}.$

9. The vertex angle of an isosceles triangle is $42°\,30'$ and its base is 24.9. Find the remaining parts of the triangle.

10. A regular polygon of n sides is inscribed in a circle with radius r. Derive a formula giving the area of this polygon.

11. Derive a formula giving the area of an n-sided polygon circumscribed about a circle with radius r.

12. A line segment of length 16 (extended if necessary) makes with the x-axis an angle of 49° 12′ 45″. Find the projections of these segments upon each of the two axes.

CUMULATIVE REVIEW IV

(May be used after page 94 of text)

1. Solve by using right triangles the triangle whose sides are 6, 7, 8.

2. State the sine formula for solving triangles. In a triangle ABC with corresponding sides a, b, c, what parts must be given so that the sine formula may be used to solve the triangle?

3. How many parts of a triangle must be given to fix the triangle? In what case is it not possible to solve the triangle by means of the sine formula? In this case what formula do you use?

4. What is the ambiguous case in the solution of triangles? Illustrate by drawing a figure. If in attempting to solve a triangle you get the value of the sine of an angle greater than unity, what is your conclusion? Give such an example and draw a figure to illustrate.

5. What is the area of a triangle whose sides are 7, 8, 9?

6. What is the radius of a circle inscribed in a triangle whose sides are 11, 14, 17? What is the radius of the circle circumscribed about this triangle?

7. What are the angles of a triangle whose sides are 4, 5, 6? What are the angles of a triangle whose sides are 3, 4, 5?

8. State and prove the law of cosines. If two sides and the included angle of a triangle are given, can you solve the triangle by using the law of cosines and sines? In practice, what formula do you use in solving the triangle in this case? Why?

9. Find the area of triangle ABC if $\angle A = 61° 31′ 15″$, $b = 171.42$, $c = 207.84$.

10. Find the radii of the inscribed and circumscribed circles of a triangle whose sides are 14, 15, 16.

11. Describe how a simple survey may be made. How many straight lines would be measured directly?

12. State and prove the law of tangents for solving triangles. How would you decide when this law should be used in solving a triangle?

13. What parts of an isosceles triangle must be given in order that the remaining parts may be found?

14. If $\overline{1}.64286$ is a logarithm, multiply it by 3; also divide it by 3.

15. State what is meant by sin $A = 9.21063 - 10$.

16. Solve the triangle ABC if $\angle A = 15° 38′$, $\angle B = 61° 43′$ and $a = 318.4$.

17. Solve the triangle ABC if $\angle A = 49° 14′ 30″$, $c = 192.84$, and $a = 179.86$. Give all solutions.

18. If in example 17 a is given as 127.49, what is the solution?

19. If in the same example a is given as 251.24, what is the solution?

CUMULATIVE REVIEW V

(May be used after page 104 of text)

Find the value of A in each of the following.

1. $\sin 2A = \cos 4A$.

2. $\tan (A - 30°) = \cot (A + 30°)$.

3. $\sec (3A - 15°) = \csc (6A - 30°)$.

4. Give the values of tangent, cotangent, secant, and cosecant in terms of sine and cosine.

5. Give a relation connecting the tangent and secant of an angle; also one connecting the cotangent and cosecant.

Prove the following identities.

6. $\dfrac{\cos^2 A}{\tan^2 A} = \cos^4 A \csc^2 A$. **7.** $\dfrac{\tan x}{\sec x} = \sin x$.

8. $\sin^2 x \cot x = \sin x \cos x$. **9.** $(\sin A - \cos A)^2 = 1 - 2 \sin A \cos A$.

10. $\sin^2 A - \cos^2 A$ **11.** $(\tan^2 A + 1) \cos^2 A = 1$.

$\qquad = 1 - 2 \cos^2 A$.

12. $(\cot^2 A + 1) \sin^2 A = 1$. **13.** $\sin^4 A - \cos^4 A = 2 \sin^2 A - 1$.

14. $\sin A = \dfrac{1}{\csc A}$. **15.** $\cos A = \dfrac{1}{\sec A}$.

16. $\tan A = \dfrac{1}{\cot A}$. **17.** $\tan A = \dfrac{\sin A}{\cos A}$.

18. $\cot A = \dfrac{\cos A}{\sin A}$. **19.** $\sin^2 A + \cos^2 A = 1$.

20. $\sec^2 A = 1 + \tan^2 A$. **21.** $\csc^2 A = 1 + \cot^2 A$.

CUMULATIVE REVIEW VI

(May be used after page 110 of text)

Find the values of the following.

1. $\dfrac{2.91 \sin 31° 10' \times \tan 81° 50'}{\sqrt[3]{8.76} \cos 49° 8' \times \cot 73° 18'}$. **2.** $\dfrac{(1.06)^5 \times 589 \times \sqrt[3]{1.025}}{76^{\frac{1}{4}} \times 48^{\frac{1}{3}} \times 64^{\frac{1}{4}}}$.

3. If $\cos A = \frac{3}{4}$, find the values of the other functions of A.

4. Express the other five functions of an angle in terms of the sine.

5. Express the other five functions of an angle in terms of the secant.

In each of the following find the value of x.

6. $\cot (4x - 20°) = \tan (3x + 10°)$.

7. $\csc (2x + 40°) = \sec (3x + 20°)$.

8. $\cos (60° - 2x) = \sin (4x - 10°)$.

9. In $\triangle ABC$, $A = 72° 14'$, $b = 19.8$, $c = 24.3$. Find the remaining parts of the triangle.

10. Find the angles of a triangle whose sides are 15, 18, 23.

11. Find the radius of a circle circumscribed about a triangle whose sides are 12, 14, and 18.

12. Make a list of relations between the trigonometric functions. Give all functions in terms of sine and cosine.

CUMULATIVE REVIEW VII

(May be used after page 114 of text)

Prove the following identities.

1. $\tan A \sin A + \cos A = \sec A$.

2. $\dfrac{\tan A \sin A}{\tan A - \sin A} = \dfrac{\sin A}{1 - \cos A}$.

3. $\dfrac{\cos A + \cot A}{\sec A + \tan A} = \cos A \cot A$.

4. $\dfrac{\csc A + 1}{\cot A} = \dfrac{\cot A}{\csc A - 1}$.

5. $\cot^4 A + \cot^2 A = \csc^4 A - \csc^2 A$.

6. $\dfrac{\cot A - \cos A}{\cos^2 A} = \dfrac{\cos A \csc A}{1 + \sin A}$.

7. $\tan A + (1 - 2 \sin^2 A) \sec A \csc A = \cot A$.

8. $1 + \dfrac{1}{\cot^2 A} = \sec^2 A$.

11. $\sec^4 x (1 - \sin^4 x) = \sec^2 x + \tan^2 x$.

9. $\dfrac{\tan x - \sin x}{\sin^2 x} = \dfrac{\sin x \sec x}{1 + \cos x}$.

12. $\dfrac{1}{1 + \cos x} + \dfrac{1}{1 - \cos x} = 2 \csc^2 x$.

10. $\dfrac{1}{\csc x - \cot x} = \csc x + \cot x$.

13. $\csc^4 x - 1 = 2 \cot^2 x + \cot^4 x$.

14. $\dfrac{\sin x \sec x + \sin y \sec y}{\sin x \sec x - \sin y \sec y} = -\dfrac{\cos x \csc x + \cos y \csc y}{\cos x \csc x - \cos y \csc y}$.

15. $\sec^4 x - \tan^4 x = \sec^2 x + \tan^2 x = 1 + 2 \tan^2 x$.

16. $(\csc x - \cot x)^2 = \dfrac{1 - \cos x}{1 + \cos x}$.

17. $(\tan x + \cot x)^2 = \sec^2 x + \csc^2 x$.

18. $\cot^2 x - \cos^2 x = \cos^2 x \cot^2 x$.

19. Attempt to solve a triangle in which $A = 61°\ 40'$, $b = 97.8$, and $a = 31.4$. What is your conclusion?

20. Solve completely the triangle ABC if $A = 45°\ 45'$, $b = 172.4$, and $a = 161.3$.

CUMULATIVE REVIEW VIII

(May be used after page 114 of the text)

1. If $\sin A = \frac{1}{2}$ and $\sin B = \frac{1}{3}$, find $\sin (A + B)$ and also $\cos (A + B)$.

2. If $\tan A = \frac{3}{4}$, find $\cot 2 A$.

3. Express the other five functions of A in terms of $\tan A$.

4. Give the relations of functions of complementary angles.

5. Prove the relations of functions of supplementary angles.

6. If A, B, C are the angles of a triangle, show that $\sin (A + B) = \sin C$, and also that $\sin \frac{1}{2} (A + B) = \cos \frac{1}{2} C$.

Prove the following identities.

7. $\sin A + \sin 2A = 2 \sin \dfrac{3A}{2} \cos \dfrac{A}{2}$.

8. $\sin 4A - \sin 2A = 2 \sin A \cos 3A$.

9. $\cos 2A + \cos 6A = 2 \cos 4A \cos 2A$.

10. $\cos 7A - \cos A = -2 \sin 4A \sin 3A.$

11. $\dfrac{\sin 75° + \sin 15°}{\cos 75° - \cos 15°} = -\cot 30°.$

12. $\dfrac{\sin 75° - \sin 15°}{\cos 75° + \cos 15°} = \tan 30°.$

13. $\sin 5A \cos 3A = \frac{1}{2} (\sin 8A + \sin 2A).$

14. $\sin 3A \cos 5A = \frac{1}{2} (\sin 8A - \sin 2A).$

15. $\cos 5A \cos 3A = \frac{1}{2} (\cos 2A + \cos 8A).$

16. $\sin 5A \sin 3A = \frac{1}{2} (\cos 2A - \cos 8A).$

17. $\sin 60° \cos 20° = \frac{1}{2} (\sin 80° + \sin 40°).$

18. $\sin 20° \cos 60° = \frac{1}{2} (\sin 80° - \sin 40°).$

19. $\cos 60° \cos 20° = \frac{1}{2} (\cos 40° + \cos 80°).$

20. $\sin 60° \sin 20° = \frac{1}{2} (\cos 40° - \cos 80°).$

21. $\dfrac{\sin 13A - \sin 9A + \sin 5A - \sin A}{\cos 13A - \cos 9A - \cos 5A + \cos A} = -\cot 4A.$

22. $(\sin 3A + \sin A) \sin A + (\cos 3A - \cos A) \cos A = 0.$

23. $2 \sin 2A \cos A + 2 \cos 4A \sin A = \sin 5A + \sin A.$

24. $2 \cos 2A \cos A - 2 \sin 4A \sin A = \cos A + \cos 5A.$

CUMULATIVE REVIEW IX

(May be used after page 114 of the text)

1. Express each of the following as a function of an angle between 0° and 45°.

$\sin 172° \, 40'$, $\cos 93° \, 35'$, $\cot 139° \, 10'$, $\tan 163° \, 50'$, $\sec 171° \, 40'$, $\csc 129° \, 20'$.

2. If $\tan x = \frac{3}{4}$, find $\tan 2x$.

3. Find $\cot (A + 45°)$ and $\cot (A - 45°)$.

Prove the following identities.

4. $\cot x - \tan x = 2 \cot 2x.$

5. $\sin (A - B) \cos B + \cos (A - B) \sin B = \sin A.$

6. $\cos (n - 1) A \cos A - \sin (n - 1) A \sin A = \cos n A.$

7. $\sin A \sec A - \sin B \sec B = \sin (A - B) \sec A \sec B.$

8. $\cos (A + B) \cos A + \sin (A + B) \sin A = \cos B.$

9. $(\cos A + \cos B)^2 + (\sin A + \sin B)^2 = 4 \cos^2 \dfrac{A - B}{2}.$

10. $(\cos A - \cos B)^2 + (\sin A - \sin B)^2 = 4 \sin^2 \dfrac{A - B}{2}.$

11. $\dfrac{\sin 2A}{1 + \cos 2A} = \sin A \sec A.$

12. $\csc A \, (1 - \cos 2A) = 2 \sin A \sec A.$

13. $\dfrac{1 + \sin A - \cos A}{1 + \sin A + \cos A} = \sin \dfrac{A}{2} \sec \dfrac{A}{2}.$

14. $\dfrac{\tan A - \tan B}{\cot A + \tan B} = \tan (A - B) \tan A.$

15. $\tan (A + B + C) = \dfrac{\tan A + \tan B + \tan C - \tan A \tan B \tan C}{1 - \tan A \tan B - \tan B \tan C - \tan C \tan A}.$

182. Supplementary work on simple survey.—In a series of
courses such as AB, BC,
CD, DE, EF, FG in the figure the measured lines will
usually not lie on level
ground. It is then necessary to measure the incline
of each line. The data obtained in the field may then
be as shown at the right.
The "lengths" now mean
measured length, not horizontal length. The first
step is then to make up a
column giving the horizontal lengths. These are found
by multiplying the meas-
ured lengths by the cosines
of the incline. Then complete as on page 59.

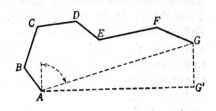

Course	Bearing	Incline	Length
AB	N.17°47′W.	+ 8°15′	693.4
BC	N. 9°21′ E.	+11°25′	714.2
CD	N.83° E.	− 3°52′	439.8
DE	S. 78° 5′ E.	− 4°17′	314.3
EF	N.81°40′ E.	+ 5°38′	587.7
FG	S. 79°21′ E.	+ 2°16′	398.9

EXERCISES

1. From the data given above, find the length and bearing of GA. Note
that the length you find is the horizontal component of this course.

2. Find whether the point G is above or below the point A, and how
much. Put your work in a neat form.

The area of a polygonal figure may be computed when the
length and bearing of each side are known. The method used
in practice is called the **double-meridian-distance** (D.M.D.)
method. We will now give a brief description of this method.

Suppose it is required to find the area of a
quadrilateral $ABCD$ shown in the figure. Let
SN be a line through one vertex of the figure
and meeting it at no other point. For convenience SN is taken as the north and south
line (the meridian) through the most western
vertex. The lines BB', CC', and DD' are
drawn perpendicular to SN. Then we have
two triangles $AB'B$ and $AD'D$, and two trap-
ezoids $B'BCC'$ and $C'CDD'$. Clearly the required area is equal to $B'BCC' + C'CDD' -
AB'B - AD'D$. The method consists in
finding the area of each of these and then the area of the figure.

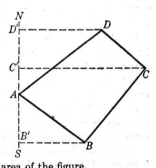

The D. M. D. of a course is the sum of the distances of its end
points from the meridian line SN.
Thus the D. M. D. of AB is $B'B$, of
BC is $B'B + C'C$, etc. It is easily
seen that the D. M. D. of a course
multiplied by its latitude gives twice
the area of the corresponding triangle
or trapezoid. The D. M. D.'s of the
courses are found in order around the
figure, the D. M. D. of any course
being found by means of the rule:

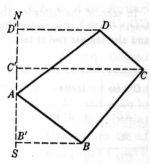

The D. M. D. of a course is equal to
the D. M. D. of the preceding course, plus the departure of the pre-
ceding course, plus the departure of the course itself.
The proof of this rule is left to the student.

This rule must be used, having regard to the sign of the departure of each
course. That is, the addition is algebraic. When the figure is taken as
suggested above, the D. M. D. of every course is positive.

Example 1. Find the area of the figure $ABCD$, using the data given in the
first three columns below.

Course	Bearing	Length	Lat.	Dept.	D.M.D.	Double Areas
AB	S. 41° 30′ E.	683.2	− 511.69	452.70	452.7	− 231,650
BC	N. 57° 20′ E.	847.8	457.60	713.69	1619.1	+ 740,900
CD	N. 21° 50′ W.	1084.0	1006.2	−403.15	1929.6	+1,941,600
DA	S. 38° 45′ W.	1220.5	− 951.84	−763.94	762.51	− 725,790

The double areas are found by multiplying the D. M. D.'s by the latitudes. Each result is carried to only five significant figures. The net area
is found by taking the algebraic sum of the double areas and then dividing
by 2. If the dimensions are given in feet, find the number of acres by dividing by 43,560, the number of square feet in an acre.

Note that in this example the sums of the positive latitudes and longitudes
are almost exactly equal to the sums of the negative latitudes and longitudes.
This would be exactly the case if the measurements were exact. In practice
these are usually not equal, however, due to inaccuracy of measuring, and
certain corrections, called balancing the survey, are necessary.

This will not be considered here, but information about it may be obtained
from any of the standard works on surveying.

EXERCISES

In each of the following the courses have the same bearing. Find the length of the course connecting the first and the last point in each example, and also the net rise or fall.

1

Course	Incline	Measured Length
AB	+ 3° 40′	398.4
BC	− 12° 10′	1222.0
CD	+ 6° 20′	1784.0

2

Course	Incline	Measured Length
AB	+ 8° 20′	816.3
BC	+ 13° 10′	513.7
CD	− 7° 30′	1481.0

3

Course	Incline	Measured Length
AB	− 4° 45′	186.7
BC	− 7° 40′	482.3
CD	− 11° 50′	712.5

4

Course	Incline	Measured Length
AB	+ 7° 20′	1983.0
BC	+ 9° 40′	784.2
CD	+ 3° 50′	1167.0

5

Course	Incline	Measured Length
AB	− 7° 25′	652.1
BC	− 3° 50′	361.4
CD	+ 4° 30′	229.6
DE	+ 28° 10′	814.7

6

Course	Incline	Measured Length
AB	+ 41° 20′	287.4
BC	+ 6° 15′	1296.4
CD	− 9° 10′	739.2
DE	− 2° 40′	889.3

Find the length and bearing of the closing course in each of the following level surveys.

7

Course	Bearing	Length of Course
AB	S. 54° 40′ W.	128.6
BC	S. 12° 3′ W.	84.7
CD	S. 71° E.	917.2
DE	N. 83° E.	346.3

8

Course	Bearing	Length of Course
AB	N. 37° 10′ E.	2862.0
BC	S. 42° 20′ E.	1363.0
CD	S. 8° 50′ E.	5916
DC	S. 21° 40′ W.	3815.0

Find the area in acres in each of the following, the lengths of the courses being given in feet. In each case it is necessary to find first the length and bearing of the closing course, using the method of §182.

9

Course	Bearing	Length of Course
AB	S. 18° 20' E.	817.2
BC	S. 83° 10' E.	1262.0
CD	N. 6° 50' W.	2281.0
DA		

10

Course	Bearing	Length of Course
AB	S. 49° E.	176.4
BC	N. 64° 20' E.	854.6
CD	N. 71° 10' W.	631.7
DA		

11

Course	Bearing	Length of Course
AB	S. 19° 20' E.	217.8
BC	S. 68° 30' E.	884.3
CD	N. 23° 50' E.	527.6
DE	N. 53° 10' W.	391.7
EA		

12

Course	Bearing	Length of Course
AB	S. 61° E.	1984.0
BC	S. 48° 50' E.	729.6
CD	N. 8° 10' W.	2162.0
DE	N. 29° W.	317.2
EA		

In practice the length and bearing of the closing course are measured directly when that is convenient, since this affords an excellent check on the whole survey. There may, however, be difficulties in measuring this course, such as are suggested in example 3, p. 89. In such cases the method suggested here must be used.

Problems in Physics

183. Components of force.—If a force f is acting along a line AB and if AC makes an angle α with AB, then there is a component of f acting along AC which is equal to $f \cos \alpha$. See also problems 14, 15, pages 63 and 64.

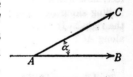

Thus if a weight resting on a horizontal table is subject to a pull of 50 lbs. in a direction making an angle of 25° with the surface of the table, then there is a force of 50 cos 25° tending to drag the weight along the surface of the table, while there is a force of 50 cos 65° tending to lift the weight vertically.

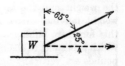

EXERCISES

1. If an automobile weighing 3500 pounds is standing on a road which slopes 15°, what force tends to pull it down the hill?

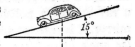

2. Two forces a and b act in the directions AB and AC and are represented in magnitude by these segments. Complete the parallelogram $ABDC$ and prove that the sum of the components of a and b along the diagonal AD is equal to AD.

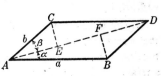

3. A weight of 340 pounds rests on an inclined plane which makes an angle of 7° with the horizontal. What is the force acting at right angles to this plane?

4. A guy-rope with a breaking strength of 6000 pounds makes an angle of 53° with a post at the point A. What part of this strength can be used to withstand a force acting at right angles to the post at this point and in the direction opposite to the side on which the rope is fastened?

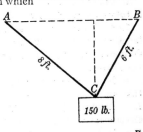

5. In the figure the points A and B are in the same horizontal line. If the ropes AC and BC, supporting a weight of 150 lbs., are 8 feet and 6 feet long, respectively, and if AB = 9 feet, what is the strain on each rope?

Suggestion: The horizontal component of the two forces must be equal.

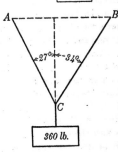

6. Using the dimensions and the weight indicated in the figure, what is the strain on each of the ropes AC and BC? If the distance AB is 7 feet, how much force must be added to the line pulling along BC to move the weight one foot to the right? In that case what would be the pull along AC?

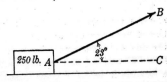

7. A weight of 250 lbs. rests on a horizontal table, and it is found that a pull of 75 lbs. in the direction AB is sufficient to overcome the friction between the weight and the table and start the weight moving. How many pounds of this force are pulling along the line AC which is parallel to the table? How many pounds act vertically upward so as to diminish weight resting on the table?

184. Reflection of light.—The path of a ray of light passing through a homogeneous medium is a straight line. When such a ray strikes a polished surface, such as a mirror, it is *reflected* according to the law that *the angle of incidence is equal to the angle of reflection.*

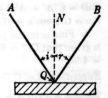

In the figure the ray AQ strikes the reflecting surface at Q and is reflected in the direction QB. If NQ is perpendicular to the surface (NQ is called the *normal* to the surface), then the law of reflection may be stated by saying that AQ and BQ make equal angles with NQ. The angles AQN and BQN are called, respectively, the angle of incidence (i) and the angle of reflection (r).

EXERCISES

1. Prove that if a mirror is rotated through an angle α, then a reflected ray is rotated through an angle 2α.

2. A light is placed at a point in the perpendicular to the center of a circular mirror and at a distance of 6 feet from it. If the mirror is 10 inches in diameter, find the angle between an incident and reflected ray at the edge of the mirror.

3. In an experiment a mirror is placed at B so that an object at A is seen at C. If $AB = 8.92$, $BC = 9.34$, and $AC = 10.63$, find the angle which the surface of the mirror makes with the line AB.

4. In the figure, AB represents a horizontal reflecting surface (the surface of a smooth lake), C represents the eye of an observer at a vertical distance a above the lake, D represents the top of a mountain, and E the reflection of the mountain in the lake as seen from C. The light from D striking the lake at F is reflected to C and C, F, E are in a straight line. At C the angle of elevation of D is α and the angle of depression of E is β. Find in terms of a, α, and β the distance from C to D.

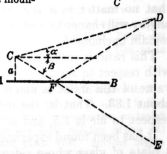

5. The mirror AB in a dresser swings about a support at C. This mirror is tipped back through an angle α so that the line AD is perpendicular to it. The lines CC' and CA and the angle α are measured and it is required to develop a formula in terms of these quantities giving the length of the line $C'D$.

If CC' is 6.84 feet, $CA = 1.8$ feet, and $\alpha = 11° 30'$, find $C'D$.

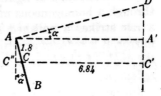

Suggestion:

$AA' = CC' + CC'' = CC' + AC$ sin α

and

$C'D = C'A' + A'D = C''A + AA'$ tan α

$\quad = CA \cos \alpha + (CC' + AC \sin \alpha) \tan \alpha.$

6. Find α in the preceding example, if it is given that $CC' = 6.84$, $AC = 1.8$ and $C'D = 4.36$.

Suggestion: Let $C'D = a$, $AC = b$, and $CC' = c$.

Then $a = b \cos \alpha + (c + b \sin \alpha) \tan \alpha$

$\quad$ or $a = b \sqrt{1 - \sin^2 \alpha} + (c + b \sin \alpha) \dfrac{\sin \alpha}{\sqrt{1 - \sin^2 \alpha}}.$

Then $a \sqrt{1 - \sin^2 \alpha} = b - b \sin^2 \alpha + c \sin \alpha + b \sin^2 \alpha = b + c \sin \alpha.$
Solve for $\sin \alpha$ and substitute values of a, b, c.

185. Refraction of light.—When light passes from one transparent medium into another, it does not generally continue in a straight line, but changes its direction.

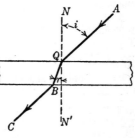

Thus if a ray of light is passing through air and meets a glass surface at Q, then that part of the light which is not reflected passes through the glass in the direction QB. If the line NQN' is perpendicular to the glass at Q, then $\angle AQN$ (i) is the **angle of incidence** and BQN' (r) is the **angle of refraction.**

It has been shown by a large number of experiments that for any particular kind of glass, the ratio at the right is the same for all different values of i. This means that no matter how the angle i is changed, the angle r will change in such a way that this ratio will remain unchanged.

$$\frac{\sin i}{\sin r}$$

This ratio is called the **index of refraction** of one substance with respect to another. For certain kinds of glass and air the value of this index is about 1.5, while for water and air it is about 1.33. That is, the index of refraction of the glass with respect to air is 1.5, and of water with respect to air is 1.33.

It has been found experimentally that if a ray passes through a plate of glass whose sides are parallel, then after emerging from the glass the path of the ray will be parallel to its original path. That is, in the figure, BC is parallel to AQ.

EXERCISES

1. In finding the index of refraction of glass with respect to air, i and r were found to be 40° and 24° 42′ respectively. What was the index?

2. Denoting the index of refraction by n, show how to find each one of the quantities, i, r, n when the other two are given.

3. A ray of light passes through a glass plate ⅜ of an inch thick. Find the amount by which this ray is displaced if $i = 35°\ 40′$ and the index of refraction is 1.49.

4. A ray of light is passed through a triangular prism as shown in the figure. What must be the angle of incidence of the ray AB if the index of refraction is 1.5, if a cross-section of the prism is an equilateral triangle, and if BC is parallel to one side of the prism? Under these same conditions find the angle through which the ray is turned in passing through the prism.

5. A stick partly submerged in water appears to change its direction at the point where it enters the water. What is the apparent direction of the stick under water if its real inclination to the surface is 47° and if the index of refraction of water with respect to air is 1.33?

MISCELLANEOUS THEOREMS AND PROBLEMS

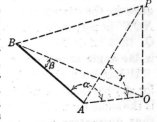

1. The line AB lies in a horizontal plane and P represents a mountain peak visible from both A and B. To find the height of P above the plane of AB and the horizontal distance from A to P, the following measurements are made: $AB = a$, $\angle OAB = \alpha$, $\angle ABO = \beta$, and $\angle OAP = \gamma$. Find formulas giving AO and OP in terms of a, α, β, γ.

Note that while O represents a point in the same horizontal plane with AB and lies inside the mountain, angles α, β, and γ can be measured directly.

2. Two parts of the roof of a house have their ridges at right angles to each other and meet, forming a valley. If each part has an incline of 45°, what is the incline of the line of intersection of these parts of the roof (the valley)?

3. A vertical wall is a feet high and stands on a horizontal plane. If α is the altitude of the sun and if the sun is in the same vertical plane with a line at right angles to the wall, what is the width of the shadow?

4. What is the width of the shadow in example 3 if the sun is in the same vertical plane with a horizontal line which makes an angle β with the wall?

5. A mountain slope makes an angle α with a horizontal plane. Find the incline of a path up the slope if its projection on the horizontal plane makes an angle β with the intersection of the slope and the horizontal plane at its foot.

6. In the preceding example what is the angle between the path and the intersection of the slope with the horizontal plane?

7. In general field-work in geology, and in particular in mining geology, there is a problem of frequent occurrence which amounts to the following. A surveyor is standing at a point A. Along a line AX there is level ground, and some- 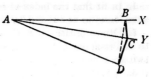 what to the right of this line there is a deep canyon in which a point D is visible. The points A, X, D determine a plane and he wishes to find the angle which this plane makes with the horizontal. To do this he measures the angle XAY so that the line AY is vertically above D. Then he measures the angle YAD. If $\angle XAY = \alpha$ and $DAY = \beta$, find a formula giving $\tan CBD$, the plane DCB being perpendicular to the line AX.

8. A pyramid with a square base of sides a has its apex a distance b above the base. Find the angle between the base and a line running from the apex to a corner of the base.

9. The legs of a tripod are $5\frac{1}{3}$ feet long and open so that the distance between two legs where they meet the ground is $4\frac{1}{2}$ feet. Find the angle which each leg makes with a plumb line from the apex of the tripod. The tripod is assumed to stand on level ground and the legs are assumed to come together at the apex.

10. In the figure, AB and BC represent the connecting-rod and dish-crank, respectively, of a steam engine. The angle which the dish-crank makes with the line AC is represented by α. Derive a formula giving the length of AC in terms of α, AB, and BC.

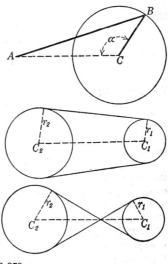

11. In the figure, C_1 and C_2 are the centers of two pulleys with radii r_1 and r_2. Find in terms of r_1, r_2 and $\overline{C_1C_2}$ the length of the belt required.

12. Using the same data as in example 11, find the length of the belt if it is to cross over as shown in the second figure.

13. Two straight stretches of railway, if extended, would meet at a point P, making an angle α. These two stretches are to be connected by means of a circular arc AB. If the radius of this arc is r, what is the distance from P to A?

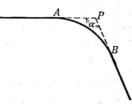

14. The length of a degree of longitude on the equator is 60 nautical miles. What is the length of a degree of longitude at latitude α, assuming the earth to be spherical?

15. Assuming the earth to be a sphere with radius r, derive a formula giving the distance from a point the distance h above the surface to the farthest point that can be seen on the surface.   If the radius of the earth is 3960 miles, how far out at sea can a mountain be seen if it is 15,000 feet high?

16. Three points, A, B, C, are known to be at distances a, b, c from each other as indicated in the figure.   From a point D these points subtend angles α and β as indicated.   The problem is to find the distances from D to each of the points A, B, and C.   (This is called Pothenot's problem.)

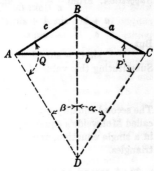

Suggestion: Since the distances a, b, c are known, the angles of the triangle ABC may be found and we may regard these as known. Denote the angles DCB and DAB by P and Q, respectively.   If these angles can be found, the problem is solved, for then the triangles DCB and DAB can be solved.

By the law of sines we have,

$$DB = a\,\frac{\sin P}{\sin \alpha} = c\,\frac{\sin Q}{\sin \beta}.$$

Hence,

$$\frac{\sin P}{\sin Q} = \frac{c \sin \alpha}{a \sin \beta}.$$

and

$$\frac{\sin P - \sin Q}{\sin P + \sin Q} = \frac{c \sin \alpha - a \sin \beta}{c \sin \alpha + a \sin \beta}.$$

By proceeding as in §90 we obtain

$$\frac{\tan \frac{1}{2}(P - Q)}{\tan \frac{1}{2}(P + Q)} = \frac{c \sin \alpha - a \sin \beta}{c \sin \alpha + a \sin \beta}. \tag{1}$$

But

$$P + Q + B + \alpha + \beta = 4 \text{ right } \angle\text{s}$$

and

$$\tfrac{1}{2}(P + Q) = 180° - \tfrac{1}{2}(B + \alpha + \beta).$$

Hence $\frac{1}{2}(P + Q)$ can be found.   Substituting this value in (1), $\frac{1}{2}(P - Q)$ is found.   Since $\frac{1}{2}(P + Q)$ and $\frac{1}{2}(P - Q)$ can be found, P and Q may be found.

17. If in the preceding example $a = 248.6$, $b = 381.2$, $c = 306.3$, $\alpha = 21°$ $35'$, $\beta = 19° 25'$, find DA, DB, DC.

18. If a projectile is fired at an initial velocity v_0 and at an angle α with the horizontal plane, then, neglecting atmospheric resistance, $y = v_0 t \sin \alpha - \frac{1}{2} g t^2$ and $x = v_0 t \cos \alpha$, where y is the vertical component of the motion, x the horizontal component, and t the time in seconds from the instant of firing.   Find the distance from the gun to the point where the projectile strikes the ground, the plane on which the firing takes place being horizontal.

Suggestion: If $y = 0$, then $t = \dfrac{2v_0}{g} \sin \alpha$.

Substitute this value of t in $x = v_0 t \cos \alpha$ and obtain $x = \dfrac{v_0^2}{g} \sin 2\alpha$.

What is the value of α which gives the maximum range?

19. Prove that in any triangle

$$\frac{a+b}{c} = \frac{\cos \frac{1}{2}(A-B)}{\sin \frac{1}{2}C}, \quad \frac{a-b}{c} = \frac{\sin \frac{1}{2}(A-B)}{\cos \frac{1}{2}C}.$$

Suggestion: From $\dfrac{a}{c} = \dfrac{\sin A}{\sin C}$ and $\dfrac{b}{c} = \dfrac{\sin B}{\sin C}$, we have, by adding,

$$\frac{a+b}{c} = \frac{\sin A + \sin B}{\sin C} = \frac{2 \sin \frac{1}{2}(A+B) \cos \frac{1}{2}(A-B)}{\sin C}.$$

But

$$\sin C = \sin (A+B) = 2 \sin \tfrac{1}{2}(A+B) \cos \tfrac{1}{2}(A+B).$$

Substituting this value of $\sin C$ and canceling,

$$\frac{a+b}{c} = \frac{\cos \frac{1}{2}(A-B)}{\cos \frac{1}{2}(A+B)} = \frac{\cos \frac{1}{2}(A-B)}{\sin \frac{1}{2}C}.$$

The second equality may be found in a similar manner. These formulas are called Mollweide's equations. Since all six elements of a triangle are involved in a single equation, these formulas are often used as checks in computing triangles.

20. A second proof of the law of tangents.

Let ABC be any triangle in which c is greater than b. With A as a center and c as radius, construct a semicircle meeting AC produced in D and E. Join B to D and E.

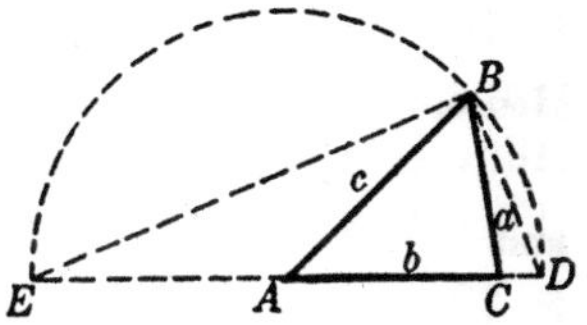

Then

$$EC = EA + b = c + b,$$
$$CD = AD - b = c - b.$$

Since $AB = AD$, $\angle ABD = \angle ADB$

and

$$\angle ABD + \angle ADB = 180° - \angle A = \angle B + \angle C.$$

Hence,

$$\angle ADB = \angle ABD = \tfrac{1}{2}(B+C),$$

and

$$\angle CBD = \angle ABD - \angle B = \tfrac{1}{2}(B+C) - \angle B = \tfrac{1}{2}(C-B).$$

But $\angle EBD$ is a right angle.

Hence,

$$\angle CEB = 90° - \angle CDB = 90° - \tfrac{1}{2}(C+B), \quad \sin CEB = \cos \tfrac{1}{2}(C+B).$$

Similarly,

$$\sin EBC = \cos \tfrac{1}{2}(C-B).$$

By the law of sines we have in the triangle CBD,

$$\frac{c-b}{a} = \frac{\sin CBD}{\sin CDB} = \frac{\sin \frac{1}{2}(C-B)}{\sin \frac{1}{2}(C+B)}.$$

Similarly from triangle ECB,

$$\frac{c+b}{a} = \frac{\sin EBC}{\sin CEB} = \frac{\cos \frac{1}{2}(C-B)}{\cos \frac{1}{2}(C+B)}.$$

Hence by division,

$$\frac{c-b}{c+b} = \frac{\tan \frac{1}{2}(C-B)}{\tan \frac{1}{2}(C+B)}.$$

186. LIST OF FORMULAS IN PLANE TRIGONOMETRY

P. 11

[1] $\sin A = \dfrac{\text{opposite side}}{\text{hypotenuse}} = \dfrac{a}{c}$ [4] $\csc A = \dfrac{\text{hypotenuse}}{\text{opposite side}} = \dfrac{c}{a}$.

[2] $\cos A = \dfrac{\text{adjacent side}}{\text{hypotenuse}} = \dfrac{b}{c}$ [5] $\sec A = \dfrac{\text{hypotenuse}}{\text{adjacent side}} = \dfrac{c}{b}$

[3] $\tan A = \dfrac{\text{opposite side}}{\text{adjacent side}} = \dfrac{a}{b}$ [6] $\cot A = \dfrac{\text{adjacent side}}{\text{opposite side}} = \dfrac{b}{a}$

P. 14

[7] $\sin A = \cos (90° - A)$ [10] $\cot A = \tan (90° - A)$

[8] $\cos A = \sin (90° - A)$ [11] $\sec A = \csc (90° - A)$

[9] $\tan A = \cot (90° - A)$ [12] $\csc A = \sec (90° - A)$

P. 59

[13] Departure = length of course × sine of bearing.

[14] Latitude = length of course × cosine of bearing.

P. 70

[15] $\sin A = \sin (180° - A)$ [18] $\cot A = -\cot (180° - A)$

[16] $\cos A = -\cos (180° - A)$ [19] $\sec A = -\sec (180° - A)$

[17] $\tan A = -\tan (180° - A)$ [20] $\csc A = \csc (180° - A)$

P. 73

[21] $c^2 = a^2 + b^2 - 2ab \cos C$

P. 74

[22] $\dfrac{\sin A}{\sin B} = \dfrac{a}{b},\qquad \dfrac{\sin B}{\sin C} = \dfrac{b}{c},\qquad \dfrac{\sin C}{\sin A} = \dfrac{c}{a}$

P. 78

[23] $\dfrac{\tan \frac{1}{2}(A - B)}{\tan \frac{1}{2}(A + B)} = \dfrac{a - b}{a + b}$

P. 80

[24] $S = \frac{1}{2} ac \sin B = \frac{1}{2} ab \sin C$ [25] $S = \dfrac{a^2 \sin B \sin C}{2 \sin A}$

P. 81

[26] $S = \frac{1}{2} ch = \sqrt{s (s - a)(s - b)(s - c)}$

[27] $r = \dfrac{1}{s}\sqrt{s (s - a)(s - b)(s - c)}$

[28] $R = \dfrac{abc}{4\sqrt{s (s - a)(s - b)(s - c)}}$

P. 82

[29] $\tan \frac{1}{2} A = \dfrac{r}{s - a}$

P. 96

[30] $\sin \theta = 1/\csc \theta$, $\csc \theta = 1/\sin \theta$

[31] $\cos \theta = 1/\sec \theta$, $\sec \theta = 1/\cos \theta$

[32] $\tan \theta = 1/\cot \theta$, $\cot \theta = 1/\tan \theta$

[33] $\tan \theta = \sin \theta / \cos \theta$ [34] $\cot \theta = \cos \theta / \sin \theta$

P. 97

[35] $\sin^2\theta + \cos^2\theta = 1$ [37] $\cot^2\theta + 1 = \csc^2\theta$

[36] $\tan^2\theta + 1 = \sec^2\theta$

P. 105

[38] $\sin (A + B) = \sin A \cos B + \cos A \sin B$

[39] $\sin (A - B) = \sin A \cos B - \cos A \sin B$

[40] $\cos (A + B) = \cos A \cos B - \sin A \sin B$

[41] $\cos (A - B) = \cos A \cos B + \sin A \sin B$

P. 108

[42] $\sin 2A = 2 \sin A \cos A$ [44] $\sin \dfrac{P}{2} = \pm\sqrt{\dfrac{1 - \cos P}{2}}$

[43] $\cos 2A = \cos^2 A - \sin^2 A$ [45] $\cos \dfrac{P}{2} = \pm\sqrt{\dfrac{1 + \cos P}{2}}$

P. 109

[46] $\tan (A + B) = \dfrac{\tan A + \tan B}{1 - \tan A \tan B}$

[47] $\tan (A - B) = \dfrac{\tan A - \tan B}{1 + \tan A \tan B}$

[48] $\cot (A + B) = \dfrac{\cot A \cot B - 1}{\cot A + \cot B}$

[49] $\cot (A - B) = \dfrac{\cot A \cot B + 1}{\cot B - \cot A}$

[50] $\tan 2A = \dfrac{2 \tan A}{1 - \tan^2 A}$ [51] $\cot 2A = \dfrac{\cot^2 A - 1}{2 \cot A}$

P. 111

[52] $\sin P + \sin Q = 2 \sin \dfrac{P + Q}{2} \cos \dfrac{P - Q}{2}$

[53] $\sin P - \sin Q = 2 \cos \dfrac{P + Q}{2} \sin \dfrac{P - Q}{2}$

[54] $\cos P + \cos Q = 2 \cos \dfrac{P + Q}{2} \cos \dfrac{P - Q}{2}$

[55] $\cos P - \cos Q = - 2 \sin \dfrac{P + Q}{2} \sin \dfrac{P - Q}{2}$

P. 112

[56] $\sin A \cos B = \frac{1}{2} \sin (A + B) + \frac{1}{2} \sin (A - B)$

[57] $\cos A \sin B = \frac{1}{2} \sin (A + B) - \frac{1}{2} \sin (A - B)$

[58] $\cos A \cos B = \frac{1}{2} \cos (A + B) + \frac{1}{2} \cos (A - B)$

[59] $\sin A \sin B = - \frac{1}{2} \cos (A + B) + \frac{1}{2} \cos (A - B)$

P. 113

[60] $\sin \dfrac{A}{2} = \sqrt{\dfrac{(s-b)\,(s-c)}{bc}}$

[61] $\cos \dfrac{A}{2} = \sqrt{\dfrac{s\,(s-a)}{bc}}$ [62] $\tan \dfrac{A}{2} = \sqrt{\dfrac{(s-b)\,(s-c)}{s\,(s-a)}}$

P. 121

[63] $\sin\,(\theta + 180°) = -\sin \theta$ [66] $\cot\,(\theta + 180°) = \cot \theta$

[64] $\cos\,(\theta + 180°) = -\cos \theta$ [67] $\sec\,(\theta + 180°) = -\sec \theta$

[65] $\tan\,(\theta + 180°) = \tan \theta$ [68] $\csc\,(\theta + 180°) = -\csc \theta$

P. 123

[69] $\sin\,(180° - \theta) = \sin \theta$ [72] $\cot\,(180° - \theta) = -\cot \theta$

[70] $\cos\,(180° - \theta) = -\cos \theta$ [73] $\sec\,(180° - \theta) = -\sec \theta$

[71] $\tan\,(180° - \theta) = -\tan \theta$ [74] $\csc\,(180° - \theta) = \csc \theta$

P. 135

[75] $\sin A = \sin\,[n\pi + (-1)^n A]$ [76] $\cos A = \cos\,(2n\pi \pm A)$

[77] $\sec A = \sec\,(2n\pi \pm A)$ [78] $\csc A = \csc\,[n\pi + (-1)^n A]$

P. 136

[79] $\tan A = \tan\,(n\pi + A)$ [80] $\cot A = \cot\,(n\pi + A)$

P. 150

[81] $(\cos \varphi + i \sin \varphi)^n = \cos n\varphi + i \sin n\varphi$

P. 152

[82] $\sqrt[n]{r\,(\cos \varphi + i \sin \varphi}} = r^{\frac{1}{n}} \left(\cos \dfrac{2k\pi + \varphi}{n} + i \sin \dfrac{2k + \varphi}{n} \right)$

P. 154

[83] $\cos n\varphi = \cos^n \varphi - \dfrac{n\,(n-1)}{2} \cos^{n-2} \varphi \sin^2 \varphi +$

$$\dfrac{n\,(n-1)\,(n-2)\,(n-3)}{2 \cdot 3 \cdot 4} \cos^{n-4} \varphi \sin^4 \varphi \ldots$$

[84] $\sin n\varphi = n \cos^{n-1} \varphi \sin \varphi -$

$$\dfrac{n\,(n-1)\,(n-2)}{2 \cdot 3} \cos^{n-3} \varphi \sin^3 \varphi +$$

$$\dfrac{n\,(n-1)\,(n-2)\,(n-3)\,(n-4)}{2 \cdot 3 \cdot 4 \cdot 5} \cos^{n-5} \varphi \sin^5 \varphi - \ldots$$

P. 156

[85] $\sin x = \dfrac{e^{xi} - e^{-xi}}{2i}$ [86] $\cos x = \dfrac{e^{xi} + e^{-xi}}{2}$

P. 159

[87] $\sin A = -\sin\,(-A)$ [88] $\cos A = \cos\,(-A)$

P. 160

[89] $\sin\,(A + 90°) = \cos A$ [91] $\cos\,(A + 90°) = -\sin A$

[90] $\sin\,(A - 90°) = -\cos A$ [92] $\cos\,(A - 90°) = \sin A$

CHAPTER XIV

SPHERICAL TRIGONOMETRY

SPHERICAL trigonometry deals with figures which lie on the surface of a sphere. The purpose of this chapter is to study the solution of certain problems related to spherical triangles.

187. Preliminary definitions and theorems.—The following definitions and theorems, which are developed in solid geometry, are given here for convenient reference. They are simple enough to be understood by a student who reads them for the first time.

The intersection of a plane with a sphere is a circle. If the plane passes through the center of the sphere, the circle is a **great circle** of the sphere; otherwise it is a **small circle** of the sphere.

A diameter of the sphere perpendicular to the plane of a circle

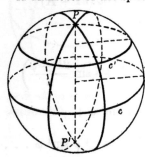

is called the **axis** of the circle. The points in which the axis of a circle meets the sphere are called the **poles** of the circle. In the figure P' and P are poles of each of the circles c' and c.

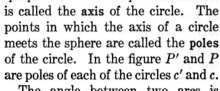

The angle between two arcs is measured by the angle between their tangents at a point of intersection. Thus in the second figure, $\angle APB$ is measured by $\angle RPT$.

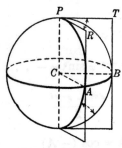

A **spherical triangle** is a figure on the surface of a sphere formed by three arcs of three great circles, not passing through the same point. Thus in the figure, APB is a spherical triangle.

Since the sides of such a triangle are arcs, they are measured in degrees or radians, as are also the angles of the triangle.

The sum of the sides of a spherical triangle is less than 360°.

The sum of the angles of a spherical triangle is greater than 180° and less than 540°.

189

188. The spherical triangle and its trihedral angle.—The planes determined by the three sides of a spherical triangle form a trihedral angle whose vertex is at the center of the sphere. If we designate the angles of the spherical triangle by A, B, and C, and the sides opposite them by a, b, and c, as we have done in plane trigonometry, then, O being the center of the sphere, it is evident from the fig-

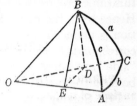

ure that $\angle AOB = c$, $\angle BOC = a$, $\angle COA = b$. Likewise the measure of the dihedral angle A-OB-C is equal to that of angle B; and similarly B-OC-$A = C$ and C-OA-$B = A$.

189. Polar triangles.—Using the vertices of a spherical tri-

angle ABC as poles, construct three great circles of the sphere. Denote by A' that point of intersection of the arcs whose poles are B and C which is on the same side of BC as A. Determine B' and C' in a similar way. Then $A'B'C'$ is the **polar triangle** of ABC.

The following theorems are proved in solid geometry.

If one spherical triangle is the polar triangle of a second, then the second is the polar triangle of the first.

An angle of any spherical triangle is the supplement of the opposite side in the polar triangle.

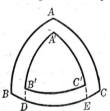

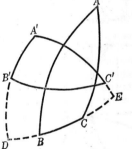

Thus if ABC and $A'B'C'$ are polar triangles and a, b, c and a', b', c' are the corresponding sides, then

$$A = 180° - a' \qquad A' = 180° - a$$
$$B = 180° - b' \qquad B' = 180° - b$$
$$C = 180° - c' \qquad C' = 180° - c$$

190. Duality in spherical trigonometry.—Suppose that any proposition has been proved for a spherical triangle ABC. Then this same proposition holds of the polar triangle $A'B'C'$ of ABC. Hence from the relations stated in §189, using §188, a proposition is deduced for ABC which, with certain changes in signs, corresponds to the original proposition except that "angle" and "side" are interchanged. This principle, known as **duality,** will be used frequently in the following pages.

191. Solving a spherical triangle.—It will appear in this chapter that if three of the six parts of a spherical triangle are given, the triangle is determined. Solving a spherical triangle is the process of finding the three unknown parts when three parts are known.

If the actual lengths of the sides are required, the radius of the sphere must be known. The determination of such length is then a simple process. A problem in spherical trigonometry is regarded as solved when the values of the sides and angles are found in circular measure.

192. Right spherical triangles.—If one of the angles of a spherical triangle is 90°, the triangle is designated as a **right spherical triangle.** In order to solve such a triangle two parts besides the right angle must be given. From the five parts, two known and three unknown, ten combinations of three may be formed. Each of the ten necessary formulas will contain three parts of the triangle. Obviously if any two of these parts are known, the third may be found.

In the derivation of these formulas, use is made of the trihedral angle corresponding to the given spherical triangle, as described in §188. Attention is called to the fact that in an equality of the form DOB = arc a, there is no implication that the two geometric entities can be made to coincide. The equality merely expresses the fact that the numerical measures of the two quantities are the same.

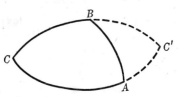

It will be noted that in the figure upon which this derivation of formulas is based, the arcs a and b are both less than 90°. For completeness the student should carry through the proof for the case in which both are greater than 90°. The figure at the left will suggest a method. Arcs CBC' and CAC' are great circle arcs of 180° each, forming a lune. Angles C and C' are equal. Arcs CB and BC' are supplementary, as are also CA and AC'.

193. Formulas for solving right spherical triangles.—Let ABC be a right spherical triangle whose right angle is at C. Let O be the center of its sphere, the radius of which is unity. Let both a and b be less than $90°$. Draw $BD \perp OC$ and $DE \perp OA$. Then BE is $\perp OA$.

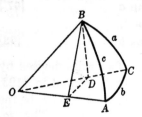

Note that in writing, as below, equations like $\angle DOB = a$ and $\angle EOB = c$ we mean to state that the radian measures of the angles and the arcs are the same.

In the figure

$$\angle DEB = A, \qquad \angle DOB = a, \qquad \angle EOB = c$$
$$DB = \sin a, \qquad OD = \cos a, \qquad EB = \sin c, \qquad OE = \cos c$$

$$\text{Then, } ED = DB \cot A = \sin a \cot A \tag{1}$$
$$ED = EB \cos A = \sin c \cos A \tag{2}$$
$$ED = OD \sin b = \cos a \sin b \tag{3}$$
$$ED = OE \tan b = \cos c \tan b \tag{4}$$

Equating in pairs these values of ED, we obtain the required ten formulas as follows.

From (1) and (2), $\sin a \cot A = \sin c \cos A$,

and hence $\qquad\qquad \sin a = \sin A \sin c$ $\qquad\qquad$ [93]

Then by symmetry, $\sin b = \sin B \sin c$ $\qquad\qquad$ [93']

From (1) and (3), $\sin a \cot A = \cos a \sin b$,

and hence $\qquad\qquad \sin b = \tan a \cot A$ $\qquad\qquad$ [94]

Then by symmetry, $\sin a = \tan b \cot B$ $\qquad\qquad$ [94']

From (1) and (4), $\sin a \cot A = \cos c \tan b$,

and hence $\qquad\qquad \cos c = \dfrac{\sin a \cot A}{\tan b}$.

Substituting from [94'],

$$\cos c = \frac{\tan b \cot B \cot A}{\tan b},$$

and hence, $\qquad\qquad \cos c = \cot A \cot B$ $\qquad\qquad$ [95]

From (2) and (3), $\sin c \cos A = \cos a \sin b$,

and therefore $\qquad\qquad \cos A = \dfrac{\cos a \sin b}{\sin c}$.

Substituting from [95],

$$\cos A = \sin B \cos a \qquad\qquad [96]$$

and by symmetry, $\qquad \cos B = \sin A \cos b \qquad\qquad [96']$

From (2) and (4), $\sin c \cos A = \cos c \tan b,$

or $\cos A = \cot c \tan b$ [97]

and by symmetry, $\cos B = \cot c \tan a$ [97']

From (3) and (4), $\cos a \sin b = \cos c \tan b,$

and hence $\cos c = \cos a \cos b$ [98]

194. Napier's rules of circular parts.—Two rules devised by Napier help in remembering the ten formulas stated in §193. In a right spherical triangle ABC, with sides a, b, c, let C be the

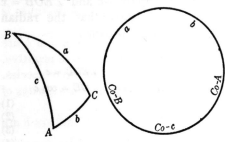

right angle. The so-called circular parts of this triangle are the sides a and b, and the complements of the angles A and B and of the side c. Denote these complements by Co-A, Co-B and Co-c respectively and arrange the circular parts in order as indicated in the circle.

Corresponding to any one of the circular parts there are two **adjacent parts** and two others which are referred to as **opposite parts**.

Then Napier's rules are:

(1) *The sine of any circular part is equal to the product of the tangents of the two adjacent circular parts.*

(2) *The sine of any circular part is equal to the product of the cosines of the two opposite circular parts.*

Applying rule (1) to the circular part b, for example, we have

$$\sin b = \tan (Co\text{-}A) \tan a$$

or $\sin b = \tan a \cot A.$

From rule (2),

$$\sin b = \cos (Co\text{-}c) \cos (Co\text{-}B)$$

or $\sin b = \sin c \sin B.$

These are formulas [94] and [93'].

The repetition of a in the words *tangent* and *adjacent*, and of o in *cosine* and *opposite*, will be a further aid to the memory.

Exercise: Develop each of the formulas of §193 by using Napier's rules

195. Species.—If each of two parts of a spherical triangle is less than 90°, or each greater than 90°, then the parts are said to be of the same species. Formulas [93] to [98] taken as a whole determine whether a part found is in the first or second quadrant, but in an individual case, a part found from its sine is indeterminate. The following rules determine the quadrant for all cases in right triangles except one. This case, the ambiguous case, is considered in the next paragraph.

RULE I: *The hypotenuse is less than 90° when the sides of the right angle are of the same species, otherwise the hypotenuse is greater than 90°; and conversely.*

For by [98], cos c = cos a cos b. Hence, when a and b are in the same quadrant, cos c is positive; otherwise it is negative. Conversely if cos c is positive, a and b are of the same species.

RULE II: *An oblique angle and its opposite side are always of the same species.*

For by [96'], sin A = cos B/cos b. Hence cos B and cos b are of like sign; that is, B and b are of the same species.

196. The ambiguous case.—If the parts given are a side and its opposite angle, the remaining parts are found from their sines. Hence there are two supplementary values for each. The relation of the

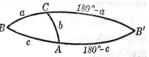

two triangles is shown in the figure for the case in which B and b are the given parts. B and B' are equal, BB' being a lune.

197. Use of logarithms.—The formulas developed for solving spherical triangles are all suitable for logarithmic computation and the computation is carried out as in plane trigonometry.

When negative values occur, the numerical results may still be found by using logarithms, the quality being determined by the number of negative factors. In such cases, the letter n may well be placed after any logarithm, the antilogarithm of which is negative. The quality of the result is then immediately determinable. In the solution of Example 3 on page 196 a suitable form is shown.

When the characteristic of a logarithm is negative, − 10 may be written after the mantissa. In this work there is seldom any ambiguity in such cases. It is therefore possible to omit the − 10 in all cases. In the examples worked out in the following pages this procedure has been adopted.

198. Solving right triangles.—If two parts of a spherical triangle are given, formulas involving each of the unknown parts with both of the known parts can be formed by the use of Napier's rules. From these the unknown parts may be found, and then as a check on these, the formula involving all three of them may be applied. The quadrant in which each magnitude lies may be determined by the principles of §195 if the formula used leaves any ambiguity. The form of the work will be clear from illustrative examples.

Example 1. Solve the spherical triangle ABC given: $C = 90°$, $c = 78°$ 25', $A = 36° 42' 30''$.

Solution: Using formulas from §193 (or Napier's rules), $\sin a = \sin A \sin c$ from [93], $\tan b = \cos A \tan c$ from [97], $\cot B = \cos c \tan A$ from [95]. Use $\sin a = \tan b \cot B$ from [94'] as a check.

log sin A = 9.77652	log cos c = 9.30275
log sin c = 9.99106	log tan A = 9.87251
log sin a = 9.76758	log cot B = 9.17526
a = 35° 50' 37''	B = 81° 29' 6''
or 144° 9' 23''	

log cos A = 9.90401	*check*
log tan c = 0.68832	log tan b = 0.59233
log tan b = 0.59233	log cot B = 9.17526
b = 75° 39' 31''	log sin a = 9.76759

Since $c < 90°$ and $b < 90°$, $a < 90°$. Hence the unknown parts in the triangle are $a = 35° 50' 37''$, $B = 81° 29' 6''$, $b = 75° 39' 31''$.

Example 2. Solve the right spherical triangle ABC, given the following. $C = 90°$, $b = 136° 35'$, $B = 107° 21'$.

Solution: The formulas to be used are

$\sin a = \tan b \cot B$	$\sin A = \cos B/\cos b$
$\sin c = \sin b/\sin B$	(*check*) $\sin a = \sin A \sin c$
log tan b = 9.97598 (n)	log cos B = 9.47452 (n)
log cot B = 9.49474 (n)	log cos b = 9.86116 (n)
log sin a = 9.47072	log sin A = 9.61336
a = 17° 11' 40''	A = 24° 14' 21''
or 162° 48' 20''	or 155° 45' 39''

log sin b = 9.83715	*check*
log sin B = 9.97978	log sin A = 9.61336
log sin c = 9.85737	log sin c = 9.85737
c = 46° 3' 35''	log sin a = 9.47073
or 133° 56' 25''	

When the smaller value of c is used then a and b are of the same species; when the larger value is used, a and b are of different species. In both cases A must be of the same species as a. Hence the results are

$$\begin{cases} c_1 = 46° \ 3' \ 35'' \\ a_1 = 162° \ 48' \ 20'' \\ A_1 = 155° \ 45' \ 39'' \end{cases} \quad \text{and} \quad \begin{cases} c_2 = 133° \ 56' \ 25'' \\ a_2 = 17° \ 11' \ 40'' \\ A_2 = 24° \ 14' \ 21'' \end{cases}$$

Example 3. Solve the right spherical triangle ABC given $c = 112° \ 25'$, $A = 36° \ 42' \ 30''$.

Solution:

$$\sin a = \sin A \sin c \qquad\qquad \tan b = \cos A \tan c$$
$$\cot B = \cos c \tan A \qquad (check) \ \sin a = \tan b \cot B$$

log sin A = 9.77652	log cos A = 9.90401
log sin c = 9.96588	log tan c = 0.38456 (n)
log sin a = 9.74240	log tan b = 0.28857 (n)
$a = 33° \ 32' \ 41''$	$b = 117° \ 13' \ 41''$
or $\quad 146° \ 27' \ 19''$	

By §195, the latter is not admissible.

log cos c = 9.58131 (n)		*check*
log tan A = 9.87251	log tan b = 0.28857 (n)
log cot B = 9.45382 (n)	log cot B = 9.45382 (n)
$B = 105° \ 52' \ 19''$	log sin a = 9.74239

EXERCISES

Solve the following triangles, C in each case being $90°$.

GROUP A

1. $\begin{cases} a = 28° \ 41' \\ B = 71° \ 32' \end{cases}$ 5. $\begin{cases} b = 29° \ 55' \\ B = 42° \ 18' \end{cases}$ 9. $\begin{cases} b = 111° \ 33' \\ A = 49° \ 9' \end{cases}$

2. $\begin{cases} a = 81° \ 44' \\ b = 42° \ 12' \end{cases}$ 6. $\begin{cases} c = 82° \ 38' \\ A = 36° \ 11' \end{cases}$ 10. $\begin{cases} c = 12° \ 18' \\ B = 67° \ 21' \end{cases}$

3. $\begin{cases} A = 21° \ 19' \\ b = 112° \ 15' \end{cases}$ 7. $\begin{cases} b = 117° \ 30' \\ c = 83° \ 48' \end{cases}$ 11. $\begin{cases} A = 62° \ 35' \\ c = 71° \ 17' \end{cases}$

4. $\begin{cases} a = 121° \ 48' \\ c = 50° \ 29' \end{cases}$ 8. $\begin{cases} B = 20° \ 58' \\ c = 45° \ 13' \end{cases}$ 12. $\begin{cases} a = 39° \ 20' \\ b = 70° \ 29' \end{cases}$

GROUP B

1. $\begin{cases} b = 98° \ 8' \\ c = 77° \ 42' \end{cases}$ 5. $\begin{cases} c = 120° \ 18' \\ B = 67° \ 48' \end{cases}$ 9. $\begin{cases} b = 53° \ 15' \\ a = 59° \ 45' \end{cases}$

2. $\begin{cases} B = 61° \ 21' \\ a = 76° \ 14' \end{cases}$ 6. $\begin{cases} a = 48° \ 47' \\ c = 74° \ 51' \end{cases}$ 10. $\begin{cases} B = 70° \ 40' \\ c = 79° \ 13' \end{cases}$

3. $\begin{cases} a = 49° \ 45' \\ b = 61° \ 18' \end{cases}$ 7. $\begin{cases} c = 79° \ 50' \\ B = 49° \ 7' \end{cases}$ 11. $\begin{cases} A = 80° \ 17' \\ c = 85° \ 25' \end{cases}$

4. $\begin{cases} b = 37° \ 40' \\ A = 77° \ 24' \end{cases}$ 8. $\begin{cases} a = 28° \ 45' \\ A = 64° \ 20' \end{cases}$ 12. $\begin{cases} A = 74° \ 5' \\ B = 62° \ 55' \end{cases}$

199. Quadrantal and isosceles triangles.—A quadrantal spherical triangle is one which has a side equal to 90°. Hence the polar triangle of a quadrantal triangle is a right triangle. Thus, in order to solve a quadrantal triangle, the polar triangle may be solved, and the values of the unknown parts of the quadrantal triangle are then known immediately.

An isosceles spherical triangle has two sides equal. The arc drawn from the vertex perpendicular to the base bisects the base and the vertical angle, forming two equal right spherical triangles. If three parts of the isosceles triangle are given, three parts of the right triangles are known, hence the remaining parts may all be found by using the formulas for solving right triangles.

EXERCISES

Solve the triangles of which parts are given.

1. $\begin{cases} a = 51° 31' \\ b = 63° 20' \\ c = 90° \end{cases}$
   6. $\begin{cases} B = 65° 11' \\ A = 85° 22' \\ c = 90° \end{cases}$
   11. $\begin{cases} A = 119° 30' \\ B = 45° 40' \\ c = 90° \end{cases}$

2. $\begin{cases} a = 38° 41' \\ B = 77° 12' \\ c = 90° \end{cases}$
   7. $\begin{cases} b = 71° 13' \\ A = 118° 30' \\ c = 90° \end{cases}$
   12. $\begin{cases} a = 100° 40' \\ b = 112° 19' \\ c = 90° \end{cases}$

3. $\begin{cases} b = 82° 25' \\ C = 68° 35' \\ c = 90° \end{cases}$
   8. $\begin{cases} a = 112° \\ b = 90° \\ c = 90° \end{cases}$
   13. $\begin{cases} b = 67° 43' \\ C = 53° 18' \\ c = 90° \end{cases}$

4. $\begin{cases} b = 96° 45' \\ B = 38° 17' \\ c = 90° \end{cases}$
   9. $\begin{cases} b = 53° 55' \\ B = 77° 50' \\ c = 90° \end{cases}$
   14. $\begin{cases} A = 24° 15' \\ B = 43° 42' \\ c = 90° \end{cases}$

5. $\begin{cases} B = 18° 50' \\ C = 48° 29' \\ c = 90° \end{cases}$
   10. $\begin{cases} a = 37° 35' \\ C = 82° 12' \\ c = 90° \end{cases}$
   15. $\begin{cases} b = 62° 15' \\ A = 104° 10' \\ c = 90° \end{cases}$

ISOSCELES TRIANGLES

In the following △s, $a = b$ and $A = B$. Find the parts not given.

1. $\begin{cases} b = 24° 48' \\ B = 39° 22' \end{cases}$
   5. $\begin{cases} a = 72° 50' \\ A = 56° 50' \end{cases}$
   9. $\begin{cases} a = 58° 27' \\ B = 26° 43' \end{cases}$

2. $\begin{cases} a = 82° 15' \\ C = 130° 24' \end{cases}$
   6. $\begin{cases} b = 19° 42' \\ c = 46° 20' \end{cases}$
   10. $\begin{cases} c = 48° 42' \\ C = 108° 18' \end{cases}$

3. $\begin{cases} b = 78° 18' \\ B = 98° 36' \end{cases}$
   7. $\begin{cases} b = 59° 19' \\ C = 69° 29' \end{cases}$
   11. $\begin{cases} A = 72° 19' \\ C = 55° 26' \end{cases}$

4. $\begin{cases} a = 16° 38' \\ c = 30° 46' \end{cases}$
   8. $\begin{cases} c = 99° 10' \\ C = 78° 24' \end{cases}$
   12. $\begin{cases} a = 42° 38' \\ A = 59° 21' \end{cases}$

200. Solution of general spherical triangles.—For spherical triangles in general three parts must be given to determine the triangle. Formulas for finding the remaining parts when any three parts are given will be developed in the following paragraphs.

201. The law of sines.—*The sines of the sides of a spherical triangle are proportional to the sines of the opposite angles.*

In symbols, $$\frac{\sin a}{\sin A} = \frac{\sin b}{\sin B} = \frac{\sin c}{\sin C} \qquad [99]$$

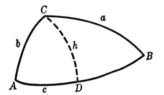 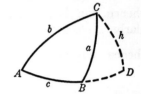

Proof: In the triangle ABC (either figure) drop the perpendicular h from the vertex C to the opposite side AB (extended, if necessary).

Then by Napier's rules or [93], in the right triangle ADC,

$$\sin h = \sin b \sin A,$$

and in triangle CDB,

$$\sin h = \sin a \sin B.$$

Hence $\sin b \sin A = \sin a \sin B,$

or

$$\frac{\sin a}{\sin A} = \frac{\sin b}{\sin B}.$$

Similarly we may prove

$$\frac{\sin a}{\sin A} = \frac{\sin c}{\sin C} \text{ and } \frac{\sin b}{\sin B} = \frac{\sin c}{\sin C}.$$

This law may be used for finding one of the remaining parts of any spherical triangle when two *opposite* parts of the triangle are among the three that are known.

202. The law of cosines.—(*a*) *The cosine of any side of a spherical triangle is equal to the product of the cosines of the other two sides plus the product of the sines of these two sides and the cosine of their included angle,* and

(b) *The cosine of any angle of a spherical triangle is equal to minus the product of the cosines of the other two angles plus the product of the sines of these two angles and the cosine of their included side.*

Proof of (a): It is evident from the figures, page 198, that when direction is considered

$$c = AD + DB, \text{ or } DB = c - AD.$$

From Napier's rules, or [97],

$$\cos A = \tan AD \cot b$$

and hence $\tan AD = \tan b \cos A.$

Similarly $\cos b = \cos h \cos AD$

and hence $\cos AD = \dfrac{\cos b}{\cos h}.$

But $\sin AD = \tan AD \cos AD$
$$= \tan b \cos A \cos b / \cos h.$$

Also $\cos a = \cos h \cos DB$
$$= \cos h \cos (c - AD)$$
$$= \cos h \cos c \cos AD + \cos h \sin c \sin AD.$$

Substituting in this last equation for $\cos AD$ and $\sin AD$,

$$\cos a = \frac{\cos h \cos c \cos b}{\cos h} + \frac{\cos h \sin c \tan b \cos A \cos b}{\cos h},$$

or $\cos a = \cos b \cos c + \sin b \sin c \cos A$ [100]

Similarly,

$$\cos b = \cos c \cos a + \sin c \sin a \cos B \qquad [100']$$
$$\cos c = \cos a \cos b + \sin a \sin b \cos C \qquad [100'']$$

This is the law of cosines for sides.

Proof of (b): If $A'B'C'$ is the polar triangle of any given triangle ABC, then formula [100] holds for $A'B'C'$.

That is, $\cos a' = \cos b' \cos c' + \sin b' \sin c' \cos A'.$
But $\cos a' = -\cos A, \cos b' = -\cos B, \cos c' = -\cos C,$
$\sin b' = \sin B, \sin C' = \sin C,$ and $\cos A' = -\cos a.$
Hence $\cos A = -\cos B \cos C + \sin B \sin C \cos a$ [101]
Similarly, $\cos B = -\cos C \cos A + \sin C \sin A \cos b$ [101']
$\cos C = -\cos A \cos B + \sin A \sin B \cos c$ [101'']

This is the law of cosines for angles.

203. The half-angle formulas.—From [100],

$$\cos A = \frac{\cos a - \cos b \cos c}{\sin b \sin c}.$$

Hence $1 - \cos A = \dfrac{\sin b \sin c - \cos a + \cos b \cos c}{\sin b \sin c}$

$$= \frac{\cos (b - c) - \cos a}{\sin b \sin c} \qquad \text{by [41]}$$

$$= \frac{2 \sin \frac{1}{2} (a + b - c) \sin \frac{1}{2} (a - b + c)}{\sin b \sin c} \qquad \text{by [55]}$$

If we let $a + b + c = 2s$, so that $\frac{1}{2} (a + b - c) = s - c$, $\frac{1}{2} (a + c - b) = s - b$ and $\frac{1}{2} (b + c - a) = s - a$, we have

$$1 - \cos A = \frac{2 \sin (s - b) \sin (s - c)}{\sin b \sin c}.$$

Similarly $1 + \cos A = \dfrac{\sin b \sin c + \cos a - \cos b \cos c}{\sin b \sin c}$

$$= \frac{\cos a - \cos (b + c)}{\sin b \sin c}$$

$$= \frac{2 \sin \frac{1}{2} (a + b + c) \sin \frac{1}{2} (b + c - a)}{\sin b \sin c}$$

$$= \frac{2 \sin s \sin (s - a)}{\sin b \sin c}.$$

But $\quad \sin^2 \dfrac{A}{2} = \dfrac{1 - \cos A}{2}$ and $\cos^2 \dfrac{A}{2} = \dfrac{1 + \cos A}{2}.$ (§124)

Hence,

$$\sin^2 \frac{A}{2} = \frac{\sin (s - b) \sin (s - c)}{\sin b \sin c} \qquad (1)$$

and

$$\cos^2 \frac{A}{2} = \frac{\sin s \sin (s - a)}{\sin b \sin c}. \qquad (2)$$

By dividing these and taking square roots,

$$\tan \frac{A}{2} = \sqrt{\frac{\sin (s - b) \sin (s - c)}{\sin s \sin (s - a)}}$$

$$= \frac{1}{\sin (s - a)} \sqrt{\frac{\sin (s - a) \sin (s - b) \sin (s - c)}{\sin s}}.$$

If we now denote this radical by r, we obtain

$$\tan \frac{A}{2} = \frac{r}{\sin (s - a)} \qquad [102]$$

Similarly, $\tan \dfrac{B}{2} = \dfrac{r}{\sin (s-b)}$ [102'] and $\tan \dfrac{C}{2} = \dfrac{r}{\sin (s-c)}$ [102'']

From these formulas, the three angles may be found when the three sides are given.

204. The half-side formulas.—If A', B', C', a', b', c' are the parts of the polar triangle of ABC, then by [102]

$$\tan \tfrac{1}{2} A' = \frac{r'}{\sin (s' - a')} \tag{1}$$

where $r' = \sqrt{\dfrac{\sin (s' - a') \sin (s' - b') \sin (s' - c')}{\sin s}}$

and $\qquad s' = \tfrac{1}{2} (a' + b' + c')$.

Then $s' = \tfrac{1}{2} (180° - A + 180° - B + 180° - C)$

$\qquad\quad = 270° - \tfrac{1}{2} (A + B + C) = 270° - S$,

where $\qquad S = \tfrac{1}{2} (A + B + C)$.

Then $\quad s' - a' = 270° - S - 180° + A = 90° - (S - A)$,

and similar relations for b' and c'. Then we have

$$r' = \sqrt{\frac{\cos (S - A) \cos (S - B) \cos (S - C)}{- \cos S}},$$

which we will denote by $1/R$.

Furthermore,

$$\tan \tfrac{1}{2} A' = \tan \left(90° - \frac{a}{2}\right) = \cot \frac{a}{2}.$$

Substituting in (1) above,

$$\cot \tfrac{1}{2} a = \frac{1}{R \cos (S - A)}$$

or $\qquad\qquad \tan \tfrac{1}{2} a = R \cos (S - A)$ $\qquad$ [103]

Similarly $\qquad \tan \tfrac{1}{2} b = R \cos (S - B)$ $\qquad$ [103']

and $\qquad\qquad \tan \tfrac{1}{2} c = R \cos (S - C)$ $\qquad$ [103'']

where $\quad R = \sqrt{\dfrac{- \cos S}{\cos (S - A) \cos (S - B) \cos (S - C)}}$.

In this expression, $\cos S$ is negative since S is always greater than 90° and less than 270°.

Since $a' < b' + c'$,

$\qquad\qquad 180° - A < 180° - B + 180° - C$

and $\qquad B + C - A < 180°$ so that $S - A < 90°$.

But $\qquad B + C - A > - 180°$, so that $S - A > - 90°$.

Hence $\cos (S - A)$ is positive. In a similar way it is seen that $\cos (S - B)$ and $\cos (S - C)$ are also positive. The value of R is accordingly real in all cases.

Formulas [103] to [103''] are sufficient for finding the three sides when the three angles are given.

205. Napier's analogies.—Dividing $\tan \dfrac{A}{2}$ by $\tan \dfrac{B}{2}$ in [102] and [102'],

$$\frac{\tan \dfrac{A}{2}}{\tan \dfrac{B}{2}} = \frac{\sin (s - b)}{\sin (s - a)}.$$

Taking this proportion by composition and division,

$$\frac{\tan \dfrac{A}{2} + \tan \dfrac{B}{2}}{\tan \dfrac{A}{2} - \tan \dfrac{B}{2}} = \frac{\sin (s - b) + \sin (s - a)}{\sin (s - b) - \sin (s - a)}.$$

Substituting for tangent in terms of sine and cosine, and applying formulas [52] and [53] to the right member,

$$\frac{\sin \dfrac{A}{2} \cos \dfrac{B}{2} + \cos \dfrac{A}{2} \sin \dfrac{B}{2}}{\sin \dfrac{A}{2} \cos \dfrac{B}{2} - \cos \dfrac{A}{2} \sin \dfrac{B}{2}} = \frac{\sin \frac{1}{2} (2s - a - b) \cos \frac{1}{2} (a - b)}{\cos \frac{1}{2} (2s - a - b) \sin \frac{1}{2} (a - b)}.$$

That is,

$$\frac{\sin \frac{1}{2} (A + B)}{\sin \frac{1}{2} (A - B)} = \frac{\tan \dfrac{c}{2}}{\tan \frac{1}{2} (a - b)} \qquad [104]$$

Again, multiplying $\tan \dfrac{A}{2}$ by $\tan \dfrac{B}{2}$ in [102] and [102'],

$$\tan \frac{A}{2} \tan \frac{B}{2} = \frac{\sin (s - c)}{\sin s},$$

or

$$\frac{\sin \dfrac{A}{2} \sin \dfrac{B}{2}}{\cos \dfrac{A}{2} \cos \dfrac{B}{2}} = \frac{\sin (s - c)}{\sin s}.$$

Then taking the proportion by division and composition and applying [52] and [53],

$$\frac{\cos \dfrac{A}{2} \cos \dfrac{B}{2} - \sin \dfrac{A}{2} \sin \dfrac{B}{2}}{\cos \dfrac{A}{2} \cos \dfrac{B}{2} + \sin \dfrac{A}{2} \sin \dfrac{B}{2}} = \frac{\sin s - \sin (s - c)}{\sin s + \sin (s - c)}$$

$$= \frac{\cos \frac{1}{2} (2s - c) \sin \dfrac{c}{2}}{\sin \frac{1}{2} (2s - c) \cos \dfrac{c}{2}}.$$

That is,

$$\frac{\cos \frac{1}{2}(A+B)}{\cos \frac{1}{2}(A-B)} = \frac{\tan \frac{c}{2}}{\tan \frac{1}{2}(a+b)} \qquad [105]$$

By using the values of $\tan \frac{a}{2}$ and $\tan \frac{b}{2}$ from [103] and [103'], and proceeding in a similar manner we obtain

$$\frac{\sin \frac{1}{2}(a+b)}{\sin \frac{1}{2}(a-b)} = \frac{\cot \frac{C}{2}}{\tan \frac{1}{2}(A-B)} \qquad [104']$$

$$\frac{\cos \frac{1}{2}(a+b)}{\cos \frac{1}{2}(a-b)} = \frac{\cot \frac{C}{2}}{\tan \frac{1}{2}(A+B)} \qquad [105']$$

The details of the proof of these two formulas are left to the student.

Formulas [104], [105], [104'], and [105'] are known as **Napier's analogies.** From these, the third side and third angle can be found when two sides and the angles opposite are known.

EXERCISES

1. Derive formula [104'] for the triangle ABC on the assumption that formula [104] holds for the polar triangle $A'B'C'$.

Solution: For the polar triangle, formula [104] is

$$\frac{\sin \frac{1}{2}(A'+B')}{\sin \frac{1}{2}(A'-B')} = \frac{\tan \frac{1}{2}c'}{\tan \frac{1}{2}(a'-b')}$$

From the relations between parts of polar triangles, $A' = 180° - a$, $B' = 180° - b$, $a' = 180° - A$, $b' = 180° - B$, $c' = 180° - C$.

Substituting, we have

$$\frac{\sin \frac{1}{2}(180° - a + 180° - b)}{\sin \frac{1}{2}(180° - a - 180° + b)} = \frac{\tan \frac{1}{2}(180° - C)}{\tan \frac{1}{2}(180° - A - 180° + B)}$$

That is,

$$\frac{\sin [180° - \frac{1}{2}(a+b)]}{\sin \frac{1}{2}(b-a)} = \frac{\tan \left(90° - \frac{C}{2}\right)}{\tan \frac{1}{2}(B-A)}$$

Hence,

$$\frac{\sin \frac{1}{2}(a+b)}{\sin \frac{1}{2}(a-b)} = \frac{\cot \frac{C}{2}}{\tan \frac{1}{2}(A-B)}, \text{ which is [104']}.$$

2. Derive formula [105'] from [105] by the use of the polar triangle.

206. Gauss's equations, or Delambre's analogies.—From (1) and (2) of §203 we obtain

$$\sin \frac{A}{2} \cos \frac{B}{2} = \frac{\sin (s - b)}{\sin c} \sqrt{\frac{\sin s \sin (s - c)}{\sin a \sin b}}$$

$$= \frac{\sin (s - b)}{\sin c} \cos \frac{C}{2}$$

and

$$\cos \frac{A}{2} \sin \frac{B}{2} = \frac{\sin (s - a)}{\sin c} \sqrt{\frac{\sin s \sin (s - c)}{\sin a \sin b}}$$

$$= \frac{\sin (s - a)}{\sin c} \cos \frac{C}{2}.$$

Adding and applying [38] and [52] we have,

$$\sin \frac{A + B}{2} = \frac{\sin (s - a) + \sin (s - b)}{\sin c} \cos \frac{C}{2}$$

$$= \frac{2 \sin \frac{1}{2} (2s - a - b) \cos \frac{1}{2} (b - a)}{2 \sin \frac{c}{2} \cos \frac{c}{2}} \cos \frac{C}{2}$$

$$= \frac{2 \sin \frac{1}{2} c \cos \frac{1}{2} (a - b)}{2 \sin \frac{c}{2} \cos \frac{c}{2}} \cos \frac{C}{2}.$$

Hence

$$\sin \frac{A + B}{2} = \frac{\cos \frac{1}{2} (a - b)}{\cos \frac{c}{2}} \cos \frac{C}{2} \qquad [106]$$

Similarly,

$$\sin \frac{A - B}{2} = \frac{\sin \frac{1}{2} (a - b)}{\sin \frac{c}{2}} \cos \frac{C}{2} \qquad [106']$$

$$\cos \frac{A + B}{2} = \frac{\cos \frac{1}{2} (a + b)}{\cos \frac{c}{2}} \sin \frac{C}{2} \qquad [106'']$$

and

$$\cos \frac{A - B}{2} = \frac{\sin \frac{1}{2} (a + b)}{\sin \frac{c}{2}} \sin \frac{C}{2} \qquad [106''']$$

These formulas are known as **Gauss's equations** or **Delambre's analogies.**

EXERCISE

Show in detail the derivation of the last three of the above formulas.

207. A rule of species.—When two of the three given parts of a triangle are opposite elements, the law of sines is applicable, in some such form as:

$$\sin A = \frac{\sin a \sin B}{\sin b}$$

Since there are two values of A both less than 180°, the possibility of ambiguity arises, as was the case in the solution of plane triangles.

In formula [105]

$$\frac{\cos \frac{1}{2} (A + B)}{\cos \frac{1}{2} (A - B)} = \frac{\tan \frac{1}{2} c}{\tan \frac{1}{2} (a + b)},$$

$\tan \frac{1}{2} c$ and $\cos \frac{1}{2} (A - B)$ are always positive since $\frac{1}{2} c$ and $\frac{1}{2} (A - B)$ are less than 90°. It follows that $\cos \frac{1}{2} (A + B)$ and $\tan \frac{1}{2} (a + b)$ are of the same sign. We therefore have the following rule of species.

Half the sum of two angles of a spherical triangle is of the same species as half the sum of the opposite sides.

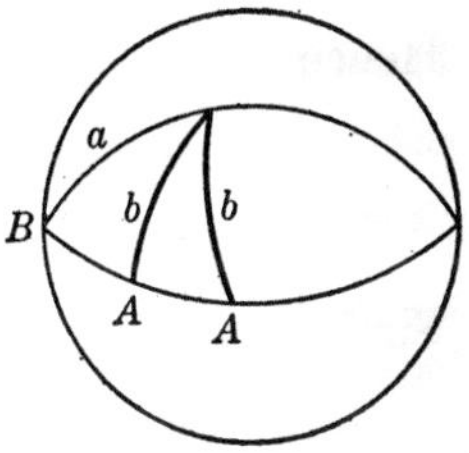

This rule may determine that one of the two supplementary values of A is not admissible. If this is not the case, there are two triangles which satisfy the given conditions. The relative position of the various parts in one such case is shown in the figure.

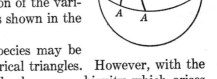

Several other rules for species may be established for general spherical triangles. However, with the formulas suggested in this book, any ambiguity which arises can be settled by the rule stated above.

208. Solution of general triangles.—In the solution of general spherical triangles we consider six cases according to the parts given.

Case   I. Three sides.

Case II. Three angles.

Case III. Two sides and their included angle.

Case IV. Two angles and their included side.

Case   V. Two sides and the angle opposite one of them.

Case VI. Two angles and the side opposite one of them.

Case I. If the three sides of a triangle are given, the angles may be found by using formulas [102] to [102″]. No ambiguity of sign can arise in this case. The solutions obtained can be checked readily by the sine law. The method of solution will be shown by an example.

Example. Find the angles of the triangle ABC, given:

$$a = 48° 55', \; b = 73° 21', \; c = 81° 38'$$

Solution:
$$r = \sqrt{\frac{\sin (s - a) \sin (s - b) \sin (s - c)}{\sin s}}.$$

$$\tan \frac{A}{2} = \frac{r}{\sin (s - a)}, \; \tan \frac{B}{2} = \frac{r}{\sin (s - b)}, \; \tan \frac{C}{2} = \frac{r}{\sin (s - c)}$$

$a =$	48° 55′	log sin $(s - a) = 9.90254$
$b =$	73° 21′	log sin $(s - b) = 9.68006$
$c =$	81° 38′	log sin $(s - c) = 9.54059$
$2s =$	202° 114′	colog sin $s = 0.00952$
$s =$	101° 57′	log $r^2 = 9.13271$
$s - a =$	53° 2′	log $r = 9.56636$
$s - b =$	28° 36′	log tan $\frac{1}{2} A = 9.66382$
$s - c =$	20° 19′	log tan $\frac{1}{2} B = 9.88630$
$s =$	101° 57′	log tan $\frac{1}{2} C = 0.02577$

Therefore, $\dfrac{A}{2} = 24° 45' 20'', \dfrac{B}{2} = 37° 35' 2'', \dfrac{C}{2} = 46° 41' 55''$

and $A = 49° 30' 40'', B = 74° 10' 4'', C = 93° 23' 50''.$

Check.
$$\frac{\sin a}{\sin A} = \frac{\sin b}{\sin B} = \frac{\sin c}{\sin C}$$

log sin $a = 9.87723$	log sin $b = 9.98140$	log sin $c = 9.99535$
log sin $A = 9.88112$	log sin $B = 9.98528$	log sin $C = 9.99923$
9.99611	9.99612	9.99612

Case II. If the three angles are given, the procedure is very similar to that shown above, but on the basis of formulas [103] to [103″]; viz.,

$$R = \sqrt{\frac{- \cos S}{\cos (S - A) \cos (S - B) \cos (S - C)}},$$

$$\tan \frac{a}{2} = R \cos (S - A),$$

$$\tan \frac{b}{2} = R \cos (S - B),$$

$$\tan \frac{c}{2} = R \cos (S - C).$$

EXERCISES

Find parts not given in the following:

1. $\begin{cases} a = 38° 18' \\ b = 46° 28' \\ c = 69° 44' \end{cases}$
   5. $\begin{cases} a = 71° 21' \\ b = 84° 19' \\ c = 20° 50' \end{cases}$
   9. $\begin{cases} A = 55° 40' \\ B = 69° 22' \\ C = 75° 10' \end{cases}$

2. $\begin{cases} a = 112° 25' \\ b = 96° 20' \\ c = 28° 35' \end{cases}$
   6. $\begin{cases} A = 36° 30' \\ B = 118° 17' \\ C = 78° 35' \end{cases}$
   10. $\begin{cases} a = 126° 35' \\ b = 75° 5' \\ c = 79° 40' \end{cases}$

3. $\begin{cases} A = 70° 32' \\ B = 62° 48' \\ C = 48° 34' \end{cases}$
   7. $\begin{cases} A = 88° 55' \\ B = 53° 25' \\ C = 61° 20' \end{cases}$
   11. $\begin{cases} A = 84° 26' \\ B = 56° 46' \\ C = 95° 24' \end{cases}$

4. $\begin{cases} A = 68° 10' \\ B = 76° 18' \\ C = 154° 36' \end{cases}$
   8. $\begin{cases} a = 116° 30' \\ b = 36° 24' \\ c = 82° 6' \end{cases}$
   12. $\begin{cases} a = 33° 18' \\ b = 46° 25' \\ c = 59° 41' \end{cases}$

Case III. When two sides and the included angle are given, the sum and difference of the two unknown angles can be found by formulas [104'] and [105'], and hence the values of the angles determined. Then by [104] the unknown side can be found and [105] furnishes a check for the computation.

Example. Solve the spherical triangle ABC, given: $b = 118° 12'$, $c = 52° 41'$, $A = 78° 36'$.

Solution:

$$\tan \tfrac{1}{2}(B+C) = \frac{\cos \tfrac{1}{2}(b-c)}{\cos \tfrac{1}{2}(b+c)} \cot \tfrac{1}{2} A. \qquad \tan \tfrac{1}{2}(B-C) = \frac{\sin \tfrac{1}{2}(b-c)}{\sin \tfrac{1}{2}(b+c)} \cot \tfrac{1}{2} A.$$

$\log \cos \tfrac{1}{2}(b-c)$	$= 9.92477$	$\log \sin \tfrac{1}{2}(b-c)$ $= 9.73328$
$\log \cot \tfrac{1}{2} A$	$= 0.08699$	$\log \cot \tfrac{1}{2} A$ $= 0.08699$
$\text{colog} \cos \tfrac{1}{2}(b+c)$	$= 1.09977$	$\text{colog} \sin \tfrac{1}{2}(b+c)$ $= 0.00137$
$\log \tan \tfrac{1}{2}(B+C)$	$= 1.11153$	$\log \tan \tfrac{1}{2}(B-C) = 9.82164$
$\tfrac{1}{2}(B+C)$	$= 85° 34' 37''$	$\tfrac{1}{2}(B-C) = 33° 33' 7''$

$$B = 85° 34' 37'' + 33° 33' 7'' = 119° 7' 44''$$
$$C = 85° 34' 37'' - 33° 33' 7'' = 52° 1' 30''$$

$$\tan \frac{a}{2} = \frac{\sin \tfrac{1}{2}(B+C)}{\sin \tfrac{1}{2}(B-C)} \tan \tfrac{1}{2}(b-c). \qquad \tan \frac{a}{2} = \frac{\cos \tfrac{1}{2}(B+C)}{\cos \tfrac{1}{2}(B-C)} \tan \tfrac{1}{2}(b+c)$$

$\log \sin \tfrac{1}{2}(B+C)$	$= 9.99871$	$\log \cos \tfrac{1}{2}(B+C) = 8.88716$
$\log \tan \tfrac{1}{2}(b-c)$	$= 9.80850$	$\log \tan \tfrac{1}{2}(b+c) = 1.09840$
$\text{colog} \sin \tfrac{1}{2}(B-C)$	$= 0.25752$	$\text{colog} \cos \tfrac{1}{2}(B-C) = 0.07915$
$\log \tan \tfrac{1}{2}a$	$= 0.06473$	$\log \tan \tfrac{1}{2}a$ $= 0.06471$
$\tfrac{1}{2}a$	$= 49° 15' 14''$	a $= 98° 30' 28''$

In this case, after the two angles have been found the law of sines may be used to find the remaining side, and a check is furnished by using the other parts in the law of sines. If this procedure is used, the rule for species given in §207 must be used to determine whether the final side is greater than, or less than, 90°.

Case IV. When two angles and the included side are given, the procedure is similar to that in Case III. The formulas used are [104] and [105] to find the unknown sides, [104'] to find the remaining angle, and then [105'] may be used as a check. As before, the law of sines may be applied after the two unknown sides have been found.

EXERCISES

Solve the following triangles.

1. $\begin{cases} a = 44° 50' \\ b = 29° 10' \\ C = 75° 16' \end{cases}$
    4. $\begin{cases} A = 29° 35' \\ C = 70° 17' \\ b = 57° 44' \end{cases}$
    7. $\begin{cases} a = 96° 34' \\ c = 63° 46' \\ B = 71° 54' \end{cases}$

2. $\begin{cases} A = 49° 26' \\ B = 67° 38' \\ c = 55° 22' \end{cases}$
    5. $\begin{cases} a = 12° 26' \\ b = 32° 44' \\ C = 98° 30' \end{cases}$
    8. $\begin{cases} B = 38° 42' \\ C = 59° 56' \\ a = 118° 30' \end{cases}$

3. $\begin{cases} B = 78° 31' \\ C = 62° 15' \\ a = 50° 32' \end{cases}$
    6. $\begin{cases} b = 124° 12' \\ c = 83° 40' \\ A = 76° 26' \end{cases}$
    9. $\begin{cases} a = 117° 58' \\ b = 82° 12' \\ C = 57° 36' \end{cases}$

Case V. When two sides and the angle opposite one of them are given, a second angle may be found by the law of sines.

If A, b and a are given, then

$$\sin B = \frac{\sin b \sin A}{\sin a}.$$

If $\sin a < \sin b \sin A$, then $\sin B > 1$ and no triangle exists for the given data. If $\sin a = \sin b \sin A$, $\sin B = 1$ and the triangle is a right triangle.

If $\sin a > \sin b \sin A$, two supplementary values of B result. Reference must then be made to §207 in order to determine whether both are possible, and if not to determine which one is to be used.

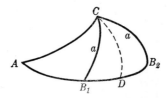

The figure shows the relation of two such triangles. Arc CD is perpendicular to arc AB. From Napier's rules, §194, $\sin CD = \sin b \sin A$.

When two sides and the angles opposite them are known, the remaining side may be found from formula [104], the remaining angle from [104']. These two parts and the given opposite parts may then be used in the law of sines as a check on the work.

Example. Solve the spherical triangle ABC, given $a = 72° 35'$, $b = 51° 6'$, $B = 38° 28'$.

Solution:
$$\sin A = \frac{\sin a \sin B}{\sin b}$$
$$\cot \frac{C}{2} = \frac{\sin \frac{1}{2}(a+b)}{\sin \frac{1}{2}(a-b)} \tan \frac{1}{2}(A-B)$$
$$\tan \frac{c}{2} = \frac{\sin \frac{1}{2}(A+B)}{\sin \frac{1}{2}(A-B)} \tan \frac{1}{2}(a-b)$$

log sin a = 9.97962	$\therefore$ $A = 49° 41' 55''$
log sin B = 9.79383	or $130° 18' 5''$
colog sin b = 0.10888	both of which are possible,
log sin A = 9.88233	according to §207

(a) Using the smaller value of A:

$a + b = 123° 41'$	$A + B = 88°$ $9' 55''$
$\dfrac{a+b}{2} = 61° 50' 30''$	$\dfrac{A+B}{2} = 44°$ $4' 58''$
$a - b = 21° 29'$	$A - B = 11° 13' 55''$
$\dfrac{a-b}{2} = 10° 44' 30''$	$\dfrac{A-B}{2} = 5° 36' 58''$

log sin $\frac{1}{2}(a-b)$ = 9.94530	log sin $\frac{1}{2}(A-B)$ = 9.84242
log tan $\frac{1}{2}(A-B)$ = 8.99271	log tan $\frac{1}{2}(a-b)$ = 9.27808
colog sin $\frac{1}{2}(a-b)$ = 0.72960	colog sin $\frac{1}{2}(A-B)$ = 1.00938
log cot $\frac{1}{2}C$ = 9.66761	log tan $\frac{1}{2}c$ = 0.12988
$\frac{1}{2}C$ = 65° 3' 13''	$\frac{1}{2}c$ = 53° 26' 33''
C = 130° 6' 26''	c = 106° 53' 6''

Check. $\dfrac{\sin b}{\sin B} = \dfrac{\sin c}{\sin C}$

log sin b = 9.89112	log sin c = 9.98087
log sin B = 9.79383	log sin C = 9.88357
0.09729	0.09730

(b) Using the larger value of A:

$A + B = 168° 46' 5''$	$A - B = 91° 50' 5''$
$\dfrac{A+B}{2} = 84° 23' 3''$	$\dfrac{A-B}{2} = 45° 55' 3''$

log sin $\frac{1}{2}(a-b)$ = 9.94530	log sin $\frac{1}{2}(A-B)$ = 9.99791
log tan $\frac{1}{2}(A-B)$ = 0.01391	log tan $\frac{1}{2}(a-b)$ = 0.27808
colog sin $\frac{1}{2}(a-b)$ = 0.72960	colog sin $\frac{1}{2}(A-B)$ = 0.14367
log cot $\frac{1}{2}C$ = 0.68881	log tan $\frac{1}{2}c$ = 0.41966
$\frac{1}{2}C$ = 11° 34' 14''	$\frac{1}{2}c$ = 14° 43' 32''
C = 23° 8' 28''	c = 29° 27' 4''

Check. log sin c = 9.69168
log sin C = 9.59439

0.09729, as above.

Case VI. When two angles and the side opposite one of them are given, the side opposite the second given side may be found by use of the law of sines, and the remaining parts by [105] and [105'].

EXERCISES

Solve the following triangles.

GROUP A

1. $\begin{cases} a = 37° 50' \\ b = 63° 10' \\ B = 70° 18' \end{cases}$
2. $\begin{cases} b = 75° 28' \\ c = 83° 21' \\ C = 40° 33' \end{cases}$
3. $\begin{cases} a = 49° 45' \\ A = 58° 26' \\ C = 32° 20' \end{cases}$

4. $\begin{cases} a = 68° 18' \\ c = 56° 32' \\ C = 32° 55' \end{cases}$
5. $\begin{cases} a = 82° 6' \\ b = 69° 15' \\ A = 118° 20' \end{cases}$
6. $\begin{cases} B = 78° 36' \\ C = 84° 16' \\ c = 66° 42' \end{cases}$

7. $\begin{cases} a = 65° 26' \\ c = 53° 14' \\ A = 85° 28' \end{cases}$
8. $\begin{cases} b = 50° 20' \\ c = 58° 46' \\ B = 98° 10' \end{cases}$
9. $\begin{cases} A = 70° 23' \\ B = 88° 13' \\ b = 81° 34' \end{cases}$

GROUP B

1. $\begin{cases} a = 78° 20' \\ b = 59° 18' \\ A = 68° 16' \end{cases}$
2. $\begin{cases} B = 87° 30' \\ C = 71° 22' \\ b = 75° 45' \end{cases}$
3. $\begin{cases} a = 71° 27' \\ c = 47° 34' \\ A = 62° 12' \end{cases}$

4. $\begin{cases} A = 51° 28' \\ B = 67° 32' \\ b = 70° 40' \end{cases}$
5. $\begin{cases} A = 103° 30' \\ C = 58° 8' \\ c = 47° 13' \end{cases}$
6. $\begin{cases} a = 70° 32' \\ b = 72° 16' \\ B = 81° 7' \end{cases}$

7. $\begin{cases} B = 60° 50' \\ C = 48° 27' \\ c = 27° 48' \end{cases}$
8. $\begin{cases} a = 74° 14' \\ c = 82° 17' \\ C = 107° 20' \end{cases}$
9. $\begin{cases} A = 93° 11' \\ B = 81° 13' \\ a = 73° 40' \end{cases}$

GROUP C

1. $\begin{cases} A = 78° 12' \\ B = 63° 48' \\ a = 50° 27' \end{cases}$
2. $\begin{cases} b = 82° 42' \\ c = 110° 33' \\ C = 85° 50' \end{cases}$
3. $\begin{cases} a = 74° 35' \\ A = 62° 28' \\ C = 98° 8' \end{cases}$

4. $\begin{cases} A = 96° 47' \\ C = 105° 52' \\ c = 72° 11' \end{cases}$
5. $\begin{cases} A = 85° 10' \\ C = 82° 19' \\ a = 56° 35' \end{cases}$
6. $\begin{cases} a = 83° 10' \\ c = 64° 45' \\ C = 58° 20' \end{cases}$

7. $\begin{cases} B = 62° 37' \\ C = 73° 21' \\ b = 49° 41' \end{cases}$
8. $\begin{cases} b = 105° 25' \\ c = 116° 32' \\ B = 48° 44' \end{cases}$
9. $\begin{cases} a = 68° 50' \\ b = 25° 35' \\ A = 112° 30' \end{cases}$

209. Applications to measurements on the surface of the earth.—The earth is very nearly, but not exactly, spherical in shape. Computations can therefore be made of distances and directions on the earth's surface by means of the formulas of spherical trigonometry with errors so small as to be negligible in simple applications. An example will illustrate some of these applications.

Example. Find the distance along a great circle of the earth from a point A (Longitude 75° W., Latitude 28° N.), to a point B, (Longitude 115° W., Latitude 47° N.).

Solution: In the figure $Q'FDQ$ is the equator, N the north pole. The difference in longitude of the two places, 40°, is measured by the arc FD; hence angle $ANB = 40°$. Also

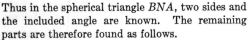

$$\text{Arc } AN = 90° - 28° = 62°$$
$$\text{Arc } NB = 90° - 47° = 43°$$

Thus in the spherical triangle BNA, two sides and the included angle are known. The remaining parts are therefore found as follows.

Denote AN by b, BN by a, and BA by n. We solve the triangle according to case III.

Then $N = 40°$, $\frac{1}{2}(b - a) = 9°\,30'$, $\frac{1}{2}(b + a) = 52°\,30'$.

$$\tan \tfrac{1}{2}(B + A) = \frac{\cos \frac{1}{2}(b - a)}{\cos \frac{1}{2}(b + a)} \cot \tfrac{1}{2} N, \quad \tan \tfrac{1}{2}(B - A) = \frac{\sin \frac{1}{2}(b - a)}{\sin \frac{1}{2}(b + a)} \cot \tfrac{1}{2} N$$

log cos $\frac{1}{2}(b - a)$	= 9.99400	log sin $\frac{1}{2}(b - a)$ = 9.21761
log cot $\frac{1}{2} N$	= 0.43893	log cot $\frac{1}{2} N$ = 0.43893
colog cos $\frac{1}{2}(b + a)$	= 0.21555	colog sin $\frac{1}{2}(b + a)$ = 0.10053
log tan $\frac{1}{2}(B + A)$	= 0.64848	log tan $\frac{1}{2}(B - A)$ = 9.75707
$\frac{1}{2}(B + A)$	= 77° 20′ 18″	$\frac{1}{2}(B - A)$ = 29° 45′ 4″

$$B = 77°\,20'\,18'' + 29°\,45'\,4'' = 107°\ 5'\,22''$$
$$A = 77°\,20'\,18'' - 29°\,45'\,4'' = \ 47°\,35'\,14''$$

$$\tan \frac{n}{2} = \frac{\sin \frac{1}{2}(B + A)}{\sin \frac{1}{2}(B - A)} \tan \tfrac{1}{2}(b - a), \quad \tan \frac{n}{2} = \frac{\cos \frac{1}{2}(B + A)}{\cos \frac{1}{2}(B - A)} \tan \tfrac{1}{2}(b + a)$$

log sin $\frac{1}{2}(B + A)$ = 9.98931	log cos $\frac{1}{2}(B + A)$ = 9.34083
log tan $\frac{1}{2}(b - a)$ = 9.22361	log tan $\frac{1}{2}(b + a)$ = 0.11502
colog sin $\frac{1}{2}(B - A)$ = 0.30430	colog cos $\frac{1}{2}(B - A)$ = 0.06139
log tan $\dfrac{n}{2}$ = 9.51722	log tan $\dfrac{n}{2}$ = 9.51724

$$\frac{n}{2} = 18°\,12'\,45''$$

$$n = 36°\,25'\,30'' = 36.42°$$

The average distance along the earth's surface corresponding to 1° along a great circle is about 69.16 miles. It follows that the distance from A to B is

$$d = 36.42 \times 69.16 = 2519 \text{ miles}$$

The above solution shows also that the initial direction from A to B is N. 47° 35′ 14″ W. It is evident that in general a great circle arc does not maintain the same direction.

EXERCISES

Using 69.16 miles as the distance corresponding to 1° along a great circle of the earth, find the shortest distance between the places named below. The latitudes and longitudes are shown below.

1. From Boston to San Francisco.
2. From New York to Cape of Good Hope.
3. From Greenwich to Auckland.
4. From Gibraltar to Calcutta.
5. From New York to Yokohama.
6. From Cape Horn to Cape of Good Hope.
7. From Havana to Valparaiso.
8. Find the direction at which an airplane should start from San Francisco in order to follow the arc of a great circle to Yokohama.
9. Find the angle at which the great circle from Baltimore to San Francisco cuts a meridian through Havana.
10. Find the angles of the spherical triangle whose vertices are New York, Cape Horn and Cape of Good Hope. (Use results from Examples 2 and 6.)

	LATITUDE	LONGITUDE
Boston..............	42° 21′ N.	71° 41′ W.
San Francisco.........	37° 48′ N.	122° 28′ W.
New York............	40° 43′ N.	74° 0′ W.
Calcutta.............	22° 33′ N.	88° 19′ E.
Greenwich............	51° 29′ N.	0
Baltimore............	39° 17′ N.	76° 37′ W.
Havana..............	23° 9′ N.	82° 23′ W.
Gibraltar.............	36° 9′ N.	5° 21′ W.
Cape of Good Hope....	34° 22′ S.	18° 29′ E.
Auckland.............	36° 51′ S.	174° 50′ E.
Yokohama............	35° 27′ N.	139° 41′ E.
Cape Horn...........	55° 59′ S.	67° 16′ W.
Valparaiso............	33° 2′ S.	71° 41′ W.

210. Applications in astronomy.—The celestial sphere is what we think of as the sky. It is an apparent sphere of indefinite but very great radius upon which the celestial objects seem to be located. The point on this sphere directly overhead for an observer is his *zenith*. The plane of the horizon passes through the observer and is perpendicular to the line from the observer to his zenith. This plane cuts the celestial sphere in the *horizon*, a great circle whose pole is the zenith. The *north celestial pole* is the point on the celestial sphere directly overhead for an observer at the north pole of the earth. The *south celestial pole* is a corresponding point with respect to the south pole of the

earth. These two points are the points in which the line of the earth's axis cuts the celestial sphere and are the poles of the great circle known as the *celestial equator.*

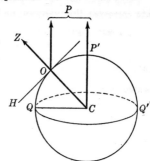

The upper figure opposite represents the earth, C being the center, QQ' the equator, P the pole, O the position of an observer, and OH the plane of the horizon for the observer. It is evident that the angle between the line to the zenith, CZ, and the direction of the earth's axis, CP', is equal to the complement of the latitude of the observer.[1]

Great circles passing through the zenith, Z (see figure), and therefore perpendicular to the horizon are *vertical circles.* The corresponding set passing through the poles, P and P', are hour circles. The angular distance from the horizon, measured along a vertical circle, to any celestial object is the *altitude* of that object. The angular distance from the celestial equator, measured along an hour circle, to the object is its *declination.*

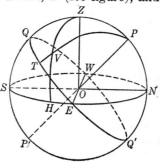

The sun apparently moves westward approximately parallel to the celestial equator, 15° per hour, in its diurnal motion. At midnight it is on the hour circle through N; at 6 A.M. on that through E, at noon on that through Q and S, and at 6 P.M. on that through W.

Thus the angle between the hour circle through the sun and the arc PNQ' determines the time. The following example shows how the time of day can be determined if the altitude of the sun (above the horizon) and its declination are known. The latter information is available from tables, but the former must be measured by the observer.

---

[1] In comparison with the radius of the celestial sphere, the radius of the earth is negligible. The center of the earth may be considered as the center of the celestial sphere. The location of the observer is necessary to determine the horizon.

Example. Find the time of day at which the altitude of the sun is 35° when the declination is 8° N. for an observation made at a point whose latitude is 43° N.

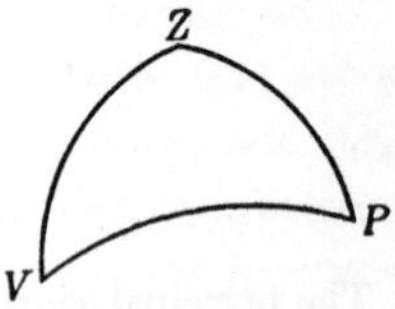

Using small letters v, z, p to denote the arcs opposite corresponding vertices, we have

$$v = 90° - 43° = 47°, \quad p = 90° - 35° = 55°,$$
$$z = 90° - 8° = 82°.$$

$$\tan \frac{P}{2} = \frac{v}{s-p}, \quad v = \frac{\sin (s-v) \sin (s-p) \sin (s-z)}{\sin s}$$

where $2s = v + p + z$

$v =$	$47°$	$\log \sin (s - v) = \ 9.84949$
$p =$	$55°$	$\log \sin (s - p) = \ 9.77946$
$z =$	$82°$	$\log \sin (s - z) = \ 9.23967$
$2s =$	$184°$	$\text{colog} \sin s = 10.00026$
$s =$	$92°$	$\log r^2 = 38.86888$
$s - v =$	$45°$	$\log r = \ 9.43444$
$s - p =$	$37°$	$\log \sin (s - p) = \ 9.77946$
$s - z =$	$10°$	$\log \tan \tfrac{1}{2} p = \ 9.65498$
$s =$	$92°$	$\tfrac{1}{2} p = 24° 18.9'$

The required hour angle is therefore 48° 37.8′. It follows that the time is 48° 37.8′ ÷ 15° = 3.24 hours either before or after noon. The required time is either 3:14.4 P.M. or 8:45.6 A.M.

EXERCISES

1. A forenoon observation made at a place whose latitude is 27° N. shows that the altitude of the sun is 33°. The declination of the sun is known to be − 6°. Find the time of day.

2. An observation of the sun is made at 4 P.M. The altitude proves to be 28°. The declination of the sun is known to be 12° N. What is the latitude of the observer? (Note that in this case, two sides and the angle opposite one of them are known.)

3. If the declination of the sun is 19°, what is its altitude as observed at 9 A.M. at a point whose latitude is 46° N.?

4. At what time in the afternoon is the altitude of the sun 20° as observed at a place whose latitude is 47° N. on a day when the declination is − 19°?

5. A star (in position V in the figure on the preceding page) is known to have a declination of 28°. Its altitude is observed to be 49° when its hour angle ZPV is 35°. Find the latitude of the observer.

6. A star is observed (as in the preceding exercise) to have an altitude of 40° and its hour angle is measured and found to be 18°. If the latitude of the observer is known to be 34° N., find the declination of the star.

7. Look up in the American Ephemeris the declination of some bright star, such as Vega, Altair, Regulus or Capella. Take an evening observation on the star, measuring, or estimating as closely as possible, its altitude and hour angle. Then compute your own latitude and compare with the information furnished by a map.

CHAPTER XV

HISTORICAL SKETCH

The principal sources used in compiling this historical sketch are:

(1) Moritz Cantor, *Vorlesungen über Geschichte der Mathematik*, fourth edition, 1906.

(2) Florian Cajori, *A History of Mathematics*, second edition, 1924.

(3) W. W. Rouse Ball, *A Short Account of the History of Mathematics*, 1893.

(4) Heinrich Wieleitner, *Geschichte der Mathematik*, (Sammlung Schubert, LXIV) 1921.

THE historical development of any science, or even of culture as a whole, often appears piecemeal and illogical. Parts which later are closely connected by apparently inevitable logical relations appear at great intervals of time and in widely separated geographical regions. Nor do these parts necessarily appear in the order of their simplicity, when simplicity is measured by the comparative difficulty of understanding, once the discovery has been made. A submerged continent is rising out of the sea: an island, a chain of islands, and then a whole region appear; later other islands and regions arise in distant places, and in time these are all connected as the continent emerges. The early spots give little promise of the final unit, and their significance is apparent only when the event has been consummated.

But the figure is not wholly fortunate. The beginnings of a science are often developed as parts of other and more general sciences. The epoch-making events in the history of science are the discovery of new methods of attack and new general theories. and points of view, quite as much as the discovery of new facts. Until these appear, investigations by means of the older methods are frequently pushed to their very limit. Great intellects achieve surprising results, while that which at a later time appears simple and obvious remains unnoticed. The history of the development of trigonometry furnished numerous instances. Many of its more difficult theorems were stated and proved long before the invention of the system of numerals which we now study in our grade schools.

Greek Trigonometry

Elementary trigonometry is essentially a combination of geometry and methods of computation, with a rather slight admixture of algebra. The geometry derives from the Greeks, the system of numerals and the algebra from the Hindus and Arabs, and some of the methods and means of computation, notably logarithms, from more recent European times. It is nevertheless true that trigonometry originated with the Greeks. To understand what they contributed to this science, and what they failed to contribute, we must know what was the main field of Greek work in mathematics, and also something about the limitations under which they labored.

Beyond any reasonable comparison the greatest mathematical work of the Greeks was in geometry. Using methods with which we are in part familiar from our study in the secondary schools, they pushed their investigations farther than any subsequent workers who were limited as they were. The whole geometric basis for trigonometry was perfected by them. But they were cramped by certain shortcomings, which made it impossible for them to develop the science as we know it today, though to us it is vastly simpler than the results in pure geometry obtained by such geniuses as Archimedes and Apollonius.

The three theorems (6), (9), (10), on page 10, which contain the substance of the cosine formula, $a^2 = b^2 + c^2 - 2bc \cos A$, are found in Euclid's *Elements*, but there is a vast gap between these theorems and the complete formula as we understand it. Greek geometry made little use of numbers. With them, for instance, the product of two lines (or the square of a line) was a rectangle, while with us it is the product of two numbers representing the lengths of the lines. With the Greeks the idea of number was essentially limited to positive (or unsigned) integers. Fractions caused them great trouble and they were wholly ignorant of our decimal notation. In Euclid's *Elements* a complete theory of proportion is developed on a purely geometric basis with no reference to numbers. Apparently it did not occur to them that the same relations exist between numbers. With such limitations it is evident that they could not develop in its entirety what is now to a large extent a computational science. But they did a great deal.

The sine formula, $\dfrac{a}{\sin A} = \dfrac{b}{\sin B}$, which is the fundamental theorem in the computational part of trigonometry, was not stated explicitly, but was contained implicitly in other theorems. If the Greeks had stated this theorem it would run in substance thus: *The sides of a triangle are in the same ratio as the chords of twice the opposite angles.* This is at once evident from the adjoining figure. The

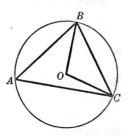

side *BC* is the chord of the angle *BOC* (the Greeks thought of it as the chord of the *arc BC*) which is twice the angle *A*. Tables of chords which are thus seen to be essentially equivalent to tables of natural sines were constructed and used. Hipparchus, the most eminent of Greek astronomers, who lived in the second century before Christ, is generally regarded as the creator of the subject of trigonometry. He is known to have constructed a table of chords, but we do not know what methods he used.

Ptolemy of Alexandria, who flourished about the middle of the second century A.D., collected and organized the then existing science of astronomy in his great work, the *Almagest*. It is not known how much of this work was original with Ptolemy, though it is certain that a large part of it was due to Hipparchus and other investigators.

The *Almagest* is divided into thirteen books. In the first book he gives (along with other matter) an account of trigonometry, including a table of chords and the method used in computing them. Use was made of the following fundamental theorem, the so-called Ptolemaic theorem:

If a quadrilateral is inscribed in a circle, then the product of its diagonals is equal to the sum of the products of the two pairs of opposite sides.

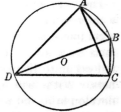

Thus in the figure $AC \times DB = AB \times DC + BC \times AD$. By means of this theorem the chords of the sum or of the difference of two arcs may be found when the chords of the arcs themselves are known, as may also the chord of half an arc or twice an arc.

Thus suppose the chords AB and BC are known, and it is required to find the chord AC.

Let DB be a diameter of known length.

Then $AC = \dfrac{AB \times DC + BC \times AD}{DB}$.

Since DCB and DAB are right angles,

$$DC = \sqrt{DB^2 - BC^2} \text{ and } AD = \sqrt{DB^2 - AB^2},$$

and $AC = \dfrac{AB \sqrt{DB^2 - BC^2} + BC \sqrt{DB^2 - AB^2}}{DB}.$

By similar constructions, the chord of the difference of two arcs and the chord of half an arc are found.

By beginning with arcs of known chords such as 60° and 72°, through successive halving, subtracting, and adding of arcs, Ptolemy obtained the chords of a series of arcs such as 30°, 15°, $7\frac{1}{2}$°, 12°, 6°, 3°, $1\frac{1}{2}$°, etc. Ptolemy gives the chords of arcs at 30 minute intervals. To do this it was necessary to find the chord of one degree. This was done by means of a method of approximation based on an ingenious theorem.

The Greeks from Hipparchus on divided the circle into 360°, one degree into 60', and one minute into 60". That is, they used the sexagesimal system in dealing with arcs and angles, while their general number system was decimal, as ours is. It is fairly certain that this system was borrowed from the Babylonians who used it in general. It is not known, however, why the Babylonians came to divide the circle into 360 parts, though many conjectures have been made. Perhaps the most plausible of these conjectures is that one of the equal angles of an equilateral triangle was regarded as a unit angle. Using sexagesimal division then gives 60° in such an angle, or 360° in the whole circle.

The form which the Greeks used in constructing their tables is interesting. The radius of the circle was divided into 60 equal parts, and the chords were given in terms of one of these parts as a unit. To get closer approximations this unit was divided into 60 parts, called minute parts, and one of these minute parts was again divided into 60 parts, called second minute parts. So a chord was given as so many parts, so many minute parts, and so many second minute parts. Thus the chord of the arc of 20° 30′ is given as 21° 21′ 12″. This means that this chord is $\dfrac{21}{60} + \dfrac{21}{3600} + \dfrac{12}{216000}$ of the radius. It is interesting that the number of each of these parts was given in the decimal number system, but of course in a system of numerals very different from ours—a system which was much like that of the Romans, though somewhat clumsier. When translated into Latin these smaller parts were written *partes minutæ* and *partes minutæ secundæ*. Hence we have our *minutes* and *seconds*.

A table of proportional parts was given for interpolation between each successive half-degree of arc, the assumption being that within these narrow limits the chords change in proportion to the arc. This is precisely the assumption which we have made for the much narrower limit of one minute of arc. As in the main table, so also in the table of proportional parts, the sexagesimal system is used both for arcs and for chords.

The value of π used by Ptolemy is $3°8′30″ = 3 + \dfrac{8}{60} + \dfrac{30}{3600} =$ 3.141666, the radius being unity.

Heron of Alexandria, who lived in the latter part of the second century B.C., discovered the formula $A = \sqrt{s(s-a)(s-b)(s-c)}$ giving the area of the triangle (see page 81). He illustrated the use of this formula by finding the area of a triangle whose sides are 13, 14, 15. In finding this formula, Heron departed from the ways of the Greeks. Ball says of him:

> Hero [Heron] did nothing to extend a knowledge of abstract mathematics; ... he was interested in science only on account of its practical applications, and so long as his results were true he cared nothing for the logical accuracy of the process by which he arrived at them. Thus in finding the area of a triangle he took the square root of the product of four lines. The classical Greek geometricians permitted the use of the square or the cube of a line [or the product of any two or three lines] because these could be represented geometrically, but a figure of four dimensions is inconceivable, and certainly they would have rejected a proof involving such a conception.

It is to be noted that the astronomers and not the mathematicians developed trigonometry in Greece. Hipparchus and Ptolemy were astronomers. For this reason spherical trigonometry was developed more fully than plane.

This account of Greek contribution to trigonometry may be
closed appropriately with the following quotation from Cantor:

The ancients did not make use of trigonometry either in their theory of
plane areas or in their practice in surveying, with the single exception of
the numerical formulas of Heron for the areas of regular polygons. This fact
may appear surprising at first sight, but an explanation does not appear
difficult.

Trigonometric expressions are not thinkable as a basis upon which to build
other species of magnitudes so long as there is not available an organized
system of mathematical symbols. In the absence of such a symbolism,
trigonometric expressions expressed in tables of lines give only approximately
correct results. But the scientific geometrician was not inclined to be satisfied with mere approximations no matter how close these might be. The
practical surveyor on the other hand was disinclined to master the science
which was indispensable in order to employ trigonometric computation. So
it came about that they left the disrespected or feared methods of trigonometry to the astronomer who, being less highly critical than the geometrician and intellectually less indolent than the surveyor, made cheerful use
of their approximate results.

Hindu and Arab Contributions to Trigonometry

The earliest known Hindu writings containing elements of
trigonometry date from the fifth or sixth century of our era,
and the latest Arab contributions were made about the year
1250. From intrinsic evidence in their writings, as well as from
general probability, it is safe to assume that these Eastern
peoples had learned from the Greeks. But the science was
largely transformed, if not greatly extended, in their hands.
As the Greeks were masters in dealing with purely geometric
problems, so the particular genius of the Hindus and Arabs was
in dealing with numbers and in computation, including the more
general computation of algebra. Even Greek algebra was geometric in character. The unknown was a line if of the first
degree, and its square represented an area. With the Hindus
and the Arabs these were pure numbers, as they are with us.
The system of numerals which we now use had been invented
in India, the essential element of this system being the principle
of place value. As a consequence trigonometric functions came
to be used as symbols representing numerical values and practical computation was greatly facilitated.

One of the most far-reaching innovations made by the Hindus
was the replacing of the chord of an arc by half the chord of

double the arc—that is by its sine as we now have it. Their method of computing also differed somewhat from that of the Greeks. Like the Greeks, and before them the Babylonians, the Hindus divided the circle into 360 degrees and these into minutes and seconds. But here a difference arises. The 360 degrees in the circle equal 21,600 minutes. While the Greeks divided the radius into 60 equal parts, the Hindus raised the question as to the number of these minutes of arc which was equal in length to the radius. Using 3.1416 as the value of π, they found this number to be 3,438 when taken to the nearest unit. That is, using the length of a minute of arc as a unit they wrote $r = 3438$. Aryabhata (born 476 A.D.) proceeds as follows to find $\sin \frac{\alpha}{2}$, when $\sin \alpha$ is known. In the figure let

arc $AB = \alpha$ and $AE = \frac{\alpha}{2}$.

Then (using the Hindu definition of sine)

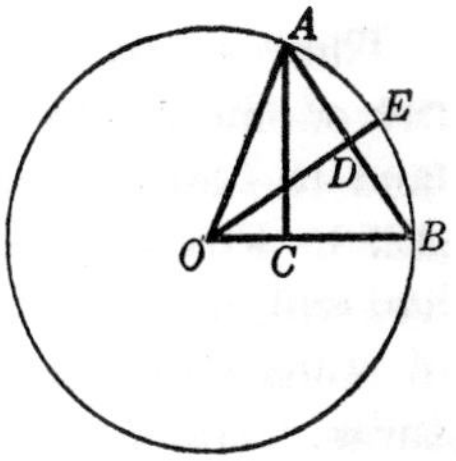

$\sin \alpha = CA$ and $\sin \frac{\alpha}{2} = DA$.

But $AB^2 = AC^2 + CB^2 = (r + OC)\,(r - OC) + (r - OC)^2 = 2r^2 - 2r \cdot OC$.

Hence $\sin^2 \frac{\alpha}{2} = \dfrac{r^2 - r \cdot OC}{2} = \dfrac{r}{2}\,(r - OC)$,

and

$\sin \frac{\alpha}{2} = \sqrt{\dfrac{r}{2}\,(r - OC)}$.

If OC is denoted by $\cos \alpha$ and $r = 3438$, we have

$$\sin \frac{\alpha}{2} = \sqrt{1719\,(3438 - \cos \alpha)}$$

But it was known that $\sin^2 \alpha + \cos^2 \alpha = r^2$ and that hence $\cos \alpha$ could be computed.

With this formula [or its equivalent], says Cajori, and with the sines of 90°, 60°, 45°, and 30° as starting-points, they reckoned the sines of half the angles [arcs?], thus obtaining the sines of 22°30, 15°, 11°15, 7°30, 3°45. They now figured out the sines of the complements of these angles [arcs?], namely, the sines of 86°15, 82°30, 78°45, 75°, 67°30; then they calculated the sines of half these angles [arcs?]; then of their complements; then, again, of half their complements; and so on. By this very simple process they got the sines of angles [arcs?] at intervals of 3°45.

Values of sin 15°, sin 7° 30', sin 3° 45' contained in the earliest known Hindu writings on mathematics were probably obtained by this method.

But [to quote from Cantor], Bhaskara [born 1114] was not satisfied with these tables. He computed sines and cosines as fractions of the radius: sin $225 = \dfrac{100}{1529}$, cos $225 = \dfrac{466}{467}$; sin $1° = \dfrac{10}{573}$, cos $1° = \dfrac{6568}{6569}$, when each fraction is a fraction of the radius.

As a final estimate of Hindu contribution to trigonometry Cantor says:

Trigonometry as the computation of parts of any triangle by means of functions of angles did not exist for the Hindus. By them all problems on triangles were reduced to problems on right triangles, and then they were able to solve the problems that appeared.

As essential progress of trigonometry in India there remains therefore the table of sines. Chords were permanently displaced by the half chords [sines].

It is safe to say that this exceptionally fortunate throw of the Hindus was achieved quite by accident, since they did not understand the far-reaching importance of this step. This was reserved for their followers, the Arabs.

There is not space to sketch even in outline the story of the rise of the Arabs. When the eastern branch of the Mohammedans had organized their capital in Bagdad, their rulers began to seek the aid of scholars among the many peoples they had subdued or rather absorbed into their own faith. A period of translation ensued. Natives of Syria, Persia, Greece, and India, residing at Bagdad, translated literary and scientific treasures from their own vernaculars. So it came about that before the end of the ninth century Arab scholars had at their disposal practically all the science that had existed up to that time. Like the Greeks and the Hindus, they accepted the sexagesimal division of the angle, but they used the Hindu table of sines instead of the chords of the Greeks.

As was the case with the Greeks and the Hindus, Arab trigonometry, with one notable exception, was developed as a part of astronomy; but important advances were made. All the trigonometric functions that are now used were introduced. Al-Battani (877–929) used arcs with unit radius and in reality regarded the functions as ratios. He was the first to prepare a table of cotangents and he probably knew the law of sines.

Abu'l Wefa (940–98) introduced all the present functions and constructed tables of tangents and cotangents. In considering the shadow triangle he used the secant and cosecant.

He invented a method for computing a table of sines which gives the sine of half a degree to nine decimal places. [Cajori.]

The history of the origin of the word *sine* is interesting.

The work of Al-Battani, De scientia stellarum, was translated into Latin by Plato Tiburtinus, in the twelfth century. Out of this translation sprang the word "sinus," as the name of a trigonometric function. The Arabic word for "sine" jiba was derived from the Sanskrit jiva, and resembled the Arabic word jaib, meaning an indentation or gulf. Hence the Latin "sinus."

It remains to mention Nasir-Eddin (1200–74), who more than any of his predecessors dissociated trigonometry from astronomy and who seems to have been the first to state explicitly the sine formula for plane triangles in practically its present form. To quote Cajori:

During the supremacy of Hulagu, lived Nasir-Eddin, a man of broad culture and an able astronomer. He persuaded Hulagu to build him and his associates a large observatory at Maraga. Treatises on algebra, geometry, arithmetic, and a translation of Euclid's *Elements*, were prepared by him. He for the first time elaborated trigonometry independently of astronomy and to such great perfection that, had his work been known, Europeans of the fifteenth century might have spared their labors.

It must be admitted that the contributions of the Arabs were in no sense revolutionary. They elaborated and amplified, but they were commentators rather than creators of new theories and methods. Ball expresses himself as follows:

The general impression left on my mind is that the Arabs were quick to appreciate the work of others—notably the Greek masters and of the Hindoo mathematicians—but, like the ancient Chinese and Egyptians, they were unable to systematically develop a subject to any considerable extent. Their schools may be taken to have lasted in all for about 650 years, and if the work produced be compared with that of Greek or modern European writers it is as a whole second-rate both in quantity and quality.

TRIGONOMETRY IN MODERN EUROPE

In what respect did the trigonometry of Nasir-Eddin differ from the elementary parts of the modern science? This question is best answered by enumerating those parts of the subject contained in a text such as the present which were not in the Arab treatise.

There was still wanting the algebraic notation which we now have. None of the present symbols of operation was in existence. The smoothness of modern algebraic operations, due very largely to a perfected notation, was impossible. There was also lacking an effective set of symbols to represent the trigonometric functions. For these reasons the derivation of formulas was much more difficult than at present.

Logarithms had not been invented and all computations were made by the ordinary processes of elementary arithmetic. Formulas specially adapted to logarithmic computation, such as the tangent formula, were of course wanting.

There was no system of coordinates such as we now use in giving general definitions of the trigonometric functions, the existence of negative numbers was scarcely realized, and consequently general definitions of the functions were impossible. Another three hundred years passed before the formula $a^2 = b^2 + c^2 - 2bc \cos A$ could be stated with its present complete meaning, though the facts which it represents were formulated into rigorously proved theorems by the Greeks.

The periodicity of the functions, as considered in Chapter IX, was obviously not recognized because of the restrictions on the definitions. Inverse functions in the more general sense and the multiplicity of solutions of trigonometric equations, the representation of the functions by means of infinite series, and such special developments as De Moivre's theorem were wholly lacking.

While a general decimal system of notation was in use, fractions continued to be written in the sexagesimal base until about 1620. Thus Leonardo of Pisa in the year 1225 wrote 1.3688081075 as $1.22' \ 7'' \ 42''' \ 33'''' \ 4^{V} \ 40^{VI}$.

The trigonometry of Nasir-Eddin would enable a competent mathematician to solve all problems in this text involving mensuration, but the work would be extremely laborious. Tables of natural trigonometric functions could be constructed, but the process was much more tedious than it is when series are available.

The use of trigonometry in higher mathematics and its applications in science were of course wanting—the mathematics and the science were not in existence.

The story of the further development of algebra and of the

invention of a system of coordinates will not be considered in this chapter. We will confine ourselves to the remaining elements which are now parts of an introductory course such as the present.

The Arabs guarded their scientific treasures jealously, especially from the Christians. But little by little they were "smuggled" into Christian Europe. There were adventurous spirits, such as Adelhard of Bath, who about 1120 attended lectures at Cordova under the guise of a Mohammedan student; learned Jewish rabbis left Spain for Christian Europe; there was considerable commercial intercourse between Italy and the Arabs both west and east. So by a gradual process the principal manuscripts that had been translated into Arabic, or which had been created by the Arabs themselves, came into the hands of European scholars. (The work of Nasir-Eddin seems to be an exception.) Upon the basis of this body of knowledge the contributions of Europe were made.

The earliest European writings on trigonometry are due to Thomas Bradwardine (1290–1349), Archbishop of Canterbury. He speaks of tangent (umbra versa) and cotangent (umbra recta). Regiomontanus (John Mueller) (1435–76) studied trigonometry at Vienna. He translated the *Almagest* and constructed a table of tangents. Immediately after the time of Regiomontanus, the Germans calculated many tables, some of them very extensive. One of these calculators of tables, generally called Raetius, was the first to construct the right triangle and make use of it in defining the functions. That is, he made them depend upon the *angle* and not upon the arc, as had been done up to this time.

Logarithms were invented by John Napier, Baron of Merchiston, Scotland, and a table was published in 1614. Napier's logarithms were made to depend upon a correspondence between an arithmetic and a geometric series, and were in no way related to exponents. The latter came into use many years later. It was only in the time of Euler, about 1750, that logarithms came to be regarded as exponents.

Napier's tables differed in many respects from those we now use. His friend Briggs constructed a table using the base 10, the general plan for the Briggsian table being the joint product of Napier and Briggs. Napier died in 1617, but Briggs in 1624

published his *Arithmetica logarithmica* containing 14-place logarithms of numbers from 1 to 20,000 and from 90,000 to 100,000.
The gap was filled by Adrian Vlacq, who was born in Holland
and lived in London and Paris. In 1628 he published the complete table up to 100,000, 70,000 of which were computed by
himself. Says Cajori:

Briggs and Vlacq published four fundamental works, the results of which
have not been superseded by any subsequent calculations until very recently.

The word "characteristic," as used in logarithms, first occurs in Briggs'
Arithmetica logarithmica, 1624; the word "mantissa" was introduced by
John Wallis, 1693.

Briggs divided a degree into 100 parts, as was done also by N. Roe in 1633,
W. Oughtred in 1657, and John Newton in 1658, but owing to the publica-
tion by Vlacq of trigonometrical tables constructed on the old sexagesimal
division, Briggs' innovation did not prevail.

Edmund Gunter of London found the logarithmic sines and
tangents for every minute to seven places. He was the inventor
of the words cosine and cotangent.

Abraham de Moivre (1667–1754), the author of the theorem
known by his name (page 150), was of French descent and lived
in London, where he enjoyed the high respect of the mathematicians of his time.

Newton himself, in the later years of his life, used to reply to inquiries
respecting mathematics, even respecting his Principia: "Go to Mr. De
Moivre: he knows these things better than I do." . . . Shortly before his
death he declared it necessary for him to sleep ten or twenty minutes longer
every day. The day after he had reached the total of over twenty-three
hours, he slept exactly twenty-four hours and then passed away in his sleep.
[Cajori.]

Oughtred invented the slide rule (1621), Daniel Bernouli
(1729) used AS to represent arcsine ($\sin^{-1}$), and Leonard Euler
(1736) used At for arctangent. The theorem now known as
Mollweide's theorem (Ex. 19, page 185) was first published by
Simpson (1748), and in part by Newton in his *Universal Arithmetic* (1707). Mollweide rediscovered this theorem a century
after Newton's original discovery.

The exponential forms given in Chapter XII, and infinite
series used in computing trigonometric functions, were by-
products of extensive investigations in many fields of mathematics in the eighteenth century. The series resulted from the

work of Taylor and Maclaurin and the exponential forms are due mainly to Euler. The geometric representation of the imaginary, $\sqrt{-1}$, is due to Wessel (1797), to Argand (1806), and to Gauss, who published a fuller exposition in 1831. The systematic use of A, B, C, a, b, c to represent the angles and sides of a triangle was first adopted by Euler, but was used at times in earlier writings. The periodicity of the trigonometric functions was known by Cotes (1682–1716), but was developed later by Euler.

ANSWERS

Page 13

1. No. Because the hypotenuse must be longer than a side of a right triangle. **3.** Less than 45°. Because the tangent is less than 1. Greater than 45°. Because the tangent is greater than 1. **5.** No. Because the hypotenuse must be longer than a side of a right triangle. **7.** 5/3. **9.** 3/5. **11.** *A*.

Page 23

1. 9.27. **3.** 83.19. **5.** 12.96. **7.** 1.901. **9.** 34°. **11.** 40°. **13.** 37°. **15.** 81.12. **17.** 195.02.

Page 27

1. .3665. **3.** .9044. **5.** .4305. **7.** .7968. **9.** .4557. **11.** 4.0910. **13.** .2954. **15.** 1.4152. **17.** 25.4512. **19.** 20°22′. **21.** 47°37′. **23.** 35°41′. **25.** 67°24′. **27.** 43°12′. **29.** 18°5′. **31.** 33°53′. **33.** 76°18′. **35.** 81°38′.

Page 28

1. $A = 33°41′$, $B = 56°19′$, $c = 14.42$. **3.** $A = 55°46′$, $B = 34°14′$, $b = 42.19$. **5.** $B = 44°$, $b = 27.04$, $c = 38.93$. **7.** $A = 76°$, $b = .2318$, $c = .9024$. **9.** $A = 59°23′$, $B = 30°37′$, $a = 155.4$. **11.** $B = 37°$, $a = 11.15$, $c = 13.96$. **13.** $A = 73°$, $a = 17.50$, $c = 18.30$. **15.** $B = 48°$, $a = 61.69$, $b = 68.52$. **17.** $A = 33°$, $a = 4.384$, $b = 6.752$. **19.** $B = 38°$, $a = 22.27$, $c = 28.26$. **21.** $A = 25°11′$, $B = 64°49′$, $b = 78.90$. **23.** $A = 47°$, $b = 7.497$, $c = 10.99$.

Page 29

1. $B = 31°48′$, $c = 10.08$, $b = 5.313$. **3.** $B = 60°55′$, $a = 882.7$, $b = 1586$. **5.** $A = 31°10′$, $B = 58°50′$, $a = 461.9$. **7.** $A = 19°36′$, $B = 70°24′$, $b = 719.1$. **9.** $A = 53°49′$, $a = .01801$, $c = .02231$. **11.** $A = 21°13′$, $a = 46.60$, $c = 128.8$. **13.** $A = 22°59′$, $a = .8395$, $b = 1.979$. **15.** $A = 51°43′$, $B = 38°17′$, $b = 602.2$. **17.** $A = 61°19′$, $B = 28°41′$, $a = .02413$. **19.** $B = 43°2′$, $b = 110.4$, $c = 161.7$.

Page 31

GROUP A

1. 138.3725. **3.** 41°. **5.** 33°41′. **7.** 53°8′; 36°52′. **9.** 50°25′.

GROUP B

1. 166.009. **3.** 49°16′. **5.** 2/5. **7.** 30°58′. **9.** 7°50′.

GROUP C

1. 56.5045. **3.** 69°27′. **5.** 35°. **7.** 83.7378. **9.** N 64°48′ E.

Page 40

1. 45.11. 3. 4762. 5. .4918. 7. 469.83. 9. .049132. 11. 46.668.
13. 4.9091. 15. .0045175. 17. .00046993. 19. .046875. 21. 478.78.
23. .045646. 25. .47788. 27. 46823. 29. .047746.

Page 45

1. 303.44. 3. 9438. 5. 897,320. 7. 3.0519. 9. 1771.3. 11. 778.2.

Page 47

GROUP A

1. .052574. 3. 4.3235. 5. .2947. 7. .11185. 9. .017264. 11. .63481.
13. .69306. 15. 4.945. 17. 7.7483.

GROUP B

1. .78322. 3. 1.5384. 5. .015650. 7. 2.4969. 9. .86196. 11. 1.0841.
13. 3.6358. 15. 4.7913. 17. .69358.

GROUP C

1. .0036803. 3. .093558. 5. .98548. 7. 3.4442. 9. .83282. 11. 196.42.
13. 8.597. 15. .052865. 17. .015465.

Page 48

1. 9.50336 − 10. 3. 9.52829 − 10. 5. 9.97628 − 10. 7. .48480.
9. 9.97625 − 10. 11. 9.53092 − 10. 13. 18°36′25″. 15. 18°18′30″.
17. 71°10′24″.

Page 50

GROUP A

1. 85.878. 3. 160.41. 5. .54723. 7. .06824. 9. 355.05. 11. .0040874.
13. .13672. 15. .30131. 17. .97785. 19. 2.6133. 21. .05581. 23. .0034569.

GROUP B

1. 55.10. 3. 33.306. 5. 14.612. 7. .66837. 9. 5.453. 11. .00051082.
13. 2863. 15. 1.7007. 17. .029091. 19. .54519. 21. 4.8699.

GROUP C

1. 68.432. 3. 342.42. 5. .33532. 7. .36579. 9. 4.3093. 11. 3.7496.
13. 3251.7. 15. .79283. 17. 21.784. 19. 402.52. 21. 413.19. 23. .4022.

Page 53

GROUP A

1. $B = 54°47′$, $b = 73.202$, $c = 89.60$. 3. $B = 15°31′$, $a = 35.122$,
$b = 9.751$. 5. $A = 52°40′36″$, $B = 37°19′24″$, $b = 65.73$. 7. $B = 67°11′$,
$b = 100.26$, $c = 108.77$. 9. $B = 52°33′$, $a = 28.974$, $b = 37.828$.
11. $A = 67°42′$, $B = 12°18′$, $b = 66.523$. 13. $B = 18°44′$, $b = 9.3738$,
$c = 29.186$. 15. $B = 6°36′$, $a = 62.323$, $b = 7.211$. 17. $A = 41°37′24″$,
$B = 48°22′36″$, $b = 20.537$.

GROUP B

1. $B = 48°35'$, $b = 19.906$, $c = 26.544$. **3.** $B = 60°10'$, $a = 48.339$, $b = 84.292$. **5.** $A = 48°45'16''$, $B = 41°14'44''$, $b = 225.57$. **7.** $B = 81°40'$, $b = 187.20$, $c = 189.19$. **9.** $B = 52°12'$, $a = 240.75$, $b = 310.38$. **11.** $A = 32°13'6''$, $B = 57°46'54''$, $b = 146.75$. **13.** $B = 12°48'$, $b = 10.824$, $c = 48.854$. **15.** $B = 24°5'$, $a = 308.52$, $b = 137.90$. **17.** $A = 40°37'1''$, $B = 49°22'59''$, $b = 486.42$.

GRADE C

1. $B = 47°6'$, $b = 26.688$, $c = 36.432$. **3.** $B = 18°48'$, $a = 269$, $b = 91.574$. **5.** $A = 39°30'50''$, $B = 50°29'10''$, $b = 110.04$. **7.** $B = 13°33'$, $b = 37.143$, $c = 158.53$. **9.** $B = 36°10'$, $a = 231.25$, $b = 169.04$. **11.** $A = 44°4'40''$, $B = 45°55'20''$, $b = 67.622$. **13.** $B = 66°44'$, $b = 96.538$, $c = 105.09$. **15.** $B = 16°5'$, $a = 82.47$, $b = 23.778$. **17.** $A = 43°59'55''$, $B = 46°5''$, $b = 198.42$.

Page 55

1. $AB = 21.772$, $CD = 10.276$. **3.** $AB = 91.408$, $AC = 51.559$. **5.** $\angle A = 35°14'$, $CD = 56.676$. **7.** $AC = 55.631$, $DC = 26.488$. **9.** $AC = 1265.3$, $DC = 935.34$. **11.** $AD = 78.193$, $DC = 58.107$. **13.** One side and an angle, two unequal sides, the altitude and an angle, or the altitude and one side.

Page 56

1. $r = 9.7083$, $h = 9.233$. **3.** $a = 6.8403$, $h = 9.397$. **5.** $a = 3.9206$, area $= 1248.6$.

Page 59

1. Bearing S 85°58'20'' E, length of course 2494.8.

Page 60

GROUP A

1. 6.4487. **3.** 78.922. **5.** 41°5'20'', 48°54'40''. **7.** 26°34', 63°26', 63°26'. **9.** 48°59'8'', 48°59'8'', 82°1'44''.

GROUP B

1. 612.57. **3.** 41°48'40''. **5.** 22°23'32'', 22°23'32'', 135°12'56''. **7.** 12°12'45''. **9.** 5.346.

GROUP C

1. 172.7. **3.** 1716.8. **5.** 15.827. **7.** 61°49'15''. **9.** 18.4343.

Page 62

1. 2.097. **3.** 519.98. **5.** 7.1526. **9.** $a + a \cot \alpha \tan \beta$. **13.** 108.766. **17.** 54°44'7'', 35°15'53''. **19.** 450 ft., 49°56'. **21.** 45°12'45''. **23.** 4.5195, horizontal distance; .68889 mi., height of mountain.

Page 70

1. $\sin = .79547$, $\log \sin = 9.90063 - 10$.
3. $\cos = -.92499$, $\log \cos = 9.96614 - 10$.
5. $\tan = -2.4373$, $\log \tan = .38690$.
7. $\sin = .32218$, $\log \sin = 9.50809 - 10$.
9. $\cot = -.8758$, $\log \cot = 9.94241 - 10$.
11. $\sin = .99550$, $\log \sin = 9.99804 - 10$.

Page 73

1. $C = 100°15'$, $a = 65.633$, $b = 47.503$. 3. $A = 49°27'30''$, $B = 58°45'5''$, $C = 71°47'24''$.

Page 75

3. $C = 97°13'$, $a = 789.88$, $c = 919.4$.

Page 77

1. $B = 59°43'$, $C = 72°24'$, $c = 163.59$; $B = 120°17'$, $C = 11°50'$, $c = 35.192$.
3. Impossible. 5. $A = 28°31'26''$, $B = 39°7'34''$, $a = 441.71$.
7. $A = 62°54'18''$, $C = 65°53'42''$, $c = 366.24$; $A = 117°5'42''$, $C = 11°42'18''$,
$c = 81.40$. 9. $A = 44°9'$, $a = 459.2$, $c = 642.87$. 11. Impossible.

Page 80

1. $B = 40°39'31''$, $C = 77°46'29''$, $a = 42.379$. 3. $A = 45°22'1''$,
$B = 61°8'59''$, $c = 3898.9$.

Page 82

1. In. $= 3.873$, Cir. $= 8.2622$. 3. In. $= 12.069$, Cir. $= 24.304$.
5. $a = 34.062$, In. $= 8.6694$, Cir. $= 17.925$. 7. 860.22. 9. 60741.
11. 57310.

Page 83

1. $A = 85°44'40''$, $B = 26°26'10''$, $C = 67°49'20''$. 3. $A = 75°6'40''$,
$B = 42°40'44''$, $C = 62°12'40''$. 5. $A = 24°18'52''$, $B = 119°32'20''$,
$C = 36°8'50''$. 7. $A = 80°3'44''$, $B = 54°5'48''$, $C = 45°50'20''$.
9. $A = 31°20'34''$, $B = 36°32'38''$, $C = 112°6'54''$. 11. $A = 51°37'44''$,
$B = 57°37'40''$, $C = 70°44'34''$.

Page 85

Group A

1. $C = 37°44'35''$, $a = 396.95$, $b = 232.18$. 3. $B = 81°3'30''$, $C = 33°11'25''$,
$c = 65.784$; $B = 98°56'30''$, $C = 15°18'25''$, $c = 31.725$. 5. Impossible.
7. $B = 14°15'5''$, $b = 6.9717$, $c = 17.166$. 9. $A = 48°16'44''$, $B = 60°5'36''$,
$C = 71°37'40''$. 11. $A = 16°46'46''$, $C = 140°30'34''$, $c = 28.314$.

Group B

1. $B = 69°40'25''$, $C = 38°29'5''$, $a = 277.48$. 3. $A = 16°54'6''$,
$B = 105°54'46''$, $C = 57°11'8''$. 5. Impossible. 7. $A = 48°33'37''$,

$B = 93°13'43''$, $c = 62.887$.   9. $C = 60°18'20''$, $a = .16551$, $b = .1924$.
11. $B = 88°13'34''$, $C = 6°23'56''$, $a = 9186.5$.

GROUP C

1. $A = 32°29'48''$, $B = 49°32'22''$, $C = 97°47'44''$.   3. $B = 63°5'43''$,
$C = 9°43'57''$, $c = 30.864$.   5. $A = 105°3'20''$, $a = 901.68$, $b = 190.17$.
7. $A = 118°31'5''$, $B = 5°48'25''$, $a = 91738$.   9. Impossible.   11. $C = 46°23'55''$,
$a = 133.52$, $c = 182.92$.

Page 86

1. $AG = 55,145$; $BG = 57,324$; $AH = 6494.2$; $BH = 12,123$; $GH = 48,793$.

Page 88

GROUP A

1. $A = 46°51'42''$, $B = 71°42'14''$, $C = 61°26'4''$;   area $= 152,550$.
3. $AB = 539.2$.   5. 116.51, 180.49 area $= 20850$.   7. $54,734,000$.
9. $A = 46°34'6''$, $B = 75°31'24''$, $C = 104°28'36''$, $D = 133°26'$; area $= 78.428$.
11. $AB = 2106$.

GROUP B

1. $52°20'56''$; yes.   3. $CD = 359.73$, $BD = 622.77$.   5. 17.489, 8.9594,
area $= 151.32$.   7. $63,063,000$ or $116,600,000$.   9. $A = 49°27'34''$,
$B = 130°32'34''$, $C = 71°47'20''$, $D = 108°12'40''$;   area $= 106.389$.
11. $AB = 924.58$.

GROUP C

1. $A = 101°55'50''$, $B = 53°45'8''$, $C = 126°56'8''$, $D = 77°22'54''$,
$DB = 327.4$.   3. $AB = 644.05$.   5. 29.204, 35.798,   area $= 993.92$.
7. $33,478,000$ or $124,260,000$.   9. Median $= 24.229$.

Page 93

1. 6.044.   3. $\tan B = \dfrac{b \sin A}{c - b \cos A}$; $B = \tan^{-1} \dfrac{b \sin A}{c - b \cos A}$;

$a = \dfrac{x}{\cos B} = \dfrac{c - b \cos A}{\cos B}$; $C = 180° - A - B$. This takes more time and
more computation.   5. 2356.62.   7. $AC = 78,800$ ft.; $AD = 126,480$ ft.;
$CD = 129,490$ ft.   9. 373.35.   11. 301.27.

Page 98

1. $\sec = 7/3$, $\sin \dfrac{2\sqrt{10}}{7}$, $\tan = \dfrac{2\sqrt{10}}{3}$, $\csc = \dfrac{7\sqrt{10}}{20}$, $\cot \dfrac{3\sqrt{10}}{20}$.

3. $\tan = 8/7$, $\sin \dfrac{8\sqrt{113}}{113}$, $\cos = \dfrac{7\sqrt{113}}{113}$, $\csc = \dfrac{\sqrt{113}}{8}$, $\sec \dfrac{\sqrt{113}}{7}$.

Page 100

1. All positive in the first quadrant.

3. *3rd quadrant*   *4th quadrant*

$-, -, -, +$	$-, +, -, -$
$-, -, -, +$	$+, +, -, -$
$-, -, +, +$	$+, -, -, -$
$-, -, +, +$	$+, -, -, -$
$-, -, -, +$	$+, +, -, -$
$-, -, -, +$	$-, +, -, -$

Page 102

GROUP A

1. $\sin^2 \alpha + 2 \sin \alpha \cos \beta + \cos^2 \beta$.
3. $\sin^2 \alpha \cos \beta$.   5. $\sin^2 \alpha - \frac{1}{2}$.   7. $(\cos^2 \alpha - \cos \beta)(\cos^2 \alpha + \cos \beta)$.
9. $(\tan \alpha - \cot \alpha)^2$.   11. $(\sin \alpha - 3 \sec \alpha)(\sin \alpha + 2 \sec \alpha)$.

13. $\dfrac{\sin \alpha \sin \beta + \cos \alpha \cos \beta}{\sin^2 \beta \cos^2 \beta}$.

GROUP B

1. $\sin \alpha \cos \alpha + \sin \beta \cos \alpha + \sin \alpha \sin \beta + \sin^2 \beta$.   3. $\dfrac{\cos^2 \alpha + \cot \beta}{\cos \alpha \tan \beta}$.

5. $\tan^2 \alpha + \frac{1}{3}$.   7. $\sin \alpha \cos \alpha (\sin \alpha - \cos \alpha)$.   9. $(\sin \alpha + \cos \alpha)^2$.

11. $(\cos \alpha + 2 \sin^2 \alpha)(\cos \alpha - \sin^2 \alpha)$.   13. $\dfrac{\tan^2 \alpha - \cot^2 \alpha}{\tan^2 \alpha + \cot^2 \alpha}$.

Page 108

1. $.96593$.   3. $\dfrac{6\sqrt{2} + \sqrt{7}}{12}$ or $.93274$; $\dfrac{6\sqrt{2} - \sqrt{7}}{12}$ or $.48150$.

5. $\dfrac{1 + 2\sqrt{6}}{6} = .98317$.

Page 110

GROUP A

1. $\dfrac{24}{25}$, $7/25$.   3. $2 + \sqrt{3} = 3.7321$.   5. $2 - \sqrt{3} = .2679$.   7. $1, 1/7$.

GROUP B

1. $\dfrac{4\sqrt{5}}{9}, -\dfrac{1}{9}$.   3. $-2 - \sqrt{3} = -3.7321$.   5. $-2 + \sqrt{3} = -.2679$.

7. $-2, \frac{1}{2}$.

Page 114

1. $\sin \frac{1}{2} B = \sqrt{\dfrac{(s-a)(s-c)}{ac}}$, $\sin \frac{1}{2} C = \sqrt{\dfrac{(s-a)(s-b)}{ab}}$.

3. $\tan \frac{1}{2} B = \sqrt{\dfrac{(s-a)(s-c)}{s(s-b)}}$, $\tan \frac{1}{2} C = \sqrt{\dfrac{(s-a)(s-b)}{s(s-c)}}$.

5. $A = 60°17'12''$, $B = 72°28'28''$, $C = 47°14'24''$.

Page 124

3. $-\sin 30°$, $-\cos 30°$, $\tan 30°$, $\cot 30°$, $-\sec 30°$, $-\csc 30°$.

5. $\sin (\theta + n \cdot 180°) = \sin \theta$
$\cos (\theta + n \cdot 180°) = \cos \theta$ when n is even.

7. $\tan (\theta + n \cdot 180°) = \tan \theta$
$\cot (\theta + n \cdot 180°) = \cot \theta$ when n is odd.
$\tan (\theta + n \cdot 180°) = \tan \theta$
$\cot (\theta + n \cdot 180°) = \cot \theta$ when n is even.

Page 125

1. 1.309, 1.466, 1.693, 1.998.

Page 126

1. .17, .64, .94.

Page 130

1. .175, .349, .524, .698, .873, 1.047, 1.222, 1.396, 1.571. **3.** .017, .035, .052, .070, .087, .105, .122, .140, .157. **5.** (a) .163, (b) 1.10, (c) .43, (d) 1.30, (e) 1.97. **7.** 47.124 ft. per sec.

9.

x	0	$\pi/6$	$\pi/4$	$\pi/3$	$\pi/2$	$2\pi/3$	$3\pi/4$	$5\pi/6$	2π
$1 + \sin x$	1	1.5	1.71	1.87	2.	1.87	1.71	1.5	1.
$x + \sin x$	0	1.02	1.49	1.91	2.57	2.96	3.06	3.12	6.28

15. $\dfrac{\cos \theta + \sqrt{3} \sin \theta}{2}$. **17.** $\dfrac{\cos \theta - \sqrt{3} \sin \theta}{2}$

Page 133

1. 45°. **3.** 45°. **5.** 30°. **7.** $\dfrac{\sqrt{3}}{2}$. **9.** $\dfrac{3}{4}$. **11.** $\dfrac{3}{5}$. **13.** $\dfrac{1}{x}$.

Page 134

1. 30°, 150°, 390°. **3.** 45°, 135°, 405°. **5.** 90°, 450°, 810°. **7.** 60°, 300°, 420°. **9.** 45°, 315°, 405°. **11.** 0°, 360°, 720°. **13.** 135°, 315°, 495°. **15.** 120°, 300°, 480°. **17.** 150°, 330°, 510°. **19.** 144°44′, 324°44′, 504°44′. **21.** 135°, 315°, 495°. **23.** 120°, 300°, 480°. **25.** 0°, 360°, 720°. **27.** 45°, 315°, 405°. **29.** 45°, 315°, 405°. **31.** 270°, 630°, 990°. **33.** 26°38′, 153°22′, 386°38′.

Page 136

1. 49°, 131°, 409°, 491°; 229°, 311°, 589°, 671°. **3.** 45°, 225°, 405°, 585°.

Page 138

11. $\dfrac{32}{9}$. **13.** $\dfrac{36}{37}$. **15.** $x\sqrt{1-4x^2}+2x\sqrt{1-x^2}$. **17.** $\dfrac{53}{\sqrt{10\cdot17\cdot37}}$.

19. $\dfrac{3(1-\sqrt5+\sqrt{21}-\sqrt{15\cdot63})}{1-\sqrt{45}-\sqrt{15\cdot63}-\sqrt{3\cdot63}}$. **21.** $-\dfrac{3}{\sqrt{34}}$.

Page 140

1. $2n\pi\pm\cos^{-1}\left(\dfrac{-1+\sqrt5}{2}\right)$, $2n\pi\pm\dfrac{\pi}{2}$.

3. $n\pi\pm\dfrac{\pi}{2}$. **5.** $2n\pi\pm\cos^{-1}\left(\dfrac{\pm1\sqrt5}{5}\right)$.

7. $2n\pi\pm\frac{2}{3}\pi$. **9.** $2n\pi\pm\dfrac{\pi}{2}$, $2n\pi+\frac{2}{3}\pi$. **11.** $2n\pi\pm\dfrac{\pi}{3}$.

13. $n\pi$, $2n\pi\pm\dfrac{\pi}{3}$. **15.** $2n\pi\pm\dfrac{\pi}{2}$, $2n\pi\pm\sin^{-1}\left(-\dfrac{3}{5}\right)$. **17.** $n\pi\pm\dfrac{\pi}{2}$,

$n\pi\pm\dfrac{\pi}{4}$. **19.** $n\pi\pm\dfrac{\pi}{6}$. **21.** $2n\pi\pm\dfrac{\pi}{4}$, $2n\pi\pm\frac{3}{4}\pi$, $2n\pi\pm\dfrac{\pi}{3}$, $2n\pi=\frac{2}{3}\pi$.

23. $n\pi\pm\dfrac{\pi}{4}$, $n\pi\pm\frac{3}{4}\pi$. **25.** $n\pi$, $2n\pi\pm\sin^{-1}\left(\dfrac{\pm\sqrt{2\pm\sqrt3}}{2}\right)$.

Page 143

1. $x=\tan^{-1}\dfrac{4}{15}+\cos^{-1}\dfrac{\sqrt{241}}{24}$, $y=\tan^{-1}\dfrac{4}{15}-\cos^{-1}\dfrac{\sqrt{241}}{24}$.

3. $y=\cos^{-1}\dfrac{a\pm\sqrt{b+2-a^2}}{2}$, $x=\cos^{-1}\dfrac{a\mp\sqrt{b+2-a^2}}{2}$.

5. $r=\pm3\sqrt{41}$, $x=\sin^{-1}2/3$, $y=\tan^{-1}5/4$.

7. $r=\pm\sqrt{47}$, $x=\tan^{-1}\dfrac{2\sqrt5}{3\sqrt3}$.

9. $r=\pm2\sqrt6$, $x=\sin^{-1}\dfrac{1}{\sqrt2}$, $y=\tan^{-1}\sqrt{\dfrac{7}{5}}$.

Page 144

1. $\pm\dfrac{1}{\sqrt2}$. **3.** ±1. **5.** $\sqrt{\dfrac{3}{28}}$. **7.** $\frac{1}{2}$. **9.** $\pm\frac{1}{6}\sqrt6$. **11.** $\pm\dfrac{25}{24}$.

Page 152

1. $\cos\dfrac{\varphi}{4}+i\sin\dfrac{\varphi}{4}$, $\cos\dfrac{2\pi+\varphi}{4}+i\sin\dfrac{2\pi+\varphi}{4}$, $\cos\dfrac{4\pi+\varphi}{4}+i\sin\dfrac{4\pi+\varphi}{4}$,

$\cos\dfrac{6\pi+\varphi}{4}+i\sin\dfrac{6\pi+\varphi}{4}$. **3.** $\cos\dfrac{\pi}{4}+i\sin\dfrac{\pi}{4}$, $\cos\dfrac{\pi}{2}+i\sin\dfrac{\pi}{2}$,

$\cos \frac{3}{4}\pi + i\sin \frac{3}{4}\pi$, $\cos \pi + i\sin \pi$, $\cos \frac{5}{4}\pi + i\sin \frac{5}{4}\pi$, $\cos \frac{3}{2}\pi + i\sin \frac{3}{2}\pi$,

$\cos \frac{7}{4}\pi + i\sin \frac{7}{4}\pi$, $\cos 2\pi + i\sin 2\pi$.

Page 153

3. $-i$, $-\frac{\sqrt{3}}{2} + \frac{i}{2}$, $\frac{\sqrt{3}}{2} + \frac{i}{2}$.

Page 154

5. $\cos\theta\,[4\cos^2\theta - 3]$. **7.** $\cos\theta\,[16\cos^4\theta - 20\cos^2\theta + 5]$.

Page 162

13. Minus the reciprocal.

Page 164

15. $\dfrac{\sin[(n+1)A]\sin\frac{n}{2}A}{\sin\frac{A}{2}}$. **17.** $\dfrac{\sin[(2n-1)A]\sin nA}{\sin A}$.

Page 169
CUMULATIVE REVIEW I

1. $\sin A = a/c$, $\cos A = b/c$, $\tan A = a/b$, $\cot A = b/a$, $\csc A = c/a$, $\sec A = c/b$. **3.** $\sin A = 3/4$, $\cos A = \sqrt{7}/4$, $\tan A = 3/\sqrt{7}$, $\csc A = 4/3$, $\sec A = 4/\sqrt{7}$, $\cot A = \sqrt{7}/3$. **5.** Cofunctions of complementary angles are equal. **9.** $\sin 40°50' = .6799$, $\cos 42°50' = .7333$, $\tan 42°50' = .9272$,

CUMULATIVE REVIEW II

1. $\sin x = \sqrt{65/9}$, $\tan x = \sqrt{65/4}$, $\sec x = 9/4$, $\csc x = 9/\sqrt{65}$, $\cot x = 4/\sqrt{65}$. **3.** $b = a\cot A$, $c = a/\sin A$. **9.** $\csc 12°$, $\sec 41°$, $\cos 34°$, $\sin 7°$, $\cot 26°$, $\tan 21°$. **11.** 1.885. **13.** 6.9953. **15.** $40°41'40''$. **17.** $34°34'47''$.

Page 170
CUMULATIVE REVIEW III

1. Proj. on $OX - A_1B_1 = AB\cos A$; proj. on $OY - A_2B_2 = AB\sin A$. **3.** $\sin 82°$, $-\cos 6°$, $-\tan 45°$, $-\cot 53°$, $-\sec 31°$, $\csc 16°$. **5.** 431.9, 463.1. **7.** 5.0034. **9.** Sides, 34.351; angles $68°45'$. **11.** $A = nr^2\tan 180°/n$.

Page 171
CUMULATIVE REVIEW IV

1. $57°54'36''$, $46°34'3''$, $75°31'21''$. **5.** 26.833. **7.** $82°49'10''$, $55°46'16''$, $41°24'36''$; $90°$, $53°7'48''$, $36°52'12''$. **9.** 15659. **13.** One angle and one side.

17. $B = 76°27'3''$, $C = 54°18'27''$, $b = 230.83$; $B = 5°3'57''$, $C = 125°41'33''$, $b = 20.966$.   **19.** $B = 95°12'30''$, $C = 35°33'$, $b = 330.32$.

Page 172

CUMULATIVE REVIEW V

1. $135°15'$.   **3.** $15°55'$.   **5.** $\tan^2 A + 1 = \sec^2 A$, $\cot^2 A + 1 = \csc^2 A$.

CUMULATIVE REVIEW VI

1. 25.933.   **3.** $\sin A = \sqrt{7}/4$, $\tan A = \sqrt{7}/3$, $\csc A = 4/\sqrt{7}$, $\sec A = 4/3$, $\cot A = 3/\sqrt{7}$.   **5.** $\cos A = \dfrac{1}{\sec A}$, $\sin A = \dfrac{\sqrt{\sec^2 A - 1}}{\sec A}$,

$\tan A = \sqrt{\sec^2 A - 1}$, $\cot A = \dfrac{1}{\sqrt{\sec^2 A - 1}}$, $\csc A = \dfrac{\sec A}{\sqrt{\sec^2 A - 1}}$.

7. $6°$.   **9.** $B = 45°55'21''$, $C = 61°50'39''$, $a = 26.247$.   **11.** 9.0102.

CUMULATIVE REVIEW VII

19. No triangle.

CUMULATIVE REVIEW VIII

1. $\sin (A + B) = \dfrac{2\sqrt{2} + 3}{6}$, $\cos (A + B) = \dfrac{2\sqrt{6} - 1}{6}$.   **3.** $\cot A = \dfrac{1}{\tan A}$, $\sec A = \sqrt{1 + \tan^2 A}$, $\cos A = \dfrac{1}{\sqrt{1 + \tan^2 A}}$, $\sin A = \dfrac{\tan A}{\sqrt{1 + \tan^2 A}}$, $\csc A = \dfrac{\sqrt{1 + \tan^2 A}}{\tan A}$.

CUMULATIVE REVIEW IX

1. $\sin 7°20'$, $-\sin 3°35'$, $-\cot 40°50'$, $-\tan 16°10'$, $-\sec 8°20'$, $\sec 39°20'$.
3. $\cot (A + 45°) = \dfrac{1 - \tan A}{1 + \tan A}$, $\cot (A - 45°) = \dfrac{\tan A + 1}{\tan A - 1}$.

Page 175

1. S $50°24'$ W. 2124.4.

Page 177

1. Net fall, 35.278, L. C. 3365.255.   **3.** Net fall, 341.811, L. C. 2643.182.
5. Net rise, 294.249, L. C. 1954.33.
7. $116.4.366$, S $69°11'$ E.   **9.** 1824.269, N $42°46'$ E, $A = 123.236$.
11. 17.558.

Page 179

1. 905.87.   **3.** 337.467.   **5.** AC is 75.06, BC is 115.78.
7. 69.0375, 29.30475.

Page 180

3. $54°25'10''$. **5.** 3.2288.

Page 182

1. 1.5383. **3.** $.089$. **5.** $59°47'38''$.

Page 182

1. $AO = \dfrac{a \sin \beta}{\sin (\alpha + \beta)}$, $OP = \dfrac{a \sin \beta \tan \gamma}{\sin (\alpha + \beta)}$. **3.** $b = \dfrac{a}{\tan \alpha}$.

5. $\sin \Theta = \sin \alpha \cos \beta$. **7.** $\dfrac{\tan \beta}{\sin \alpha}$. **9.** $25°58'$.

11. $\sqrt{\overline{C_2C_1}^2 - (r_1 r_2)^2} + \pi (r_2 + r_1) + 2 (r_2 - r_1) \sin \dfrac{r_2 - r_1}{C_2 C_1}$. **13.** $r \cot \dfrac{\alpha}{2}$.

15. 150.027. **17.** $DA = 383.294$, $DC = 332.126$, $DB = 526.704$.

Page 196

GROUP A

1. $A = 33°41'0''$, $b = 55°10'16''$, $c = 59°55'52''$.
3. $a = 19°51'29''$, $B = 97°54'42''$, $c = 110°51'46''$.
5. $c = 47°49'16''$, $A = 58°34'43''$, $a = 39°13'30''$.
7. $B = 63°9'20''$, $A = 102°2'43''$, $a = 103°31'34''$.
9. $a = 47°5'12''$, $B = 106°7'55''$, $c = 104°29'0''$.
11. $a = 57°13'8''$, $B = 58°15'30''$, $b = 53°39'16''$.

GROUP B

1. Impossible. **3.** $A = 53°24'14''$, $B = 67°19'19''$, $c = 71°55'25''$.
5. $b = 53°4'20''$, $A = 141°1'53''$, $a = 147°6'49''$.
7. $b = 48°5'22''$, $A = 78°28'34''$, $a = 74°40'40''$.
9. $A = 64°57'16''$, $B = 57°10'32''$, $c = 72°27'28''$.
11. $a = 79°16'0''$, $B = 64°58'58''$, $b = 64°35'35''$.

Page 197

1. $A = 45°51'55''$, $B = 55°1'0''$, $C = 113°31'52''$.
3. $B = 67°20'24''$, $a = 139°58'6''$, $A = 160°24'14''$.
5. $b = 25°32'24''$, $a = 162°25'34''$, $A = 135°32'45''$.
7. $a = 116°51'19''$, $B = 68°50'37''$, $C = 80°5'1''$.
9. Impossible. **11.** $a = 122°1'57''$, $b = 49°37'28''$, $C = 69°52'17''$.
13. $B = 47°53'33''$, $a = 145°33'42''$, $A = 153°2'14''$.
15. $a = 102°30'33''$, $B = 61°30'52''$, $C = 83°17'48''$.

Page 197

ISOSCELES TRIANGLES

1. $C = 39°18'57''$, $C = 106°38'41''$. **3.** $C = 73°26'14''$, $c = 71°39'46''$.
5. $C = 131°23'24''$, $c = 121°5'48''$. **7.** $A = 70°30'41''$, $c = 58°41'38''$.
9. $c = 110°59'29''$, $C = 150°29'30''$. **11.** $a = 52°38'21''$, $c = 43°23'29''$.

Page 207

1. $A = 36°34'20''$, $B = 44°11'0''$, $C = 115°36'0''$.
3. $a = 17°33'40''$, $b = 16°32'12''$, $c = 13°52'56''$.
5. $A = 50°3'13''$, $B = 126°22'27''$, $C = 16°43'29''$.
7. $a = 64°21'56''$, $b = 46°23'36''$, $c = 52°17'56''$.
9. $a = 43°41'3''$, $b = 51°30'48''$, $c = 53°57'12''$.
11. $a = 86°52'19''$, $b = 57°3'4''$, $c = 92°49'9''$.

Page 208

1. $A = 74°30'18''$, $B = 41°46'3''$, $c = 45°2'16''$.
3. $b = 58°21'24''$, $c = 50°14'39''$, $A = 62°42'16''$.
5. $A = 20°59'48''$, $B = 64°8'40''$, $c = 36°27'38''$.
7. $A = 104°12'14''$, $C = 61°5'0''$, $b = 76°55'10''$.
9. $A = 125°20'35''$, $B = 66°12'27''$, $c = 66°5'42''$.

Page 210

GROUP A

1. $A = 40°19'40''$, $C = 93°25'22''$, $c = 71°6'24''$.
3. $c = 28°37'37''$, $B = 102°44'18''$, $b = 60°53'2''$.
5. $B = 56°12'0''$, $c = 24°35'36''$, $C = 21°42'18''$.
7. $C = 61°24'40''$, $B = 60°12'50''$, $b = 52°21'15''$.
9. $a = 68°47'0''$, $C = 72°33'18''$, $c = 70°45'38''$.

GROUP B

1. $B = 54°38'45''$, $C = 112°4'26''$, $c = 102°18'51''$.
3. $C = 43°31'23''$, $B = 111°10'31''$, $b = 92°11'38''$.
5. Two solutions: $a = 57°10'15''$, $B = 29°26'26''$, $b = 25°8'4''$;
   $a = 122°49'45''$, $B = 111°37'29''$, $b = 126°32'54''$.
7. Two solutions: $b = 32°58'9''$, $A = 78°50'19''$, $a = 37°41'37''$;
   $b = 147°1'51''$, $A = 165°40'36''$, $a = 171°7'56''$.
9. $b = 71°46'45''$, $C = 18°42'0''$, $c = 17°56'53''$.

GROUP C

1. $b = 44°58'28''$, $C = 54°8'38''$, $c = 39°40'24''$.   3. Impossible.
5. $c = 56°6'47''$, $B = 22°23'18''$, $b = 18°36'20''$.
7. Two solutions: $c = 55°21'20''$, $A = 67°8'49''$, $a = 52°18'22''$;
   $c = 124°38'40''$, $A = 162°28'0''$, $a = 165°0'22''$.
9. $B = 25°19'47''$, $c = 56°25'36''$, $C = 55°38'6''$.

Page 212

1. 2251 mi.   3. 11,429 mi.   5. 6762.776 mi.   7. 3949.174 mi.
9. $A = 106°7'7''$ or $73°52'53''$.

Page 214

1. $8^h 47^m 42^s$.   3. $44°19'$.   5. $61°54'44''$, $4°3'45''$.

INDEX

FIVE-PLACE TABLES

LOGARITHMS
LOGARITHMIC FUNCTIONS
NATURAL FUNCTIONS

COMPILED BY

N. J. LENNES

AND

A. S. MERRILL

University of Montana

HARPER & BROTHERS PUBLISHERS
NEW YORK AND LONDON

CONTENTS

PREFACE

ANOTHER set of five-place tables of logarithms and trigonometric functions requires justification. Such justification, we believe, is to be found in the exceptionally convenient form of these tables, in the attractiveness and general excellence of the typography, and in a degree of accuracy which is known to be almost, if not entirely, absolute.

The type is of good size and body, all numerals are of the same height, and the general result is such as to make continued use particularly easy. In every case, that part of a number which is to be prefixed to the numerals given is found by looking above in the same column. This avoids the use of asterisks and the looking across the page each time a logarithm is to be found. The result is a real advantage both in elementary instruction and in practical use.

An accurate set of five-place tables is perhaps not as common as one might expect. The set from which the original copy for these tables was made had several scores of errors. Our random selection for this purpose may have been unfortunate.

The manuscript of logarithms of numbers and of logarithmic functions was corrected by reading against Bremiker's edition of Vega's seven-place tables. No table of natural functions of known reliability being available, this part of the table was recomputed completely. For this purpose the logarithms of these functions were found in Schrön's seven-place table and the numbers finally determined by using the tables of the U. S. Coast and Geodetic Survey. Schrön's table, using a system indicating plus or minus after the last figure, gives each logarithm to within 5 in the eighth place. This left no doubt as to the figure in the fifth place of the numbers except in about a half-dozen cases where the correct value is almost exactly half way between two consecutive five-place numbers. It is possible that in some of these cases accuracy might be improved by changing the figure in the fifth place, but we know that the maximum improvement that is thus possible is one unit in the seventh place.

3

The cast proof of the tables of logarithms and logarithmic functions was read by separate teams against the Schrön and the Bruhn tables, this reading disclosing in all five errors. In every case the final figure was decided upon by using the Schrön table with its final plus and minus marking. The logarithms of numbers were also read against the ten-place table of the U. S. Coast and Geodetic Survey. No discrepancies between these tables were detected except one error in a heading in the Bruhn table.

The cast proof of the table of natural functions was read against Loomis' six-place table, which however fails to decide the last figure in our table, in about seven hundred cases. These were recomputed. In this reading and recomputing of the cast table of natural functions one error was found. Also one error was found in the Loomis table which gives cot 32° 24′ = 1.57555 instead of 1.57575. If the very high degree of accuracy of the Loomis table had been known to us we could have spared ourselves much computing, though it would still remain to settle cases of doubtful last figures.

The tables of differences were computed directly from the columns of logarithms and this provided an additional check against gross errors in the tables of logarithms and logarithmic functions.

As an introduction, when the tables are bound separately, the chapter on logarithms in our trigonometry has been used. This affords the most convenient arrangement for the initial study of the use of the tables that has come to our attention. For instance on page XII (in *Trigonometry*, p. 38) there is the first study of finding logarithms of numbers and this refers solely to the table on the page opposite. Finding antilogarithms is introduced on page XIV (p. 40) and the page of table opposite contains all of the logarithms that are used. A similar arrangement is made on pages XXII and XXIII (pp. 48 and 49) for learning to use the table of logarithmic functions. Appropriate exercises are given at each step so that the table may be used readily in the class room for practice in the use of logarithms without arranging additional material.

N. J. LENNES
A. S. MERRILL

LOGARITHMS OF NUMBERS[1]

[1] From Five-Place Tables compiled by N. J. Lennes and A. S. Merrill, Harper & Brothers, Publishers.

Numbers 100–150 Logs 00000–17869

N	0	1	2	3	4	5	6	7	8	9
100	00 000	00 043	00 087	00 130	00 173	00 217	00 260	00 303	00 346	00 389
101	432	475	518	561	604	647	689	732	775	817
102	860	903	945	988	01 030	01 072	01 115	01 157	01 199	01 242
103	01 284	01 326	01 368	01 410	452	494	536	578	620	662
104	703	745	787	828	870	912	953	995	02 036	02 078
105	02 119	02 160	02 202	02 243	02 284	02 325	02 366	02 407	449	490
106	531	572	612	653	694	735	776	816	857	898
107	938	979	03 019	03 060	03 100	03 141	03 181	03 222	03 262	03 302
108	03 342	03 383	423	463	503	543	583	623	663	703
109	743	782	822	862	902	941	981	04 021	04 060	04 100
110	04 139	04 179	04 218	04 258	04 297	04 336	04 376	04 415	04 454	04 493
111	532	571	610	650	689	727	766	805	844	883
112	922	961	999	05 038	05 077	05 115	05 154	05 192	05 231	05 269
113	05 308	05 346	05 385	423	461	500	538	576	614	652
114	690	729	767	805	843	881	918	956	994	06 032
115	06 070	06 108	06 145	06 183	06 221	06 258	06 296	06 333	06 371	408
116	446	483	521	558	595	633	670	707	744	781
117	819	856	893	930	967	07 004	07 041	07 078	07 115	07 151
118	07 188	07 225	07 262	07 298	07 335	372	408	445	482	518
119	555	591	628	664	700	737	773	809	846	882
120	07 918	07 954	07 990	08 027	08 063	08 099	08 135	08 171	08 207	08 243
121	08 279	08 314	08 350	386	422	458	493	529	565	600
122	636	672	707	743	778	814	849	884	920	955
123	991	09 026	09 061	09 096	09 132	09 167	09 202	09 237	09 272	09 307
124	09 342	377	412	447	482	517	552	587	621	656
125	691	726	760	795	830	864	899	934	968	10 003
126	10 037	10 072	10 106	10 140	10 175	10 209	10 243	10 278	10 312	346
127	380	415	449	483	517	551	585	619	653	687
128	721	755	789	823	857	890	924	958	992	11 025
129	11 059	11 093	11 126	11 160	11 193	11 227	11 261	11 294	11 327	361
130	11 394	11 428	11 461	11 494	11 528	11 561	11 594	11 628	11 661	11 694
131	727	760	793	826	860	893	926	959	992	12 024
132	12 057	12 090	12 123	12 156	12 189	12 222	12 254	12 287	12 320	352
133	385	418	450	483	516	548	581	613	646	678
134	710	743	775	808	840	872	905	937	969	13 001
135	13 033	13 066	13 098	13 130	13 162	13 194	13 226	13 253	13 290	322
136	354	386	418	450	481	513	545	577	609	640
137	672	704	735	767	799	830	862	893	925	956
138	988	14 019	14 051	14 082	14 114	14 145	14 176	14 203	14 239	14 270
139	14 301	333	364	395	426	457	489	520	551	582
140	14 613	14 644	14 675	14 706	14 737	14 763	14 799	14 829	14 860	14 891
141	922	953	983	15 014	15 045	15 076	15 106	15 137	15 168	15 198
142	15 229	15 259	15 290	320	351	381	412	442	473	503
143	534	564	594	625	655	685	715	746	776	806
144	836	866	897	927	957	987	16 017	16 047	16 077	16 107
145	16 137	16 167	16 197	16 227	16 256	16 286	316	346	376	406
146	435	465	495	524	554	584	613	643	673	702
147	732	761	791	820	850	879	909	938	967	997
148	17 026	17 056	17 085	17 114	17 143	17 173	17 202	17 231	17 260	17 289
149	319	348	377	406	435	464	493	522	551	580
150	17 609	17 638	17 667	17 696	17 725	17 754	17 782	17 811	17 840	17 869
N	0	1	2	3	4	5	6	7	8	9

P.P.

	43	42	41
1	4.3	4.2	4.1
2	8.6	8.4	8.2
3	12.9	12.6	12.3
4	17.2	16.8	16.4
5	21.5	21.0	20.5
6	25.8	25.2	24.6
7	30.1	29.4	28.7
8	34.4	33.6	32.8
9	38.7	37.8	36.9

	40	39	38
1	4.0	3.9	3.8
2	8.0	7.8	7.6
3	12.0	11.7	11.4
4	16.0	15.6	15.2
5	20.0	19.5	19.0
6	24.0	23.4	22.8
7	28.0	27.3	26.6
8	32.0	31.2	30.4
9	36.0	35.1	34.2

	37	36	35
1	3.7	3.6	3.5
2	7.4	7.2	7.0
3	11.1	10.8	10.5
4	14.8	14.4	14.0
5	18.5	18.0	17.5
6	22.2	21.6	21.0
7	25.9	25.2	24.5
8	29.6	28.8	28.0
9	33.3	32.4	31.5

	34	33	32
1	3.4	3.3	3.2
2	6.8	6.6	6.4
3	10.2	9.9	9.6
4	13.6	13.2	12.8
5	17.0	16.5	16.0
6	20.4	19.8	19.2
7	23.8	23.1	22.4
8	27.2	26.4	25.6
9	30.6	29.7	28.8

	31	30	29
1	3.1	3.0	2.9
2	6.2	6.0	5.8
3	9.3	9.0	8.7
4	12.4	12.0	11.6
5	15.5	15.0	14.5
6	18.6	18.0	17.4
7	21.7	21.0	20.3
8	24.8	24.0	23.2
9	27.9	27.0	26.1

N	0	1	2	3	4	5	6	7	8	9
150	17 609	17 638	17 667	17 696	17 725̄	17 754	17 782	17 811	17 840	17 869
151	898	926	955	984	18 013	18 041	18 070	18 099	18 127	18 156
152	18 184	18 213	18 241	18 270	298	327	355	384	412	441
153	469	498	526	554	583	611	639	667	696	724
154	752	780	808	837	865̄	893	921	949	977	19 005
155	19 033	19 061	19 089	19 117	19 145	19 173	19 201	19 229	19 257	285̄
156	312	340	368	396	424	451	479	507	535̄	562
157	590	618	645	673	700	728	756	783	811	838
158	866	893	921	948	976	20 003	20 030	20 058	20 085	20 112
159	20 140	20 167	20 194	20 222	20 249	276	303	330	358	385̄
160	20 412	20 439	20 466	20 493	20 520	20 548	20 575̄	20 602	20 629	20 656
161	683	710	737	763	790	817	844	871	898	925̄
162	952	978	21 005	21 032	21 059	21 085	21 112	21 139	21 165	21 192
163	21 219	21 245	272	299	325	352	378	405̄	431	458
164	484	511	537	564	590	617	643	669	696	722
165	748	775̄	801	827	854	880	906	932	958	985̄
166	22 011	22 037	22 063	22 089	22 115	22 141	22 167	22 194	22 220	22 246
167	272	298	324	350	376	401	427	453	479	505̄
168	531	557	583	608	634	660	686	712	737	763
169	789	814	840	866	891	917	943	968	994	23 019
170	23 045̄	23 070	23 096	23 121	23 147	23 172	23 198	23 223	23 249	23 274
171	300	325	350	376	401	426	452	477	502	528̄
172	553	578	603	629	654	679	704	729	754	779
173	805̄	830	855	880	905̄	930	955	980	24 005̄	24 030
174	24 055̄	24 080	24 105̄	24 130	24 155̄	24 180	24 204	24 229	254	279
175	304	329	353	378	403	428	452	477	502	527̄
176	551	576	601	625	650	674	699	724	748	773
177	797	822	846	871	895	920	944	969	993	25 018
178	25 042	25 066	25 091	25 115	25 139	25 164	25 188	25 212	25 237	261
179	285̄	310	334	358	382	406	431	455̄	479	503
180	25 527	25 551	25 575̄	25 600	25 624	25 648	25 672	25 696	25 720	25 744
181	768	792	816	840	864	888	912	935	959	983
182	26 007	26 031	26 055̄	26 079	26 102	26 126	26 150	26 174	26 198	26 221
183	245	269	293	316	340	364	387	411	435̄	458
184	482	505̄	529	553	576	600	623	647	670	694
185	717	741	764	788	811	834	858	881	905̄	928
186	951	975̄	998	27 021	27 045̄	27 068	27 091	27 114	27 138	27 161
187	27 184	27 207	27 231	254	277	300	323	346	370	393
188	416	439	462	485	508	531	554	577	600	623
189	646	669	692	715	738	761	784	807	830	852
190	27 875̄	27 898	27 921	27 944	27 967	27 989	28 012	28 035̄	28 058	28 081
191	28 103	28 126	28 149	28 171	28 194	28 217	240	262	285̄	307
192	330	353	375	398	421	443	466	488	511	533
193	556	578	601	623	646	668	691	713	735	758
194	780	803	825̄	847	870	892	914	937	959	981
195	29 003	29 026	29 048	29 070	29 092	29 115̄	29 137	29 159	29 181	29 203
196	226	248	270	292	314	336	358	380	403	425̄
197	447	469	491	513	535̄	557	579	601	623	645̄
198	667	688	710	732	754	776	798	820	842	863
199	885	907	929	951	973	994	30 016	30 038	30 060	30 081
200	30 103	30 125̄	30 146	30 168	30 190	30 211	30 233	30 255̄	30 276	30 298
N	0	1	2	3	4	5	6	7	8	9

P.P.

	29	28		27	26		25	24		23	22		21
1	2.9	2.8	1	2.7	2.6	1	2.5	2.4	1	2.3	2.2	1	2.1
2	5.8	5.6	2	5.4	5.2	2	5.0	4.8	2	4.6	4.4	2	4.2
3	8.7	8.4	3	8.1	7.8	3	7.5	7.2	3	6.9	6.6	3	6.3
4	11.6	11.2	4	10.8	10.4	4	10.0	9.6	4	9.2	8.8	4	8.4
5	14.5	14.0	5	13.5	13.0	5	12.5	12.0	5	11.5	11.0	5	10.5
6	17.4	16.8	6	16.2	15.6	6	15.0	14.4	6	13.8	13.2	6	12.6
7	20.3	19.6	7	18.9	18.2	7	17.5	16.8	7	16.1	15.4	7	14.7
8	23.2	22.4	8	21.6	20.8	8	20.0	19.2	8	18.4	17.6	8	16.8
9	26.1	25.2	9	24.3	23.4	9	22.5	21.6	9	20.7	19.8	9	18.9

Numbers 200–250   Logs 30103–39950

N	0	1	2	3	4	5	6	7	8	9
200	30 103	30 125	30 146	30 168	30 190	30 211	30 233	30 255	30 276	30 298
201	320	341	363	384	406	428	449	471	492	514
202	535	557	578	600	621	643	664	685	707	728
203	750	771	792	814	835	856	878	899	920	942
204	963	984	31 006	31 027	31 048	31 069	31 091	31 112	31 133	31 154
205	31 175	31 197	218	239	260	281	302	323	345	366
206	387	408	429	450	471	492	513	534	555	576
207	597	618	639	660	681	702	723	744	765	785
208	806	827	848	869	890	911	931	952	973	994
209	32 015	32 035	32 056	32 077	32 098	32 118	32 139	32 160	32 181	32 201
210	32 222	32 243	32 263	32 284	32 305	32 325	32 346	32 366	32 387	32 408
211	428	449	469	490	510	531	552	572	593	613
212	634	654	675	695	715	736	756	777	797	818
213	838	858	879	899	919	940	960	980	33 001	33 021
214	33 041	33 062	33 082	33 102	33 122	33 143	33 163	33 183	203	224
215	244	264	284	304	325	345	365	385	405	425
216	445	465	486	506	526	546	566	586	606	626
217	646	666	686	706	726	746	766	786	806	826
218	846	866	885	905	925	945	965	985	34 005	34 025
219	34 044	34 064	34 084	34 104	34 124	34 143	34 163	34 183	203	223
220	34 242	34 262	34 282	34 301	34 321	34 341	34 361	34 380	34 400	34 420
221	439	459	479	498	518	537	557	577	596	616
222	635	655	674	694	713	733	753	772	792	811
223	830	850	869	889	908	928	947	967	986	35 005
224	35 025	35 044	35 064	35 083	35 102	35 122	35 141	35 160	35 180	199
225	218	238	257	276	295	315	334	353	372	392
226	411	430	449	468	488	507	526	545	564	583
227	603	622	641	660	679	698	717	736	755	774
228	793	813	832	851	870	889	908	927	946	965
229	984	36 003	36 021	36 040	36 059	36 078	36 097	36 116	36 135	36 154
230	36 173	36 192	36 211	36 229	36 248	36 267	36 286	36 305	36 324	36 342
231	361	380	399	418	436	455	474	493	511	530
232	549	568	586	605	624	642	661	680	698	717
233	736	754	773	791	810	829	847	866	884	903
234	922	940	959	977	996	37 014	37 033	37 051	37 070	37 088
235	37 107	37 125	37 144	37 162	37 181	199	218	236	254	273
236	291	310	328	346	365	383	401	420	438	457
237	475	493	511	530	548	566	585	603	621	639
238	658	676	694	712	731	749	767	785	803	822
239	840	858	876	894	912	931	949	967	985	38 003
240	38 021	38 039	38 057	38 075	38 093	38 112	38 130	38 148	38 166	38 184
241	202	220	238	256	274	292	310	328	346	364
242	382	399	417	435	453	471	489	507	525	543
243	561	578	596	614	632	650	668	686	703	721
244	739	757	775	792	810	828	846	863	881	899
245	917	934	952	970	987	39 005	39 023	39 041	39 058	39 076
246	39 094	39 111	39 129	39 146	39 164	182	199	217	235	252
247	270	287	305	322	340	358	375	393	410	428
248	445	463	480	498	515	533	550	568	585	602
249	620	637	655	672	690	707	724	742	759	777
250	39 794	39 811	39 829	39 846	39 863	39 881	39 898	39 915	39 933	39 950
N	0	1	2	3	4	5	6	7	8	9

P.P.

	22	21	20	19	18	17
1	2.2	2.1	2.0	1.9	1.8	1.7
2	4.4	4.2	4.0	3.8	3.6	3.4
3	6.6	6.3	6.0	5.7	5.4	5.1
4	8.8	8.4	8.0	7.6	7.2	6.8
5	11.0	10.5	10.0	9.5	9.0	8.5
6	13.2	12.6	12.0	11.4	10.8	10.2
7	15.4	14.7	14.0	13.3	12.6	11.9
8	17.6	16.8	16.0	15.2	14.4	13.6
9	19.8	18.9	18.0	17.1	16.2	15.3

Numbers 250–300   Logs 39794–47842

N	0	1	2	3	4	5	6	7	8	9
250	39 794	39 811	39 829	39 846	39 863	39 881	39 898	39 915	39 933	39 950
251	967	985	40 002	40 019	40 037	40 054	40 071	40 088	40 106	40 123
252	40 140	40 157	175	192	209	226	243	261	278	295
253	312	329	346	364	381	398	415	432	449	466
254	483	500	518	535	552	569	586	603	620	637
255	654	671	688	705	722	739	756	773	790	807
256	824	841	858	875	892	909	926	943	960	976
257	993	41 010	41 027	41 044	41 061	41 078	41 095	41 111	41 128	41 145
258	41 162	179	196	212	229	246	263	280	296	313
259	330	347	363	380	397	414	430	447	464	481
260	41 497	41 514	41 531	41 547	41 564	41 581	41 597	41 614	41 631	41 647
261	664	681	697	714	731	747	764	780	797	814
262	830	847	863	880	896	913	929	946	963	979
263	996	42 012	42 029	42 045	42 062	42 078	42 095	42 111	42 127	42 144
264	42 160	177	193	210	226	243	259	275	292	308
265	325	341	357	374	390	406	423	439	455	472
266	488	504	521	537	553	570	586	602	619	635
267	651	667	684	700	716	732	749	765	781	797
268	813	830	846	862	878	894	911	927	943	959
269	975	991	43 008	43 024	43 040	43 056	43 072	43 088	43 104	43 120
270	43 136	43 152	43 169	43 185	43 201	43 217	43 233	43 249	43 265	43 281
271	297	313	329	345	361	377	393	409	425	441
272	457	473	489	505	521	537	553	569	584	600
273	616	632	648	664	680	696	712	727	743	759
274	775	791	807	823	838	854	870	886	902	917
275	933	949	965	981	996	44 012	44 028	44 044	44 059	44 075
276	44 091	44 107	44 122	44 138	44 154	170	185	201	217	232
277	248	264	279	295	311	326	342	358	373	389
278	404	420	436	451	467	483	498	514	529	545
279	560	576	592	607	623	638	654	669	685	700
280	44 716	44 731	44 747	44 762	44 778	44 793	44 809	44 824	44 840	44 855
281	871	886	902	917	932	948	963	979	994	45 010
282	45 025	45 040	45 056	45 071	45 086	45 102	45 117	45 133	45 148	163
283	179	194	209	225	240	255	271	286	301	317
284	332	347	362	378	393	408	423	439	454	469
285	484	500	515	530	545	561	576	591	606	621
286	637	652	667	682	697	712	728	743	758	773
287	788	803	818	834	849	864	879	894	909	924
288	939	954	969	984	46 000	46 015	46 030	46 045	46 060	46 075
289	46 090	46 105	46 120	46 135	150	165	180	195	210	225
290	46 240	46 255	46 270	46 285	46 300	46 315	46 330	46 345	46 359	46 374
291	389	404	419	434	449	464	479	494	509	523
292	538	553	568	583	598	613	627	642	657	672
293	687	702	716	731	746	761	776	790	805	820
294	835	850	864	879	894	909	923	938	953	967
295	982	997	47 012	47 026	47 041	47 056	47 070	47 085	47 100	47 114
296	47 129	47 144	159	173	188	202	217	232	246	261
297	276	290	305	319	334	349	363	378	392	407
298	422	436	451	465	480	494	509	524	538	553
299	567	582	596	611	625	640	654	669	683	698
300	47 712	47 727	47 741	47 756	47 770	47 784	47 799	47 813	47 828	47 842
N	0	1	2	3	4	5	6	7	8	9

P.P.

	18		17		16		15		14
1	1.8	1	1.7	1	1.6	1	1.5	1	1.4
2	3.6	2	3.4	2	3.2	2	3.0	2	2.8
3	5.4	3	5.1	3	4.8	3	4.5	3	4.2
4	7.2	4	6.8	4	6.4	4	6.0	4	5.6
5	9.0	5	8.5	5	8.0	5	7.5	5	7.0
6	10.8	6	10.2	6	9.6	6	9.0	6	8.4
7	12.6	7	11.9	7	11.2	7	10.5	7	9.8
8	14.4	8	13.6	8	12.8	8	12.0	8	11.2
9	16.2	9	15.3	9	14.4	9	13.5	9	12.6

Numbers 300–350   Logs 47712–54518

N	0	1	2	3	4	5	6	7	8	9
300	47 712	47 727	47 741	47 756	47 770	47 784	47 799	47 813	47 828	47 842
301	857	871	885	900	914	929	943	958	972	986
302	48 001	48 015	48 029	48 044	48 058	48 073	48 087	48 101	48 116	48 130
303	144	159	173	187	202	216	230	244	259	273
304	287	302	316	330	344	359	373	387	401	416
305	430	444	458	473	487	501	515	530	544	558
306	572	586	601	615	629	643	657	671	686	700
307	714	728	742	756	770	785	799	813	827	841
308	855	869	883	897	911	926	940	954	968	982
309	996	49 010	49 024	49 038	49 052	49 066	49 080	49 094	49 108	49 122
310	49 136	49 150	49 164	49 178	49 192	49 206	49 220	49 234	49 248	49 262
311	276	290	304	318	332	346	360	374	388	402
312	415	429	443	457	471	485	499	513	527	541
313	554	568	582	596	610	624	638	651	665	679
314	693	707	721	734	748	762	776	790	803	817
315	831	845	859	872	886	900	914	927	941	955
316	969	982	996	50 010	50 024	50 037	50 051	50 065	50 079	50 092
317	50 106	50 120	50 133	147	161	174	188	202	215	229
318	243	256	270	284	297	311	325	338	352	365
319	379	393	406	420	433	447	461	474	488	501
320	50 515	50 529	50 542	50 556	50 569	50 583	50 596	50 610	50 623	50 637
321	651	664	678	691	705	718	732	745	759	772
322	786	799	813	826	840	853	866	880	893	907
323	920	934	947	961	974	987	51 001	51 014	51 028	51 041
324	51 055	51 068	51 081	51 095	51 108	51 121	135	148	162	175
325	188	202	215	228	242	255	268	282	295	308
326	322	335	348	362	375	388	402	415	428	441
327	455	468	481	495	508	521	534	548	561	574
328	587	601	614	627	640	654	667	680	693	706
329	720	733	746	759	772	786	799	812	825	838
330	51 851	51 865	51 878	51 891	51 904	51 917	51 930	51 943	51 957	51 970
331	983	996	52 009	52 022	52 035	52 048	52 061	52 075	52 088	52 101
332	52 114	52 127	140	153	166	179	192	205	218	231
333	244	257	270	284	297	310	323	336	349	362
334	375	388	401	414	427	440	453	466	479	492
335	504	517	530	543	556	569	582	595	608	621
336	634	647	660	673	686	699	711	724	737	750
337	763	776	789	802	815	827	840	853	866	879
338	892	905	917	930	943	956	969	982	994	53 007
339	53 020	53 033	53 046	53 058	53 071	53 084	53 097	53 110	53 122	135
340	53 148	53 161	53 173	53 186	53 199	53 212	53 224	53 237	53 250	53 263
341	275	288	301	314	326	339	352	364	377	390
342	403	415	428	441	453	466	479	491	504	517
343	529	542	555	567	580	593	605	618	631	643
344	656	668	681	694	706	719	732	744	757	769
345	782	794	807	820	832	845	857	870	882	895
346	908	920	933	945	958	970	983	995	54 008	54 020
347	54 033	54 045	54 058	54 070	54 083	54 095	54 108	54 120	133	145
348	158	170	183	195	208	220	233	245	258	270
349	283	295	307	320	332	345	357	370	382	394
350	54 407	54 419	54 432	54 444	54 456	54 469	54 481	54 494	54 506	54 518
N	0	1	2	3	4	5	6	7	8	9

P.P.

	15		14		13		12
1	1.5	1	1.4	1	1.3	1	1.2
2	3.0	2	2.8	2	2.6	2	2.4
3	4.5	3	4.2	3	3.9	3	3.6
4	6.0	4	5.6	4	5.2	4	4.8
5	7.5	5	7.0	5	6.5	5	6.0
6	9.0	6	8.4	6	7.8	6	7.2
7	10.5	7	9.8	7	9.1	7	8.4
8	12.0	8	11.2	8	10.4	8	9.6
9	13.5	9	12.6	9	11.7	9	10.8

Numbers 350–400   Logs 54407–60304

N	0	1	2	3	4	5	6	7	8	9
350	54 407	54 419	54 432	54 444	54 456	54 469	54 481	54 494	54 506	54 518
351	531	543	555	568	580	593	605	617	630	642
352	654	667	679	691	704	716	728	741	753	765
353	777	790	802	814	827	839	851	864	876	888
354	900	913	925	937	949	962	974	986	998	55 011
355	55 023	55 035	55 047	55 060	55 072	55 084	55 096	55 108	55 121	133
356	145	157	169	182	194	206	218	230	242	255
357	267	279	291	303	315	328	340	352	364	376
358	388	400	413	425	437	449	461	473	485	497
359	509	522	534	546	558	570	582	594	606	618
360	55 630	55 642	55 654	55 666	55 678	55 691	55 703	55 715	55 727	55 739
361	751	763	775	787	799	811	823	835	847	859
362	871	883	895	907	919	931	943	955	967	979
363	991	56 003	56 015	56 027	56 038	56 050	56 062	56 074	56 086	56 098
364	56 110	122	134	146	158	170	182	194	205	217
365	229	241	253	265	277	289	301	312	324	336
366	348	360	372	384	396	407	419	431	443	455
367	467	478	490	502	514	526	538	549	561	573
368	585	597	608	620	632	644	656	667	679	691
369	703	714	726	738	750	761	773	785	797	808
370	56 820	56 832	56 844	56 855	56 867	56 879	56 891	56 902	56 914	56 926
371	937	949	961	972	984	996	57 008	57 019	57 031	57 043
372	57 054	57 066	57 078	57 089	57 101	57 113	124	136	148	159
373	171	183	194	206	217	229	241	252	264	276
374	287	299	310	322	334	345	357	368	380	392
375	403	415	426	438	449	461	473	484	496	507
376	519	530	542	553	565	576	588	600	611	623
377	634	646	657	669	680	692	703	715	726	738
378	749	761	772	784	795	807	818	830	841	852
379	864	875	887	898	910	921	933	944	955	967
380	57 978	57 990	58 001	58 013	58 024	58 035	58 047	58 058	58 070	58 081
381	58 092	58 104	115	127	138	149	161	172	184	195
382	206	218	229	240	252	263	274	286	297	309
383	320	331	343	354	365	377	388	399	410	422
384	433	444	456	467	478	490	501	512	524	535
385	546	557	569	580	591	602	614	625	636	647
386	659	670	681	692	704	715	726	737	749	760
387	771	782	794	805	816	827	838	850	861	872
388	883	894	906	917	928	939	950	961	973	984
389	995	59 006	59 017	59 028	59 040	59 051	59 062	59 073	59 084	59 095
390	59 106	59 118	59 129	59 140	59 151	59 162	59 173	59 184	59 195	59 207
391	218	229	240	251	262	273	284	295	306	318
392	329	340	351	362	373	384	395	406	417	428
393	439	450	461	472	483	494	506	517	528	539
394	550	561	572	583	594	605	616	627	638	649
395	660	671	682	693	704	715	726	737	748	759
396	770	780	791	802	813	824	835	846	857	868
397	879	890	901	912	923	934	945	956	966	977
398	988	999	60 010	60 021	60 032	60 043	60 054	60 065	60 076	60 086
399	60 097	60 108	119	130	141	152	163	173	184	195
400	60 206	60 217	60 228	60 239	60 249	60 260	60 271	60 282	60 293	60 304
N	0	1	2	3	4	5	6	7	8	9

P.P.

	13		12		11		10
1	1.3		1.2		1.1		1.0
2	2.6		2.4		2.2		2.0
3	3.9		3.6		3.3		3.0
4	5.2		4.8		4.4		4.0
5	6.5		6.0		5.5		5.0
6	7.8		7.2		6.6		6.0
7	9.1		8.4		7.7		7.0
8	10.4		9.6		8.8		8.0
9	11.7		10.8		9.9		9.0

12

Numbers 400–450　Logs 60206–65408

N	0	1	2	3	4	5	6	7	8	9
400	60 206	60 217	60 228	60 239	60 249	60 260	60 271	60 282	60 293	60 304
401	314	325	336	347	358	369	379	390	401	412
402	423	433	444	455	466	477	487	498	509	520
403	531	541	552	563	574	584	595	606	617	627
404	638	649	660	670	681	692	703	713	724	735
405	746	756	767	778	788	799	810	821	831	842
406	853	863	874	885	895	906	917	927	938	949
407	959	970	981	991	61 002	61 013	61 023	61 034	61 045	61 055
408	61 066	61 077	61 087	61 098	109	119	130	140	151	162
409	172	183	194	204	215	225	236	247	257	268
410	61 278	61 289	61 300	61 310	61 321	61 331	61 342	61 352	61 363	61 374
411	384	395	405	416	426	437	448	458	469	479
412	490	500	511	521	532	542	553	563	574	584
413	595	606	616	627	637	648	658	669	679	690
414	700	711	721	731	742	752	763	773	784	794
415	805	815	826	836	847	857	868	878	888	899
416	909	920	930	941	951	962	972	982	993	62 003
417	62 014	62 024	62 034	62 045	62 055	62 066	62 076	62 086	62 097	107
418	118	128	138	149	159	170	180	190	201	211
419	221	232	242	252	263	273	284	294	304	315
420	62 325	62 335	62 346	62 356	62 366	62 377	62 387	62 397	62 408	62 418
421	428	439	449	459	469	480	490	500	511	521
422	531	542	552	562	572	583	593	603	613	624
423	634	644	655	665	675	685	696	706	716	726
424	737	747	757	767	778	788	798	808	818	829
425	839	849	859	870	880	890	900	910	921	931
426	941	951	961	972	982	992	63 002	63 012	63 022	63 033
427	63 043	63 053	63 063	63 073	63 083	63 094	104	114	124	134
428	144	155	165	175	185	195	205	215	225	236
429	246	256	266	276	286	296	306	317	327	337
430	63 347	63 357	63 367	63 377	63 387	63 397	63 407	63 417	63 428	63 438
431	448	458	468	478	488	498	508	518	528	538
432	548	558	568	579	589	599	609	619	629	639
433	649	659	669	679	689	699	709	719	729	739
434	749	759	769	779	789	799	809	819	829	839
435	849	859	869	879	889	899	909	919	929	939
436	949	959	969	979	988	998	64 008	64 018	64 028	64 038
437	64 048	64 058	64 068	64 078	64 088	64 098	108	118	128	137
438	147	157	167	177	187	197	207	217	227	237
439	246	256	266	276	286	296	306	316	326	335
440	64 345	64 355	64 365	64 375	64 385	64 395	64 404	64 414	64 424	64 434
441	444	454	464	473	483	493	503	513	523	532
442	542	552	562	572	582	591	601	611	621	631
443	640	650	660	670	680	689	699	709	719	729
444	738	748	758	768	777	787	797	807	816	826
445	836	846	856	865	875	885	895	904	914	924
446	933	943	953	963	972	982	992	65 002	65 011	65 021
447	65 031	65 040	65 050	65 060	65 070	65 079	65 089	099	108	118
448	128	137	147	157	167	176	186	196	205	215
449	225	234	244	254	263	273	283	292	302	312
450	65 321	65 331	65 341	65 350	65 360	65 369	65 379	65 389	65 398	65 408
N	0	1	2	3	4	5	6	7	8	9

P.P.

11: 1 1.1 | 2 2.2 | 3 3.3 | 4 4.4 | 5 5.5 | 6 6.6 | 7 7.7 | 8 8.8 | 9 9.9

10: 1 1.0 | 2 2.0 | 3 3.0 | 4 4.0 | 5 5.0 | 6 6.0 | 7 7.0 | 8 8.0 | 9 9.0

9: 1 .9 | 2 1.8 | 3 2.7 | 4 3.6 | 5 4.5 | 6 5.4 | 7 6.3 | 8 7.2 | 9 8.1

Numbers 450–500   Logs 65321–69975

N	0	1	2	3	4	5	6	7	8	9
450	65 321	65 331	65 341	65 350	65 360	65 369	65 379	65 389	65 398	65 408
451	418	427	437	447	456	466	475	485	495	504
452	514	523	533	543	552	562	571	581	591	600
453	610	619	629	639	648	658	667	677	686	696
454	706	715	725	734	744	753	763	772	782	792
455	801	811	820	830	839	849	858	868	877	887
456	896	906	916	925	935	944	954	963	973	982
457	992	66 001	66 011	66 020	66 030	66 039	66 049	66 058	66 068	66 077
458	66 087	096	106	115	124	134	143	153	162	172
459	181	191	200	210	219	229	238	247	257	266
460	66 276	66 285	66 295	66 304	66 314	66 323	66 332	66 342	66 351	66 361
461	370	380	389	398	408	417	427	436	445	455
462	464	474	483	492	502	511	521	530	539	549
463	558	567	577	586	596	605	614	624	633	642
464	652	661	671	680	689	699	708	717	727	736
465	745	755	764	773	783	792	801	811	820	829
466	839	848	857	867	876	885	894	904	913	922
467	932	941	950	960	969	978	987	997	67 006	67 015
468	67 025	67 034	67 043	67 052	67 062	67 071	67 080	67 089	099	108
469	117	127	136	145	154	164	173	182	191	201
470	67 210	67 219	67 228	67 237	67 247	67 256	67 265	67 274	67 284	67 293
471	302	311	321	330	339	348	357	367	376	385
472	394	403	413	422	431	440	449	459	468	477
473	486	495	504	514	523	532	541	550	560	569
474	578	587	596	605	614	624	633	642	651	660
475	669	679	688	697	706	715	724	733	742	752
476	761	770	779	788	797	806	815	825	834	843
477	852	861	870	879	888	897	906	916	925	934
478	943	952	961	970	979	988	997	68 006	68 015	68 024
479	68 034	68 043	68 052	68 061	68 070	68 079	68 088	097	106	115
480	68 124	68 133	68 142	68 151	68 160	68 169	68 178	68 187	68 196	68 205
481	215	224	233	242	251	260	269	278	287	296
482	305	314	323	332	341	350	359	368	377	386
483	395	404	413	422	431	440	449	458	467	476
484	485	494	502	511	520	529	538	547	556	565
485	574	583	592	601	610	619	628	637	646	655
486	664	673	681	690	699	708	717	726	735	744
487	753	762	771	780	789	797	806	815	824	833
488	842	851	860	869	878	886	895	904	913	922
489	931	940	949	958	966	975	984	993	69 002	69 011
490	69 020	69 028	69 037	69 046	69 055	69 064	69 073	69 082	69 090	69 099
491	108	117	126	135	144	152	161	170	179	188
492	197	205	214	223	232	241	249	258	267	276
493	285	294	302	311	320	329	338	346	355	364
494	373	381	390	399	408	417	425	434	443	452
495	461	469	478	487	496	504	513	522	531	539
496	548	557	566	574	583	592	601	609	618	627
497	636	644	653	662	671	679	688	697	705	714
498	723	732	740	749	758	767	775	784	793	801
499	810	819	827	836	845	854	862	871	880	888
500	69 897	69 906	69 914	69 923	69 932	69 940	69 949	69 958	69 966	69 975
N	0	1	2	3	4	5	6	7	8	9

P.P.

10		9		8	
1	1.0	1	0.9	1	0.8
2	2.0	2	1.8	2	1.6
3	3.0	3	2.7	3	2.4
4	4.0	4	3.6	4	3.2
5	5.0	5	4.5	5	4.0
6	6.0	6	5.4	6	4.8
7	7.0	7	6.3	7	5.6
8	8.0	8	7.2	8	6.4
9	9.0	9	8.1	9	7.2

Numbers 500–550   Logs 69897–74107

N	0	1	2	3	4	5	6	7	8	9	P.P.
500	69 897	69 906	69 914	69 923	69 932	69 940	69 949	69 958	69 966	69 975	**9**
501	984	992	70 001	70 010	70 018	70 027	70 036	70 044	70 053	70 062	1 0.9
502	70 070	70 079	088	096	105	114	122	131	140	148	2 1.8
503	157	165	174	183	191	200	209	217	226	234	3 2.7
504	243	252	260	269	278	286	29$\overline{5}$	303	312	321	4 3.6
505	329	338	346	35$\overline{5}$	364	372	381	389	398	406	5 4.5
506	415	424	432	441	449	458	467	475	484	492	6 5.4
507	501	50$\overline{9}$	518	526	535	544	552	561	569	578	7 6.3
508	586	59$\overline{5}$	603	612	621	629	638	646	65$\overline{5}$	663	8 7.2
509	672	680	689	697	706	714	723	731	740	749	9 8.1
510	70 757	70 766	70 774	70 783	70 791	70 800	70 808	70 817	70 825	70 834	
511	842	851	859	868	876	88$\overline{5}$	893	902	91$\overline{0}$	919	
512	927	935	944	952	961	969	978	986	99$\overline{5}$	71 003	
513	71 012	71 020	71 029	71 037	71 046	71 054	71 063	71 071	71 079	088	
514	096	10$\overline{5}$	113	122	130	139	147	155	164	172	
515	181	189	198	206	214	223	231	240	248	257	
516	26$\overline{5}$	273	282	290	299	307	315	324	332	341	
517	349	357	366	374	383	39$\overline{1}$	399	408	416	42$\overline{5}$	
518	433	441	450	458	466	47$\overline{5}$	483	492	500	508	
519	517	525	533	542	550	559	567	575	584	592	
520	71 600	71 609	71 617	71 625	71 634	71 642	71 650	71 659	71 667	71 675	**8**
521	684	692	700	709	717	725	734	742	750	759	1 0.8
522	767	775	784	792	800	809	817	825	834	842	2 1.6
523	850	858	867	875	883	892	900	908	917	92$\overline{5}$	3 2.4
524	933	941	950	958	966	97$\overline{5}$	983	991	999	72 008	4 3.2
525	72 016	72 024	72 032	72 041	72 049	72 057	72 066	72 074	72 082	090	5 4.0
526	099	107	11$\overline{5}$	123	132	140	148	156	16$\overline{5}$	173	6 4.8
527	181	189	198	206	214	222	230	239	247	255	7 5.6
528	263	272	280	288	296	304	313	321	329	337	8 6.4
529	346	354	362	370	378	387	39$\overline{5}$	403	411	419	9 7.2
530	72 428	72 436	72 444	72 452	72 460	72 469	72 477	72 48$\overline{5}$	72 493	72 501	
531	509	518	526	534	542	550	558	567	57$\overline{5}$	583	
532	591	599	607	616	624	632	640	648	656	66$\overline{5}$	
533	673	681	689	697	705	713	722	730	738	746	
534	754	762	770	779	787	79$\overline{5}$	803	811	819	827	
535	835	843	852	860	868	876	884	892	900	908	
536	916	92$\overline{5}$	933	941	949	957	965	973	981	989	
537	997	73 006	73 014	73 022	73 030	73 038	73 046	73 054	73 062	73 070	
538	73 078	086	094	102	111	119	127	13$\overline{5}$	143	151	
539	159	167	17$\overline{5}$	183	191	199	207	215	223	231	
540	73 239	73 247	73 255	73 263	73 272	73 280	73 288	73 296	73 304	73 312	**7**
541	320	328	336	344	352	360	368	376	384	392	1 0.7
542	400	408	416	424	432	440	448	456	464	472	2 1.4
543	480	488	496	504	512	520	528	536	544	552	3 2.1
544	560	568	576	584	592	600	608	616	624	632	4 2.8
545	640	648	656	664	672	679	687	695	703	711	5 3.5
546	719	727	735	743	751	759	767	77$\overline{5}$	783	791	6 4.2
547	799	807	81$\overline{5}$	823	830	838	846	854	862	870	7 4.9
548	878	886	894	902	910	918	926	933	941	949	8 5.6
549	957	965	973	981	989	997	74 00$\overline{5}$	74 013	74 020	74 028	9 6.3
550	74 036	74 044	74 052	74 060	74 068	74 076	74 084	74 092	74 099	74 107	
N	0	1	2	3	4	5	6	7	8	9	

Numbers 550–600 Logs 74036–77880

N	0	1	2	3	4	5	6	7	8	9
550	74 036	74 044	74 052	74 060	74 068	74 076	74 084	74 092	74 099	74 107
551	115	123	131	139	147	155	162	170	178	186
552	194	202	210	218	225	233	241	249	257	265
553	273	280	288	296	304	312	320	327	335	343
554	351	359	367	374	382	390	398	406	414	421
555	429	437	445	453	461	468	476	484	492	500
556	507	515	523	531	539	547	554	562	570	578
557	586	593	601	609	617	624	632	640	648	656
558	663	671	679	687	695	702	710	718	726	733
559	741	749	757	764	772	780	788	796	803	811
560	74 819	74 827	74 834	74 842	74 850	74 858	74 865	74 873	74 881	74 889
561	896	904	912	920	927	935	943	950	958	966
562	974	981	989	997	75 005	75 012	75 020	75 028	75 035	75 043
563	75 051	75 059	75 066	75 074	082	089	097	105	113	120
564	128	136	143	151	159	166	174	182	189	197
565	205	213	220	228	236	243	251	259	266	274
566	282	289	297	305	312	320	328	335	343	351
567	358	366	374	381	389	397	404	412	420	427
568	435	442	450	458	465	473	481	488	496	504
569	511	519	526	534	542	549	557	565	572	580
570	75 587	75 595	75 603	75 610	75 618	75 626	75 633	75 641	75 648	75 656
571	664	671	679	686	694	702	709	717	724	732
572	740	747	755	762	770	778	785	793	800	808
573	815	823	831	838	846	853	861	868	876	884
574	891	899	906	914	921	929	937	944	952	959
575	967	974	982	989	997	76 005	76 012	76 020	76 027	76 035
576	76 042	76 050	76 057	76 065	76 072	080	087	095	103	110
577	118	125	133	140	148	155	163	170	178	185
578	193	200	208	215	223	230	238	245	253	260
579	268	275	283	290	298	305	313	320	328	335
580	76 343	76 350	76 358	76 365	76 373	76 380	76 388	76 395	76 403	76 410
581	418	425	433	440	448	455	462	470	477	485
582	492	500	507	515	522	530	537	545	552	559
583	567	574	582	589	597	604	612	619	626	634
584	641	649	656	664	671	678	686	693	701	708
585	716	723	730	738	745	753	760	768	775	782
586	790	797	805	812	819	827	834	842	849	856
587	864	871	879	886	893	901	908	916	923	930
588	938	945	953	960	967	975	982	989	997	77 004
589	77 012	77 019	77 026	77 034	77 041	77 048	77 056	77 063	77 070	078
590	77 085	77 093	77 100	77 107	77 115	77 122	77 129	77 137	77 144	77 151
591	159	166	173	181	188	195	203	210	217	225
592	232	240	247	254	262	269	276	283	291	298
593	305	313	320	327	335	342	349	357	364	371
594	379	386	393	401	408	415	422	430	437	444
595	452	459	466	474	481	488	495	503	510	517
596	525	532	539	546	554	561	568	576	583	590
597	597	605	612	619	627	634	641	648	656	663
598	670	677	685	692	699	706	714	721	728	735
599	743	750	757	764	772	779	786	793	801	808
600	77 815	77 822	77 830	77 837	77 844	77 851	77 859	77 866	77 873	77 880
N	0	1	2	3	4	5	6	7	8	9

P.P.

8

1	0.8
2	1.6
3	2.4
4	3.2
5	4.0
6	4.8
7	5.6
8	6.4
9	7.2

7

1	0.7
2	1.4
3	2.1
4	2.8
5	3.5
6	4.2
7	4.9
8	5.6
9	6.3

Numbers 600–650 Logs 77815–81351

N	0	1	2	3	4	5	6	7	8	9	P.P.
600	77 815	77 822	77 830	77 837	77 844	77 851	77 859	77 866	77 873	77 880	**8**
601	887	895	902	909	916	924	931	938	945	952	1 0.8
602	960	967	974	981	988	996	78 003	78 010	78 017	78 025	2 1.6
603	78 032	78 039	78 046	78 053	78 061	78 068	075	082	089	097	3 2.4
604	104	111	118	125	132	140	147	154	161	168	4 3.2
605	176	183	190	197	204	211	219	226	233	240	5 4.0
606	247	254	262	269	276	283	290	297	305	312	6 4.8
607	319	326	333	340	347	355	362	369	376	383	7 5.6
608	390	398	405	412	419	426	433	440	447	455	8 6.4
609	462	469	476	483	490	497	504	512	519	526	9 7.2
610	78 533	78 540	78 547	78 554	78 561	78 569	78 576	78 583	78 590	78 597	
611	604	611	618	625	633	640	647	654	661	668	
612	675	682	689	696	704	711	718	725	732	739	
613	746	753	760	767	774	781	789	796	803	810	
614	817	824	831	838	845	852	859	866	873	880	
615	888	895	902	909	916	923	930	937	944	951	
616	958	965	972	979	986	993	79 000	79 007	79 014	79 021	
617	79 029	79 036	79 043	79 050	79 057	79 064	071	078	085	092	
618	099	106	113	120	127	134	141	148	155	162	
619	169	176	183	190	197	204	211	218	225	232	
620	79 239	79 246	79 253	79 260	79 267	79 274	79 281	79 288	79 295	79 302	**7**
621	309	316	323	330	337	344	351	358	365	372	1 0.7
622	379	386	393	400	407	414	421	428	435	442	2 1.4
623	449	456	463	470	477	484	491	498	505	511	3 2.1
624	518	525	532	539	546	553	560	567	574	581	4 2.8
625	588	595	602	609	616	623	630	637	644	650	5 3.5
626	657	664	671	678	685	692	699	706	713	720	6 4.2
627	727	734	741	748	754	761	768	775	782	789	7 4.9
628	796	803	810	817	824	831	837	844	851	858	8 5.6
629	865	872	879	886	893	900	906	913	920	927	9 6.3
630	79 934	79 941	79 948	79 955	79 962	79 969	79 975	79 982	79 989	79 996	
631	80 003	80 010	80 017	80 024	80 030	80 037	80 044	80 051	80 058	80 065	
632	072	079	085	092	099	106	113	120	127	134	
633	140	147	154	161	168	175	182	188	195	202	
634	209	216	223	229	236	243	250	257	264	271	
635	277	284	291	298	305	312	318	325	332	339	
636	346	353	359	366	373	380	387	393	400	407	
637	414	421	428	434	441	448	455	462	468	475	
638	482	489	496	502	509	516	523	530	536	543	
639	550	557	564	570	577	584	591	598	604	611	
640	80 618	80 625	80 632	80 638	80 645	80 652	80 659	80 665	80 672	80 679	**6**
641	686	693	699	706	713	720	726	733	740	747	1 0.6
642	754	760	767	774	781	787	794	801	808	814	2 1.2
643	821	828	835	841	848	855	862	868	875	882	3 1.8
644	889	895	902	909	916	922	929	936	943	949	4 2.4
645	956	963	969	976	983	990	996	81 003	81 010	81 017	5 3.0
646	81 023	81 030	81 037	81 043	81 050	81 057	81 064	070	077	084	6 3.6
647	090	097	104	111	117	124	131	137	144	151	7 4.2
648	158	164	171	178	184	191	198	204	211	218	8 4.8
649	224	231	238	245	251	258	265	271	278	285	9 5.4
650	81 291	81 298	81 305	81 311	81 318	81 325	81 331	81 338	81 345	81 351	
N	0	1	2	3	4	5	6	7	8	9	

N	0	1	2	3	4	5	6	7	8	9	P.P.
						Numbers 650–700		**Logs 81291–84566**			
650	81 291	81 298	81 305̅	81 311	81 318	81 325̅	81 331	81 338	81 345̅	81 351	**7**
651	358̲	365̅	371	378̲	385̲	391	398	405̅	411	418̲	1 0.7
652	425̲	431	438	445	451	458	465̅	471	478	485̅	2 1.4
653	491	498	505̅	511	518	525̅	531	538	544	551	3 2.1
654	558	564	571	578	584	591	598	604	611	617	4 2.8
655	624	631	637	644	651	657	664	671	677	684	5 3.5
656	690	697	704	710	717	723	730	737	743	750	6 4.2
657	757	763	770	776	783	790	796	803	809	816	7 4.9
658	823	829	836	842	849	856	862	869	875	882	8 5.6
659	889	895	902	908	915̅	921	928	935̅	941	948	9 6.3
660	81 954	81 961	81 968	81 974	81 981	81 987	81 994	82 000	82 007	82 014	
661	82 020	82 027	82 033	82 040	82 046	82 053	82 060	066	073	079	
662	086	092	099	105	112	119	125	132	138	145̅	
663	151	158	164	171	178	184	191	197	204	210	
664	217	223	230	236	243	249	256	263	269	276	
665	282	289	295	302	308	315̅	321	328	334	341	
666	347	354	360	367	373	380	387	393	400	406	
667	413	419	426	432	439	445	452	458	465̅	471	
668	478	484	491	497	504	510	517	523	530̲	536	
669	543	549̲	556	562	569	575	582	588	595̲	601	
670	82 607	82 614	82 620	82 627	82 633	82 640	82 646	82 653	82 659	82 666	**6**
671	672	679	685	692	698	705̅	711	718	724	730	1 0.6
672	737	743	750	756	763	769	776	782	789	795	2 1.2
673	802	808	814	821	827	834	840	847	853	860	3 1.8
674	866	872	879	885	892	898	905̅	911	918	924	4 2.4
675	930̲	937	943	950	956	963	969	975	982	988	5 3.0
676	995̅	83 001	83 008	83 014	83 020	83 027	83 033	83 040	83 046	83 052	6 3.6
677	83 059	065	072	078	085̅	091	097	104	110	117	7 4.2
678	123	129	136	142	149	155̅	161	168	174	181	8 4.8
679	187	193	200	206	213	219	225	232	238	245̅	9 5.4
680	83 251	83 257	83 264	83 270	83 276	83 283	83 289	83 296	83 302	83 308	
681	315̅	321	327	334	340	347	353	359	366	372	
682	378̲	385̅	391̲	398	404	410	417	423	429	436	
683	442	448	455̅	461	467	474	480	487	493	499	
684	506	512	518	525̅	531	537	544	550	556	563	
685	569	575	582	588	594	601	607	613	620	626	
686	632	639	645	651	658	664	670	677	683	689	
687	696	702	708	715̅	721	727	734	740	746	753	
688	759	765	771̲	778	784	790	797	803	809	816	
689	822	828	835̅	841	847	853	860	866	872	879	
690	83 885̅	83 891	83 897	83 904	83 910	83 916	83 923	83 929	83 935	83 942	
691	948	954	960	967	973	979	985	992	998	84 004	
692	84 011	84 017	84 023	84 029	84 036	84 042	84 048	84 055̅	84 061	067	
693	073	080	086	092	098	105̅	111	117	123	130	
694	136	142̲	148	155̅	161	167	173	180	186	192̲	
695	198	205̲	211	217	223	230	236	242	248	255̅	
696	261	267	273	280	286	292	298	305̅	311	317	
697	323	330	336	342	348	354	361	367	373	379	
698	386	392	398	404	410	417	423	429	435	442	
699	448	454	460	466	473	479	485̅	491	497	504	
700	84 510	84 516	84 522	84 528	84 535̅	84 541	84 547	84 553	84 559	84 566	
N	0	1	2	3	4	5	6	7	8	9	

Numbers 700–750   Logs 84510–87558

N	0	1	2	3	4	5	6	7	8	9
700	84 510	84 516	84 522	84 528	84 535	84 541	84 547	84 553	84 559	84 566
701	572	578	584	590	597	603	609	615	621	628
702	634	640	646	652	658	665	671	677	683	689
703	696	702	708	714	720	726	733	739	745	751
704	757	763	770	776	782	788	794	800	807	813
705	819	825	831	837	844	850	856	862	868	874
706	880	887	893	899	905	911	917	924	930	936
707	942	948	954	960	967	973	979	985	991	997
708	85 003	85 009	85 016	85 022	85 028	85 034	85 040	85 046	85 052	85 058
709	065	071	077	083	089	095	101	107	114	120
710	85 126	85 132	85 138	85 144	85 150	85 156	85 163	85 169	85 175	85 181
711	187	193	199	205	211	217	224	230	236	242
712	248	254	260	266	272	278	285	291	297	303
713	309	315	321	327	333	339	345	352	358	364
714	370	376	382	388	394	400	406	412	418	425
715	431	437	443	449	455	461	467	473	479	485
716	491	497	503	509	516	522	528	534	540	546
717	552	558	564	570	576	582	588	594	600	606
718	612	618	625	631	637	643	649	655	661	667
719	673	679	685	691	697	703	709	715	721	727
720	85 733	85 739	85 745	85 751	85 757	85 763	85 769	85 775	85 781	85 788
721	794	800	806	812	818	824	830	836	842	848
722	854	860	866	872	878	884	890	896	902	908
723	914	920	926	932	938	944	950	956	962	968
724	974	980	986	992	998	86 004	86 010	86 016	86 022	86 028
725	86 034	86 040	86 046	86 052	86 058	064	070	076	082	088
726	094	100	106	112	118	124	130	136	141	147
727	153	159	165	171	177	183	189	195	201	207
728	213	219	225	231	237	243	249	255	261	267
729	273	279	285	291	297	303	308	314	320	326
730	86 332	86 338	86 344	86 350	86 356	86 362	86 368	86 374	86 380	86 386
731	392	398	404	410	415	421	427	433	439	445
732	451	457	463	469	475	481	487	493	499	504
733	510	516	522	528	534	540	546	552	558	564
734	570	576	581	587	593	599	605	611	617	623
735	629	635	641	646	652	658	664	670	676	682
736	688	694	700	705	711	717	723	729	735	741
737	747	753	759	764	770	776	782	788	794	800
738	806	812	817	823	829	835	841	847	853	859
739	864	870	876	882	888	894	900	906	911	917
740	86 923	86 929	86 935	86 941	86 947	86 953	86 958	86 964	86 970	86 976
741	982	988	994	999	87 005	87 011	87 017	87·023	87 029	87 035
742	87 040	87 046	87 052	87 058	064	070	075	081	087	093
743	099	105	111	116	122	128	134	140	146	151
744	157	163	169	175	181	186	192	198	204	210
745	216	221	227	233	239	245	251	256	262	268
746	274	280	286	291	297	303	309	315	320	326
747	332	338	344	349	355	361	367	373	379	384
748	390	396	402	408	413	419	425	431	437	442
749	448	454	460	466	471	477	483	489	495	500
750	87 506	87 512	87 518	87 523	87 529	87 535	87 541	87 547	87 552	87 558
N	0	1	2	3	4	5	6	7	8	9

P.P.

7		6		5	
1	0.7	1	0.6	1	0.5
2	1.4	2	1.2	2	1.0
3	2.1	3	1.8	3	1.5
4	2.8	4	2.4	4	2.0
5	3.5	5	3.0	5	2.5
6	4.2	6	3.6	6	3.0
7	4.9	7	4.2	7	3.5
8	5.6	8	4.8	8	4.0
9	6.3	9	5.4	9	4.5

N	0	1	2	3	4	5	6	7	8	9	P.P.
						Numbers 750–800		Logs 87506–90358			
750	87 506	87 512	87 518	87 523	87 529	87 535	87 541	87 547	87 552	87 558	**6**
751	564	570	576	581	587	593	599	604	610	616	
752	622	628	633	639	645	651	656	662	668	674	1 0.6
753	679	685	691	697	703	708	714	720	726	731	2 1.2
754	737	743	749	754	760	766	772	777	783	789	3 1.8
755	795	800	806	812	818	823	829	835	841	846	4 2.4
756	852	858	864	869	875	881	887	892	898	904	5 3.0
757	910	915	921	927	933	938	944	950	955	961	6 3.6
758	967	973	978	984	990	996	88 001	88 007	88 013	88 018	7 4.2
759	88 024	88 030	88 036	88 041	88 047	88 053	058	064	070	076	8 4.8
760	88 081	88 087	88 093	88 098	88 104	88 110	88 116	88 121	88 127	88 133	9 5.4
761	138	144	150	156	161	167	173	178	184	190	
762	195	201	207	213	218	224	230	235	241	247	
763	252	258	264	270	275	281	287	292	298	304	
764	309	315	321	326	332	338	343	349	355	360	
765	366	372	377	383	389	395	400	406	412	417	
766	423	429	434	440	446	451	457	463	468	474	
767	480	485	491	497	502	508	513	519	525	530	
768	536	542	547	553	559	564	570	576	581	587	
769	593	598	604	610	615	621	627	632	638	643	
770	88 649	88 655	88 660	88 666	88 672	88 677	88 683	88 689	88 694	88 700	**5**
771	705	711	717	722	728	734	739	745	750	756	
772	762	767	773	779	784	790	795	801	807	812	1 0.5
773	818	824	829	835	840	846	852	857	863	868	2 1.0
774	874	880	885	891	897	902	908	913	919	925	3 1.5
775	930	936	941	947	953	958	964	969	975	981	4 2.0
776	986	992	997	89 003	89 009	89 014	89 020	89 025	89 031	89 037	5 2.5
777	89 042	89 048	89 053	059	064	070	076	081	087	092	6 3.0
778	098	104	109	115	120	126	131	137	143	148	7 3.5
779	154	159	165	170	176	182	187	193	198	204	8 4.0
780	89 209	89 215	89 221	89 226	89 232	89 237	89 243	89 248	89 254	89 260	9 4.5
781	265	271	276	282	287	293	298	304	310	315	
782	321	326	332	337	343	348	354	360	365	371	
783	376	382	387	393	398	404	409	415	421	426	
784	432	437	443	448	454	459	465	470	476	481	
785	487	492	498	504	509	515	520	526	531	537	
786	542	548	553	559	564	570	575	581	586	592	
787	597	603	609	614	620	625	631	636	642	647	
788	653	658	664	669	675	680	686	691	697	702	
789	708	713	719	724	730	735	741	746	752	757	
790	89 763	89 768	89 774	89 779	89 785	89 790	89 796	89 801	89 807	89 812	
791	818	823	829	834	840	845	851	856	862	867	
792	873	878	883	889	894	900	905	911	916	922	
793	927	933	938	944	949	955	960	966	971	977	
794	982	988	993	998	90 004	90 009	90 015	90 020	90 026	90 031	
795	90 037	90 042	90 048	90 053	059	064	069	075	080	086	
796	091	097	102	108	113	119	124	129	135	140	
797	146	151	157	162	168	173	179	184	189	195	
798	200	206	211	217	222	227	233	238	244	249	
799	255	260	266	271	276	282	287	293	298	304	
800	90 309	90 314	90 320	90 325	90 331	90 336	90 342	90 347	90 352	90 358	
N	0	1	2	3	4	5	6	7	8	9	

Numbers 800–850   Logs 90309–92988

N	0	1	2	3	4	5	6	7	8	9	P.P.
800	90 309	90 314	90 320	90 325	90 331	90 336	90 342	90 347	90 352	90 358	**6**
801	363	369	374	380	385̄	390	396	401	407	412	1 0.6
802	417	423	428	434	439	445̄	450	455	461	466	2 1.2
803	472	477	482	488	493	499	504	509	515̄	520	3 1.8
804	526	531	536	542	547	553	558	563	569	574	4 2.4
805	580	585̄	590	596	601	607	612	617	623	628	5 3.0
806	634	639	644	650	655	660	666	671	677	682	6 3.6
807	687	693	698	703	709	714	720	725	730	736	7 4.2
808	741	747	752	757	763	768	773	779	784	789	8 4.8
809	795̄	800	806	811	816	822	827	832	838	843	9 5.4
810	90 849	90 854	90 859	90 865̄	90 870	90 875	90 881	90 886	90 891	90 897	
811	902	907	913	918	924	929	934	940	945̄	950	
812	956	961	966	972	977	982	988	993	998	91 004	
813	91 009	91 014	91 020	91 025	91 030	91 036	91 041	91 046	91 052	057	
814	062	068	073	078	084	089	094	100	105	110	
815	116	121	126	132	137	142	148	153	158	164	
816	169	174	180	185̄	190	196	201	206	212	217	
817	222	228	233	238	243	249	254	259	265̄	270	
818	275	281	286	291	297	302	307	312	318	323	
819	328	334	339	344	350	355̄	360	365	371	376	
820	91 381	91 387	91 392	91 397	91 403	91 408	91 413	91 418	91 424	91 429	**5**
821	434	440	445̄	450	455	461	466	471	477	482̄	1 0.5
822	487	492	498	503	508	514	519	524	529	535̄	2 1.0
823	540	545	551	556	561	566	572	577	582	587	3 1.5
824	593	598	603	609	614	619	624	630	635̄	640	4 2.0
825	645	651	656	661	666	672	677	682	687	693	5 2.5
826	698	703	709	714	719	724	730	735̄	740	745	6 3.0
827	751	756	761	766	772	777	782	787	793	798	7 3.5
828	803	808	814	819	824	829	834	840	845̄	850	8 4.0
829	855	861	866	871	876	882	887	892	897	903	9 4.5
830	91 908	91 913	91 918	91 924	91 929	91 934	91 939	91 944	91 950	91 955̄	
831	960	965	971	976	981	986	991	997	92 002	92 007	
832	92 012	92 018	92 023	92 028	92 033	92 038	92 044	92 049	054	059	
833	065	070	075̄	080	085	091	096	101	106	111	
834	117	122	127	132	137	143	148	153	158	163	
835	169	174	179	184	189	195̄	200	205	210	215	
836	221	226	231	236	241	247	252	257	262	267	
837	273	278	283	288	293	298	304	309	314	319	
838	324	330	335̄	340	345	350	355	361	366	371	
839	376	381	387	392	397	402	407	412	418	423	
840	92 428	92 433	92 438	92 443	92 449	92 454	92 459	92 464	92 469	92 474	
841	480	485̄	490	495	500	505	511	516	521	526	
842	531	536	542	547	552	557	562	567	572	578	
843	583	588	593	598	603	609	614	619	624	629	
844	634	639	645̄	650	655̄	660	665	670	675	681	
845	686	691	696	701	706	711	716	722	727	732	
846	737	742	747	752	758	763	768	773	778	783	
847	788	793	799	804	809	814	819	824	829	834	
848	840	845̄	850	855̄	860	865	870	875	881	886	
849	891	896	901	906	911	916	921	927	932	937	
850	92 942	92 947	92 952	92 957	92 962	92 967	92 973	92 978	92 983	92 988	
N	0	1	2	3	4	5	6	7	8	9	

N	0	1	2	3	4	5	6	7	8	9	P.P.
850	92 942	92 947	92 952	92 957	92 962	92 967	92 973	92 978	92 983	92 988	**6**
851	993	998	93 003	93 008	93 013	93 018	93 024	93 029	93 034	93 039	
852	93 044	93 049	054	059	064	069	075	080	085	090	1 0.6
853	095	100	105	110	115	120	125	131	136	141	2 1.2 · 3 1.8
854	146	151	156	161	166	171	176	181	186	192	4 2.4
855	197	202	207	212	217	222	227	232	237	242	5 3.0
856	247	252	258	263	268	273	278	283	288	293	6 3.6
857	298	303	308	313	318	323	328	334	339	344	7 4.2
858	349	354	359	364	369	374	379	384	389	394	8 4.8
859	399	404	409	414	420	425	430	435	440	445	9 5.4
860	93 450	93 455	93 460	93 465	93 470	93 475	93 480	93 485	93 490	93 495	
861	500	505	510	515	520	526	531	536	541	546	
862	· 551	556	561	566	571	576	581	586	591	596	
863	601	606	611	616	621	626	631	636	641	646	
864	651	656	661	666	671	676	682	687	692	697	
865	702	707	712	717	722	727	732	737	742	747	
866	752	757	762	767	772	777	782	787	792	797	
867	802	807	812	817	822	827	832	837	842	847	
868	852	857	862	867	872	877	882	887	892	897	
869	902	907	912	917	922	927	932	937	942	947	
870	93 952	93 957	93 962	93 967	93 972	93 977	93 982	93 987	93 992	93 997	**5**
871	94 002	94 007	94 012	94 017	94 022	94 027	94 032	94 037	94 042	94 047	
872	052	057	062	067	072	077	082	086	091	096	1 0.5
873	101	106	111	116	121	126	131	136	141	146	2 1.0 · 3 1.5
874	151	156	161	166	171	176	181	186	191	196	4 2.0
875	201	206	211	216	221	226	231	236	240	245	5 2.5
876	250	255	260	265	270	275	280	285	290	295	6 3.0
877	300	305	310	315	320	325	330	335	340	345	7 3.5
878	349	354	359	364	369	374	379	384	389	394	8 4.0
879	399	404	409	414	419	424	429	433	438	443	9 4.5
880	94 448	94 453	94 458	94 463	94 468	94 473	94 478	94 483	94 488	94 493	
881	498	503	507	512	517	522	527	532	537	542	
882	547	552	557	562	567	571	576	581	586	591	
883	596	601	606	611	616	621	626	630	635	640	
884	645	650	655	660	665	670	675	680	685	689	
885	694	699	704	709	714	719	724	729	734	738	
886	743	748	753	758	763	768	773	778	783	787	
887	792	797	802	807	812	817	822	827	832	836	
888	841	846	851	856	861	866	871	876	880	885	
889	890	895	900	905	910	915	919	924	929	934	
890	94 939	94 944	94 949	94 954	94 959	94 963	94 968	94 973	94 978	94 983	**4**
891	988	993	998	95 002	95 007	95 012	95 017	95 022	95 027	95 032	
892	95 036	95 041	95 046	051	056	061	066	071	075	080	1 0.4
893	085	090	095	100	105	109	114	119	124	129	2 0.8 · 3 1.2
894	134	139	143	148	153	158	163	168	173	177	4 1.6
895	182	187	192	197	202	207	211	216	221	226	5 2.0
896	231	236	240	245	250	255	260	265	270	274	6 2.4
897	279	284	289	294	299	303	308	313	318	323	7 2.8
898	328	332	337	342	347	352	357	361	366	371	8 3.2
899	376	381	386	390	395	400	405	410	415	419	9 3.6
900	95 424	95 429	95 434	95 439	95 444	95 448	95 453	95 458	95 463	95 468	
N	0	1	2	3	4	5	6	7	8	9	

Numbers 900–950			Logs 95424–97813								P.P.
N	**0**	**1**	**2**	**3**	**4**	**5**	**6**	**7**	**8**	**9**	
900	95 424	95 429	95 434	95 439	95 444	95 448	95 453	95 458	95 463	95 468	**5**
901	472	477	482	487	492	497	501	506	511	516	1 0.5
902	521	525	530	535	540	545̄	550	554	559	564	2 1.0
903	569	574	578	583	588	593	598	602	607	612	3 1.5
904	617	622	626	631	636	641	646	650	655	660	4 2.0
905	665̄	670	674	679	684	689	694	698	703	708	5 2.5
906	713	718	722	727	732	737	742	746	751	756	6 3.0
907	761	766	770	775	780	785̄	789	794	799	804	7 3.5
908	809	813	818	823	828	832	837	842	847	852	8 4.0
909	856	861	866	871	875	880	885	890	895̄	899	9 4.5
910	95 904	95 909	95 914	95 918	95 923	95 928	95 933	95 938	95 942	95 947	
911	952	957	961	966	971	976	980	985	990	995̄	
912	999	96 004	96 009	96 014	96 019	96 023	96 028	96 033	96 038	96 042	
913	96 047	052	057	061	066	071	076	080	085	090	
914	095̄	099	104	109	114	118	123	128	133	137	
915	142	147	152	156	161	166	171	175	180	185̄	
916	190	194	199	204	209	213	218	223	227	232	
917	237	242	246	251	256	261	265	270	275̄	280	
918	284	289	294	298	303	308	313	317	322	327	
919	332	336	341	346	350	355	360	365̄	369	374	
920	96 379	96 384	96 388	96 393	96 398	96 402	96 407	96 412	96 417	96 421	**4**
921	426	431	435	440	445̄	450	454	459	464	468	1 0.4
922	473	478	483	487	492	497	501	506	511	515	2 0.8
923	520	525̄	530	534	539	544	548	553	558	562	3 1.2
924	567	572	577	581	586	591	595	600	605̄	609	4 1.6
925	614	619	624	628	633	638	642	647	652	656	5 2.0
926	661	666	670	675	680	685̄	689	694	699	703	6 2.4
927	708	713	717	722	727	731	736	741	745	750	7 2.8
928	755̄	759	764	769	774	778	783	788	792	797	8 3.2
929	802	806	811	816	820	825̄	830	834	839	844	9 3.6
930	96 848	96 853	96 858	96 862	96 867	96 872	96 876	96 881	96 886	96 890	
931	895̄	900	904	909	914	918	923	928	932	937	
932	942	946	951	956	960	965̄	970	974	979	984	
933	988	993	997	97 002	97 007	97 011	97 016	97 021	97 025	97 030	
934	97 035̄	97 039	97 044	049	053	058	063	067	072	077	
935	081	086	090	095	100	104	109	114	118	123	
936	128	132	137	142	146	151	155	160	165̄	169	
937	174	179	183	188	192	197	202	206	211	216	
938	220	225̄	230	234	239	243	248	253	257	262	
939	267	271	276	280	285	290	294	299	304	308	
940	97 313	97 317	97 322	97 327	97 331	97 336	97 340	97 345	97 350	97 354	
941	359	364	368	373	377	382	387	391	396	400	
942	405	410	414	419	424	428	433	437	442	447	
943	451	456	460	465̄	470	474	479	483	488	493	
944	497	502	506	511	516	520	525̄	529	534	539	
945	543	548	552	557	562	566	571	575	580	585̄	
946	589	594	598	603	607	612	617	621	626	630	
947	635̄	640	644	649	653	658	663	667	672	676	
948	681	685	690	695̄	699	704	708	713	717	722	
949	727	731	736	740	745̄	749	754	759	763	768	
950	97 772	97 777	97 782	97 786	97 791	97 795	97 800	97 804	97 809	97 813	
N	**0**	**1**	**2**	**3**	**4**	**5**	**6**	**7**	**8**	**9**	

Numbers 950-1000 Logs 97772-00039

23

N	0	1	2	3	4	5	6	7	8	9
950	97 772	97 777	97 782	97 786	97 791	97 795	97 800	97 804	97 809	97 813
951	818	823	827	832	836	841	845	850	855	859
952	864	868	873	877	882	886	891	896	900	905
953	909	914	918	923	928	932	937	941	946	950
954	955	959	964	968	973	978	982	987	991	996
955	98 000	98 005	98 009	98 014	98 019	98 023	98 028	98 032	98 037	98 041
956	046	050	055	059	064	068	073	078	082	087
957	091	096	100	105	109	114	118	123	127	132
958	137	141	146	150	155	159	164	168	173	177
959	182	186	191	195	200	204	209	214	218	223
960	98 227	98 232	98 236	98 241	98 245	98 250	98 254	98 259	98 263	98 268
961	272	277	281	286	290	295	299	304	308	313
962	318	322	327	331	336	340	345	349	354	358
963	363	367	372	376	381	385	390	394	399	403
964	408	412	417	421	426	430	435	439	444	448
965	453	457	462	466	471	475	480	484	489	493
966	498	502	507	511	516	520	525	529	534	538
967	543	547	552	556	561	565	570	574	579	583
968	588	592	597	601	605	610	614	619	623	628
969	632	637	641	646	650	655	659	664	668	673
970	98 677	98 682	98 686	98 691	98 695	98 700	98 704	98 709	98 713	98 717
971	722	726	731	735	740	744	749	753	758	762
972	767	771	776	780	784	789	793	798	802	807
973	811	816	820	825	829	834	838	843	847	851
974	856	860	865	869	874	878	883	887	892	896
975	900	905	909	914	918	923	927	932	936	941
976	945	949	954	958	963	967	972	976	981	985
977	989	994	998	99 003	99 007	99 012	99 016	99 021	99 025	99 029
978	99 034	99 038	99 043	047	052	056	061	065	069	074
979	078	083	087	092	096	100	105	109	114	118
980	99 123	99 127	99 131	99 136	99 140	99 145	99 149	99 154	99 158	99 162
981	167	171	176	180	185	189	193	198	202	207
982	211	216	220	224	229	233	238	242	247	251
983	255	260	264	269	273	277	282	286	291	295
984	300	304	308	313	317	322	326	330	335	339
985	344	348	352	357	361	366	370	374	379	383
986	388	392	396	401	405	410	414	419	423	427
987	432	436	441	445	449	454	458	463	467	471
988	476	480	484	489	493	498	502	506	511	515
989	520	524	528	533	537	542	546	550	555	559
990	99 564	99 568	99 572	99 577	99 581	99 585	99 590	99 594	99 599	99 603
991	607	612	616	621	625	629	634	638	642	647
992	651	656	660	664	669	673	677	682	686	691
993	695	699	704	708	712	717	721	726	730	734
994	739	743	747	752	756	760	765	769	774	778
995	782	787	791	795	800	804	808	813	817	822
996	826	830	835	839	843	848	852	856	861	865
997	870	874	878	883	887	891	896	900	904	909
998	913	917	922	926	930	935	939	944	948	952
999	957	961	965	970	974	978	983	987	991	996
1000	00 000	00 004	00 009	00 013	00 017	00 022	00 026	00 030	00 035	00 039
N	0	1	2	3	4	5	6	7	8	9

P.P.

5
1 0.5
2 1.0
3 1.5
4 2.0
5 2.5
6 3.0
7 3.5
8 4.0
9 4.5

4
1 0.4
2 0.8
3 1.2
4 1.6
5 2.0
6 2.4
7 2.8
8 3.2
9 3.6

Numbers 1000–1050		Logs 0000000–0215614								
N	**0**	**1**	**2**	**3**	**4**	**5**	**6**	**7**	**8**	**9**
1000	000 0000	0434	0869	1303	1737	2171	2605̄	3039	3473	3907
01	4341	4775̄	5203	5642	6076	6510	6943	7377	7810	8244
02	8677	9111	9544	9977	*0411	*0844	*1277	*1710	*2143	*2576
03	001 3009	3442	3875	4308	4741	5174	5607	6039	6472	6905̄
04	7337	7770	8202	8635̄	9067	9499	9932	*0364	*0796	*1228
05	002 1661	2093	2525̄	2957	3389	3821	4253	4685̄	5116	5548
06	5980	6411	6843	7275̄	7706	8138	8569	9001	9432	9863
07	003 0295̄	0726	1157	1588	2019	2451	2882	3313	3744	4174
08	4605̄	5036	5467	5898	6328	6759	7190	7620	8051	8481
09	8912	9342	9772	*0203	*0633	*1063	*1493	*1924	*2354	*2784
1010	004 3214	3644	4074	4504	4933	5363	5793	6223	6652	7082
11	7512	7941	8371	8800	9229	9659	*0088	*0517	*0947	*1376
12	005 1805	2234	2663	3092	3521	3950	4379	4808	5237	5666
13	6094	6523	6952	7380	7809	8238	8666	9094	9523	9951
14	006 0380	0808	1236	1664	2092	2521	2949	3377	3805̄	4233
15	4660	5088̄	5516	5944	6372	6799	7227	7655̄	8082	8510
16	8937	9365̄	9792	*0219	*0647	*1074	*1501	*1928	*2355	*2782
17	007 3210	3637	4064	4490	4917	5344	5771	6198	6624	7051
18	7478	7904	8331	8757	9184	9610	*0037	*0463	*0889	*1316
19	008 1742	2168	2594	3020	3446	3872	4298	4724	5150	5576
1020	6002	6427	6853	7279	7704	8130	8556	8981	9407	9832
21	009 0257	0683	1108	1533	1959	2384	2809	3234	3659	4084
22	4509	4934	5359	5784	6208	6633	7058	7483	7907	8332
23	8756	9181	9605̄	*0030	*0454	*0878	*1303	*1727	*2151	*2575̄
24	010 3000	3424	3848	4272	4696	5120	5544	5967	6391	6815̄
25	7239	7662	8086	8510	8933	9357	9780	*0204	*0627	*1050
26	011 1474	1897	2320	2743	3166	3590	4013	4436	4859	5282
27	5704	6127	6550	6973	7396	7818	8241	8664	9086	9509
28	9931	*0354	*0776	*1198	*1621	*2043	*2465̄	*2887	*3310	*3732
29	012 4154	4576	4998	5420	5842	6264	6685̄	7107	7529	7951
1030	8372	8794	9215̄	9637	*0059	*0480	*0901	*1323	*1744	*2165̄
31	013 2587	3008	3429	3850	4271	4692	5113	5534	5955̄	6376
32	6797	7218	7639	8059	8480	8901	9321	9742	*0162	*0583
33	014 1003	1424	1844	2264	2685̄	3105̄	3525̄	3945̄	4365̄	4785̄
34	5205̄	5625̄	6045̄	6465̄	6885̄	7305̄	7725̄	8144	8564	8984
35	9403	9823	*0243	*0662	*1082	*1501	*1920	*2340	*2759	*3178
36	015 3598	4017	4436	4855̄	5274	5693	6112	6531	6950	7369
37	7788	8206	8625̄	9044	9462	9881	*0300	*0718	*1137	*1555̄
38	016 1974	2392	2810	3229	3647	4065̄	4483	4901	5319	5737
39	6155̄	6573	6991	7409	7827	8245̄	8663	9080	9498	9916
1040	017 0333	0751	1168	1586	2003	2421	2838	3256	3673	4090
41	4507	4924	5342	5759	6176	6593	7010	7427	7844	8260
42	8677	9094	9511	9927	*0344	*0761	*1177	*1594	*2010	*2427
43	018 2843	3259	3676	4092	4508	4925̄	5341	5757	6173	6589
44	7005̄	7421	7837	8253	8669	9084	9500	9916	*0332	*0747
45	019 1163	1578	1994	2410	2825̄	3240	3656	4071	4486	4902
46	5317	5732	6147	6562	6977	7392	7807	8222	8637	9052
47	9467	9882	*0296	*0711	*1126	*1540	*1955̄	*2369	*2784	*3198
48	020 3613	4027	4442	4856	5270	5684	6099	6513	6927	7341
49	7755̄	8169	8583	8997	9411	9824	*0238	*0652	*1066	*1479
1050	021 1893	2307	2720	3134	3547	3961	4374	4787	5201	5614
N	**0**	**1**	**2**	**3**	**4**	**5**	**6**	**7**	**8**	**9**

N	0	1	2	3	4	5	6	7	8	9
				Numbers 1050–1100		Logs 0211893–0417479				
1050	021 1893	2307	2720	3134	3547	3961	4374	4787	5201	5614
51	6027	6440	6854	7267	7680	8093	8506	8919	9332	974$\overline{5}$
52	022 0157	0570	0983	1396	1808	2221	2634	3046	3459	3871
53	4284	4696	5109	5521	5933	6345	6758	7170	7582	7994
54	8406	8818	9230	9642	*0054	*0466	*0878	*1289	*1701	*2113
55	023 252$\overline{5}$	2936	3348	3759	4171	4582	4994	5405	5817	6228
56	6639	7050	7462	7873	8284	8695	9106	9517	9928	*0339
57	024 0750	1161	1572	1982	2393	2804	3214	3625	4036	4446
58	4857	5267	5678	6088	6498	6909	7319	7729	8139	8549
59	8960	9370	9780	*0190	*0600	*1010	*1419	*1829	*2239	*2649
1060	025 3059	3468	3878	4288	4697	5107	5516	5926	6335	6744
61	7154	7563	7972	8382	8791	9200	9609	*0018	*0427	*0836
62	026 1245	1654	2063	2472	2881	3289	3698	4107	4515	4924
63	5333	5741	6150	6558	6967	737$\overline{5}$	7783	8192	8600	9008
64	9416	9824	*0233	*0641	*1049	*1457	*186$\overline{5}$	*2273	*2680	*3088
65	027 3496	3904	4312	4719	5127	553$\overline{5}$	5942	6350	6757	7165
66	7572	7979	8387	8794	9201	9609	*0016	*0423	*0830	*1237
67	028 1644	2051	2458	2865	3272	3679	4086	4492	4899	5306
68	5713	6119	6526	6932	7339	7745	8152	8558	8964	9371
69	9777	*0183	*0590	*0996	*1402	*1808	*2214	*2620	*3026	*3432
1070	029 3838	4244	4649	5055	5461	5867	6272	6678	7084	7489
71	789$\overline{5}$	8300	8706	9111	9516	9922	*0327	*0732	*1138	*1543
72	030 1948	2353	2758	3163	3568	3973	4378	4783	5188	5592
73	5997	6402	6807	7211	7616	8020	8425	8830	9234	9638
74	031 0043	0447	0851	1256	1660	2064	2468	2872	3277	3681
75	408$\overline{5}$	4489	4893	5296	5700	6104	6508	6912	7315	7719
76	8123	8526	8930	9333	9737	*0140	*0544	*0947	*1350	*1754
77	032 2157	2560	2963	3367	3770	4173	4576	4979	5382	578$\overline{5}$
78	6188	6590	6993	7396	7799	8201	8604	9007	9409	9812
79	033 0214	0617	1019	1422	1824	2226	2629	3031	3433	3835
1080	4238	4640	5042	5444	5846	6248	6650	7052	7453	7855
81	8257	8659	9060	9462	9864	*0265	*0667	*1068	*1470	*1871
82	034 2273	2674	3075	3477	3878	4279	4680	5081	5482	5884
83	628$\overline{5}$	6686	7087	7487	7888	8289	8690	9091	9491	9892
84	035 0293	0693	1094	149$\overline{5}$	1895	2296	2696	3096	3497	3897
85	4297	4698	5098	5498	5898	6298	6698	7098	7498	7898
86	8298	8698	9098	9498	9898	*0297	*0697	*1097	*1496	*1896
87	036 2295	269$\overline{5}$	3094	3494	3893	4293	4692	5091	5491	5890
88	6289	6688	7087	7486	7885	8284	8683	9082	9481	9880
89	037 0279	0678	1076	1475	1874	2272	2671	3070	3468	3867
1090	426$\overline{5}$	4663	5062	5460	5858	6257	665$\overline{5}$	7053	7451	7849
91	8248	8646	9044	9442	9839	*0237	*0635	*1033	*1431	*1829
92	038 2226	2624	3022	3419	3817	4214	4612	5009	5407	5804
93	6202	6599	6996	7393	7791	8188	8585	8982	9379	9776
94	039 0173	0570	0967	1364	1761	2158	2554	2951	3348	374$\overline{5}$
95	4141	4538	4934	5331	5727	6124	6520	6917	7313	7709
96	8106	8502	8898	9294	9690	*0086	*0482	*0878	*1274	*1670
97	040 2066	2462	2858	3254	3650	4045	4441	4837	5232	5628
98	6023	6419	6814	7210	7605	8001	8396	8791	9187	9582
99	9977	*0372	*0767	*1162	*1557	*1952	*2347	*2742	*3137	*3532
1100	041 3927	4322	4716	5111	5506	5900	6295	6690	7084	7479
N	0	1	2	3	4	5	6	7	8	9

LOGARITHMS OF
TRIGONOMETRIC FUNCTIONS[1]

[1] From Five-Place Tables compiled by N. J. Lennes and A. S. Merrill, Harper & Brothers, Publishers.

′	L. Sin.	d.	L. Tang.	c. d.	L. Cotg.	L. Cos.	′	P. P.		
0	.....		.....			10.00 000	60			
1	6.46 373	30103	6.46 373	30103	3.53 627	000	59	1′	5800	4576	3779
2	6.76 476	17609	6.76 476	17609	3.23 524	000	58	10″	967	763	630
3	6.94 085	12494	6.94 085	12494	3.05 915	000	57	20″	1933	1525	1260
4	7.06 579	9691	7.06 579	9691	2.93 421	000	56	30″	2900	2288	1890
5	7.16 270	7918	7.16 270	7918	2.83 730	000	55	40″	3867	3051	2519
6	7.24 188	6694	7.24 188	6694	2.75 812	000	54	50″	4833	3813	3149
7	7.30 882	5800	7.30 882	5800	2.69 118	000	53				
8	7.36 682	5115	7.36 682	5115	2.63 318	000	52	1′	3218	2802	2483
9	7.41 797	4576	7.41 797	4576	2.58 203	000	51	10″	536	467	414
10	7.46 373	4139	7.46 373	4139	2.53 627	10.00 000	50	20″	1073	934	828
11	7.50 512	3779	7.50 512	3779	2.49 488	000	49	30″	1609	1401	1242
12	7.54 291	3476	7.54 291	3476	2.45 709	000	48	40″	2145	1868	1655
13	7.57 767	3218	7.57 767	3219	2.42 233	000	47	50″	2682	2335	2069
14	7.60 985	2997	7.60 986	2996	2.39 014	000	46	1′	2227	2021	1848
15	7.63 982	2802	7.63 982	2803	2.36 018	000	45				
16	7.66 784	2633	7.66 785	2633	2.33 215	000	44	10″	371	337	308
17	7.69 417	2483	7.69 418	2482	2.30 582	9.99 999	43	20″	742	674	616
18	7.71 900	2348	7.71 900	2348	2.28 100	999	42	30″	1114	1011	924
19	7.74 248	2227	7.74 248	2228	2.25 752	999	41	40″	1485	1347	1232
20	7.76 475	2119	7.76 476	2119	2.23 524	9.99 999	40	50″	1856	1684	1540
21	7.78 594	2021	7.78 595	2020	2.21 405	999	39	1′	1704	1579	1472
22	7.80 615	1930	7.80 615	1931	2.19 385	999	38	10″	284	263	245
23	7.82 545	1848	7.82 546	1848	2.17 454	999	37	20″	568	526	491
24	7.84 393	1773	7.84 394	1773	2.15 606	999	36	30″	852	790	736
25	7.86 166	1704	7.86 167	1704	2.13 833	999	35	40″	1136	1053	981
26	7.87 870	1639	7.87 871	1639	2.12 129	999	34	50″	1420	1316	1227
27	7.89 509	1579	7.89 510	1579	2.10 490	999	33				
28	7.91 088	1524	7.91 089	1524	2.08 911	999	32	1′	1379	1297	1223
29	7.92 612	1472	7.92 613	1473	2.07 387	998	31	10″	230	216	204
30	7.94 084	1424	7.94 086	1424	2.05 914	9.99 998	30	20″	460	432	408
31	7.95 508	1379	7.95 510	1379	2.04 490	998	29	30″	690	649	612
32	7.96 887	1336	7.96 889	1336	2.03 111	998	28	40″	919	865	815
33	7.98 223	1297	7.98 225	1297	2.01 775	998	27	50″	1149	1081	1019
34	7.99 520	1259	7.99 522	1259	2.00 478	998	26	1′	1158	1100	1046
35	8.00 779	1223	8.00 781	1223	1.99 219	998	25				
36	8.02 002	1190	8.02 004	1190	1.97 996	998	24	10″	193	183	174
37	8.03 192	1158	8.03 194	1159	1.96 806	997	23	20″	386	367	349
38	8.04 350	1128	8.04 353	1128	1.95 647	997	22	30″	579	550	523
39	8.05 478	1100	8.05 481	1100	1.94 519	997	21	40″	772	733	697
40	8.06 578	1072	8.06 581	1072	1.93 419	9.99 997	20	50″	965	917	872
41	8.07 650	1046	8.07 653	1047	1.92 347	997	19	1′	999	954	914
42	8.08 696	1022	8.08 700	1022	1.91 300	997	18	10″	167	159	152
43	8.09 718	999	8.09 722	998	1.90 278	997	17	20″	333	318	305
44	8.10 717	976	8.10 720	976	1.89 280	996	16	30″	500	477	457
45	8.11 693	954	8.11 696	955	1.88 304	996	15	40″	666	636	609
46	8.12 647	934	8.12 651	934	1.87 349	996	14	50″	833	795	762
47	8.13 581	914	8.13 585	915	1.86 415	996	13				
48	8.14 495	896	8.14 500	895	1.85 500	996	12	1′	877	843	812
49	8.15 391	877	8.15 395	878	1.84 605	996	11	10″	146	141	135
50	8.16 268	860	8.16 273	860	1.83 727	9.99 995	10	20″	292	281	271
51	8.17 128	843	8.17 133	843	1.82 867	995	9	30″	439	422	406
52	8.17 971	827	8.17 976	828	1.82 024	995	8	40″	585	562	541
53	8.18 798	812	8.18 804	812	1.81 196	995	7	50″	731	703	677
54	8.19 610	797	8.19 616	797	1.80 384	995	6	1′	782	755	730
55	8.20 407	782	8.20 413	782	1.79 587	994	5				
56	8.21 189	769	8.21 195	769	1.78 805	994	4	10″	130	126	122
57	8.21 958	755	8.21 964	756	1.78 036	994	3	20″	261	252	243
58	8.22 713	743	8.22 720	742	1.77 280	994	2	30″	391	378	365
59	8.23 456	730	8.23 462	730	1.76 538	994	1	40″	521	503	487
60	8.24 186		8.24 192		1.75 808	9.99 993	0	50″	652	629	608

′	L. Cos.	d.	L. Cotg.	c. d.	L. Tang.	L. Sin.	′			

'	L. Sin.	d.	L. Tang.	c. d.	L. Cotg.	L. Cos.	'
0	8.24 186	717	8.24 192	718	1.75 808	9.99 993	60
1	903	706	910	706	090	993	59
2	8.25 609	695	8.25 616	696	1.74 384	993	58
3	8.26 304	684	8.26 312	684	1.73 688	993	57
4	988	673	996	673	004	992	56
5	8.27 661	663	8.27 669	663	1.72 331	992	55
6	8.28 324	653	8.28 332	654	1.71 668	992	54
7	977	644	986	643	014	992	53
8	8.29 621	634	8.29 629	634	1.70 371	992	52
9	8.30 255	624	8.30 263	625	1.69 737	991	51
10	8.30 879	616	8.30 888	617	1.69 112	9.99 991	50
11	8.31 495	608	8.31 505	607	1.68 495	991	49
12	8.32 103	599	8.32 112	599	1.67 888	990	48
13	702	590	711	591	289	990	47
14	8.33 292	583	8.33 302	584	1.66 698	990	46
15	875	575	886	575	114	990	45
16	8.34 450	568	8.34 461	568	1.65 539	989	44
17	8.35 018	560	8.35 029	561	1.64 971	989	43
18	578	553	590	553	410	989	42
19	8.36 131	547	8.36 143	546	1.63 857	989	41
20	8.36 678	539	8.36 689	540	1.63 311	9.99 988	40
21	8.37 217	533	8.37 229	533	1.62 771	988	39
22	750	526	762	527	238	988	38
23	8.38 276	520	8.38 289	520	1.61 711	987	37
24	796	514	809	514	191	987	36
25	8.39 310	508	8.39 323	509	1.60 677	987	35
26	818	502	832	502	168	986	34
27	8.40 320	496	8.40 334	496	1.59 666	986	33
28	816	491	830	491	170	986	32
29	8.41 307	485	8.41 321	486	1.58 679	985	31
30	8.41 792	480	8.41 807	480	1.58 193	9.99 985	30
31	8.42 272	474	8.42 287	475	1.57 713	985	29
32	746	470	762	470	238	984	28
33	8.43 216	464	8.43 232	464	1.56 768	984	27
34	680	459	696	460	304	984	26
35	8.44 139	455	8.44 156	455	1.55 844	983	25
36	594	450	611	450	389	983	24
37	8.45 044	445	8.45 061	446	1.54 939	983	23
38	489	441	507	441	493	982	22
39	930	436	948	437	052	982	21
40	8.46 366	433	8.46 385	432	1.53 615	9.99 982	20
41	799	427	817	428	183	981	19
42	8.47 226	424	8.47 245	424	1.52 755	981	18
43	650	419	669	420	331	981	17
44	8.48 069	416	8.48 089	416	1.51 911	980	16
45	485	411	505	412	495	980	15
46	896	408	917	408	083	979	14
47	8.49 304	404	8.49 325	404	1.50 675	979	13
48	708	400	729	401	271	979	12
49	8.50 108	396	8.50 130	397	1.49 870	978	11
50	8.50 504	393	8.50 527	393	1.49 473	9.99 978	10
51	897	390	920	390	080	977	9
52	8.51 287	386	8.51 310	386	1.48 690	977	8
53	673	382	696	383	304	977	7
54	8.52 055	379	8.52 079	380	1.47 921	976	6
55	434	376	459	376	541	976	5
56	810	373	835	373	165	975	4
57	8.53 183	369	8.53 208	370	1.46 792	975	3
58	552	367	578	367	422	974	2
59	919	363	945	363	055	974	1
60	8.54 282		8.54 308		1.45 692	9.99 974	0
'	L. Cos.	d.	L. Cotg.	c. d.	L. Tang.	L. Sin.	'

P. P.

1'	717	673	644
10"	120	112	107
20"	239	224	215
30"	359	337	322
40"	478	449	429
50"	598	561	537
1'	616	590	568
10"	103	98	95
20"	205	197	189
30"	308	295	284
40"	411	393	379
50"	513	492	473
1'	547	533	520
10"	91	89	87
20"	182	178	173
30"	274	267	260
40"	365	355	347
50"	456	444	433
1'	508	496	485
10"	85	83	81
20"	169	165	162
30"	254	248	243
40"	339	331	323
50"	423	413	404
1'	474	464	455
10"	79	77	76
20"	158	155	152
30"	237	232	228
40"	316	309	303
50"	395	387	379
1'	445	436	427
10"	74	73	71
20"	148	145	142
30"	223	218	214
40"	297	291	285
50"	371	363	356
1'	419	411	404
10"	70	69	67
20"	140	137	135
30"	210	206	202
40"	279	274	269
50"	349	343	337
1'	396	390	382
10"	66	65	64
20"	132	130	127
30"	198	195	191
40"	264	260	255
50"	330	325	318
1'	376	369	363
10"	63	62	61
20"	125	123	121
30"	188	185	182
40"	251	246	242
50"	313	308	303

88°

'	L. Sin.	d.	L. Tang.	c. d.	L. Cotg.	L. Cos.	'
0	8.54 282	360	8.54 308	361	1.45 692	9.99 974	60
1	642	357	669	358	331	973	59
2	999	355	8.55 027	355	1.44 973	973	58
3	8.55 354	351	382	352	618	972	57
4	705	349	734	349	266	972	56
5	8.56 054	346	8.56 083	346	1.43 917	971	55
6	400	343	429	344	571	971	54
7	743	341	773	341	227	970	53
8	8.57 084	337	8.57 114	338	1.42 886	970	52
9	421	336	452	336	548	969	51
10	8.57 757	332	8.57 788	333	1.42 212	9.99 969	50
11	8.58 089	330	8.58 121	330	1.41 879	968	49
12	419	328	451	328	549	968	48
13	747	325	779	326	221	967	47
14	8.59 072	323	8.59 105	323	1.40 895	967	46
15	395̄	320	428	321	572	967	45
16	715	318	749	319	251	966	44
17	8.60 033	316	8.60 068	316	1.39 932	966	43
18	349	313	384	314	616	965̄	42
19	662	311	698	311	302	964	41
20	8.60 973	309	8.61 009	310	1.38 991	9.99 964	40
21	8.61 282	307	319	307	681	963	39
22	589	305	626	305	374	963	38
23	894	302	931	303	069	962	37
24	8.62 196	301	8.62 234	301	1.37 766	962	36
25	497	298	535	299	465̄	961	35
26	795̄	296	834	297	166	961	34
27	8.63 091	294	8.63 131	295	1.36 869	960	33
28	385	293	426	292	574	960	32
29	678	290	718	291	282	959	31
30	8.63 968	288	8.64 009	289	1.35 991	9.99 959	30
31	8.64 256	287	298	287	702̄	958	29
32	543	284	585	285	415̄	958	28
33	827	283	870	284	130	957	27
34	8.65 110	281	8.65 154	281	1.34 846	956	26
35	391	279	435	280	565̄	956	25
36	670	277	715̄	278	285	955	24
37	947	276	993	276	007	955̄	23
38	8.66 223	274	8.66 269	274	1.33 731	954	22
39	497	272	543	273	457	954	21
40	8.66 769	270	8.66 816	271	1.33 184	9.99 953	20
41	8.67 039	269	8.67 087	269	1.32 913	952	19
42	308	267	356	268	644	952	18
43	575	266	624	266	376	951	17
44	841	263	890	264	110	951	16
45	8.68 104	263	8.68 154	263	1.31 846	950	15
46	367	260	417	261	583	949	14
47	627	259	678	260	322	949	13
48	886	258	938	258	062	948	12
49	8.69 144	256	8.69 196	257	1.30 804	948	11
50	8.69 400	254	8.69 453	255	1.30 547	9.99 947	10
51	654	253	708	254	292	946	9
52	907	252	962	252	038	946	8
53	8.70 159	250	8.70 214	251	1.29 786	945̄	7
54	409	249	465̄	249	535	944	6
55	658	247	714	248	286	944	5
56	905̄	246	962	246	038	943	4
57	8.71 151	244	8.71 208	245	1.28 792	942	3
58	395	243	453	244	547	942	2
59	638	242	697	243	303	941	1
60	8.71 880		8.71 940		1.28 060	9.99 940	0
'	L. Cos.	d.	L. Cotg.	c. d.	L. Tang.	L. Sin.	'

P. P.

1'	360	350	340
1"	6.0	5.8	5.7
2"	12.0	11.7	11.3
3"	18.0	17.5	17.0
4"	24.0	23.3	22.7
5"	30.0	29.2	28.3
6"	36.0	35.0	34.0
7"	42.0	40.8	39.7
8"	48.0	46.7	45.3
9"	54.0	52.5	51.0

1'	330	320	310
1"	5.5	5.3	5.2
2"	11.0	10.7	10.3
3"	16.5	16.0	15.5
4"	22.0	21.3	20.7
5"	27.5	26.7	25.8
6"	33.0	32.0	31.0
7"	38.5	37.3	36.2
8"	44.0	42.7	41.3
9"	49.5	48.0	46.5

1'	300	290	285
1"	5.0	4.8	4.8
2"	10.0	9.7	9.5
3"	15.0	14.5	14.3
4"	20.0	19.3	19.0
5"	25.0	24.2	23.8
6"	30.0	29.0	28.5
7"	35.0	33.8	33.3
8"	40.0	38.7	38.0
9"	45.0	43.5	42.8

1'	280	275	270
1"	4.7	4.6	4.5
2"	9.3	9.2	9.0
3"	14.0	13.8	13.5
4"	18.7	18.3	18.0
5"	23.3	22.9	22.5
6"	28.0	27.5	27.0
7"	32.7	32.1	31.5
8"	37.3	36.7	36.0
9"	42.0	41.3	40.5

1'	265	260	255
1"	4.4	4.3	4.3
2"	8.8	8.7	8.5
3"	13.3	13.0	12.8
4"	17.7	17.3	17.0
5"	22.1	21.7	21.3
6"	26.5	26.0	25.5
7"	30.9	30.3	29.8
8"	35.3	34.7	34.0
9"	39.8	39.0	38.3

1'	250	245	240
1"	4.2	4.1	4.0
2"	8.3	8.2	8.0
3"	12.5	12.3	12.0
4"	16.7	16.3	16.0
5"	20.8	20.4	20.0
6"	25.0	24.5	24.0
7"	29.2	28.6	28.0
8"	33.3	32.7	32.0
9"	37.5	36.8	36.0

′	L. Sin.	d.	L. Tang.	c. d.	L. Cotg.	L. Cos.	′
0	8.71 880	240	8.71 940	241	1.28 060	9.99 940	60
1	8.72 120	239	8.72 181	239	1.27 819	940	59
2	359	238	420	239	580	939	58
3	597	237	659	237	341	938	57
4	834	235	896	236	104	938	56
5	8.73 069	234	8.73 132	234	1.26 868	937	55
6	303	232	366	234	634	936	54
7	535	232	600	232	400	936	53
8	767	230	832	231	168	935	52
9	997	229	8.74 063	229	1.25 937	934	51
10	8.74 226	228	8.74 292	229	1.25 708	9.99 934	50
11	454	226	521	227	479	933	49
12	680	226	748	226	252	932	48
13	906	224	974	225	026	932	47
14	8.75 130	223	8.75 199	224	1.24 801	931	46
15	353	222	423	222	577	930	45
16	575̄	220	645	222	355̄	929	44
17	795	220	867	220	133	929	43
18	8.76 015	219	8.76 087	219	1.23 913	928	42
19	234	217	306	219	694	927	41
20	8.76 451	216	8.76 525̄	217	1.23 475	9.99 926	40
21	667	216	742	216	258	926	39
22	883	214	958	215	042	925	38
23	8.77 097	213	8.77 173	214	1.22 827	924	37
24	310	212	387	213	613	923	36
25	522	211	600	211	400	923	35
26	733	210	811	211	189	922	34
27	943	209	8.78 022	210	1.21 978	921	33
28	8.78 152	208	232	209	768	920	32
29	360	208	441	208	559	920	31
30	8.78 568	206	8.78 649	206	1.21 351	9.99 919	30
31	774	205	855	206	145̄	918	29
32	979	204	8.79 061	205	1.20 939	917	28
33	8.79 183	203	266	204	734	917	27
34	386	202	470	203	530	916	26
35	588	201	673	202	327	915	25
36	789	201	875	201	125̄	914	24
37	990	199	8.80 076	201	1.19 924	913	23
38	8.80 189	199	277	199	723	913	22
39	388	197	476	198	524	912	21
40	8.80 585	197	8.80 674	198	1.19 326	9.99 911	20
41	782	196	872	196	128	910	19
42	978	195	8.81 068	196	1.18 932	909	18
43	8.81 173	194	264	195	736	909	17
44	367	193	459	194	541	908	16
45	560	192	653	193	347	907	15
46	752	192	846	192	154	906	14
47	944	190	8.82 038	192	1.17 962	905	13
48	8.82 134	190	230	190	770	904	12
49	324	189	420	190	580	904	11
50	8.82 513	188	8.82 610	189	1.17 390	9.99 903	10
51	701	187	799	188	201	902	9
52	888	187	987	188	013	901	8
53	8.83 075̄	186	8.83 175̄	186	1.16 825	900	7
54	261	185	361	186	639	899	6
55	446	184	547	185	453	898	5
56	630	183	732	184	268	898	4
57	813	183	916	184	084	897	3
58	996	181	8.84 100	182	1.15 900	896̄	2
59	8.84 177	181	282	182	718	895̄	1
60	8.84 358		8.84 464		1.15 536	9.99 894	0
′	L. Cos.	d.	L. Cotg.	c. d.	L. Tang.	L. Sin.	′

P. P.

1′	241	237	233
1″	4.0	4.0	3.9
2″	8.0	7.9	7.8
3″	12.1	11.9	11.7
4″	16.1	15.8	15.5
5″	20.1	19.8	19.4
6″	24.1	23.7	23.3
7″	28.1	27.7	27.2
8″	32.1	31.6	31.1
9″	36.2	35.6	35.0

1′	229	225	221
1″	3.8	3.8	3.7
2″	7.6	7.5	7.4
3″	11.5	11.3	11.1
4″	15.3	15.0	14.7
5″	19.1	18.8	18.4
6″	22.9	22.5	22.1
7″	26.7	26.3	25.8
8″	30.5	30.0	29.5
9″	34.4	33.8	33.2

1′	217	213	209
1″	3.6	3.6	3.5
2″	7.2	7.1	7.0
3″	10.9	10.7	10.5
4″	14.5	14.2	13.9
5″	18.1	17.8	17.4
6″	21.7	21.3	20.9
7″	25.3	24.9	24.4
8″	28.9	28.4	27.9
9″	32.6	32.0	31.4

1′	205	202	199
1″	3.4	3.4	3.3
2″	6.8	6.7	6.6
3″	10.3	10.1	10.0
4″	13.7	13.5	13.3
5″	17.1	16.8	16.6
6″	20.5	20.2	19.9
7″	23.9	23.6	23.2
8″	27.3	26.9	26.5
9″	30.8	30.3	29.9

1′	196	193	190
1″	3.3	3.2	3.2
2″	6.5	6.4	6.3
3″	9.8	9.7	9.5
4″	13.1	12.9	12.7
5″	16.3	16.1	15.8
6″	19.6	19.3	19.0
7″	22.9	22.5	22.2
8″	26.1	25.7	25.3
9″	29.4	29.0	28.5

1′	187	184	181
1″	3.1	3.1	3.0
2″	6.2	6.1	6.0
3″	9.4	9.2	9.1
4″	12.5	12.3	12.1
5″	15.6	15.3	15.1
6″	18.7	18.4	18.1
7″	21.8	21.5	21.1
8″	24.9	24.5	24.1
9″	28.1	27.6	27.2

′	L. Sin.	d.	L. Tang.	c. d.	L. Cotg.	L. Cos.	′
0	8.84 358	181	8.84 464	182	1.15 536	9.99 894	60
1	539	179	646	180	354	893	59
2	718	179	826	180	174	892	58
3	897	178	8.85 006	179	1.14 994	891	57
4	8.85 075	177	185	178	815	891	56
5	252	177	363	177	637	890	55
6	429	176	540	177	460	889	54
7	605̄	175	717	176	283	888	53
8	780̄	175	893	176	107	887	52
9	955̄	173	8.86 069	174	1.13 931	886	51
10	8.86 128	173	8.86 243	174	1.13 757	9.99 885	50
11	301	173	417	174	583	884	49
12	474	171	591	172	409	883	48
13	645	171	763	172	237	882	47
14	816	171	935	171	065̄	881	46
15	987	169	8.87 106	171	1.12 894	880	45
16	8.87 156	169	277	170	723	879	44
17	325	169	447	169	553	879	43
18	494	167	616	169	384	878	42
19	661	168	785̄	168	215	877	41
20	8.87 829	166	8.87 953	167	1.12 047	9.99 876	40
21	995̄	166	8.88 120	167	1.11 880	875̄	39
22	8.88 161	165	287	166	713	874	38
23	326	164	453	165	547	873	37
24	490	164	618	165	382	872	36
25	654	163	783	165	217	871	35
26	817	163	948	163	052	870	34
27	980	162	8.89 111	163	1.10 889	869	33
28	8.89 142	162	274	163	726	868	32
29	304	160	437	161	563	867	31
30	8.89 464	161	8.89 598	162	1.10 402	9.99 866	30
31	625̄	159	760	160	240	865̄	29
32	784	159	920	160	080	864	28
33	943	159	8.90 080	160	1.09 920	863	27
34	8.90 102	158	240	159	760	862	26
35	260	157	399	158	601	861	25
36	417	157	557	158	443	860	24
37	574	156	715	157	285	859	23
38	730	155	872	157	128	858	22
39	885	155	8.91 029	156	1.08 971	857	21
40	8.91 040	155	8.91 135	156	1.08 815	9.99 856	20
41	195̄	154	340	155	660	855̄	19
42	349	153	495	155	505̄	854	18
43	502	153	650	153	350	853	17
44	655	152	803	154	197	852	16
45	807	152	957	153	043	851	15
46	959	151	8.92 110	152	1.07 890	850	14
47	8.92 110	151	262	152	738	848	13
48	261	150	414	151	586	847	12
49	411	150	565	151	435	846	11
50	8.92 561	149	8.92 716	150	1.07 284	9.99 845	10
51	710	149	866	150	134	844	9
52	859	148	8.93 016	149	1.06 984	843	8
53	8.93 007	147	165	148	835	842	7
54	154	147	313	149	687	841	6
55	301	147	462	147	538	840	5
56	448	146	609	147	391	839	4
57	594	146	756	147	244	838	3
58	740	145	903	146	097	837	2
59	885	145	8.94 049	146	1.05 951	836	1
60	8.94 030		8.94 195		1.05 805̄	9.99 834	0
′	L. Cos.	d.	L. Cotg.	c. d.	L. Tang.	L. Sin.	′

P. P.

1′	181	178	175
1″	3.0	3.0	2.9
2″	6.0	5.9	5.8
3″	9.1	8.9	8.8
4″	12.1	11.9	11.7
5″	15.1	14.8	14.6
6″	18.1	17.8	17.5
7″	21.1	20.8	20.4
8″	24.1	23.7	23.3
9″	27.2	26.7	26.3

1′	173	171	169
1″	2.9	2.9	2.8
2″	5.8	5.7	5.6
3″	8.7	8.6	8.5
4″	11.5	11.4	11.3
5″	14.4	14.3	14.1
6″	17.3	17.1	16.9
7″	20.2	20.0	19.7
8″	23.1	22.8	22.5
9″	26.0	25.7	25.4

1′	167	165	163
1″	2.8	2.8	2.7
2″	5.6	5.5	5.4
3″	8.4	8.3	8.2
4″	11.1	11.0	10.9
5″	13.9	13.8	13.6
6″	16.7	16.5	16.3
7″	19.5	19.3	19.0
8″	22.3	22.0	21.7
9″	25.1	24.8	24.5

1′	161	159	157
1″	2.7	2.7	2.6
2″	5.4	5.3	5.2
3″	8.1	8.0	7.9
4″	10.7	10.6	10.5
5″	13.4	13.3	13.1
6″	16.1	15.9	15.7
7″	18.8	18.6	18.3
8″	21.5	21.2	20.9
9″	24.2	23.9	23.6

1′	155	153	151
1″	2.6	2.6	2.5
2″	5.2	5.1	5.0
3″	7.8	7.7	7.6
4″	10.3	10.2	10.1
5″	12.9	12.8	12.6
6″	15.5	15.3	15.1
7″	18.1	17.9	17.6
8″	20.7	20.4	20.1
9″	23.3	23.0	22.7

1′	149	147	145
1″	2.5	2.5	2.4
2″	5.0	4.9	4.8
3″	7.5	7.4	7.3
4″	9.9	9.8	9.7
5″	12.4	12.3	12.1
6″	14.9	14.7	14.5
7″	17.4	17.2	16.9
8″	19.9	19.6	19.3
9″	22.4	22.1	21.8

′	L. Sin.	d.	L. Tang.	c. d.	L. Cotg.	L. Cos.	′
0	8.94 030	144	8.94 195	145	1.05 805̄	9.99 834	60
1	174	143	340	145	660	833	59
2	317	144	485	145	515̄	832	58
3	461	142	630	143	370	831	57
4	603	143	773	144	227	830	56
5	746	141	917	143	083	829	55
6	887	142	8.95 060	143	1.04 940	828	54
7	8.95 029	141	202	142	798	827	53
8	170	141	344	142	656	825	52
9	310	140	486	142	514	824	51
10	8.95 450	140	8.95 627	141	1.04 373	9.99 823	50
11	589	139	767	140	233	822	49
12	728	139	908	141	092	821	48
13	867	139	8.96 047	139	1.03 953	820	47
14	8.96 005	138	187	140	813̄	819	46
15	143	138	325	138	675̄	817	45
16	280	137	464	139	536	816	44
17	417	137	602	138	398	815	43
18	553	136	739	137	261	814	42
19	689	136	877	138	123	813	41
20	8.96 825	136	8.97 013	136	1.02 987	9.99 812	40
21	960	135	150	137	850	810	39
22	8.97 095̄	135	285	135	715̄	809	38
23	229	134	421	136	579	808	37
24	363	134	556	135	444	807	36
25	496	133	691	135	309	806	35
26	629	133	825̄	134	175	804	34
27	762	133	959	134	041	803	33
28	894	132	8.98 092	133	1.01 908	802	32
29	8.98 026	132	225	133	775̄	801	31
30	8.98 157	131	8.98 358	133	1.01 642	9.99 800	30
31	288	131	490	132	510	798	29
32	419	131	622	132	378	797	28
33	549	130	753	131	247	796	27
34	679	130	884̄	131	116	795̄	26
35	808	129	8.99 015	131	1.00 985	793	25
36	937	129	145	130	855̄	792	24
37	8.99 066	129	275̄	130	725̄	791	23
38	194	128	405̄	130	595	790	22
39	322	128	534	129	466	788	21
40	8.99 450	128	8.99 662	128	1.00 338	9.99 787	20
41	577	127	791	129	209	786	19
42	704	127	919	128	081	785̄	18
43	830	126	9.00 046	127	0.99 954	783	17
44	956	126	174	128	826	782	16
45	9.00 082	126	301	127	699	781	15
46	207	125	427	126	573	780	14
47	332	125	553	126	447	778	13
48	456	124	679	126	321	777	12
49	581	125	805̄	126	195	776̄	11
50	9.00 704	123	9.00 930	125	0.99 070	9.99 775̄	10
51	828	124	9.01 055̄	125	0.98 945	773	9
52	951	123	179	124	821	772	8
53	9.01 074	123	303	124	697	771	7
54	196	122	427	124	573	769	6
55	318	122	550	123	450	768	5
56	440	122	673	123	327	767	4
57	561	121	796	123	204	765	3
58	682	121	918	122	082	764	2
59	803	121	9.02 040	122	0.97 960	763	1
60	9.01 923	120	9.02 162	122	0.97 838	9.99 761	0

′	L. Cos.	d.	L. Cotg.	c. d.	L. Tang.	L. Sin.	′

P. P.

1′	145	143	141
1″	2.4	2.4	2.4
2″	4.8	4.8	4.7
3″	7.3	7.2	7.1
4″	9.7	9.5	9.4
5″	12.1	11.9	11.8
6″	14.5	14.3	14.1
7″	16.9	16.7	16.5
8″	19.3	19.1	18.8
9″	21.8	21.5	21.2

1′	139	137	135
1″	2.3	2.3	2.3
2″	4.6	4.6	4.5
3″	7.0	6.9	6.8
4″	9.3	9.1	9.0
5″	11.6	11.4	11.3
6″	13.9	13.7	13.5
7″	16.2	16.0	15.8
8″	18.5	18.3	18.0
9″	20.9	20.6	20.3

1′	133	131	129
1″	2.2	2.2	2.2
2″	4.4	4.4	4.3
3″	6.7	6.6	6.5
4″	8.9	8.7	8.6
5″	11.1	10.9	10.8
6″	13.3	13.1	12.9
7″	15.5	15.3	15.1
8″	17.7	17.5	17.2
9″	20.0	19.7	19.4

1′	128	127	126
1″	2.1	2.1	2.1
2″	4.3	4.2	4.2
3″	6.4	6.4	6.3
4″	8.5	8.5	8.4
5″	10.7	10.6	10.5
6″	12.8	12.7	12.6
7″	14.9	14.8	14.7
8″	17.1	16.9	16.8
9″	19.2	19.1	18.9

1′	125	124	123
1″	2.1	2.1	2.1
2″	4.2	4.1	4.1
3″	6.3	6.2	6.2
4″	8.3	8.3	8.2
5″	10.4	10.3	10.3
6″	12.5	12.4	12.3
7″	14.6	14.5	14.4
8″	16.7	16.5	16.4
9″	18.8	18.6	18.5

1′	122	121	120
1″	2.0	2.0	2.0
2″	4.1	4.0	4.0
3″	6.1	6.1	6.0
4″	8.1	8.1	8.0
5″	10.2	10.1	10.0
6″	12.2	12.1	12.0
7″	14.2	14.1	14.0
8″	16.3	16.1	16.0
9″	18.3	18.2	18.0

′	L. Sin.	d.	L. Tang.	c. d.	L. Cotg.	L. Cos.	′
0	9.01 923	120	9.02 162	121	0.97 838	9.99 761	60
1	9.02 043	120	283	121	717	760	59
2	163	120	404	121	596	759	58
3	283	119	525	120	475	757	57
4	402	118	645	121	355	756	56
5	520	119	766	119	234	755	55
6	639	118	885	120	115	753	54
7	757	117	9.03 005	119	0.96 995	752	53
8	874	118	124	118	876	751	52
9	992	117	242	119	758	749	51
10	9.03 109	117	9.03 361	118	0.96 639	9.99 748	50
11	226	116	479	118	521	747	49
12	342	116	597	117	403	745	48
13	458	116	714	118	286	744	47
14	574	116	832	116	168	742	46
15	690	115	948	117	052	741	45
16	805	115	9.04 065	116	0.95 935	740	44
17	920	115	181	116	819	738	43
18	9.04 034	114	297	116	703	737	42
19	149	115	413	115	587	736	41
20	9.04 262	113	9.04 528	115	0.95 472	9.99 734	40
21	376	114	643	115	357	733	39
22	490	114	758	115	242	731	38
23	503	113	873	114	127	730	37
24	715	112	987	114	013	728	36
25	828	113	9.05 101	113	0.94 899	727	35
26	940	112	214	114	786	726	34
27	9.05 052	112	328	113	672	724	33
28	164	111	441	112	559	723	32
29	275	111	553	113	447	721	31
30	9.05 386	111	9.05 666	112	0.94 334	9.99 720	30
31	497	110	778	112	222	718	29
32	607	110	890	112	110	717	28
33	717	110	9.06 002	111	0.93 998	716	27
34	827	110	113	111	887	714	26
35	937	109	224	111	776	713	25
36	9.06 046	109	335	110	665	711	24
37	155	109	445	111	555	710	23
38	264	108	556	110	444	708	22
39	372	109	666	109	334	707	21
40	9.06 481	108	9.06 775	110	0.93 225	9.99 705	20
41	589	107	885	109	115	704	19
42	696	108	994	109	006	702	18
43	804	107	9.07 103	108	0.92 897	701	17
44	911	107	211	109	789	699	16
45	9.07 018	106	320	108	680	698	15
46	124	107	428	108	572	696	14
47	231	106	536	107	464	695	13
48	337	105	643	108	357	693	12
49	442	106	751	107	249	692	11
50	9.07 548	105	9.07 858	106	0.92 142	9.99 690	10
51	653	105	964	107	036	689	9
52	758	105	9.08 071	106	0.91 929	687	8
53	863	105	177	106	823	686	7
54	968	104	283	106	717	684	6
55	9.08 072	104	389	106	611	683	5
56	176	104	495	105	505	681	4
57	280	103	600	105	400	680	3
58	383	103	705	105	295	678	2
59	486	103	810	104	190	677	1
60	9.08 589		9.08 914		0.91 086	9.99 675	0
′	L. Cos.	d.	L. Cotg.	c. d.	L. Tang.	L. Sin.	′

P. P.

	120	119	118
1″	2.0	2.0	2.0
2″	4.0	4.0	3.9
3″	6.0	6.0	5.9
4″	8.0	7.9	7.9
5″	10.0	9.9	9.8
6″	12.0	11.9	11.8
7″	14.0	13.9	13.8
8″	16.0	15.9	15.7
9″	18.0	17.9	17.7

	117	116	115
1″	2.0	1.9	1.9
2″	3.9	3.9	3.8
3″	5.9	5.8	5.8
4″	7.8	7.7	7.7
5″	9.8	9.7	9.6
6″	11.7	11.6	11.5
7″	13.7	13.5	13.4
8″	15.6	15.5	15.3
9″	17.6	17.4	17.3

	114	113	112
1″	1.9	1.9	1.9
2″	3.8	3.8	3.7
3″	5.7	5.7	5.6
4″	7.6	7.5	7.5
5″	9.5	9.4	9.3
6″	11.4	11.3	11.2
7″	13.3	13.2	13.1
8″	15.2	15.1	14.9
9″	17.1	17.0	16.8

	111	110	109
1″	1.9	1.8	1.8
2″	3.7	3.7	3.6
3″	5.6	5.5	5.5
4″	7.4	7.3	7.3
5″	9.3	9.2	9.1
6″	11.1	11.0	10.9
7″	13.0	12.8	12.7
8″	14.8	14.7	14.5
9″	16.7	16.5	16.4

	108	107	106
1″	1.8	1.8	1.8
2″	3.6	3.6	3.5
3″	5.4	5.4	5.3
4″	7.2	7.1	7.1
5″	9.0	8.9	8.8
6″	10.8	10.7	10.6
7″	12.6	12.5	12.4
8″	14.4	14.3	14.1
9″	16.2	16.1	15.9

	105	104	103
1″	1.8	1.7	1.7
2″	3.5	3.5	3.4
3″	5.3	5.2	5.2
4″	7.0	6.9	6.9
5″	8.8	8.7	8.6
6″	10.5	10.4	10.3
7″	12.3	12.1	12.0
8″	14.0	13.9	13.7
9″	15.8	15.6	15.5

′	L. Sin.	d.	L. Tang.	c. d.	L. Cotg.	L. Cos.	′
0	9.08 589	103	9.08 914	105	0.91 086	9.99 675	60
1	692	103	9.09 019	104	0.90 981	674	59
2	795̄	102	123	104	877	672	58
3	897	102	227	103	773	670	57
4	999	102	330	104	670	669	56
5	9.09 101	101	434	103	566	667	55
6	202	102	537	103	463	666	54
7	304̲	101	640	102	360	664	53
8	405̄	101	742	103	258	663	52
9	506	100	845̄	102	155	661	51
10	9.09 606	101	9.09 947	102	0.90 053	9.99 659	50
11	707	100	9.10 049	101	0.89 951	658	49
12	807	100	150	102	850	656	48
13	907	99	252	101	748	655̄	47
14	9.10 006	100	353	101	647	653	46
15	106	99	454	101	546	651	45
16	205̄	99	555̄	101	445	650	44
17	304	98	656	100	344	648	43
18	402	99	756	100	244	647	42
19	501	98	856	100	144	645̄	41
20	9.10 599	98	9.10 956	100	0.89 044	9.99 643	40
21	697	98	9.11 056	99	0.88 944	642	39
22	795	98	155	99	845̄	640	38
23	893	97	254	99	746	638	37
24	990	97	353	99	647	637	36
25	9.11 087	97	452	99	548	635̄	35
26	184	97	551	98	449	633	34
27	281	96	649	98	351	632	33
28	377	97	747	98	253	630	32
29	474	96	845	98	155̄	629	31
30	9.11 570	96	9.11 943	97	0.88 057	9.99 627	30
31	666	95	9.12 040	98	0.87 960	625	29
32	761	96	138̲	97	862	624	28
33	857	95	235̲	97	765	622	27
34	952	95	332	96	668	620	26
35	9.12 047	95	428	97	572	618	25
36	142	94	525̄	96	475	617	24
37	236	95	621	96	379	615	23
38	331	94	717	96	283	613	22
39	425̄	94	813	96	187	612	21
40	9.12 519	93	9.12 909	95	0.87 091	9.99 610	20
41	612	94	9.13 004	95	0.86 996	608	19
42	706	93	099	95	901	607	18
43	799	93	194	95	806	605̄	17
44	892	93	289	95	711	603	16
45	985	93	384	94	616	601	15
46	9.13 078	93	478	95	522	600	14
47	171	92	573	94	427	598	13
48	263	92	667	94	333	596	12
49	355	92	761	93	239	595̄	11
50	9.13 447	92	9.13 854	94	0.86 146	9.99 593	10
51	539	91	948	93	052	591	9
52	630	92	9.14 041	93	0.85 959	589	8
53	722	91	134	93	866	588	7
54	813	91	227	93	773	586	6
55	904	90	320	92	680	584	5
56	994	91	412	92	588	582	4
57	9.14 085	90	504	92	496	581	3
58	175	91	597	93	403	579	2
59	266	90	688	91	312	577	1
60	9.14 356		9.14 780	92	0.85 220	9.99 575	0
′	L. Cos.	d.	L. Cotg.	c. d.	L. Tang.	L. Sin.	′

P. P.

	105	104	103
1′	105	104	103
1″	1.8	1.7	1.7
2″	3.5	3.5	3.4
3″	5.3	5.2	5.2
4″	7.0	6.9	6.9
5″	8.8	8.7	8.6
6″	10.5	10.4	10.3
7″	12.3	12.1	12.0
8″	14.0	13.9	13.7
9″	15.8	15.6	15.5

	102	101	100
1′	102	101	100
1″	1.7	1.7	1.7
2″	3.4	3.4	3.3
3″	5.1	5.1	5.0
4″	6.8	6.7	6.7
5″	8.5	8.4	8.3
6″	10.2	10.1	10.0
7″	11.9	11.8	11.7
8″	13.6	13.5	13.3
9″	15.3	15.2	15.0

	99	98	97
1′	99	98	97
1″	1.7	1.6	1.6
2″	3.3	3.3	3.2
3″	5.0	4.9	4.9
4″	6.6	6.5	6.5
5″	8.3	8.2	8.1
6″	9.9	9.8	9.7
7″	11.6	11.4	11.3
8″	13.2	13.1	12.9
9″	14.9	14.7	14.6

	96	95	94
1′	96	95	94
1″	1.6	1.6	1.6
2″	3.2	3.2	3.1
3″	4.8	4.8	4.7
4″	6.4	6.3	6.3
5″	8.0	7.9	7.8
6″	9.6	9.5	9.4
7″	11.2	11.1	11.0
8″	12.8	12.7	12.5
9″	14.4	14.3	14.1

	93	92	91
1′	93	92	91
1″	1.6	1.5	1.5
2″	3.1	3.1	3.0
3″	4.7	4.6	4.6
4″	6.2	6.1	6.1
5″	7.8	7.7	7.6
6″	9.3	9.2	9.1
7″	10.9	10.7	10.6
8″	12.4	12.3	12.1
9″	14.0	13.8	13.7

	90	1	2
1′	90	1	2
1″	1.5	0.02	0.03
2″	3.0	0.03	0.07
3″	4.5	0.05	0.10
4″	6.0	0.07	0.13
5″	7.5	0.08	0.17
6″	9.0	0.10	0.20
7″	10.5	0.12	0.23
8″	12.0	0.13	0.27
9″	13.5	0.15	0.30

′	L. Sin.	d.	L. Tang.	c.d.	L. Cotg.	L. Cos.	d.	′
0	9.14 356	89	9.14 780	92	0.85 220	9.99 575	1	60
1	445	89	872	91	128	574	2	59
2	535	89	963	91	037	572	2	58
3	624	90	9.15 054	91	0.84 946	570	2	57
4	714	89	145	91	855	568	2	56
5	803	88	236	91	764	566	1	55
6	891	89	327	90	673	565	2	54
7	980	89	417	91	583	563	2	53
8	9.15 069	88	508	90	492	561	2	52
9	157	88	598	90	402	559	2	51
10	9.15 245	88	9.15 688	89	0.84 312	9.99 557	1	50
11	333	88	777	90	223	556	2	49
12	421	87	867	89	133	554	2	48
13	508	88	956	90	044	552	2	47
14	596	87	9.16 046	89	0.83 954	550	2	46
15	683	87	135	89	865	548	2	45
16	770	87	224	88	776	546	1	44
17	857	87	312	88	688	545	2	43
18	944	86	401	88	599	543	2	42
19	9.16 030	86	489	88	511	541	2	41
20	9.16 116	87	9.16 577	88	0.83 423	9.99 539	2	40
21	203	86	665	88	335	537	2	39
22	289	85	753	88	247	535	2	38
23	374	86	841	87	159	533	1	37
24	460	85	928	88	072	532	2	36
25	545	86	9.17 016	87	0.82 984	530	2	35
26	631	85	103	87	897	528	2	34
27	716	85	190	87	810	526	2	33
28	801	85	277	86	723	524	2	32
29	886	84	363	87	637	522	2	31
30	9.16 970	85	9.17 450	86	0.82 550	9.99 520	2	30
31	9.17 055	84	536	86	464	518	1	29
32	139	84	622	86	378	517	2	28
33	223	84	708	86	292	515	2	27
34	307	84	794	86	206	513	2	26
35	391	83	880	85	120	511	2	25
36	474	84	965	86	035	509	2	24
37	558	83	9.18 051	85	0.81 949	507	2	23
38	641	83	136	85	864	505	2	22
39	724	83	221	85	779	503	2	21
40	9.17 807	83	9.18 306	85	0.81 694	9.99 501	2	20
41	890	83	391	85	609	499	2	19
42	973	82	475	84	525	497	2	18
43	9.18 055	82	560	84	440	495	1	17
44	137	83	644	84	356	494	2	16
45	220	82	728	84	272	492	2	15
46	302	81	812	84	188	490	2	14
47	383	82	896	83	104	488	2	13
48	465	82	979	84	021	486	2	12
49	547	81	9.19 063	83	0.80 937	484	2	11
50	9.18 628	81	9.19 146	83	0.80 854	9.99 482	2	10
51	709	81	229	83	771	480	2	9
52	790	81	312	83	688	478	2	8
53	871	81	395	83	605	476	2	7
54	952	81	478	83	522	474	2	6
55	9.19 033	80	561	82	439	472	2	5
56	113	80	643	82	357	470	2	4
57	193	80	725	82	275	468	2	3
58	273	80	807	82	193	466	2	2
59	353	80	889	82	111	464	2	1
60	9.19 433		9.19 971		0.80 029	9.99 462		0

| ′ | L. Cos. | d. | L. Cotg. | c.d. | L. Tang. | L. Sin. | d. | ′ |

P. P.

1′	92	91	90
1″	1.5	1.5	1.5
2″	3.1	3.0	3.0
3″	4.6	4.6	4.5
4″	6.1	6.1	6.0
5″	7.7	7.6	7.5
6″	9.2	9.1	9.0
7″	10.7	10.6	10.5
8″	12.3	12.1	12.0
9″	13.8	13.7	13.5

1′	89	88	87
1″	1.5	1.5	1.5
2″	3.0	2.9	2.9
3″	4.5	4.4	4.4
4″	5.9	5.9	5.8
5″	7.4	7.3	7.3
6″	8.9	8.8	8.7
7″	10.4	10.3	10.2
8″	11.9	11.7	11.6
9″	13.4	13.2	13.1

1′	86	85
1″	1.4	1.4
2″	2.9	2.8
3″	4.3	4.3
4″	5.7	5.7
5″	7.2	7.1
6″	8.6	8.5
7″	10.0	9.9
8″	11.5	11.3
9″	12.9	12.8

1′	84	83
1″	1.4	1.4
2″	2.8	2.8
3″	4.2	4.2
4″	5.6	5.5
5″	7.0	6.9
6″	8.4	8.3
7″	9.8	9.7
8″	11.2	11.1
9″	12.6	12.5

1′	82	81
1″	1.4	1.4
2″	2.7	2.7
3″	4.1	4.1
4″	5.5	5.4
5″	6.8	6.8
6″	8.2	8.1
7″	9.6	9.5
8″	10.9	10.8
9″	12.3	12.2

1′	1	2	80
1″	0.02	0.03	1.3
2″	0.03	0.07	2.7
3″	0.05	0.10	4.0
4″	0.07	0.13	5.3
5″	0.08	0.17	6.7
6″	0.10	0.20	8.0
7″	0.12	0.23	9.3
8″	0.13	0.27	10.7
9″	0.15	0.30	12.0

'	L. Sin.	d.	L. Tang.	c.d.	L. Cotg.	L. Cos.	d.	'
0	9.19 433	80	9.19 971	82	0.80 029	9.99 462	2	60
1	513	79	9.20 053	81	0.79 947	460	2	59
2	592	80	134	82	866	458	2	58
3	672	79	216	81	784	456	2	57
4	751	79	297	81	703	454	2	56
5	830	79	378	81	622	452	2	55
6	909	79	459	81	541	450	2	54
7	988	79	540	81	460	448	2	53
8	9.20 067	78	621	80	379	446	2	52
9	145	78	701	81	299	444	2	51
10	9.20 223	79	9.20 782	80	0.79 218	9.99 442	2	50
11	302	78	862	80	138	440	2	49
12	380	78	942	80	058	438	2	48
13	458	77	9.21 022	80	0.78 978	436	2	47
14	535	78	102	80	898	434	2	46
15	613	78	182	79	818	432	3	45
16	691	77	261	80	739	429	2	44
17	768	77	341	79	659	427	2	43
18	845	77	420	79	580	425	2	42
19	922	77	499	79	501	423	2	41
20	9.20 999	77	9.21 578	79	0.78 422	9.99 421	2	40
21	9.21 076	77	657	79	343	419	2	39
22	153	76	736	78	264	417	2	38
23	229	77	814	79	186	415̄	2	37
24	306	76	893	78	107	413	2	36
25	382	76	971	78	029	411	3	35
26	458	76	9.22 049	78	0.77 951	409	2	34
27	534	76	127	78	873	407	3	33
28	610	75	205	78	795̄	404	2	32
29	685	76	283	78	717	402	2	31
30	9.21 761	75	9.22 361	77	0.77 639	9.99 400	2	30
31	836	76	438	78	562	398	2	29
32	912	75	516	77	484	396	2	28
33	987	75	593	77	407	394	2	27
34	9.22 062	75	670	77	330	392	2	26
35	137	74	747	77	253	390	2	25
36	211	75	824	77	176	388	3	24
37	286	75	901	76	099	385	2	23
38	361	74	977	77	023	383	2	22
39	435̄	74	9.23 054	76	0.76 946	381	2	21
40	9.22 509	74	9.23 130	76	0.76 870	9.99 379	2	20
41	583	74	206	77	794	377̄	2	19
42	657	74	283	76	717	375̄	3	18
43	731̄	74	359	76	641	372	2	17
44	805	73	435̄	75	565	370	2	16
45	878	74	510	76	490	368	2	15
46	952	73	586	75	414	366	2	14
47	9.23 025	73	661	76	339	364	2	13
48	098	73	737	75	263	362	3	12
49	171	73	812	75	188	359	2	11
50	9.23 244	73	9.23 887	75	0 76 113	9.99 357	2	10
51	317	73	962	75	038	355	2	9
52	390	72	9.24 037	75	0.75 963	353	2	8
53	462	73	112	74	888	351	3	7
54	535̄	72	186	75	814	348	2	6
55	607	72	261	74	739	346	2	5
56	679	73	335	75	665̄	344	2	4
57	752	71	410	74	590	342	2	3
58	823	72	484	74	516	340	3	2
59	895	72	558	74	442	337	2	1
60	9.23 967		9.24 632		0.75 368	9.99 335		0
'	L. Cos.	d.	L. Cotg.	c.d.	L. Tang.	L. Sin.	d.	'

P. P.

1'	82	81	80
1"	1.4	1.4	1.3
2"	2.7	2.7	2.7
3"	4.1	4.1	4.0
4"	5.5	5.4	5.3
5"	6.8	6.8	6.7
6"	8.2	8.1	8.0
7"	9.6	9.5	9.3
8"	10.9	10.8	10.7
9"	12.3	12.2	12.0

1'	79	78	77
1"	1.3	1.3	1.3
2"	2.6	2.6	2.6
3"	4.0	3.9	3.9
4"	5.3	5.2	5.1
5"	6.6	6.5	6.4
6"	7.9	7.8	7.7
7"	9.2	9.1	9.0
8"	10.5	10.4	10.3
9"	11.9	11.7	11.6

1'	76	75
1"	1.3	1.3
2"	2.5	2.5
3"	3.8	3.8
4"	5.1	5.0
5"	6.3	6.3
6"	7.6	7.5
7"	8.9	8.8
8"	10.1	10.0
9"	11.4	11.3

1'	74	73
1"	1.2	1.2
2"	2.5	2.4
3"	3.7	3.7
4"	4.9	4.9
5"	6.2	6.1
6"	7.4	7.3
7"	8.6	8.5
8"	9.9	9.7
9"	11.1	11.0

1'	72	71
1"	1.2	1.2
2"	2.4	2.4
3"	3.6	3.6
4"	4.8	4.7
5"	6.0	5.9
6"	7.2	7.1
7"	8.4	8.3
8"	9.6	9.5
9"	10.8	10.7

1'	2	3
1"	0.03	0.05
2"	0.07	0.10
3"	0.10	0.15
4"	0.13	0.20
5"	0.17	0.25
6"	0.20	0.30
7"	0.23	0.35
8"	0.27	0.40
9"	0.30	0.45

'	L. Sin.	d.	L. Tang.	c.d.	L. Cotg.	L. Cos.	d.	'
0	9.23 967	72	9.24 632	74	0.75 368	9.99 335	2	60
1	9.24 039	71	706	73	294	333	2	59
2	110	71	779	74	221	331	3	58
3	181	72	853	73	147	328	2	57
4	253	71	926	74	074	326	2	56
5	324	71	9.25 000	73	000	324	2	55
6	395	71	073	73	0.74 927	322	3	54
7	466	70	146	73	854	319	2	53
8	536	71	219	73	781	317	2	52
9	607	70	292	73	708	315	2	51
10	9.24 677	71	9.25 365	72	0.74 635	9.99 313	3	50
11	748	70	437	73	563	310	2	49
12	818	70	510	72	490	308	2	48
13	888	70	582	73	418	306	2	47
14	958	70	655	72	345	304	3	46
15	9.25 028	70	727	72	273	301	2	45
16	098	70	799	72	201	299	2	44
17	168	69	871	72	129	297	3	43
18	237	70	943	72	057	294	2	42
19	307	69	9.26 015	71	0.73 985	292	2	41
20	9.25 376	69	9.26 086	72	0.73 914	9.99 290	2	40
21	445	69	158	71	842	288	3	39
22	514	69	229	72	771	285	2	38
23	583	69	301	71	699	283	2	37
24	652	69	372	71	628	281	3	36
25	721	69	443	71	557	278	2	35
26	790	68	514	71	486	276	2	34
27	858	69	585	70	415	274	3	33
28	927	68	655	71	345	271	2	32
29	995	68	726	71	274	269	2	31
30	9.26 063	68	9.26 797	70	0.73 203	9.99 267	3	30
31	131	68	867	70	133	264	2	29
32	199	68	937	70	063	262	2	28
33	267	68	9.27 008	71	0.72 992	260	2	27
34	335	68	078	70	922	257	2	26
35	403	68	148	70	852	255	3	25
36	470	68	218	70	782	252	2	24
37	538	67	288	70	712	250	2	23
38	605	67	357	70	643	248	3	22
39	672	67	427	69	573	245	2	21
40	9.26 739	67	9.27 496	70	0.72 504	9.99 243	2	20
41	806	67	566	69	434	241	3	19
42	873	67	635	69	365	238	2	18
43	940	67	704	69	296	236	2	17
44	9.27 007	66	773	69	227	233	2	16
45	073	67	842	69	158	231	2	15
46	140	66	911	69	089	229	3	14
47	206	67	980	69	020	226	2	13
48	273	66	9.28 049	68	0.71 951	224	3	12
49	339	66	117	69	883	221	2	11
50	9.27 405	66	9.28 186	68	0.71 814	9.99 219	2	10
51	471	66	254	69	746	217	3	9
52	537	66	323	68	677	214	2	8
53	602	65	391	68	609	212	2	7
54	668	66	459	68	541	209	2	6
55	734	66	527	68	473	207	3	5
56	799	65	595	67	405	204	2	4
57	864	65	662	68	338	202	2	3
58	930	66	730	68	270	200	3	2
59	995	65	798	67	202	197	2	1
60	9.28 060	65	9.28 865	67	0.71 135	9.99 195		0
'	L. Cos.	d.	L. Cotg.	c.d.	L. Tang.	L. Sin.	d.	'

P. P.

1'	74	73
1"	1.2	1.2
2"	2.5	2.4
3"	3.7	3.7
4"	4.9	4.9
5"	6.2	6.1
6"	7.4	7.3
7"	8.6	8.5
8"	9.9	9.7
9"	11.1	11.0

1'	72	71
1"	1.2	1.2
2"	2.4	2.4
3"	3.6	3.6
4"	4.8	4.7
5"	6.0	5.9
6"	7.2	7.1
7"	8.4	8.3
8"	9.6	9.5
9"	10.8	10.7

1'	70	69
1"	1.2	1.2
2"	2.3	2.3
3"	3.5	3.5
4"	4.7	4.6
5"	5.8	5.8
6"	7.0	6.9
7"	8.2	8.1
8"	9.3	9.2
9"	10.5	10.4

1'	68	67
1"	1.1	1.1
2"	2.3	2.2
3"	3.4	3.4
4"	4.5	4.5
5"	5.7	5.6
6"	6.8	6.7
7"	7.9	7.8
8"	9.1	8.9
9"	10.2	10.1

1'	66	65
1"	1.1	1.1
2"	2.2	2.2
3"	3.3	3.3
4"	4.4	4.3
5"	5.5	5.4
6"	6.6	6.5
7"	7.7	7.6
8"	8.8	8.7
9"	9.9	9.8

1'	2	3
1"	0.03	0.05
2"	0.07	0.10
3"	0.10	0.15
4"	0.13	0.20
5"	0.17	0.25
6"	0.20	0.30
7"	0.23	0.35
8"	0.27	0.40
9"	0.30	0.45

′	L. Sin.	d.	L. Tang.	c.d.	L. Cotg.	L. Cos.	d.	′
0	9.28 060	65	9.28 865	68	0.71 135	9.99 195	3	60
1	125̄	65	933	67	067	192	2	59
2	190	64	9.29 000	67	000	190	3	58
3	254	65	067	67	0.70 933	187	2	57
4	319	65	134	67	866	185	3	56
5	384	64	201	67	799	182	2	55
6	448	64	268	67	732	180	3	54
7	512	65	335̄	67	665	177	2	53
8	577	64	402	66	598	175̄	3	52
9	641	64	468	67	532	172	2	51
10	9.28 705̄	64	9.29 535̄	66	0.70 465	9.99 170	3	50
11	769	64	601	67	399	167	2	49
12	833	63	668	66	332	165̄	3	48
13	896	64	734	66	266	162	2	47
14	960	64	800	66	200	160	3	46
15	9.29 024	63	866	66	134	157	2	45
16	087	63	932	66	068	155̄	3	44
17	150	64	998	66	002	152	3	43
18	214	63	9.30 064	66	0.69 936	150	3	42
19	277	63	130	65	870	147	2	41
20	9.29 340	63	9.30 195	66	0.69 805̄	9.99 145	3	40
21	403	63	261	65	739	142	2	39
22	466	63	326	65	674	140	3	38
23	529	62	391	66	609	137	2	37
24	591	63	457	65	543	135̄	3	36
25	654	62	522	65	478	132	2	35
26	716	63	587	65	413	130	3	34
27	779	62	652	65	348	127	3	33
28	841	62	717	65	283	124	2	32
29	903	63	782	64	218	122	3	31
30	9.29 966	62	9.30 846	65	0.69 154	9.99 119	2	30
31	9.30 028	62	911	64	089	117	3	29
32	090	61	975	65	025̄	114	2	28
33	151	62	9.31 040	64	0.68 960	112	3	27
34	213	62	104	64	896	109	3	26
35	275̄	61	168	65	832	106	2	25
36	336	62	233	64	767	104	3	24
37	398	61	297	64	703	101	2	23
38	459	62	361	64	639	099	3	22
39	521	61	425	64	575	096	3	21
40	9.30 582	61	9.31 489	63	0.68 511	9.99 093	2	20
41	643	61	552	64	448	091	3	19
42	704	61	616	63	384	088	3	18
43	765	61	679	64	321	086	3	17
44	826	61	743	63	257	083	3	16
45	887	60	806	64	194	080	2	15
46	947	61	870	63	130	078	3	14
47	9.31 008	60	933	63	067	075̄	3	13
48	068	61	996	63	004	072	2	12
49	129	60	9.32 059	63	0.67 941	070	3	11
50	9.31 189	61	9.32 122	63	0.67 878	9.99 067	3	10
51	250	60	185	63	815̄	064	2	9
52	310	60	248	63	752	062	3	8
53	370	60	311	62	689	059	3	7
54	430	60	373	63	627	056	2	6
55	490	59	436	62	564	054	3	5
56	549	60	498	63	502	051	3	4
57	609	60	561	62	439	048	2	3
58	669	59	623	62	377	046	3	2
59	728	60	685	62	315̄	043	3	1
60	9.31 788		9.32 747		0.67 253	9.99 040		0
′	L. Cos.	d.	L. Cotg.	c.d.	L. Tang.	L. Sin.	d.	′

P. P.

	68	67
1″	1.1	1.1
2″	2.3	2.2
3″	3.4	3.4
4″	4.5	4.5
5″	5.7	5.6
6″	6.8	6.7
7″	7.9	7.8
8″	9.1	8.9
9″	10.2	10.1

	66	65
1″	1.1	1.1
2″	2.2	2.2
3″	3.3	3.3
4″	4.4	4.3
5″	5.5	5.4
6″	6.6	6.5
7″	7.7	7.6
8″	8.8	8.7
9″	9.9	9.8

	64	63
1″	1.1	1.1
2″	2.1	2.1
3″	3.2	3.2
4″	4.3	4.2
5″	5.3	5.3
6″	6.4	6.3
7″	7.5	7.4
8″	8.5	8.4
9″	9.6	9.5

	62	61
1″	1.0	1.0
2″	2.1	2.0
3″	3.1	3.1
4″	4.1	4.1
5″	5.2	5.1
6″	6.2	6.1
7″	7.2	7.1
8″	8.3	8.1
9″	9.3	9.2

	60	59
1″	1.0	1.0
2″	2.0	2.0
3″	3.0	3.0
4″	4.0	3.9
5″	5.0	4.9
6″	6.0	5.9
7″	7.0	6.9
8″	8.0	7.9
9″	9.0	8.9

	2	3
1″	0.03	0.05
2″	0.07	0.10
3″	0.10	0.15
4″	0.13	0.20
5″	0.17	0.25
6″	0.20	0.30
7″	0.23	0.35
8″	0.27	0.40
9″	0.30	0.45

'	L. Sin.	d.	L. Tang.	c.d.	L. Cotg.	L. Cos.	d.	'
0	9.31 788	59	9.32 747	63	0.67 253	9.99 040	2	60
1	847	60	810	62	190	038		59
2	907	59	872	61	128	035	3	58
3	966	59	933	62	067	032	3	57
4	9.32 025	59	995	62	005	030	2	56
5	084	59	9.33 057	62	0.66 943	027	3	55
6	143	59	119	61	881	024	3	54
7	202	59	180	62	820	022	2	53
8	261	58	242	61	758	019	3	52
9	319	59	303	62	697	016	3	51
10	9.32 378	59	9.33 365	61	0.66 635	9.99 013	2	50
11	437	58	426	61	574	011	3	49
12	495	58	487	61	513	008	3	48
13	553	59	548	61	452	005	3	47
14	612	58	609	61	391	002	2	46
15	670	58	670	61	330	000	3	45
16	728	58	731	61	269	9.98 997	3	44
17	786	58	792	61	208	994	3	43
18	844	58	853	60	147	991	2	42
19	902	58	913	61	087	989	3	41
20	9.32 960	58	9.33 974	60	0.66 026	9.98 986	3	40
21	9.33 018	57	9.34 034	61	0.65 966	983	3	39
22	075	58	095	60	905	980	2	38
23	133	57	155	60	845	978	3	37
24	190	58	215	61	785	975	3	36
25	248	57	276	60	724	972	3	35
26	305	57	336	60	664	969	2	34
27	362	58	396	60	604	967	3	33
28	420	57	456	60	544	964	3	32
29	477	57	516	60	484	961	3	31
30	9.33 534	57	9.34 576	59	0.65 424	9.98 958	2	30
31	591	56	635	60	365	955	2	29
32	647	57	695	60	305	953	3	28
33	704	57	755	59	245	950	3	27
34	761	57	814	60	186	947	3	26
35	818	56	874	59	126	944	3	25
36	874	57	933	59	067	941	3	24
37	931	56	992	59	008	938	2	23
38	987	56	9.35 051	60	0.64 949	936	3	22
39	9.34 043	57	111	59	889	933	3	21
40	9.34 100	56	9.35 170	59	0.64 830	9.98 930	3	20
41	156	56	229	59	771	927	3	19
42	212	56	288	59	712	924	3	18
43	268	56	347	58	653	921	2	17
44	324	56	405	59	595	919	3	16
45	380	56	464	59	536	916	3	15
46	436	55	523	58	477	913	3	14
47	491	56	581	59	419	910	3	13
48	547	55	640	58	360	907	3	12
49	602	56	698	59	302	904	3	11
50	9.34 658	55	9.35 757	58	0.64 243	9.98 901	3	10
51	713	56	815	58	185	898	2	9
52	769	55	873	58	127	896	3	8
53	824	55	931	58	069	893	3	7
54	879	55	989	58	011	890	3	6
55	934	55	9.36 047	58	0.63 953	887	3	5
56	989	55	105	58	895	884	3	4
57	9.35 044	55	163	58	837	881	3	3
58	099	55	221	58	779	878	3	2
59	154	55	279	57	721	875	3	1
60	9.35 209		9.36 336		0.63 664	9.98 872		0
'	L. Cos.	d.	L. Cotg.	c.d.	L. Tang.	L. Sin.	d.	'

P. P.

1'	63	62
1"	1.1	1.0
2"	2.1	2.1
3"	3.2	3.1
4"	4.2	4.1
5"	5.3	5.2
6"	6.3	6.2
7"	7.4	7.2
8"	8.4	8.3
9"	9.5	9.3

1'	61	60
1"	1.0	1.0
2"	2.0	2.0
3"	3.1	3.0
4"	4.1	4.0
5"	5.1	5.0
6"	6.1	6.0
7"	7.1	7.0
8"	8.1	8.0
9"	9.2	9.0

1'	59	58
1"	1.0	1.0
2"	2.0	1.9
3"	3.0	2.9
4"	3.9	3.9
5"	4.9	4.8
6"	5.9	5.8
7"	6.9	6.8
8"	7.9	7.7
9"	8.9	8.7

1'	57	56
1"	1.0	0.9
2"	1.9	1.9
3"	2.9	2.8
4"	3.8	3.7
5"	4.8	4.7
6"	5.7	5.6
7"	6.7	6.5
8"	7.6	7.5
9"	8.6	8.4

1'	55
1"	0.9
2"	1.8
3"	2.8
4"	3.7
5"	4.6
6"	5.5
7"	6.4
8"	7.3
9"	8.3

1'	2	3
1"	0.03	0.05
2"	0.07	0.10
3"	0.10	0.15
4"	0.13	0.20
5"	0.17	0.25
6"	0.20	0.30
7"	0.23	0.35
8"	0.27	0.40
9"	0.30	0.45

′	L. Sin.	d.	L. Tang.	c. d.	L. Cotg.	L. Cos.	d.	′	P. P.		
									1′	58	57
0	9.35 209	54	9.36 336	58	0.63 664	9.98 872	3	60	1″	1.0	1.0
1	263	55	394	58	606	869	2	59	2″	1.9	1.9
2	318	55	452	57	548	867	3	58	3″	2.9	2.9
3	373	54	509	57	491	864	3	57	4″	3.9	3.8
4	427	54	566	58	434	861	3	56	5″	4.8	4.8
5	481	55	624	57	376	858	3	55	6″	5.8	5.7
6	536	54	681	57	319	85$\overline{5}$	3	54	7″	6.8	6.7
7	590	54	738	57	262	852	3	53	8″	7.7	7.6
8	644	54	795	57	20$\overline{5}$	849	3	52	9″	8.7	8.6
9	698	54	852	57	148	846	3	51			
10	9.35 752	54	9.36 909	57	0.63 091	9.98 843	3	50	1′	56	55
11	806	54	966	57	034	840	3	49	1″	0.9	0.9
12	860	54	9.37 023	57	0.62 977	837	3	48	2″	1.9	1.8
13	914	54	080	57	920	834	3	47	3″	2.8	2.8
14	968	54	137	56	863	831	3	46	4″	3.7	3.7
15	9.36 022	53	193	57	807	828	3	45	5″	4.7	4.6
16	075	54	250	56	750	825	3	44	6″	5.6	5.5
17	129	53	306	57	694	822	3	43	7″	6.5	6.4
18	182	54	363	56	637	819	3	42	8″	7.5	7.3
19	236	53	419	57	581	816	3	41	9″	8.4	8.3
20	9.36 289	53	9.37 476	56	0.62 524	9.98 813	3	40	1′	54	53
21	342	53	532	56	468	810	3	39	1″	0.9	0.9
22	395	54	588	56	412	807	3	38	2″	1.8	1.8
23	449	53	644	56	356	804	3	37	3″	2.7	2.7
24	502	53	700	56	300	801	3	36	4″	3.6	3.5
25	55$\overline{5}$	53	756	56	244	798	3	35	5″	4.5	4.4
26	608	52	812	56	188	795	3	34	6″	5.4	5.3
27	660	53	868	56	132	792	3	33	7″	6.3	6.2
28	713	53	924	56	076	789	3	32	8″	7.2	7.1
29	766	53	980	55	020	786	3	31	9″	8.1	8.0
30	9.36 819	52	9.38 035	56	0.61 965	9.98 783	3	30	1′	52	51
31	871	53	091	56	909	780	3	29	1″	0.9	0.9
32	924	52	147	55	853	777	3	28	2″	1.7	1.7
33	976	52	202	55	798	774	3	27	3″	2.6	2.6
34	9.37 028	53	257	56	743	771	3	26	4″	3.5	3.4
35	081	52	313	55	687	768	3	25	5″	4.3	4.3
36	133	52	368	55	632	76$\overline{5}$	3	24	6″	5.2	5.1
37	185	52	423	56	577	762	3	23	7″	6.1	6.0
38	237	52	479	55	521	759	3	22	8″	6.9	6.8
39	289	52	534	55	466	756	3	21	9″	7.8	7.7
40	9.37 341	52	9.38 589	55	0.61 411	9.98 753	3	20	1′	2	
41	393	52	644	55	356	750	4	19	1″	0.03	
42	445	52	699	55	301	746	3	18	2″	0.07	
43	497	52	754	54	246	743	3	17	3″	0.10	
44	549	51	808	55	192	740	3	16	4″	0.13	
45	600	52	863	55	137	737	3	15	5″	0.17	
46	652	51	918	54	082	734	3	14	6″	0.20	
47	703	52	972	55	028	731	3	13	7″	0.23	
48	75$\overline{5}$	51	9.39 027	55	0.60 973	728	3	12	8″	0.27	
49	806	52	082	54	918	72$\overline{5}$	3	11	9″	0.30	
50	9.37 858	51	9.39 136	54	0.60 864	9.98 722	3	10	1′	3	4
51	909	51	190	55	810	719	4	9	1″	0.05	0.07
52	960	51	24$\overline{5}$	54	755	715	3	8	2″	0.10	0.13
53	9.38 011	51	299	54	701	712	3	7	3″	0.15	0.20
54	062	51	353	54	647	709	3	6	4″	0.20	0.27
55	113	51	407	54	593	706	3	5	5″	0.25	0.33
56	164	51	461	54	539	703	3	4	6″	0.30	0.40
57	215	51	515	54	48$\overline{5}$	700	3	3	7″	0.35	0.47
58	266	51	569	54	431	697	3	2	8″	0.40	0.53
59	317	51	623	54	377	694	4	1	9″	0.45	0.60
60	9.38 368		9.39 677		0.60 323	9.98 690		0			
′	L. Cos.	d.	L. Cotg.	c. d.	L. Tang.	L. Sin.	d.	′			

′	L. Sin.	d.	L. Tang.	c.d.	L. Cotg.	L. Cos.	d.	′
0	9.38 368	50	9.39 677	54	0.60 323	9.98 690	3	60
1	418	51	731	54	269	687	3	59
2	469	50	785	53	215	684	3	58
3	519	51	838	54	162	681	3	57
4	570	50	892	53	108	678	3	56
5	620	50	945	54	055	675	4	55
6	670	51	999	53	001	671	3	54
7	721	50	9.40 052	54	0.59 948	668	3	53
8	771	50	106	53	894	665	3	52
9	821	50	159	53	841	662	3	51
10	9.38 871	50	9.40 212	54	0.59 788	9.98 659	3	50
11	921	50	266	53	734	656	4	49
12	971	50	319	53	681	652	3	48
13	9.39 021	50	372	53	628	649	3	47
14	071	50	425	53	575	646	3	46
15	121	49	478	53	522	643	3	45
16	170	50	531	53	469	640	4	44
17	220	50	584	52	416	636	3	43
18	270	49	636	53	364	633	3	42
19	319	50	689	53	311	630	3	41
20	9.39 369	49	9.40 742	53	0.59 258	9.98 627	4	40
21	418	49	795	53	205	623	3	39
22	467	49	847	52	153	620	3	38
23	517	50	900	53	100	617	3	37
24	566	49	952	52	048	614	4	36
25	615	49	9.41 005	53	0.58 995	610	3	35
26	664	49	057	52	943	607	3	34
27	713	49	109	52	891	604	3	33
28	762	49	161	53	839	601	4	32
29	811	49	214	52	786	597	3	31
30	9.39 860	49	9.41 266	52	0.58 734	9.98 594	3	30
31	909	49	318	52	682	591	3	29
32	958	48	370	52	630	588	4	28
33	9.40 006	49	422	52	578	584	3	27
34	055	48	474	52	526	581	3	26
35	103	49	526	52	474	578	4	25
36	152	48	578	51	422	574	3	24
37	200	49	629	52	371	571	3	23
38	249	48	681	52	319	568	3	22
39	297	49	733	51	267	565	4	21
40	9.40 346	48	9.41 784	52	0.58 216	9.98 561	3	20
41	394	48	836	51	164	558	3	19
42	442	48	887	52	113	555	4	18
43	490	48	939	51	061	551	3	17
44	538	48	990	51	010	548	3	16
45	586	48	9.42 041	52	0.57 959	545	4	15
46	634	48	093	51	907	541	3	14
47	682	48	144	51	856	538	3	13
48	730	48	195	51	805	535	3	12
49	778	47	246	51	754	531	3	11
50	9.40 825	48	9.42 297	51	0.57 703	9.98 528	3	10
51	873	48	348	51	652	525	4	9
52	921	47	399	51	601	521	3	8
53	968	48	450	51	550	518	3	7
54	9.41 016	47	501	51	499	515	4	6
55	063	48	552	51	448	511	3	5
56	111	47	603	50	397	508	3	4
57	158	47	653	51	347	505	4	3
58	205	47	704	51	296	501	3	2
59	252	48	755	51	245	498	4	1
60	9.41 300		9.42 805	50	0.57 195	9.98 494		0
′	L. Cos.	d.	L. Cotg.	c.d.	L. Tang.	L. Sin.	d.	′

P. P.

1′	54	53
1″	0.9	0.9
2″	1.8	1.8
3″	2.7	2.7
4″	3.6	3.5
5″	4.5	4.4
6″	5.4	5.3
7″	6.3	6.2
8″	7.2	7.1
9″	8.1	8.0

1′	52	51
1″	0.9	0.9
2″	1.7	1.7
3″	2.6	2.6
4″	3.5	3.4
5″	4.3	4.3
6″	5.2	5.1
7″	6.1	6.0
8″	6.9	6.8
9″	7.8	7.7

1′	50	49
1″	0.8	0.8
2″	1.7	1.6
3″	2.5	2.5
4″	3.3	3.3
5″	4.2	4.1
6″	5.0	4.9
7″	5.8	5.7
8″	6.7	6.5
9″	7.5	7.4

1′	48
1″	0.8
2″	1.6
3″	2.4
4″	3.2
5″	4.0
6″	4.8
7″	5.6
8″	6.4
9″	7.2

1′	47
1″	0.8
2″	1.6
3″	2.4
4″	3.1
5″	3.9
6″	4.7
7″	5.5
8″	6.3
9″	7.1

1′	3	4
1″	0.05	0.07
2″	0.10	0.13
3″	0.15	0.20
4″	0.20	0.27
5″	0.25	0.33
6″	0.30	0.40
7″	0.35	0.47
8″	0.40	0.53
9″	0.45	0.60

′	L. Sin.	d.	L. Tang.	c.d.	L. Cotg.	L. Cos.	d.	′	P. P.		
0	9.41 300	47	9.42 805	51	0.57 195	9.98 494	3	**60**	**1′**	**51**	**50**
1	347	47	856	50	144	491	3	59	1″	0.9	0.8
2	394	47	906	51	094	488	4	58	2″	1.7	1.7
3	441	47	957	50	043	484	3	57	3″	2.6	2.5
4	488	47	9.43 007	50	0.56 993	481	4	56	4″	3.4	3.3
5	535	47	057	51	943	477	3	55	5″	4.3	4.2
6	582	46	108	50	892	474	3	54	6″	5.1	5.0
7	628	47	158	50	842	471	4	53	7″	6.0	5.8
8	675	47	208	50	792	467	3	52	8″	6.8	6.7
9	722	46	258	50	742	464	4	51	9″	7.7	7.5
10	9.41 768	47	9.43 308	50	0.56 692	9.98 460	3	**50**	**1′**	**49**	**48**
11	815	46	358	50	642	457	4	49	1″	0.8	0.8
12	861	47	408	50	592	453	3	48	2″	1.6	1.6
13	908	46	458	50	542	450	3	47	3″	2.5	2.4
14	954	47	508	50	492	447	4	46	4″	3.3	3.2
15	9.42 001	46	558	49	442	443	3	45	5″	4.1	4.0
16	047	46	607	50	393	440	4	44	6″	4.9	4.8
17	093	47	657	50	343	436	4	43	7″	5.7	5.6
18	140	46	707	49	293	433	4	42	8″	6.5	6.4
19	186	46	756	50	244	429	3	41	9″	7.4	7.2
20	9.42 232	46	9.43 806	49	0.56 194	9.98 426	4	**40**	**1′**	**47**	**46**
21	278	46	855	50	145	422	3	39	1″	0.8	0.8
22	324	46	905	49	095	419	4	38	2″	1.6	1.5
23	370	46	954	50	046	415	3	37	3″	2.4	2.3
24	416	45	9.44 004	49	0.55 996	412	3	36	4″	3.1	3.1
25	461	46	053	49	947	409	4	35	5″	3.9	3.8
26	507	46	102	49	898	405	3	34	6″	4.7	4.6
27	553	46	151	50	849	402	4	33	7″	5.5	5.4
28	599	45	201	49	799	398	3	32	8″	6.3	6.1
29	644	46	250	49	750	395	4	31	9″	7.1	6.9
30	9.42 690	45	9.44 299	49	0.55 701	9.98 391	3	**30**	**1′**	**45**	
31	735	46	348	49	652	388	4	29	1″	0.8	
32	781	45	397	49	603	384	3	28	2″	1.5	
33	826	46	446	49	554	381	4	27	3″	2.3	
34	872	45	495	49	505	377	4	26	4″	3.0	
35	917	45	544	48	456	373	3	25	5″	3.8	
36	962	46	592	49	408	370	4	24	6″	4.5	
37	9.43 008	45	641	49	359	366	3	23	7″	5.3	
38	053	45	690	48	310	363	4	22	8″	6.0	
39	098	45	738	49	262	359	3	21	9″	6.8	
40	9.43 143	45	9.44 787	49	0.55 213	9.98 356	4	**20**	**1′**	**44**	
41	188	45	836	48	164	352	3	19	1″	0.7	
42	233	45	884	49	116	349	4	18	2″	1.5	
43	278	45	933	48	067	345	3	17	3″	2.2	
44	323	44	981	48	019	342	4	16	4″	2.9	
45	367	45	9.45 029	49	0.54 971	338	4	15	5″	3.7	
46	412	45	078	48	922	334	3	14	6″	4.4	
47	457	45	126	48	874	331	4	13	7″	5.1	
48	502	44	174	48	826	327	3	12	8″	5.9	
49	546	45	222	49	778	324	4	11	9″	6.6	
50	9.43 591	44	9.45 271	48	0.54 729	9.98 320	3	**10**	**1′**	**3**	**4**
51	635	45	319	48	681	317	4	9	1″	0.05	0.07
52	680	44	367	48	633	313	4	8	2″	0.10	0.13
53	724	45	415	48	585	309	4	7	3″	0.15	0.20
54	769	44	463	48	537	306	3	6	4″	0.20	0.27
55	813	44	511	48	489	302	3	5	5″	0.25	0.33
56	857	44	559	47	441	299	4	4	6″	0.30	0.40
57	901	45	606	48	394	295	4	3	7″	0.35	0.47
58	946	44	654	48	346	291	3	2	8″	0.40	0.53
59	990	44	702	48	298	288	4	1	9″	0.45	0.60
60	9.44 034		9.45 750		0.54 250	9.98 284		**0**			
′	L. Cos.	d.	L. Cotg.	c.d.	L. Tang.	L. Sin.	d.	′			

′	L. Sin.	d.	L. Tang.	c.d.	L. Cotg.	L. Cos.	d.	′
0	9.44 034	44	9.45 750	47	0.54 250	9.98 284	3	60
1	078	44	797	48	203	281	4	59
2	122	44	845	47	155	277	4	58
3	166	44	892	48	108	273	3	57
4	210	43	940	47	060	270	4	56
5	253	44	987	48	013	266	4	55
6	297	44	9.46 035	47	0.53 965	262	3	54
7	341	44	082	48	918	259	4	53
8	385	43	130	47	870	255	4	52
9	428	44	177	47	823	251	3	51
10	9.44 472	44	9.46 224	47	0.53 776	9.98 248	4	50
11	516	43	271	48	729	244	4	49
12	559	43	319	47	681	240	3	48
13	602	44	366	47	634	237	4	47
14	646	43	413	47	587	233	4	46
15	689	44	460	47	540	229	3	45
16	733	43	507	47	493	226	4	44
17	776	43	554	47	446	222	4	43
18	819	43	601	47	399	218	4	42
19	862	43	648	46	352	215	3	41
20	9.44 905	43	9.46 694	47	0.53 306	9.98 211	4	40
21	948	44	741	47	259	207	3	39
22	992	43	788	47	212	204	4	38
23	9.45 035	42	835	46	165	200	4	37
24	077	43	881	47	119	196	4	36
25	120	43	928	47	072	192	3	35
26	163	43	975	46	025	189	4	34
27	206	43	9.47 021	47	0.52 979	185	4	33
28	249	43	068	46	932	181	4	32
29	292	42	114	46	886	177	3	31
30	9.45 334	43	9.47 160	47	0.52 840	9.98 174	4	30
31	377	42	207	46	793	170	4	29
32	419	43	253	46	747	166	4	28
33	462	42	299	47	701	162	3	27
34	504	43	346	46	654	159	4	26
35	547	42	392	46	608	155	4	25
36	589	43	438	46	562	151	4	24
37	632	42	484	46	516	147	3	23
38	674	42	530	46	470	144	4	22
39	716	42	576	46	424	140	4	21
40	9.45 758	43	9.47 622	46	0.52 378	9.98 136	4	20
41	801	42	668	46	332	132	3	19
42	843	42	714	46	286	129	4	18
43	885	42	760	46	240	125	4	17
44	927	42	806	46	194	121	4	16
45	969	42	852	45	148	117	3	15
46	9.46 011	42	897	46	103	113	4	14
47	053	42	943	46	057	110	3	13
48	095	41	989	46	011	106	4	12
49	136	42	9.48 035	45	0.51 965	102	4	11
50	9.46 178	42	9.48 080	46	0.51 920	9.98 098	4	10
51	220	42	126	45	874	094	4	9
52	262	41	171	46	829	090	3	8
53	303	42	217	45	783	087	4	7
54	345	41	262	45	738	083	4	6
55	386	42	307	46	693	079	4	5
56	428	41	353	45	647	075	4	4
57	469	42	398	45	602	071	3	3
58	511	41	443	46	557	067	4	2
59	552	42	489	45	511	063	4	1
60	9.46 594		9.48 534		0.51 466	9.98 060		0
′	L. Cos.	d.	L. Cotg.	c.d.	L. Tang.	L. Sin.	d.	′

P. P.

′	48	47
1″	0.8	0.8
2″	1.6	1.6
3″	2.4	2.4
4″	3.2	3.1
5″	4.0	3.9
6″	4.8	4.7
7″	5.6	5.5
8″	6.4	6.3
9″	7.2	7.1

′	46	45
1″	0.8	0.8
2″	1.5	1.5
3″	2.3	2.3
4″	3.1	3.0
5″	3.8	3.8
6″	4.6	4.5
7″	5.4	5.3
8″	6.1	6.0
9″	6.9	6.8

′	44	43
1″	0.7	0.7
2″	1.5	1.4
3″	2.2	2.2
4″	2.9	2.9
5″	3.7	3.6
6″	4.4	4.3
7″	5.1	5.0
8″	5.9	5.7
9″	6.6	6.5

′	42
1″	0.7
2″	1.4
3″	2.1
4″	2.8
5″	3.5
6″	4.2
7″	4.9
8″	5.6
9″	6.3

′	41
1″	0.7
2″	1.4
3″	2.1
4″	2.7
5″	3.4
6″	4.1
7″	4.8
8″	5.5
9″	6.2

′	3	4
1″	0.05	0.07
2″	0.10	0.13
3″	0.15	0.20
4″	0.20	0.27
5″	0.25	0.33
6″	0.30	0.40
7″	0.35	0.47
8″	0.40	0.53
9″	0.45	0.60

′	L. Sin.	d.	L. Tang.	c.d.	L. Cotg.	L. Cos.	d.	′
0	9.46 594	41	9.48 534	45	0.51 466	9.98 060	4	60
1	635	41	579	45	421	056	4	59
2	676	41	624	45	376	052	4	58
3	717	41	669	45	331	048	4	57
4	758	42	714	45	286	044	4	56
5	800	41	759	45	241	040	4	55
6	841	41	804	45	196	036	4	54
7	882	41	849	45	151	032	3	53
8	923	41	894	45	106	029	4	52
9	964	41	939	45	061	025	4	51
10	9.47 005	40	9.48 984	45	0.51 016	9.98 021	4	50
11	045	41	9.49 029	44	0.50 971	017	4	49
12	086	41	073	45	927	013	4	48
13	127	41	118	45	882	009	4	47
14	168	41	163	44	837	005	4	46
15	209	40	207	45	793	001	4	45
16	249	41	252	44	748	9.97 997	4	44
17	290	40	296	45	704	993	4	43
18	330	41	341	44	659	989	3	42
19	371	40	385	45	615	986	4	41
20	9.47 411	41	9.49 430	44	0.50 570	9.97 982	4	40
21	452	40	474	45	526	978	4	39
22	492	41	519	44	481	974	4	38
23	533	40	563	44	437	970	4	37
24	573	40	607	45	393	966	4	36
25	613	41	652	44	348	962	4	35
26	654	40	696	44	304	958	4	34
27	694	40	740	44	260	954	4	33
28	734	40	784	44	216	950	4	32
29	774	40	828	44	172	946	4	31
30	9.47 814	40	9.49 872	44	0.50 128	9.97 942	4	30
31	854	40	916	44	084	938	4	29
32	894	40	960	44	040	934	4	28
33	934	40	9.50 004	44	0.49 996	930	4	27
34	974	40	048	44	952	926	4	26
35	9.48 014	40	092	44	908	922	4	25
36	054	40	136	44	864	918	4	24
37	094	39	180	43	820	914	4	23
38	133	40	223	44	777	910	4	22
39	173	40	267	44	733	906	4	21
40	9.48 213	39	9.50 311	44	0.49 689	9.97 902	4	20
41	252	40	355	43	645	898	4	19
42	292	40	398	44	602	894	4	18
43	332	39	442	43	558	890	4	17
44	371	40	485	44	515	886	4	16
45	411	39	529	43	471	882	4	15
46	450	40	572	44	428	878	4	14
47	490	39	616	43	384	874	4	13
48	529	39	659	44	341	870	4	12
49	568	39	703	43	297	866	5	11
50	9.48 607	40	9.50 746	43	0.49 254	9.97 861	4	10
51	647	39	789	44	211	857	4	9
52	686	39	833	43	167	853	4	8
53	725	39	876	43	124	849	4	7
54	764	39	919	43	081	845	4	6
55	803	39	962	43	038	841	4	5
56	842	39	9.51 005	43	0.48 995	837	4	4
57	881	39	048	44	952	833	4	3
58	920	39	092	43	908	829	4	2
59	959	39	135	43	865	825	4	1
60	9.48 998		9.51 178		0.48 822	9.97 821		0

′	L. Cos.	d.	L. Cotg.	c.d.	L. Tang.	L. Sin.	d.	′

P. P.

′	45	44
1″	0.8	0.7
2″	1.5	1.5
3″	2.3	2.2
4″	3.0	2.9
5″	3.8	3.7
6″	4.5	4.4
7″	5.3	5.1
8″	6.0	5.9
9″	6.8	6.6

′	43	42
1″	0.7	0.7
2″	1.4	1.4
3″	2.2	2.1
4″	2.9	2.8
5″	3.6	3.5
6″	4.3	4.2
7″	5.0	4.9
8″	5.7	5.6
9″	6.5	6.3

′	41	40
1″	0.7	0.7
2″	1.4	1.3
3″	2.1	2.0
4″	2.7	2.7
5″	3.4	3.3
6″	4.1	4.0
7″	4.8	4.7
8″	5.5	5.3
9″	6.2	6.0

′	39
1″	0.7
2″	1.3
3″	2.0
4″	2.6
5″	3.3
6″	3.9
7″	4.6
8″	5.2
9″	5.9

′	3
1″	0.05
2″	0.10
3″	0.15
4″	0.20
5″	0.25
6″	0.30
7″	0.35
8″	0.40
9″	0.45

′	4	5
1″	0.07	0.08
2″	0.13	0.17
3″	0.20	0.25
4″	0.27	0.33
5″	0.33	0.42
6″	0.40	0.50
7″	0.47	0.58
8″	0.53	0.67
9″	0.60	0.75

72°

′	L. Sin.	d.	L. Tang.	c. d.	L. Cotg.	L. Cos.	d.	′		P. P.	
0	9.48 998	39	9.51 178	43	0.48 822	9.97 821	4	60	1′	43	42
1	9.49 037	39	221	43	779	817	5	59	1″	0.7	0.7
2	076	39	264	42	736	812	4	58	2″	1.4	1.4
3	115	38	306	43	694	808	4	57	3″	2.2	2.1
4	153	39	349	43	651	804	4	56	4″	2.9	2.8
5	192	39	392	43	608	800	4	55	5″	3.6	3.5
6	231	38	435	43	565	796	4	54	6″	4.3	4.2
7	269	39	478	42	522	792	4	53	7″	5.0	4.9
8	308	39	520	43	480	788	4	52	8″	5.7	5.6
9	347	38	563	43	437	784	5	51	9″	6.5	6.3
10	9.49 385	39	9.51 606	42	0.48 394	9.97 779	4	50	1′	41	39
11	424	38	648	43	352	775	4	49	1″	0.7	0.7
12	462	38	691	43	309	771	4	48	2″	1.4	1.3
13	500	39	734	42	266	767	4	47	3″	2.1	2.0
14	539	38	776	43	224	763	4	46	4″	2.7	2.6
15	577	38	819	42	181	759	5	45	5″	3.4	3.3
16	615	39	861	42	139	754	4	44	6″	4.1	3.9
17	654	38	903	43	097	750	4	43	7″	4.8	4.6
18	692	38	946	42	054	746	4	42	8″	5.5	5.2
19	730	38	988	43	012	742	4	41	9″	6.2	5.9
20	9.49 768	38	9.52 031	42	0.47 969	9.97 738	4	40	1′	38	
21	806	38	073	42	927	734	5	39	1″	0.6	
22	844	38	115	42	885	729	4	38	2″	1.3	
23	882	38	157	43	843	725	4	37	3″	1.9	
24	920	38	200	42	800	721	4	36	4″	2.5	
25	958	38	242	42	758	717	4	35	5″	3.2	
26	996	38	284	42	716	713	5	34	6″	3.8	
27	9.50 034	38	326	42	674	708	4	33	7″	4.4	
28	072	38	368	42	632	704	4	32	8″	5.1	
29	110	38	410	42	590	700	4	31	9″	5.7	
30	9.50 148	37	9.52 452	42	0.47 548	9.97 696	5	30	1′	37	
31	185	38	494	42	506	691	4	29	1″	0.6	
32	223	38	536	42	464	687	4	28	2″	1.2	
33	261	37	578	42	422	683	4	27	3″	1.9	
34	298	38	620	41	380	679	5	26	4″	2.5	
35	336	38	661	42	339	674	4	25	5″	3.1	
36	374	37	703	42	297	670	4	24	6″	3.7	
37	411	38	745	42	255	666	4	23	7″	4.3	
38	449	37	787	42	213	662	5	22	8″	4.9	
39	486	37	829	41	171	657	4	21	9″	5.6	
40	9.50 523	38	9.52 870	42	0.47 130	9.97 653	4	20	1′	36	
41	561	37	912	41	088	649	4	19	1″	0.6	
42	598	37	953	42	047	645	5	18	2″	1.2	
43	635	38	995	42	005	640	4	17	3″	1.8	
44	673	37	9.53 037	41	0.46 963	636	4	16	4″	2.4	
45	710	37	078	42	922	632	4	15	5″	3.0	
46	747	37	120	41	880	628	5	14	6″	3.6	
47	784	37	161	41	839	623	4	13	7″	4.2	
48	821	37	202	42	798	619	4	12	8″	4.8	
49	858	38	244	41	756	615	5	11	9″	5.4	
50	9.50 896	37	9.53 285	42	0.46 715	9.97 610	4	10	1′	4	5
51	933	37	327	41	673	606	4	9	1″	0.07	0.08
52	970	37	368	41	632	602	5	8	2″	0.13	0.17
53	9.51 007	36	409	41	591	597	4	7	3″	0.20	0.25
54	043	37	450	42	550	593	4	6	4″	0.27	0.33
55	080	37	492	41	508	589	5	5	5″	0.33	0.42
56	117	37	533	41	467	584	4	4	6″	0.40	0.50
57	154	37	574	41	426	580	4	3	7″	0.47	0.58
58	191	36	615	41	385	576	5	2	8′	0.53	0.67
59	227	37	656	41	344	571	4	1	9″	0.60	0.75
60	9.51 264		9.53 697		0.46 303	9.97 567		0			
′	L. Cos.	d.	L. Cotg.	c. d.	L. Tang.	L. Sin.	d.	′			

'	L. Sin.	d.	L. Tang.	c. d.	L. Cotg.	L. Cos.	d.	'	P. P.		
0	9.51 264	37	9.53 697	41	0.46 303	9.97 567	4	60	1'	41	40
1	301	37	738	41	262	563	5	59	1″	0.7	0.7
2	338	36	779	41	221	558	4	58	2″	1.4	1.3
3	374	37	820	41	180	554	4	57	3″	2.1	2.0
4	411	36	861	41	139	550	5	56	4″	2.7	2.7
5	447	37	902	41	098	545	4	55	5″	3.4	3.3
6	484	36	943	41	057	541	5	54	6″	4.1	4.0
7	520	37	984	41	016	536	4	53	7″	4.8	4.7
8	557	36	9.54 025	40	0.45 975	532	4	52	8″	5.5	5.3
9	593	36	065	41	935	528	5	51	9″	6.2	6.0
10	9.51 629	37	9.54 106	41	0.45 894	9.97 523	4	50			
11	666	36	147	40	853	519	4	49			
12	702	36	187	41	813	515	5	48	1'	39	37
13	738	36	228	41	772	510	4	47	1″	0.7	0.6
14	774	37	269	40	731	506	5	46	2″	1.3	1.2
15	811	36	309	41	691	501	4	45	3″	2.0	1.9
16	847	36	350	40	650	497	5	44	4″	2.6	2.5
17	883	36	390	41	610	492	4	43	5″	3.3	3.1
18	919	36	431	40	569	488	4	42	6″	3.9	3.7
19	955	36	471	41	529	484	5	41	7″	4.6	4.3
20	9.51 991	36	9.54 512	40	0.45 488	9.97 479	4	40	8″	5.2	4.9
21	9.52 027	36	552	41	448	475	5	39	9″	5.9	5.6
22	063	36	593	40	407	470	4	38			
23	099	36	633	40	367	466	5	37			
24	135	36	673	41	327	461	4	36	1'	36	35
25	171	36	714	40	286	457	4	35	1″	0.6	0.6
26	207	36	754	40	246	453	5	34	2″	1.2	1.2
27	242	35	794	41	206	448	4	33	3″	1.8	1.8
28	278	36	835	40	165	444	5	32	4″	2.4	2.3
29	314	36	875	40	125	439	4	31	5″	3.0	2.9
30	9.52 350	35	9.54 915	40	0.45 085	9.97 435	5	30	6″	3.6	3.5
31	385	36	955	40	045	430	4	29	7″	4.2	4.1
32	421	35	995	40	005	426	5	28	8″	4.8	4.7
33	456	36	9.55 035	40	0.44 965	421	4	27	9″	5.4	5.3
34	492	35	075	40	925	417	5	26			
35	527	36	115	40	885	412	4	25			
36	563	35	155	40	845	408	5	24	1'	34	
37	598	36	195	40	805	403	4	23	1″	0.6	
38	634	35	235	40	765	399	5	22	2″	1.1	
39	669	36	275	40	725	394	4	21	3″	1.7	
40	9.52 705	35	9.55 315	40	0.44 685	9.97 390	5	20	4″	2.3	
41	740	35	355	40	645	385	4	19	5″	2.8	
42	775	36	395	39	605	381	5	18	6″	3.4	
43	811	35	434	40	566	376	4	17	7″	4.0	
44	846	35	474	40	526	372	5	16	8″	4.5	
45	881	35	514	40	486	367	4	15	9″	5.1	
46	916	35	554	39	446	363	5	14			
47	951	35	593	40	407	358	5	13			
48	986	35	633	40	367	353	4	12			
49	9.53 021	35	673	39	327	349	5	11	1'	4	5
50	9.53 056	36	9.55 712	40	0.44 288	9.97 344	4	10	1″	0.07	0.08
51	092	34	752	39	248	340	5	9	2″	0.13	0.17
52	126	35	791	40	209	335	4	8	3″	0.20	0.25
53	161	35	831	39	169	331	5	7	4″	0.27	0.33
54	196	35	870	40	130	326	4	6	5″	0.33	0.42
55	231	35	910	39	090	322	5	5	6″	0.40	0.50
56	266	35	949	40	051	317	5	4	7″	0.47	0.58
57	301	35	989	39	011	312	4	3	8″	0.53	0.67
58	336	34	9.56 028	39	0.43 972	308	5	2	9″	0.60	0.75
59	370	35	067	40	933	303	4	1			
60	9.53 405		9.56 107		0.43 893	9.97 299		0			
'	L. Cos.	d.	L. Cotg.	c.d.	L. Tang.	L. Sin.	d.	'			

′	L. Sin.	d.	L. Tang.	c. d.	L. Cotg.	L. Cos.	d.	′
0	9.53 405	35	9.56 107	39	0.43 893	9.97 299	5	60
1	440	35	146	39	854	294	5	59
2	475̄	34	185	39	815̄	289	4	58
3	509	35	224	40	776	285	5	57
4	544	34	264	39	736	280	4	56
5	578	35	303	39	697	276	5	55
6	613	34	342	39	658	271	5	54
7	647	35	381	39	619	266	4	53
8	682	34	420	39	580	262	5	52
9	716	35	459	39	541	257	5	51
10	9.53 751	34	9.56 498	39	0.43 502	9.97 252	4	50
11	785	34	537	39	463	248	5	49
12	819	35	576	39	424̄	243	5	48
13	854	34	615	39	385	238	4	47
14	888	34	654	39	346	234	5	46
15	922	35	693	39	307	229	5	45
16	957	34	732	39	268	224	4	44
17	991̄	34	771	39	229	220	5	43
18	9.54 025̄	34	810	39	190	215	5	42
19	059	34	849	38	151	210	4	41
20	9.54 093	34	9.56 887	39	0.43 113	9.97 206	5	40
21	127	34	926	39	074	201	5	39
22	161	34	965̄	39	035	196	4	38
23	195	34	9.57 004	38	0.42 996	192	5	37
24	229	34	042	39	958	187	5	36
25	263	34	081	39	919	182	4	35
26	297	34	120	38	880	178	5	34
27	331	34	158	39	842	173	5	33
28	365̄	34	197	38	803	168	5	32
29	399	34	235	39	765̄	163	4	31
30	9.54 433	33	9.57 274	38	0.42 726	9.97 159	5	30
31	466	34	312	39	688	154	5	29
32	500	34	351	38	649	149	4	28
33	534	33	389	39	611	145	5	27
34	567	34	428	38	572	140	5	26
35	601	34	466	38	534	135	5	25
36	635̄	33	504	39	496	130	4	24
37	668	34	543	38	457	126	5	23
38	702	33	581	38	419	121	5	22
39	735	34	619	39	381	116	5	21
40	9.54 769	33	9.57 658	38	0.42 342	9.97 111	4	20
41	802	34	696	38	304	107	5	19
42	836	33	734	38	266	102	5	18
43	869	34	772	38	228	097	5	17
44	903	33	810	39	190	092	5	16
45	936	33	849	38	151	087	4	15
46	969	34	887	38	113	083	5	14
47	9.55 003	33	925̄	38	075	078	5	13
48	036	33	963	38	037	073	5	12
49	069	33	9.58 001	38	0.41 999	068	5	11
50	9.55 102	34	9.58 039	38	0.41 961	9.97 063	4	10
51	136	33	077	38	923	059	5	9
52	169	33	115̄	38	885	054	5	8
53	202	33	153	38	847	049	5	7
54	235̄	33	191	38	809	044	5	6
55	268	33	229	38	771	039	4	5
56	301	33	267	37	733	035̄	5	4
57	334	33	304	38	696	030̄	5	3
58	367	33	342	38	658	025̄	5	2
59	400	33	380	38	620	020	5	1
60	9.55 433		9.58 418		0.41 582	9.97 015		0
′	L. Cos.	d.	L. Cotg.	c. d.	L. Tang.	L. Sin.	d.	′

P. P.

1′	40	39
1″	0.7	0.7
2″	1.3	1.3
3″	2.0	2.0
4″	2.7	2.6
5″	3.3	3.3
6″	4.0	3.9
7″	4.7	4.6
8″	5.3	5.2
9″	6.0	5.9

1′	38	37
1″	0.6	0.6
2″	1.3	1.2
3″	1.9	1.9
4″	2.5	2.5
5″	3.2	3.1
6″	3.8	3.7
7″	4.4	4.3
8″	5.1	4.9
9″	5.7	5.6

1′	35
1″	0.6
2″	1.2
3″	1.8
4″	2.3
5″	2.9
6″	3.5
7″	4.1
8″	4.7
9″	5.3

1′	34
1″	0.6
2″	1.1
3″	1.7
4″	2.3
5″	2.8
6″	3.4
7″	4.0
8″	4.5
9″	5.1

1′	33
1″	0.6
2″	1.1
3″	1.7
4″	2.2
5″	2.8
6″	3.3
7″	3.9
8″	4.4
9″	5.0

1′	4	5
1″	0.07	0.08
2″	0.13	0.17
3″	0.20	0.25
4″	0.27	0.33
5″	0.33	0.42
6″	0.40	0.50
7″	0.47	0.58
8″	0.53	0.67
9″	0.60	0.75

′	L. Sin.	d.	L. Tang.	c.d.	L. Cotg.	L. Cos.	d.	′
0	9.55 433	33	9.58 418	37	0.41 582	9.97 015	5	60
1	466	33	455	38	545	010	5	59
2	499	33	493	38	507	005	4	58
3	532	32	531	38	469	001	5	57
4	564	33	569	37	431	9.96 996	5	56
5	597	33	606	38	394	991	5	55
6	630	33	644	37	356	986	5	54
7	663	32	681	38	319	981	5	53
8	695	33	719	38	281	976	5	52
9	728	33	757	37	243	971	5	51
10	9.55 761	32	9.58 794	38	0.41 206	9.96 966	4	50
11	793	33	832	38	168	962	5	49
12	826	32	869	38	131	957	5	48
13	858	33	907	37	093	952	5	47
14	891	32	944	37	056	947	5	46
15	923	33	981	38	019	942	5	45
16	956	32	9.59 019	37	0.40 981	937	5	44
17	988	33	056	38	944	932	5	43
18	9.56 021	32	094	37	906	927	5	42
19	053	32	131	37	869	922	5	41
20	9.56 085	33	9.59 168	37	0.40 832	9.96 917	5	40
21	118	32	205	38	795	912	5	39
22	150	32	243	37	757	907	4	38
23	182	33	280	37	720	903	5	37
24	215	32	317	37	683	898	5	36
25	247	32	354	37	646	893	5	35
26	279	32	391	38	609	888	5	34
27	311	32	429	37	571	883	5	33
28	343	32	466	37	534	878	5	32
29	375	33	503	37	497	873	5	31
30	9.56 408	32	9.59 540	37	0.40 460	9.96 868	5	30
31	440	32	577	37	423	863	5	29
32	472	32	614	37	386	858	5	28
33	504	32	651	37	349	853	5	27
34	536	32	688	37	312	848	5	26
35	568	31	725	37	275	843	5	25
36	599	32	762	37	238	838	5	24
37	631	32	799	36	201	833	5	23
38	663	32	835	37	165	828	5	22
39	695	32	872	37	128	823	5	21
40	9.56 727	32	9.59 909	37	0.40 091	9.96 818	5	20
41	759	31	946	37	054	813	5	19
42	790	32	983	36	017	808	5	18
43	822	32	9.60 019	37	0.39 981	803	5	17
44	854	32	056	37	944	798	5	16
45	886	31	093	37	907	793	5	15
46	917	32	130	36	870	788	5	14
47	949	31	166	37	834	783	5	13
48	980	32	203	37	797	778	6	12
49	9.57 012	32	240	36	760	772	5	11
50	9.57 044	31	9.60 276	37	0.39 724	9.96 767	5	10
51	075	32	313	36	687	762	5	9
52	107	31	349	37	651	757	5	8
53	138	31	386	36	614	752	5	7
54	169	32	422	37	578	747	5	6
55	201	31	459	36	541	742	5	5
56	232	32	495	37	505	737	5	4
57	264	31	532	36	468	732	5	3
58	295	31	568	37	432	727	5	2
59	326	32	605	36	395	722	5	1
60	9.57 358		9.60 641		0.39 359	9.96 717		0
′	L. Cos.	d.	L. Cotg.	c.d.	L. Tang.	L. Sin.	d.	′

P. P.

1′	38	37
1″	0.6	0.6
2″	1.3	1.2
3″	1.9	1.9
4″	2.5	2.5
5″	3.2	3.1
6″	3.8	3.7
7″	4.4	4.3
8″	5.1	4.9
9″	5.7	5.6

1′	36	33
1″	0.6	0.6
2″	1.2	1.1
3″	1.8	1.7
4″	2.4	2.2
5″	3.0	2.8
6″	3.6	3.3
7″	4.2	3.9
8″	4.8	4.4
9″	5.4	5.0

1′	32
1″	0.5
2″	1.1
3″	1.6
4″	2.1
5″	2.7
6″	3.2
7″	3.7
8″	4.3
9″	4.8

1′	31
1″	0.5
2″	1.0
3″	1.6
4″	2.1
5″	2.6
6″	3.1
7″	3.6
8″	4.1
9″	4.7

1′	4
1″	0.07
2″	0.13
3″	0.20
4″	0.27
5″	0.33
6″	0.40
7″	0.47
8″	0.53
9″	0.60

1′	5	6
1″	0.08	0.10
2″	0.17	0.20
3″	0.25	0.30
4″	0.33	0.40
5″	0.42	0.50
6″	0.50	0.60
7″	0.58	0.70
8″	0.67	0.80
9″	0.75	0.90

′	L. Sin.	d.	L. Tang.	c. d.	L. Cotg.	L. Cos.	d.	′
0	9.57 358	31	9.60 641	36	0.39 359	9.96 717	6	60
1	389	31	677	37	323	711	5	59
2	420	31	714	36	286	706	5	58
3	451	31	750	36	250	701	5	57
4	482	32	786	37	214	696	5	56
5	514	31	823	36	177	691	5	55
6	545̄	31	859	36	141	686	5	54
7	576	31	895	36	105̄	681	5	53
8	607	31	931	36	069	676	6	52
9	638	31	967	37	033	670	5	51
10	9.57 669	31	9.61 004	36	0.38 996	9.96 665	5	50
11	700	31	040	36	960	660	5	49
12	731	31	076	36	924	655	5	48
13	762	31	112	36	888	650	5	47
14	793	31	148	36	852	645̄	5	46
15	824	31	184	36	816	640	6	45
16	855̄	30	220	36	780	634	5	44
17	885	31	256	36	744	629	5	43
18	916	31	292	36	708	624	5	42
19	947	31	328	36	672	619	5	41
20	9.57 978	30	9.61 364	36	0.38 636	9.96 614	6	40
21	9.58 008	31	400	36	600	608	5	39
22	039	31	436	36	564	603	5	38
23	070	31	472	36	528	598	5	37
24	101	30	508	36	492	593	5	36
25	131	31	544	35	456	588	6	35
26	162	30	579	36	421	582	5	34
27	192	31	615	36	385̄	577	5	33
28	223	30	651	36	349	572	5	32
29	253	31	687	35	313	567	5	31
30	9.58 284	30	9.61 722	36	0.38 278	9.96 562	6	30
31	314	31	758	36	242	556	5	29
32	345̄	30	794	36	206	551	5	28
33	375	31	830	35	170	546	5	27
34	406	30	865	36	135̄	541	6	26
35	436	31	901	35	099	535	5	25
36	467	30	936	36	064	530	5	24
37	497	30	972	36	028	525̄	5	23
38	527	30	9.62 008	35	0.37 992	520	6	22
39	557	31	043	36	957	514	5	21
40	9.58 588	30	9.62 079	35	0.37 921	9.96 509	5	20
41	618	30	114	36	886	504	6	19
42	648	30	150	35	850̄	498	5	18
43	678	31	185	36	815̄	493	5	17
44	709	30	221	35	779	488	6	16
45	739	30	256	36	744	483	5	15
46	769	30	292	35	708	477	6	14
47	799	30	327	35	673	472	5	13
48	829	30	362	36	638	467	6	12
49	859	30	398	35	602	461	5	11
50	9.58 889	30	9.62 433	35	0.37 567	9.96 456	5	10
51	919	30	468	36	532	451	6	9
52	949	30	504	35	496	445	5	8
53	979	30	539	35	461	440	5	7
54	9.59 009	30	574	35	426	435̄	6	6
55	039	30	609	36	391	429	5	5
56	069	29	645̄	35	355	424	5	4
57	098	30	680̄	35	320	419	6	3
58	128	30	715	35	285	413	5	2
59	158	30	750	35	250	408	5	1
60	9.59 188		9.62 785		0.37 215	9.96 403		0
′	L. Cos.	d.	L. Cotg.	c. d.	L. Tang.	L. Sin.	d.	′

P. P.

′	37	36
1″	0.6	0.6
2″	1.2	1.2
3″	1.9	1.8
4″	2.5	2.4
5″	3.1	3.0
6″	3.7	3.6
7″	4.3	4.2
8″	4.9	4.8
9″	5.6	5.4

′	35	32
1″	0.6	0.5
2″	1.2	1.1
3″	1.8	1.6
4″	2.3	2.1
5″	2.9	2.7
6″	3.5	3.2
7″	4.1	3.7
8″	4.7	4.3
9″	5.3	4.8

′	31
1″	0.5
2″	1.0
3″	1.6
4″	2.1
5″	2.6
6″	3.1
7″	3.6
8″	4.1
9″	4.7

′	30
1″	0.5
2″	1.0
3″	1.5
4″	2.0
5″	2.5
6″	3.0
7″	3.5
8″	4.0
9″	4.5

′	29
1″	0.5
2″	1.0
3″	1.5
4″	1.9
5″	2.4
6″	2.9
7″	3.4
8″	3.9
9″	4.4

′	5	6
1″	0.08	0.10
2″	0.17	0.20
3″	0.25	0.30
4″	0.33	0.40
5″	0.42	0.50
6″	0.50	0.60
7″	0.58	0.70
8″	0.67	0.80
9″	0.75	0.90

′	L. Sin.	d.	L. Tang.	c.d.	L. Cotg.	L. Cos.	d.	′
0	9.59 188	30	9.62 785	35	0.37 215	9.96 403	6	60
1	218	29	820	35	180	397	5	59
2	247	30	855	35	145	392	5	58
3	277	30	890	36	110	387	6	57
4	307	29	926	35	074	381	5	56
5	336	30	961	35	039	376	6	55
6	366	30	996	35	004	370	5	54
7	396	29	9.63 031	35	0.36 969	365	5	53
8	425	30	066	35	934	360	6	52
9	455	29	101	34	899	354	5	51
10	9.59 484	30	9.63 135	35	0.36 865	9.96 349	6	50
11	514	29	170	35	830	343	5	49
12	543	30	205	35	795	338	5	48
13	573	29	240	35	760	333	6	47
14	602	30	275	35	725	327	5	46
15	632	29	310	35	690	322	6	45
16	661	29	345	34	655	316	5	44
17	690	30	379	35	621	311	6	43
18	720	29	414	35	586	305	5	42
19	749	29	449	35	551	300	6	41
20	9.59 778	30	9.63 484	35	0.36 516	9.96 294	5	40
21	808	29	519	34	481	289	6	39
22	837	29	553	35	447	284	6	38
23	866	29	588	35	412	278	5	37
24	895	29	623	34	377	273	6	36
25	924	30	657	35	343	267	5	35
26	954	29	692	34	308	262	5	34
27	983	29	726	35	274	256	5	33
28	9.60 012	29	761	35	239	251	6	32
29	041	29	796	34	204	245	5	31
30	9.60 070	29	9.63 830	35	0.36 170	9.96 240	6	30
31	099	29	865	34	135	234	5	29
32	128	29	899	35	101	229	6	28
33	157	29	934	34	066	223	5	27
34	186	29	968	35	032	218	6	26
35	215	29	9.64 003	34	0.35 997	212	5	25
36	244	29	037	35	963	207	6	24
37	273	29	072	34	928	201	5	23
38	302	29	106	34	894	196	6	22
39	331	28	140	35	860	190	5	21
40	9.60 359	29	9.64 175	34	0.35 825	9.96 185	6	20
41	388	29	209	34	791	179	5	19
42	417	29	243	35	757	174	6	18
43	446	28	278	34	722	168	6	17
44	474	29	312	34	688	162	6	16
45	503	29	346	35	654	157	6	15
46	532	29	381	34	619	151	5	14
47	561	28	415	34	585	146	6	13
48	589	29	449	34	551	140	5	12
49	618	28	483	34	517	135	6	11
50	9.60 646	29	9.64 517	35	0.35 483	9.96 129	6	10
51	675	29	552	34	448	123	6	9
52	704	28	586	34	414	118	6	8
53	732	29	620	34	380	112	5	7
54	761	28	654	34	346	107	6	6
55	789	29	688	34	312	101	6	5
56	818	28	722	34	278	095	5	4
57	846	29	756	34	244	090	6	3
58	875	28	790	34	210	084	5	2
59	903	28	824	34	176	079	6	1
60	9.60 931		9.64 858		0.35 142	9.96 073		0

′	L. Cos.	d.	L. Cotg.	c.d.	L. Tang.	L. Sin.	d.	′

P. P.

1′	36	35
1″	0.6	0.6
2″	1.2	1.2
3″	1.8	1.8
4″	2.4	2.3
5″	3.0	2.9
6″	3.6	3.5
7″	4.2	4.1
8″	4.8	4.7
9″	5.4	5.3

1′	34	30
1″	0.6	0.5
2″	1.1	1.0
3″	1.7	1.5
4″	2.3	2.0
5″	2.8	2.5
6″	3.4	3.0
7″	4.0	3.5
8″	4.5	4.0
9″	5.1	4.5

1′	29
1″	0.5
2″	1.0
3″	1.5
4″	1.9
5″	2.4
6″	2.9
7″	3.4
8″	3.9
9″	4.4

1′	28
1″	0.5
2″	0.9
3″	1.4
4″	1.9
5″	2.3
6″	2.8
7″	3.3
8″	3.7
9″	4.2

1′	5	6
1″	0.08	0.10
2″	0.17	0.20
3″	0.25	0.30
4″	0.33	0.40
5″	0.42	0.50
6″	0.50	0.60
7″	0.58	0.70
8″	0.67	0.80
9″	0.75	0.90

Logarithmic Functions

24°

′	L. Sin.	d.	L. Tang.	c. d.	L. Cotg.	L. Cos.	d.	′	P. P.		
0	9.60 931	29	9.64 858	34	0.35 142	9.96 073	6	60	1′	34	33
1	960	28	892	34	108	067	5	59	1″	0.6	0.6
2	988	28	926	34	074	062	6	58	2″	1.1	1.1
3	9.61 016	29	960	34	040	056	6	57	3″	1.7	1.7
4	045	28	994	34	006	050	5	56	4″	2.3	2.2
5	073	28	9.65 028	34	0.34 972	045	6	55	5″	2.8	2.8
6	101	28	062	34	938	039	5	54	6″	3.4	3.3
7	129	29	096	34	904	034	6	53	7″	4.0	3.9
8	158	28	130	34	870	028	6	52	8″	4.5	4.4
9	186	28	164	33	836	022	5	51	9″	5.1	5.0
10	9.61 214	28	9.65 197	34	0.34 803	9.96 017	6	50			
11	242	28	231	34	769	011	6	49			
12	270	28	265	34	735	005	5	48	1′	29	
13	298	28	299	34	701	000	6	47	1″	0.5	
14	326	28	333	33	667	9.95 994	6	46	2″	1.0	
15	354	28	366	34	634	988	6	45	3″	1.5	
16	382	29	400	34	600	982	5	44	4″	1.9	
17	411	27	434	33	566	977	6	43	5″	2.4	
18	438	28	467	34	533	971	6	42	6″	2.9	
19	466	28	501	34	499	965	5	41	7″	3.4	
20	9.61 494	28	9.65 535	33	0.34 465	9.95 960	6	40	8″	3.9	
21	522	28	568	34	432	954	6	39	9″	4.4	
22	550	28	602	34	398	948	6	38			
23	578	28	636	33	364	942	5	37			
24	606	28	669	34	331	937	6	36			
25	634	28	703	33	297	931	6	35	1′	28	
26	662	27	736	34	264	925	5	34	1″	0.5	
27	689	28	770	33	230	920	6	33	2″	0.9	
28	717	28	803	34	197	914	6	32	3″	1.4	
29	745	28	837	33	163	908	6	31	4″	1.9	
30	9.61 773	27	9.65 870	34	0.34 130	9.95 902	5	30	5″	2.3	
31	800	28	904	33	096	897	6	29	6″	2.8	
32	828	28	937	34	063	891	6	28	7″	3.3	
33	856	27	971	33	029	885	6	27	8″	3.7	
34	883	28	9.66 004	34	0.33 996	879	6	26	9″	4.2	
35	911	28	038	33	962	873	5	25			
36	939	27	071	33	929	868	6	24	1′	27	
37	966	28	104	34	896	862	6	23	1″	0.5	
38	994	27	138	33	862	856	6	22	2″	0.9	
39	9.62 021	28	171	33	829	850	6	21	3″	1.4	
40	9.62 049	27	9.66 204	34	0.33 796	9.95 844	5	20	4″	1.8	
41	076	28	238	33	762	839	6	19	5″	2.3	
42	104	27	271	33	729	833	6	18	6″	2.7	
43	131	28	304	33	696	827	6	17	7″	3.2	
44	159	27	337	34	663	821	6	16	8″	3.6	
45	186	28	371	33	629	815	5	15	9″	4.1	
46	214	27	404	33	596	810	6	14			
47	241	27	437	33	563	804	6	13			
48	268	28	470	33	530	798	6	12			
49	296	27	503	34	497	792	6	11	1′	5	6
50	9.62 323	27	9.66 537	33	0.33 463	9.95 786	6	10	1″	0.08	0.10
51	350	27	570	33	430	780	5	9	2″	0.17	0.20
52	377	28	603	33	397	775	6	8	3″	0.25	0.30
53	405	27	636	33	364	769	6	7	4″	0.33	0.40
54	432	27	669	33	331	763	6	6	5″	0.42	0.50
55	459	27	702	33	298	757	6	5	6″	0.50	0.60
56	486	27	735	33	265	751	6	4	7″	0.58	0.70
57	513	28	768	33	232	745	6	3	8″	0.67	0.80
58	541	27	801	33	199	739	6	2	9″	0.75	0.90
59	568	27	834	33	166	733	5	1			
60	9.62 595		9.66 867		0.33 133	9.95 728		0			
′	L. Cos.	d.	L. Cotg.	c. d.	L. Tang.	L. Sin.	d.	′			

65°

′	L. Sin.	d.	L. Tang.	c.d.	L. Cotg.	L. Cos.	d.	′
0	9.62 595	27	9.66 867	33	0.33 133	9.95 728	6	60
1	622	27	900	33	100	722	6	59
2	649	27	933	33	067	716	6	58
3	676	27	966	33	034	710	6	57
4	703	27	999	33	001	704	6	56
5	730	27	9.67 032	33	0.32 968	698	6	55
6	757	27	065	33	935	692	6	54
7	784	27	098	33	902	686	6	53
8	811	27	131	32	869	680	6	52
9	838	27	163	33	837	674	6	51
10	9.62 865	27	9.67 196	33	0.32 804	9.95 668	5	50
11	892	26	229	33	771	663	6	49
12	918	27	262	33	738	657	6	48
13	945	27	295	32	705	651	6	47
14	972	27	327	33	673	645	6	46
15	999	27	360	33	640	639	6	45
16	9.63 026	26	393	33	607	633	6	44
17	052	27	426	32	574	627	6	43
18	079	27	458	33	542	621	6	42
19	106	27	491	33	509	615	6	41
20	9.63 133	26	9.67 524	32	0.32 476	9.95 609	6	40
21	159	27	556	33	444	603	6	39
22	186	27	589	33	411	597	6	38
23	213	26	622	32	378	591	6	37
24	239	27	654	33	346	585	6	36
25	266	26	687	32	313	579	6	35
26	292	27	719	33	281	573	6	34
27	319	26	752	33	248	567	6	33
28	345	27	785	32	215	561	6	32
29	372	26	817	33	183	555	6	31
30	9.63 398	27	9.67 850	32	0.32 150	9.95 549	6	30
31	425	26	882	33	118	543	6	29
32	451	27	915	32	085	537	6	28
33	478	26	947	33	053	531	6	27
34	504	27	980	32	020	525	6	26
35	531	26	9.68 012	32	0.31 988	519	6	25
36	557	26	044	33	956	513	6	24
37	583	27	077	32	923	507	7	23
38	610	26	109	33	891	500	6	22
39	636	26	142	32	858	494	6	21
40	9.63 662	27	9.68 174	32	0.31 826	9.95 488	6	20
41	689	26	206	33	794	482	6	19
42	715	26	239	32	761	476	6	18
43	741	26	271	32	729	470	6	17
44	767	27	303	33	697	464	6	16
45	794	26	336	32	664	458	6	15
46	820	26	368	32	632	452	6	14
47	846	26	400	32	600	446	6	13
48	872	26	432	33	568	440	6	12
49	898	26	465	32	535	434	7	11
50	9.63 924	26	9.68 497	32	0.31 503	9.95 427	6	10
51	950	26	529	32	471	421	6	9
52	976	26	561	32	439	415	6	8
53	9.64 002	26	593	33	407	409	6	7
54	028	26	626	32	374	403	6	6
55	054	26	658	32	342	397	6	5
56	080	26	690	32	310	391	7	4
57	106	26	722	32	278	384	6	3
58	132	26	754	32	246	378	6	2
59	158	26	786	32	214	372	6	1
60	9.64 184		9.68 818		0.31 182	9.95 366		0
′	L. Cos.	d.	L. Cotg.	c.d.	L. Tang.	L. Sin.	d.	′

P. P.

1′	33	32
1″	0.6	0.5
2″	1.1	1.1
3″	1.7	1.6
4″	2.2	2.1
5″	2.8	2.7
6″	3.3	3.2
7″	3.9	3.7
8″	4.4	4.3
9″	5.0	4.8

1′	27
1″	0.5
2″	0.9
3″	1.4
4″	1.8
5″	2.3
6″	2.7
7″	3.2
8″	3.6
9″	4.1

1′	26
1″	0.4
2″	0.9
3″	1.3
4″	1.7
5″	2.2
6″	2.6
7″	3.0
8″	3.5
9″	3.9

1′	5
1″	0.08
2″	0.17
3″	0.25
4″	0.33
5″	0.42
6″	0.50
7″	0.58
8″	0.67
9″	0.75

1′	6	7
1″	0.10	0.12
2″	0.20	0.23
3″	0.30	0.35
4″	0.40	0.47
5″	0.50	0.58
6″	0.60	0.70
7″	0.70	0.82
8″	0.80	0.93
9″	0.90	1.05

′	L. Sin.	d.	L. Tang.	c.d.	L. Cotg.	L. Cos.	d.	′
0	9.64 184	26	9.68 818	32	0.31 182	9.95 366	6	60
1	210	26	850	32	150	360	6	59
2	236	26	882	32	118	354	6	58
3	262	26	914	32	086	348	7	57
4	288	25	946	32	054	341	6	56
5	313	26	978	32	022	335	6	55
6	339	26	9.69 010	32	0.30 990	329	6	54
7	365	26	042	32	958	323	6	53
8	391	26	074	32	926	317	7	52
9	417	25	106	32	894	310	6	51
10	9.64 442	26	9.69 138	32	0.30 862	9.95 304	6	50
11	468	26	170	32	830	298	6	49
12	494	25	202	32	798	292	6	48
13	519	26	234	32	766	286	7	47
14	545̄	26	266	32	734	279	6	46
15	571	25	298	31	702	273	6	45
16	596	26	329	32	671	267	6	44
17	622	25	361	32	639	261	7	43
18	647	26	393	32	607	254	6	42
19	673	25	425̄	32	575	248	6	41
20	9 64 698	26	9.69 457	31	0.30 543	9.95 242	6	40
21	724	25	488	32	512	236	7	39
22	749	26	520	32	480	229	6	38
23	775̄	25	552	32	448	223	6	37
24	800	26	584	31	416̄	217	6	36
25	826	25	615	32	385	211	6	35
26	851	26	647	32	353	204	7	34
27	877	25	679	31	321	198	6	33
28	902	25	710	32	290	192	7	32
29	927	26	742	32	258	185	6	31
30	9.64 953	25	9.69 774	31	0.30 226	9.95 179	6	30
31	978	25	805	32	195̄	173	6	29
32	9.65 003	26	837	31	163	167	7	28
33	029	25	868	32	132	160	6	27
34	054	25	900	32	100	154	6	26
35	079	25	932	31	068	148	7	25
36	104	26	963	32	037	141	6	24
37	130	25	995̄	31	005	135̄	6	23
38	155̄	25	9.70 026	32	0.29 974	129	7	22
39	180	25	058	31	942	122	6	21
40	9.65 205	25	9.70 089	32	0.29 911	9.95 116	6	20
41	230	25	121	31	879	110	7	19
42	255	26	152	32	848	103	6	18
43	281	25	184	31	816	097	7	17
44	306	25	215	32	785̄	090	6	16
45	331	25	247	31	753	084	6	15
46	356	25	278	31	722	078	7	14
47	381	25	309	32	691	071̄	6	13
48	406	25	341	31	659	065̄	6	12
49	431	25	372	32	628	059	7	11
50	9.65 456	25	9.70 404	31	0.29 596	9.95 052	6	10
51	481	25	435̄	31	565	046	7	9
52	506	25	466	32	534	039	6	8
53	531	25	498	31	502	033	6	7
54	556	24	529	31	471	027	7	6
55	580	25	560	32	440	020	6	5
56	605	25	592	31	408	014	7	4
57	630	25	623	31	377	007	6	3
58	655	25	654	31	346	001	6	2
59	680	25	685	32	315	9.94 995	7	1
60	9.65 705̄		9.70 717		0.29 283	9.94 988		0
′	L. Cos.	d.	L. Cotg.	c.d.	L. Tang.	L. Sin.	d.	′

P. P.

	32	31
1′		
1″	0.5	0.5
2″	1.1	1.0
3″	1.6	1.6
4″	2.1	2.1
5″	2.7	2.6
6″	3.2	3.1
7″	3.7	3.6
8″	4.3	4.1
9″	4.8	4.7

	26
1′	
1″	0.4
2″	0.9
3″	1.3
4″	1.7
5″	2.2
6″	2.6
7″	3.0
8″	3.5
9″	3.9

	25
1′	
1″	0.4
2″	0.8
3″	1.3
4″	1.7
5″	2.1
6″	2.5
7″	2.9
8″	3.3
9″	3.8

	24
1′	
1″	0.4
2″	0.8
3″	1.2
4″	1.6
5″	2.0
6″	2.4
7″	2.8
8″	3.2
9″	3.6

	6	7
1′		
1″	0.10	0.12
2″	0.20	0.23
3″	0.30	0.35
4″	0.40	0.47
5″	0.50	0.58
6″	0.60	0.70
7″	0.70	0.82
8″	0.80	0.93
9″	0.90	1.05

'	L. Sin.	d.	L. Tang.	c.d.	L. Cotg.	L. Cos.	d.	'
0	9.65 705	24	9.70 717	31	0.29 283	9.94 988	6	60
1	729	25	748	31	252	982	7	59
2	754	25	779	31	221	975	6	58
3	779	25	810	31	190	969	7	57
4	804	24	841	32	159	962	6	56
5	828	25	873	31	127	956	7	55
6	853	25	904	31	096	949	6	54
7	878	24	935	31	065	943	7	53
8	902	25	966	31	034	936	6	52
9	927	25	997	31	003	930	7	51
10	9.65 952	24	9.71 028	31	0.28 972	9.94 923	6	50
11	976	25	059	31	941	917	6	49
12	9.66 001	24	090	31	910	911	7	48
13	025	25	121	32	879	904	6	47
14	050	25	153	31	847	898	7	46
15	075	24	184	31	816	891	6	45
16	099	25	215	31	785	885	7	44
17	124	24	246	31	754	878	7	43
18	148	25	277	31	723	871	7	42
19	173	24	308	31	692	865	7	41
20	9.66 197	24	9.71 339	31	0.28 661	9.94 858	6	40
21	221	25	370	31	630	852	7	39
22	246	24	401	30	599	845	6	38
23	270	25	431	31	569	839	7	37
24	295	24	462	31	538	832	6	36
25	319	24	493	31	507	826	7	35
26	343	25	524	31	476	819	6	34
27	368	24	555	31	445	813	7	33
28	392	24	586	31	414	806	7	32
29	416	25	617	31	383	799	6	31
30	9.66 441	24	9.71 648	31	0.28 352	9.94 793	7	30
31	465	24	679	30	321	786	6	29
32	489	24	709	31	291	780	7	28
33	513	24	740	31	260	773	6	27
34	537	25	771	31	229	767	7	26
35	562	24	802	31	198	760	7	25
36	586	24	833	30	167	753	6	24
37	610	24	863	31	137	747	7	23
38	634	24	894	31	106	740	6	22
39	658	24	925	30	075	734	7	21
40	9.66 682	24	9.71 955	31	0.28 045	9.94 727	7	20
41	706	25	986	31	014	720	6	19
42	731	24	9.72 017	31	0.27 983	714	7	18
43	755	24	048	30	952	707	7	17
44	779	24	078	31	922	700	6	16
45	803	24	109	31	891	694	7	15
46	827	24	140	30	860	687	7	14
47	851	24	170	31	830	680	6	13
48	875	24	201	30	799	674	7	12
49	899	23	231	31	769	667	7	11
50	9.66 922	24	9.72 262	31	0.27 738	9.94 660	6	10
51	946	24	293	30	707	654	7	9
52	970	24	323	31	677	647	7	8
53	994	24	354	30	646	640	6	7
54	9.67 018	24	384	31	616	634	7	6
55	042	24	415	30	585	627	7	5
56	066	24	445	31	555	620	6	4
57	090	23	476	30	524	614	7	3
58	113	24	506	31	494	607	7	2
59	137	24	537	30	463	600	7	1
60	9.67 161		9.72 567		0.27 433	9.94 593		0
'	L. Cos.	d.	L. Cotg.	c.d.	L. Tang.	L. Sin.	d.	'

P. P.

	32	31
1'		
1"	0.5	0.5
2"	1.1	1.0
3"	1.6	1.6
4"	2.1	2.1
5"	2.7	2.6
6"	3.2	3.1
7"	3.7	3.6
8"	4.3	4.1
9"	4.8	4.7

	30	25
1'		
1"	0.5	0.4
2"	1.0	0.8
3"	1.5	1.3
4"	2.0	1.7
5"	2.5	2.1
6"	3.0	2.5
7"	3.5	2.9
8"	4.0	3.3
9"	4.5	3.8

	24
1'	
1"	0.4
2"	0.8
3"	1.2
4"	1.6
5"	2.0
6"	2.4
7"	2.8
8"	3.2
9"	3.6

	23
1'	
1"	0.4
2"	0.8
3"	1.2
4"	1.5
5"	1.9
6"	2.3
7"	2.7
8"	3.1
9"	3.5

	6	7
1'		
1"	0.10	0.12
2"	0.20	0.23
3"	0.30	0.35
4"	0.40	0.47
5"	0.50	0.58
6"	0.60	0.70
7"	0.70	0.82
8"	0.80	0.93
9"	0.90	1.05

'	L. Sin.	d.	L. Tang.	c.d.	L. Cotg.	L. Cos.	d.	'
0	9.67 161	24	9.72 567	31	0.27 433	9.94 593	6	60
1	185̄	23	598	30	402	587	7	59
2	208	24	628	31	372	580	7	58
3	232	24	659	30	341	573	6	57
4	256	24	689	31	311	567	7	56
5	280	23	720	30	280	560	7	55
6	303	24	750	30	250	553	7	54
7	327	23	780	31	220	546	6	53
8	350	24	811	30	189	540	7	52
9	374	24	841	31	159	533	7	51
10	9.67 398	23	9.72 872	30	0.27 128	9.94 526	7	50
11	421	24	902	30	098	519	6	49
12	445̄	23	932	31	068	513	7	48
13	468	24	963	30	037	506	7	47
14	492	23	993	30	007	499	7	46
15	515	24	9.73 023	31	0.26 977	492	7	45
16	539	23	054	30	946	485	6	44
17	562	24	084	30	916	479	7	43
18	586	23	114	30	886	472	7	42
19	609	24	144	31	856	465	7	41
20	9.67 633	23	9.73 175̄	30	0.26 825	9.94 458	7	40
21	656	24	205̄	30	795	451	6	39
22	680	23	235̄	30	765̄	445̄	7	38
23	703	23	265̄	30	735̄	438	7	37
24	726	24	295̄	31	705̄	431	7	36
25	750	23	326	30	674	424	7	35
26	773	23	356	30	644	417	7	34
27	796	24	386	30	614	410	6	33
28	820	23	416	30	584	404	7	32
29	843	23	446	30	554	397	7	31
30	9.67 866	24	9.73 476	31	0.26 524	9.94 390	7	30
31	890	23	507	30	493	383	7	29
32	913	23	537	30	463	376	7	28
33	936	23	567	30	433	369	7	27
34	959	23	597	30	403	362	7	26
35	982	24	627	30	373	355	6	25
36	9.68 006	23	657	30	343	349	7	24
37	029	23	687	30	313	342	7	23
38	052	23	717	30	283	335̄	7	22
39	075	23	747	30	253	328	7	21
40	9.68 098	23	9.73 777	30	0.26 223	9.94 321	7	20
41	121	23	807	30	193	314	7	19
42	144	23	837	30	163	307	7	18
43	167	23	867	30	133	300	7	17
44	190	23	897	30	103	293	7	16
45	213	24	927	30	073	286	6	15
46	237	23	957	30	043	279	7	14
47	260	23	987	30	013	273	7	13
48	283	22	9.74 017	30	0.25 983	266	7	12
49	305	23	047	30	953	259	7	11
50	9.68 328	23	9.74 077	30	0.25 923	9.94 252	7	10
51	351	23	107	30	893	245̄	7	9
52	374	23	137	29	863	238	7	8
53	397	23	166	30	834	231	7	7
54	420	23	196	30	804	224	7	6
55	443	23	226	30	774	217	7	5
56	466	23	256	30	744	210	7	4
57	489	23	286	30	714	203	7	3
58	512	22	316	29	684	196	7	2
59	534	23	345	30	655̄	189	7	1
60	9.68 557		9.74 375		0.25 625	9.94 182		0
'	L. Cos.	d.	L. Cotg.	c.d.	L. Tang.	L. Sin.	d.	'

P. P.

1'	31	30
1"	0.5	0.5
2"	1.0	1.0
3"	1.6	1.5
4"	2.1	2.0
5"	2.6	2.5
6"	3.1	3.0
7"	3.6	3.5
8"	4.1	4.0
9"	4.7	4.5

1'	29	24
1"	0.5	0.4
2"	1.0	0.8
3"	1.5	1.2
4"	1.9	1.6
5"	2.4	2.0
6"	2.9	2.4
7"	3.4	2.8
8"	3.9	3.2
9"	4.4	3.6

1'	23
1"	0.4
2"	0.8
3"	1.2
4"	1.5
5"	1.9
6"	2.3
7"	2.7
8"	3.1
9"	3.5

1'	22
1"	0.4
2"	0.7
3"	1.1
4"	1.5
5"	1.8
6"	2.2
7"	2.6
8"	2.9
9"	3.3

1'	6	7
1"	0.10	0.12
2"	0.20	0.23
3"	0.30	0.35
4"	0.40	0.47
5"	0.50	0.58
6"	0.60	0.70
7"	0.70	0.82
8"	0.80	0.93
9"	0.90	1.05

'	L. Sin.	d.	L. Tang.	c.d.	L. Cotg.	L. Cos.	d.	'	P.P.		
0	9.68 557	23	9.74 375	30	0.25 625	9.94 182	7	60	1'	30	
1	580	23	405	30	595	175	7	59	1"	0.5	
2	603	22	435	30	565	168	7	58	2"	1.0	
3	625	23	465	29	535	161	7	57	3"	1.5	
4	648	23	494	30	506	154	7	56	4"	2.0	
5	671	23	524	30	476	147	7	55	5"	2.5	
6	694	22	554	29	446	140	7	54	6"	3.0	
7	716	23	583	30	417	133	7	53	7"	3.5	
8	739	23	613	30	387	126	7	52	8"	4.0	
9	762	22	643	30	357	119	7	51	9"	4.5	
10	9.68 784	23	9.74 673	29	0.25 327	9.94 112	7	50			
11	807	22	702	30	298	105	7	49			
12	829	23	732	30	268	098	8	48	1'	29	
13	852	23	762	29	238	090	7	47	1"	0.5	
14	875	22	791	30	209	083	7	46	2"	1.0	
15	897	23	821	30	179	076	7	45	3"	1.5	
16	920	22	851	29	149	069	7	44	4"	1.9	
17	942	23	880	30	120	062	7	43	5"	2.4	
18	965	22	910	29	090	055	7	42	6"	2.9	
19	987	23	939	30	061	048	7	41	7"	3.4	
20	9.69 010	22	9.74 969	29	0.25 031	9.94 041	7	40	8"	3.9	
21	032	23	998	30	002	034	7	39	9"	4.4	
22	055	22	9.75 028	30	0.24 972	027	7	38			
23	077	23	058	29	942	020	8	37			
24	100	22	087	30	913	012	7	36			
25	122	22	117	29	883	005	7	35	1'	23	
26	144	23	146	30	854	9.93 998	7	34	1"	0.4	
27	167	22	176	29	824	991	7	33	2"	0.8	
28	189	23	205	30	795	984	7	32	3"	1.2	
29	212	22	235	29	765	977	7	31	4"	1.5	
30	9.69 234	22	9.75 264	30	0.24 736	9.93 970	7	30	5"	1.9	
31	256	23	294	29	706	963	8	29	6"	2.3	
32	279	22	323	30	677	955	7	28	7"	2.7	
33	301	22	353	29	647	948	7	27	8"	3.1	
34	323	22	382	30	618	941	7	26	9"	3.5	
35	345	23	411	30	589	934	7	25			
36	368	22	441	29	559	927	7	24			
37	390	22	470	30	530	920	8	23	1'	22	
38	412	22	500	30	500	912	7	22	1"	0.4	
39	434	22	529	29	471	905	7	21	2"	0.7	
40	9.69 456	23	9.75 558	30	0.24 442	9.93 898	7	20	3"	1.1	
41	479	22	588	29	412	891	7	19	4"	1.5	
42	501	22	617	30	383	884	8	18	5"	1.8	
43	523	22	647	29	353	876	7	17	6"	2.2	
44	545	22	676	29	324	869	7	16	7"	2.6	
45	567	22	705	30	295	862	7	15	8"	2.9	
46	589	22	735	29	265	855	8	14	9"	3.3	
47	611	22	764	29	236	847	7	13			
48	633	22	793	29	207	840	7	12			
49	655	22	822	30	178	833	7	11	1'	7	8
50	9.69 677	22	9.75 852	29	0.24 148	9.93 826	7	10	1"	0.12	0.13
51	699	22	881	29	119	819	8	9	2"	0.23	0.27
52	721	22	910	29	090	811	7	8	3"	0.35	0.40
53	743	22	939	29	061	804	7	7	4"	0.47	0.53
54	765	22	969	29	031	797	8	6	5"	0.58	0.67
55	787	22	998	29	002	789	7	5	6"	0.70	0.80
56	809	22	9.76 027	29	0.23 973	782	7	4	7"	0.82	0.93
57	831	22	056	29	944	775	7	3	8"	0.93	1.07
58	853	22	086	29	914	768	8	2	9"	1.05	1.20
59	875	22	115	29	885	760	7	1			
60	9.69 897		9.76 144		0.23 856	9.93 753		0			
'	L. Cos.	d.	L. Cotg.	c. d.	L. Tang.	L. Sin.	d.	'			

′	L. Sin.	d.	L. Tang.	c.d.	L. Cotg.	L. Cos.	d.	′	P. P.		
0	9.69 897	22	9.76 144	29	0.23 856	9.93 753	7	60	1′	30	29
1	919	22	173	29	827	746	8	59	1″	0.5	0.5
2	941	22	202	29	798	738	7	58	2″	1.0	1.0
3	963	21	231	30	769	731	7	57	3″	1.5	1.5
4	984	22	261	29	739	724	7	56	4″	2.0	1.9
5	9.70 006	22	290	29	710	717	7	55	5″	2.5	2.4
6	028	22	319	29	681	709	7	54	6″	3.0	2.9
7	050	22	348	29	652	702	7	53	7″	3.5	3.4
8	072	21	377	29	623	695	8	52	8″	4.0	3.9
9	093	22	406	29	594	687	7	51	9″	4.5	4.4
10	9.70 115	22	9.76 435	29	0.23 565	9.93 680	7	50			
11	137	22	464	29	536	673	8	49			
12	159	21	493	29	507	665	7	48	1′	28	
13	180	22	522	29	478	658	8	47	1″	0.5	
14	202	22	551	29	449	650	7	46	2″	0.9	
15	224	21	580	29	420	643	7	45	3″	1.4	
16	245	22	609	30	391	636	8	44	4″	1.9	
17	267	21	639	29	361	628	7	43	5″	2.3	
18	288	22	668	29	332	621	7	42	6″	2.8	
19	310	22	697	28	303	614	8	41	7″	3.3	
20	9.70 332	21	9.76 725	29	0.23 275	9.93 606	7	40	8″	3.7	
21	353	22	754	29	246	599	8	39	9″	4.2	
22	375	21	783	29	217	591	7	38			
23	396	22	812	29	188	584	7	37			
24	418	21	841	29	159	577	8	36	1′	22	
25	439	22	870	29	130	569	7	35	1″	0.4	
26	461	21	899	29	101	562	8	34	2″	0.7	
27	482	22	928	29	072	554	7	33	3″	1.1	
28	504	21	957	29	043	547	8	32	4″	1.5	
29	525	22	986	29	014	539	7	31	5″	1.8	
30	9.70 547	21	9.77 015	29	0.22 985	9.93 532	7	30	6″	2.2	
31	568	22	044	29	956	525	8	29	7″	2.6	
32	590	21	073	28	927	517	7	28	8″	2.9	
33	611	22	101	29	899	510	8	27	9″	3.3	
34	633	21	130	29	870	502	7	26			
35	654	21	159	29	841	495	8	25			
36	675	22	188	29	812	487	7	24	1′	21	
37	697	21	217	29	783	480	8	23	1″	0.4	
38	718	21	246	28	754	472	7	22	2″	0.7	
39	739	22	274	29	726	465	8	21	3″	1.1	
40	9.70 761	21	9.77 303	29	0.22 697	9.93 457	7	20	4″	1.4	
41	782	21	332	29	668	450	8	19	5″	1.8	
42	803	21	361	29	639	442	7	18	6″	2.1	
43	824	22	390	28	610	435	8	17	7″	2.5	
44	846	21	418	29	582	427	7	16	8″	2.8	
45	867	21	447	29	553	420	8	15	9″	3.2	
46	888	21	476	29	524	412	7	14			
47	909	22	505	28	495	405	8	13			
48	931	21	533	29	467	397	7	12			
49	952	21	562	29	438	390	8	11	1′	7	8
50	9.70 973	21	9.77 591	28	0.22 409	9.93 382	7	10	1″	0.12	0.13
51	994	21	619	29	381	375	8	9	2″	0.23	0.27
52	9.71 015	21	648	29	352	367	7	8	3″	0.35	0.40
53	036	22	677	29	323	360	8	7	4″	0.47	0.53
54	058	21	706	28	294	352	8	6	5″	0.58	0.67
55	079	21	734	29	266	344	5	5	6″	0.70	0.80
56	100	21	763	28	237	337	7	4	7″	0.82	0.93
57	121	21	791	29	209	329	8	3	8″	0.93	1.07
58	142	21	820	29	180	322	7	2	9″	1.05	1.20
59	163	21	849	28	151	314	8	1			
60	9.71 184		9.77 877		0.22 123	9.93 307	7	0			
′	L. Cos.	d.	L. Cotg.	c.d.	L. Tang.	L. Sin.	d.	′			

'	L. Sin.	d.	L. Tang.	c.d.	L. Cotg.	L. Cos.	d.	'
0	9.71 184	21	9.77 877	29	0.22 123	9.93 307	8	60
1	205	21	906	29	094	299	8	59
2	226	21	935	28	065	291	7	58
3	247	21	963	29	037	284	8	57
4	268	21	992	28	008	276	7	56
5	289	21	9.78 020	29	0.21 980	269	8	55
6	310	21	049	28	951	261	8	54
7	331	21	077	29	923	253	7	53
8	352	21	106	29	894	246	8	52
9	373	20	135	28	865	238	8	51
10	9.71 393	21	9.78 163	29	0.21 837	9.93 230	7	50
11	414	21	192	28	808	223	8	49
12	435	21	220	29	780	215	8	48
13	456	21	249	28	751	207	7	47
14	477	21	277	29	723	200	8	46
15	498	21	306	28	694	192	8	45
16	519	20	334	29	666	184	7	44
17	539	21	363	28	637	177	8	43
18	560	21	391	28	609	169	8	42
19	581	21	419	29	581	161	7	41
20	9.71 602	20	9.78 448	28	0.21 552	9.93 154	8	40
21	622	21	476	29	524	146	8	39
22	643	21	505	28	495	138	7	38
23	664	21	533	29	467	131	8	37
24	685	20	562	28	438	123	8	36
25	705	21	590	28	410	115	7	35
26	726	21	618	29	382	108	8	34
27	747	20	647	28	353	100	8	33
28	767	21	675	29	325	092	8	32
29	788	21	704	28	296	084	7	31
30	9.71 809	20	9.78 732	28	0.21 268	9.93 077	8	30
31	829	21	760	29	240	069	8	29
32	850	20	789	28	211	061	8	28
33	870	21	817	28	183	053	7	27
34	891	20	845	29	155	046	8	26
35	911	21	874	28	126	038	8	25
36	932	20	902	28	098	030	8	24
37	952	21	930	29	070	022	8	23
38	973	21	959	28	041	014	7	22
39	994	20	987	28	013	007	8	21
40	9.72 014	20	9.79 015	28	0.20 985	9.92 999	8	20
41	034	21	043	29	957	991	8	19
42	055	20	072	28	928	983	7	18
43	075	21	100	28	900	976	8	17
44	096	20	128	28	872	968	8	16
45	116	21	156	29	844	960	8	15
46	137	20	185	28	815	952	8	14
47	157	20	213	28	787	944	8	13
48	177	21	241	28	759	936	7	12
49	198	20	269	28	731	929	8	11
50	9.72 218	20	9.79 297	29	0.20 703	9.92 921	8	10
51	238	21	326	28	674	913	8	9
52	259	20	354	28	646	905	8	8
53	279	20	382	28	618	897	8	7
54	299	21	410	28	590	889	8	6
55	320	20	438	28	562	881	7	5
56	340	20	466	29	534	874	8	4
57	360	21	495	28	505	866	8	3
58	381	20	523	28	477	858	8	2
59	401	20	551	28	449	850	8	1
60	9.72 421		9.79 579		0.20 421	9.92 842		0
'	L. Cos.	d.	L. Cotg.	c.d.	L. Tang.	L. Sin.	d.	'

P.P.

1'	29
1"	0.5
2"	1.0
3"	1.5
4"	1.9
5"	2.4
6"	2.9
7"	3.4
8"	3.9
9"	4.4

1'	28
1"	0.5
2"	0.9
3"	1.4
4"	1.9
5"	2.3
6"	2.8
7"	3.3
8"	3.7
9"	4.2

1'	21
1"	0.4
2"	0.7
3"	1.1
4"	1.4
5"	1.8
6"	2.1
7"	2.5
8"	2.8
9"	3.2

1'	20
1"	0.3
2"	0.7
3"	1.0
4"	1.3
5"	1.7
6"	2.0
7"	2.3
8"	2.7
9"	3.0

1'	7	8
1"	0.12	0.13
2"	0.23	0.27
3"	0.35	0.40
4"	0.47	0.53
5"	0.58	0.67
6"	0.70	0.80
7"	0.82	0.93
8"	0.93	1.07
9"	1.05	1.20

′	L. Sin.	d.	L. Tang.	c. d.	L. Cotg.	L. Cos.	d.	′
0	9.72 421	20	9.79 579	28	0.20 421	9.92 842	8	60
1	441	20	607	28	393	834	8	59
2	461	21	635	28	365	826	8	58
3	482	20	663	28	337	818	8	57
4	502	20	691	28	309	810	7	56
5	522	20	719	28	281	803	8	55
6	542	20	747	29	253	795	8	54
7	562	20	776	28	224	787	8	53
8	582	20	804	28	196	779	8	52
9	602	20	832	28	168	771	8	51
10	9.72 622	21	9.79 860	28	0.20 140	9.92 763	8	50
11	643	20	888	28	112	755	8	49
12	663	20	916	28	084	747	8	48
13	683	20	944	28	056	739	8	47
14	703	20	972	28	028	731	8	46
15	723	20	9.80 000	28	000	723	8	45
16	743	20	028	28	0.19 972	715	8	44
17	763	20	056	28	944	707	8	43
18	783	20	084	28	916	699	8	42
19	803	20	112	28	888	691	8	41
20	9.72 823	20	9.80 140	28	0.19 860	9.92 683	8	40
21	843	20	168	27	832	675	8	39
22	863	20	195	28	805	667	8	38
23	883	19	223	28	777	659	8	37
24	902	20	251	28	749	651	8	36
25	922	20	279	28	721	643	8	35
26	942	20	307	28	693	635	8	34
27	962	20	335	28	665	627	8	33
28	982	20	363	28	637	619	8	32
29	9.73 002	20	391	28	609	611	8	31
30	9.73 022	19	9.80 419	28	0.19 581	9.92 603	8	30
31	041	20	447	27	553	595	8	29
32	061	20	474	28	526	587	8	28
33	081	20	502	28	498	579	8	27
34	101	20	530	28	470	571	8	26
35	121	19	558	28	442	563	8	25
36	140	20	586	28	414	555	8	24
37	160	20	614	28	386	546	9	23
38	180	20	642	27	358	538	8	22
39	200	19	669	28	331	530	8	21
40	9.73 219	20	9.80 697	28	0.19 303	9.92 522	8	20
41	239	20	725	28	275	514	8	19
42	259	19	753	28	247	506	8	18
43	278	20	781	27	219	498	8	17
44	298	20	808	28	192	490	8	16
45	318	19	836	28	164	482	9	15
46	337	20	864	28	136	473	8	14
47	357	20	892	27	108	465	8	13
48	377	19	919	28	081	457	8	12
49	396	20	947	28	053	449	8	11
50	9.73 416	19	9.80 975	28	0.19 025	9.92 441	8	10
51	435	20	9.81 003	27	0.18 997	433	8	9
52	455	19	030	28	970	425	9	8
53	474	20	058	28	942	416	8	7
54	494	19	086	27	914	408	8	6
55	513	20	113	28	887	400	8	5
56	533	19	141	28	859	392	8	4
57	552	20	169	27	831	384	8	3
58	572	19	196	28	804	376	9	2
59	591	20	224	28	776	367	8	1
60	9.73 611		9.81 252		0.18 748	9.92 359		0
′	L. Cos.	d.	L. Cotg.	c. d.	L. Tang.	L. Sin.	d.	′

P. P.

	29	28
1′	29	28
1″	0.5	0.5
2″	1.0	0.9
3″	1.5	1.4
4″	1.9	1.9
5″	2.4	2.3
6″	2.9	2.8
7″	3.4	3.3
8″	3.9	3.7
9″	4.4	4.2

	27	21
1′	27	21
1″	0.5	0.4
2″	0.9	0.7
3″	1.4	1.1
4″	1.8	1.4
5″	2.3	1.8
6″	2.7	2.1
7″	3.2	2.5
8″	3.6	2.8
9″	4.1	3.2

	20	19
1′	20	19
1″	0.3	0.3
2″	0.7	0.6
3″	1.0	1.0
4″	1.3	1.3
5″	1.7	1.6
6″	2.0	1.9
7″	2.3	2.2
8″	2.7	2.5
9″	3.0	2.9

	7
1′	7
1″	0.12
2″	0.23
3″	0.35
4″	0.47
5″	0.58
6″	0.70
7″	0.82
8″	0.93
9″	1.05

	8	9
1′	8	9
1″	0.13	0.15
2″	0.27	0.30
3″	0.40	0.45
4″	0.53	0.60
5″	0.67	0.75
6″	0.80	0.90
7″	0.93	1.05
8″	1.07	1.20
9″	1.20	1.35

'	L. Sin.	d.	L. Tang.	c.d.	L. Cotg.	L. Cos.	d.	'
0	9.73 611	19	9.81 252	27	0.18 748	9.92 359	8	60
1	630	20	279	28	721	351	8	59
2	650	19	307	28	693	343	8	58
3	669	20	335	27	665	335	9	57
4	689	19	362	28	638	326	8	56
5	708	19	390	28	610	318	8	55
6	727	20	418	27	582	310	8	54
7	747	19	445	28	555	302	9	53
8	766	19	473	27	527	293	8	52
9	785	20	500	28	500	285	8	51
10	9.73 805	19	9.81 528	28	0.18 472	9.92 277	8	50
11	824	19	556	27	444	269	9	49
12	843	20	583	28	417	260	8	48
13	863	19	611	27	389	252	8	47
14	882	19	638	28	362	244	9	46
15	901	20	666	27	334	235	8	45
16	921	19	693	28	307	227	8	44
17	940	19	721	27	279	219	8	43
18	959	19	748	28	252	211	9	42
19	978	19	776	27	224	202	8	41
20	9.73 997	20	9.81 803	28	0.18 197	9.92 194	8	40
21	9.74 017	19	831	27	169	186	9	39
22	036	19	858	28	142	177	8	38
23	055	19	886	27	114	169	8	37
24	074	19	913	28	087	161	9	36
25	093	20	941	27	059	152	8	35
26	113	19	968	28	032	144	8	34
27	132	19	996	27	004	136	9	33
28	151	19	9.82 023	28	0.17 977	127	8	32
29	170	19	051	27	949	119	8	31
30	9.74 189	19	9.82 078	28	0.17 922	9.92 111	9	30
31	208	19	106	27	894	102	8	29
32	227	19	133	28	867	094	8	28
33	246	19	161	27	839	086	9	27
34	265	19	188	27	812	077	8	26
35	284	19	215	28	785	069	9	25
36	303	19	243	27	757	060	8	24
37	322	19	270	28	730	052	8	23
38	341	19	298	27	702	044	9	22
39	360	19	325	27	675	035	8	21
40	9.74 379	19	9.82 352	28	0.17 648	9.92 027	9	20
41	398	19	380	27	620	018	8	19
42	417	19	407	28	593	010	8	18
43	436	19	435	27	565	002	8	17
44	455	19	462	27	538	9.91 993	8	16
45	474	19	489	28	511	985	9	15
46	493	19	517	27	483	976	8	14
47	512	19	544	27	456	968	9	13
48	531	18	571	28	429	959	8	12
49	549	19	599	27	401	951	9	11
50	9.74 568	19	9.82 626	27	0.17 374	9.91 942	8	10
51	587	19	653	28	347	934	9	9
52	606	19	681	27	319	925	8	8
53	625	19	708	27	292	917	9	7
54	644	18	735	27	265	908	8	6
55	662	19	762	28	238	900	9	5
56	681	19	790	27	210	891	8	4
57	700	19	817	27	183	883	9	3
58	719	18	844	27	156	874	8	2
59	737	19	871	28	129	866	9	1
60	9.74 756		9.82 899		0.17 101	9.91 857		0

'	L. Cos.	d.	L. Cotg.	c.d.	L. Tang.	L. Sin.	d.	'

P. P.

1'	28	27
1"	0.5	0.5
2"	0.9	0.9
3"	1.4	1.4
4"	1.9	1.8
5"	2.3	2.3
6"	2.8	2.7
7"	3.3	3.2
8"	3.7	3.6
9"	4.2	4.1

1'	20
1"	0.3
2"	0.7
3"	1.0
4"	1.3
5"	1.7
6"	2.0
7"	2.3
8"	2.7
9"	3.0

1'	19
1"	0.3
2"	0.6
3"	1.0
4"	1.3
5"	1.6
6"	1.9
7"	2.2
8"	2.5
9"	2.9

1'	18
1"	0.3
2"	0.6
3"	0.9
4"	1.2
5"	1.5
6"	1.8
7"	2.1
8"	2.4
9"	2.7

1'	8	9
1"	0.13	0.15
2"	0.27	0.30
3"	0.40	0.45
4"	0.53	0.60
5"	0.67	0.75
6"	0.80	0.90
7"	0.93	1.05
8"	1.07	1.20
9"	1.20	1.35

'	L. Sin.	d.	L. Tang.	c.d.	L. Cotg.	L. Cos.	d.	'
0	9.74 756	19	9.82 899	27	0.17 101	9.91 857	8	60
1	775̄	19	926	27	074	849	9	59
2	794	18	953	27	047	840	8	58
3	812	19	980	28	020	832	9	57
4	831	19	9.83 008	27	0.16 992	823	8	56
5	850	18	035̄	27	965	815̄	9	55
6	868	19	062	27	938	806	8	54
7	887	19	089	28	911	798	9	53
8	906	18	117	27	883	789	8	52
9	924	19	144	27	856	781	9	51
10	9.74 943	18	9.83 171	27	0.16 829	9.91 772	9	50
11	961	19	198	27	802̄	763̄	8	49
12	980	19	225	27	775	755̄	9	48
13	999	18	252	28	748	746	8	47
14	9.75 017	19	280	27	720	738	9	46
15	036	18	307	27	693	729	9	45
16	054	19	334	27	666	720	8	44
17	073	18	361	27	639	712	9	43
18	091	19	388	27	612	703	8	42
19	110	18	415	27	585̄	695̄	9	41
20	9.75 128	19	9.83 442	28	0.16 558	9.91 686	9	40
21	147	18	470	27	530	677	8	39
22	165	19	497	27	503	669	9	38
23	184	18	524	27	476	660	9	37
24	202	19	551	27	449	651	8	36
25	221	18	578	27	422	643	9	35
26	239	19	605	27	395̄	634	8	34
27	258	18	632	27	368	625	9	33
28	276	18	659	27	341	617	8	32
29	294	19	686	27	314	608	9	31
30	9.75 313	18	9.83 713	27	0.16 287	9.91 599	9	30
31	331	19	740	28	260	591	9	29
32	350	18	768	27	232	582	9	28
33	368	18	795̄	27	205	573̄	8	27
34	386	19	822	27	178	565̄	9	26
35	405̄	18	849	27	151	556	9	25
36	423	18	876	27	124	547	9	24
37	441	18	903	27	097	538	8	23
38	459	19	930	27	070	530	9	22
39	478	18	957	27	043	521	9	21
40	9.75 496	18	9.83 984	27	0.16 016	9.91 512	9	20
41	514	19	9.84 011	27	0.15 989	504̄	9	19
42	533	18	038	27	962	495̄	9	18
43	551	18	065̄	27	935	486	9	17
44	569	18	092	27	908	477	8	16
45	587	18	119	27	881	469	9	15
46	605	19	146	27	854	460	9	14
47	624	18	173	27	827	451	9	13
48	642	18	200	27	800	442	9	12
49	660	18	227	27	773	433	8	11
50	9.75 678	18	9.84 254	26	0.15 746	9.91 425̄	9	10
51	696	18	280	27	720	416	9	9
52	714	19	307	27	693	407	8	8
53	733	18	334	27	666	398	9	7
54	751	18	361	27	639	389	9	6
55	769	18	388	27	612	381	8	5
56	787	18	415	27	585̄	372	9	4
57	805̄	18	442	27	558	363	9	3
58	823	18	469	27	531	354	9	2
59	841	18	496	27	504	345	9	1
60	9.75 859		9.84 523	27	0.15 477	9.91 336	9	0
'	L. Cos.	d.	L. Cotg.	c.d.	L. Tang.	L. Sin.	d.	'

P. P.

	28	27
1'		
1"	0.5	0.5
2"	0.9	0.9
3"	1.4	1.4
4"	1.9	1.8
5"	2.3	2.3
6"	2.8	2.7
7"	3.3	3.2
8"	3.7	3.6
9"	4.2	4.1

	26
1'	
1"	0.4
2"	0.9
3"	1.3
4"	1.7
5"	2.2
6"	2.6
7"	3.0
8"	3.5
9"	3.9

	19
1'	
1"	0.3
2"	0.6
3"	1.0
4"	1.3
5"	1.6
6"	1.9
7"	2.2
8"	2.5
9"	2.9

	18
1'	
1"	0.3
2"	0.6
3"	0.9
4"	1.2
5"	1.5
6"	1.8
7"	2.1
8"	2.4
9"	2.7

	8	9
1'		
1"	0.13	0.15
2"	0.27	0.30
3"	0.40	0.45
4"	0.53	0.60
5"	0.67	0.75
6"	0.80	0.90
7"	0.93	1.05
8"	1.07	1.20
9"	1.20	1.35

′	L. Sin.	d.	L. Tang.	c. d.	L. Cotg.	L. Cos.	d.	′
0	9.75 859	18	9.84 523	27	0.15 477	9.91 336	8	60
1	877	18	550	26	450	328	9	59
2	895	18	576	27	424	319	9	58
3	913	18	603	27	397	310	9	57
4	931	18	630	27	370	301	9	56
5	949	18	657	27	343	292	9	55
6	967	18	684	27	316	283	9	54
7	985	18	711	27	289	274	8	53
8	9.76 003	18	738	26	262	266	9	52
9	021	18	764	27	236	257	9	51
10	9.76 039	18	9.84 791	27	0.15 209	9.91 248	9	50
11	057	18	818	27	182	239	9	49
12	075	18	845	27	155	230	9	48
13	093	18	872	27	128	221	9	47
14	111	18	899	26	101	212	9	46
15	129	17	925	27	075	203	9	45
16	146	18	952	27	048	194	9	44
17	164	18	979	27	021	185	9	43
18	182	18	9.85 006	27	0.14 994	176	9	42
19	200	18	033	26	967	167	9	41
20	9.76 218	18	9.85 059	27	0.14 941	9.91 158	9	40
21	236	17	086	27	914	149	8	39
22	253	18	113	27	887	141	9	38
23	271	18	140	26	860	132	9	37
24	289	18	166	27	834	123	9	36
25	307	17	193	27	807	114	9	35
26	324	18	220	27	780	105	9	34
27	342	18	247	26	753	096	9	33
28	360	18	273	27	727	087	9	32
29	378	17	300	27	700	078	9	31
30	9.76 395	18	9.85 327	27	0.14 673	9.91 069	9	30
31	413	18	354	26	646	060	9	29
32	431	17	380	27	620	051	9	28
33	448	18	407	27	593	042	9	27
34	466	18	434	26	566	033	10	26
35	484	17	460	27	540	023	9	25
36	501	18	487	27	513	014	9	24
37	519	18	514	26	486	005	9	23
38	537	17	540	27	460	9.90 996	9	22
39	554	18	567	27	433	987	9	21
40	9.76 572	18	9.85 594	26	0.14 406	9.90 978	9	20
41	590	17	620	27	380	969	9	19
42	607	18	647	27	353	960	9	18
43	625	17	674	26	326	951	9	17
44	642	18	700	27	300	942	9	16
45	660	17	727	27	273	933	9	15
46	677	18	754	26	246	924	9	14
47	695	17	780	27	220	915	9	13
48	712	18	807	27	193	906	10	12
49	730	17	834	26	166	896	9	11
50	9.76 747	18	9.85 860	27	0.14 140	9.90 887	9	10
51	765	17	887	26	113	878	9	9
52	782	18	913	27	087	869	9	8
53	800	17	940	27	060	860	9	7
54	817	18	967	26	033	851	9	6
55	835	17	993	27	007	842	10	5
56	852	18	9.86 020	26	0.13 980	832	9	4
57	870	17	046	27	954	823	9	3
58	887	17	073	27	927	814	9	2
59	904	18	100	26	900	805	9	1
60	9.76 922		9.86 126		0.13 874	9.90 796		0
′	L. Cos.	d.	L. Cotg.	c. d.	L. Tang.	L. Sin.	d.	′

P. P.

	27	26
1″	0.5	0.4
2″	0.9	0.9
3″	1.4	1.3
4″	1.8	1.7
5″	2.3	2.2
6″	2.7	2.6
7″	3.2	3.0
8″	3.6	3.5
9″	4.1	3.9

	18
1″	0.3
2″	0.6
3″	0.9
4″	1.2
5″	1.5
6″	1.8
7″	2.1
8″	2.4
9″	2.7

	17
1″	0.3
2″	0.6
3″	0.9
4″	1.1
5″	1.4
6″	1.7
7″	2.0
8″	2.3
9″	2.6

	8
1″	0.13
2″	0.27
3″	0.40
4″	0.53
5″	0.67
6″	0.80
7″	0.93
8″	1.07
9″	1.20

	9	10
1″	0.15	0.17
2″	0.30	0.33
3″	0.45	0.50
4″	0.60	0.67
5″	0.75	0.83
6″	0.90	1.00
7″	1.05	1.17
8″	1.20	1.33
9″	1.35	1.50

'	L. Sin.	d.	L. Tang.	c.d.	L. Cotg.	L. Cos.	d.	'
0	9.76 922	17	9.86 126	27	0.13 874	9.90 796	9	60
1	939	18	153	26	847	787	10	59
2	957	17	179	27	821	777	9	58
3	974	17	206	26	794	768	9	57
4	991	18	232	27	768	759	9	56
5	9.77 009	17	259	26	741	750	9	55
6	026	17	285	27	715̄	741	9	54
7	043	18	312	26	688	731	10	53
8	061	17	338	27	662̲	722	9	52
9	078	17	365	27	635	713	9	51
10	9.77 095	17	9.86 392	26	0.13 608	9.90 704	10	50
11	112	18	418	27	582	694	9	49
12	130	17	445	26	555	685	9	48
13	147	17	471	27	529	676	9	47
14	164	17	498	26	502	667	10	46
15	181	18	524	27	476	657	9	45
16	199	17	551	26	449	648	9	44
17	216	17	577	26	423	639	9	43
18	233	17	603	27	397	630	10	42
19	250	18	630	26	370	620	9	41
20	9.77 268	17	9.86 656	27	0.13 344	9.90 611	9	40
21	285̄	17	683	26	317	602	10	39
22	302	17	709	27	291	592	9	38
23	319	17	736	26	264	583	9	37
24	336	17	762	27	238	574	9	36
25	353	17	789	26	211	565̄	10	35
26	370	17	815	27	185̄	555	9	34
27	387	18	842	26	158	546	9	33
28	405̄	17	868	26	132	537	10	32
29	422	17	894	27	106	527	9	31
30	9.77 439	17	9.86 921	26	0.13 079	9.90 518	9	30
31	456	17	947	27	053	509	10	29
32	473	17	974	26	026	499	9	28
33	490	17	9.87 000	27	000	490	10	27
34	507	17	027	26	0.12 973	480	9	26
35	524	17	053	26	947	471	9	25
36	541	17	079	27	921	462	10	24
37	558	17	106	26	894	452	9	23
38	575	17	132	27	868	443	9	22
39	592	17	158	26	842	434	10	21
40	9.77 609	17	9.87 185	27	0.12 815	9.90 424	9	20
41	626	17	211	26	789	415̄	10	19
42	643	17	238	27	762	405	9	18
43	660	17	264	26	736	396	9	17
44	677	17	290	27	710	386	10	16
45	694	17	317	26	683	377	9	15
46	711	17	343	27	657	368	10	14
47	728	16	369	26	631	358	9	13
48	744	17	396	27	604	349	10	12
49	761	17	422	26	578	339	9	11
50	9.77 778	17	9.87 448	27	0.12 552	9.90 330	10	10
51	795	17	475̄	26	525	320	9	9
52	812	17	501	26	499	311	10	8
53	829	17	527	27	473	301	9	7
54	846	16	554	26	446	292	10	6
55	862	17	580	26	420	282	9	5
56	879	17	606	27	394	273	10	4
57	896	17	633	26	367	263	9	3
58	913	17	659	26	341	254	10	2
59	930	16	685	26	315̄	244	9	1
60	9.77 946		9.87 711		0.12 289	9.90 235		0
'	L. Cos.	d.	L. Cotg.	c.d.	L. Tang.	L. Sin.	d.	'

P. P.

1'	27	26
1"	0.5	0.4
2"	0.9	0.9
3"	1.4	1.3
4"	1.8	1.7
5"	2.3	2.2
6"	2.7	2.6
7"	3.2	3.0
8"	3.6	3.5
9"	4.1	3.9

1'	18
1"	0.3
2"	0.6
3"	0.9
4"	1.2
5"	1.5
6"	1.8
7"	2.1
8"	2.4
9"	2.7

1'	17
1"	0.3
2"	0.6
3"	0.9
4"	1.1
5"	1.4
6"	1.7
7"	2.0
8"	2.3
9"	2.6

1'	16
1"	0.3
2"	0.5
3"	0.8
4"	1.1
5"	1.3
6"	1.6
7"	1.9
8"	2.1
9"	2.4

1'	9	10
1"	0.15	0.2
2"	0.30	0.3
3"	0.45	0.5
4"	0.60	0.7
5"	0.75	0.8
6"	0.90	1.0
7"	1.05	1.2
8"	1.20	1.3
9"	1.35	1.5

′	L. Sin.	d.	L. Tang.	c. d.	L. Cotg.	L. Cos.	d.	′		P. P.	
0	9.77 946	17	9.87 711	27	0.12 289	9.90 235	10	60	1′	27	
1	963	17	738	26	262	225	9	59	1″	0.5	
2	980	17	764	26	236	216	10	58	2″	0.9	
3	997	16	790	27	210	206	9	57	3″	1.4	
4	9.78 013	17	817	26	183	197	10	56	4″	1.8	
5	030	17	843	26	157	187	9	55	5″	2.3	
6	047	16	869	26	131	178	10	54	6″	2.7	
7	063	17	895	27	105̄	168	9	53	7″	3.2	
8	080	17	922	26	078	159	10	52	8″	3.6	
9	097	16	948	26	052	149	10	51	9″	4.1	
10	9.78 113	17	9.87 974	26	0.12 026	9.90 139	9	50			
11	130	17	9.88 000	27	000	130	10	49			
12	147	16	027	26	0.11 973	120	9	48	1′	26	
13	163	17	053	26	947	111	10	47	1″	0.4	
14	180	17	079	26	921	101	10	46	2″	0.9	
15	197	16	105	26	895	091	9	45	3″	1.3	
16	213	17	131	27	869	082	10	44	4″	1.7	
17	230	16	158	26	842	072	9	43	5″	2.2	
18	246	17	184	26	816	063	10	42	6″	2.6	
19	263	17	210	26	790	053	10	41	7″	3.0	
20	9.78 280	16	9.88 236	26	0.11 764	9.90 043	9	40	8″	3.5	
21	296	17	262	27	738	034	10	39	9″	3.9	
22	313	16	289	26	711	024	10	38			
23	329	17	315	26	685	014	9	37			
24	346	16	341	26	659	005̄	10	36	1′	17	
25	362	17	367	26	633	9.89 995	10	35	1″	0.3	
26	379	16	393	27	607	985	9	34	2″	0.6	
27	395	17	420	26	580	976	10	33	3″	0.9	
28	412	16	446	26	554	966	10	32	4″	1.1	
29	428̄	17	472	26	528	956	9	31	5″	1.4	
30	9.78 445	16	9.88 498	26	0.11 502	9.89 947	10	30	6″	1.7	
31	461	17	524	26	476	937	10	29	7″	2.0	
32	478	16	550	27	450	927	9	28	8″	2.3	
33	494	16	577	26	423	918	10	27	9″	2.6	
34	510	17	603	26	397	908	10	26			
35	527	16	629	26	371	898	10	25			
36	543	17	655̄	26	345	888	9	24	1′	16	
37	560	16	681	26	319	879	10	23	1″	0.3	
38	576	16	707	26	293	869	10	22	2″	0.5	
39	592	17	733	26	267	859	10	21	3″	0.8	
40	9.78 609	16	9.88 759	27	0.11 241	9.89 849	9	20	4″	1.1	
41	625	17	786	26	214	840	10	19	5″	1.3	
42	642	16	812	26	188	830	10	18	6″	1.6	
43	658	16	838	26	162	820	10	17	7″	1.9	
44	674	17	864	26	136	810	9	16	8″	2.1	
45	691	16	890	26	110	801	10	15	9″	2.4	
46	707	16	916	26	084	791	10	14			
47	723	16	942	26	058	781	10	13			
48	739	17	968	26	032	771	10	12			
49	756	16	994	26	006	761	9	11	1′	9	10
50	9.78 772	16	9.89 020	26	0.10 980	9.89 752	10	10	1″	0.15	0.2
51	788	17	046	27	954	742	10	9	2″	0.30	0.3
52	805̄	16	073	26	927	732	10	8	3″	0.45	0.5
53	821	16	099	26	901	722	10	7	4″	0.60	0.7
54	837	16	125	26	875	712	10	6	5″	0.75	0.8
55	853	16	151	26	849	702	9	5	6″	0.90	1.0
56	869	17	177	26	823	693	10	4	7″	1.05	1.2
57	886	16	203	26	797	683	10	3	8″	1.20	1.3
58	902	16	229	26	771	673	10	2	9″	1.35	1.5
59	918	16	255̄	26	745	663	10	1			
60	9.78 934		9.89 281		0.10 719	9.89 653		0			
′	L. Cos.	d.	L. Cotg.	c. d.	L. Tang.	L. Sin.	d.	′			

′	L. Sin.	d.	L. Tang.	c. d.	L. Cotg.	L. Cos.	d.	′		P. P.	
0	9.78 934	16	9.89 281	26	0.10 719	9.89 653	10	60	1′	26	25
1	950	17	307	26	693	643	10	59	1″	0.4	0.4
2	967	16	333	26	667	633	9	58	2″	0.9	0.8
3	983	16	359	26	641	624	10	57	3″	1.3	1.3
4	999	16	385	26	61$\overline{5}$	614	10	56	4″	1.7	1.7
5	9.79 015	16	411	26	589	604	10	55	5″	2.2	2.1
6	031	16	437	26	563	594	10	54	6″	2.6	2.5
7	047	16	463	26	537	584	10	53	7″	3.0	2.9
8	063	16	489	26	511	574	10	52	8″	3.5	3.3
9	079	16	515	26	48$\overline{5}$	564	10	51	9″	3.9	3.8
10	9.79 095	16	9.89 541	26	0.10 459	9.89 554	10	50			
11	111	17	567	26	433	544	10	49			
12	128	16	593	26	407	534	10	48	1′	17	16
13	144	16	619	26	381	524	10	47	1″	0.3	0.3
14	160	16	645	26	35$\overline{5}$	514	10	46	2″	0.6	0.5
15	176	16	671	26	329	504	9	45	3″	0.9	0.8
16	192	16	697	26	303	49$\overline{5}$	10	44	4″	1.1	1.1
17	208	16	723	26	277	48$\overline{5}$	10	43	5″	1.4	1.3
18	224	16	749	26	251	47$\overline{5}$	10	42	6″	1.7	1.6
19	240	16	775	26	22$\overline{5}$	46$\overline{5}$	10	41	7″	2.0	1.9
20	9.79 256	16	9.89 801	26	0.10 199	9.89 455	10	40	8″	2.3	2.1
21	272	16	827	26	173	445	10	39	9″	2.6	2.4
22	288	16	853	26	147	43$\overline{5}$	10	38			
23	304	15	879	26	121	42$\overline{5}$	10	37			
24	319	16	90$\overline{5}$	26	095	41$\overline{5}$	10	36	1′	15	
25	335	16	931	26	069	405	9	35	1″	0.3	
26	351	16	957	26	043	39$\overline{5}$	10	34	2″	0.5	
27	367	16	983	26	017	38$\overline{5}$	10	33	3″	0.8	
28	383	16	9.90 009	26	0.09 991	37$\overline{5}$	11	32	4″	1.0	
29	399	16	03$\overline{5}$	26	965	364	10	31	5″	1.3	
30	9.79 41$\overline{5}$	16	9.90 061	25	0.09 939	9.89 354	10	30	6″	1.5	
31	431	16	086	26	914	344	10	29	7″	1.8	
32	447	16	112	26	888	334	10	28	8″	2.0	
33	463	15	138	26	862	324	10	27	9″	2.3	
34	478	16	164	26	836	314	10	26			
35	494	16	190	26	810	304	10	25			
36	510	16	216	26	784	294	10	24			
37	526	16	242	26	758	284	10	23	1′	9	
38	542	16	268	26	732	274	10	22	1″	0.15	
39	558	15	294	26	706	264	10	21	2″	0.30	
40	9.79 573	16	9.90 320	26	0.09 680	9.89 254	10	20	3″	0.45	
41	589	16	346	25	654	244	11	19	4″	0.60	
42	60$\overline{5}$	16	371	26	629	233	10	18	5″	0.75	
43	621	15	397	26	603	223	10	17	6″	0.90	
44	636	16	423	26	577	213	10	16	7″	1.05	
45	652	16	449	26	551	203	10	15	8″	1.20	
46	668	16	47$\overline{5}$	26	525	193	10	14	9″	1.35	
47	684	15	501	26	499	183	10	13			
48	699	16	527	26	473	173	11	12			
49	715	16	553	25	447	162	10	11	1′	10	11
50	9.79 731	15	9.90 578	26	0.09 422	9.89 152	10	10	1″	0.2	0.2
51	746	16	604	26	396	142	10	9	2″	0.3	0.4
52	762	16	630	26	370	132	10	8	3″	0.5	0.6
53	778	15	656	26	344	122	10	7	4″	0.7	0.7
54	793	16	682	26	318	112	11	6	5″	0.8	0.9
55	809	16	708	26	292	101	10	5	6″	1.0	1.1
56	82$\overline{5}$	15	734	25	266	091	10	4	7″	1.2	1.3
57	840	16	759	26	241	081	10	3	8″	1.3	1.5
58	856	16	785	26	21$\overline{5}$	071	11	2	9″	1.5	1.7
59	872	15	811	26	189	060	10	1			
60	9.79 887		9.90 837		0.09 163	9.89 050		0			
′	L. Cos.	d.	L. Cotg.	c. d.	L. Tang.	L. Sin.	d.	′			

'	L. Sin.	d.	L. Tang.	c.d.	L. Cotg.	L. Cos.	d.	'
0	9.79 887	16	9.90 837	26	0.09 163	9.89 050	10	60
1	903	15	863	26	137	040	10	59
2	918	16	889	25	111	030	10	58
3	934	16	914	26	086	020	10	57
4	950	15	940	26	060	009	11	56
5	965	16	966	26	034	9.88 999	10	55
6	981	15	992	26	008	989	10	54
7	996	16	9.91 018	25	0.08 982	978	11	53
8	9.80 012	15	043	26	957	968	10	52
9	027	16	069	26	931	958	10	51
10	9.80 043	15	9.91 095	26	0.08 905	9.88 948	10	50
11	058	16	121	26	879	937	11	49
12	074	15	147	25	853	927	10	48
13	089	16	172	26	828	917	10	47
14	105	15	198	26	802	906	11	46
15	120	16	224	26	776	896	10	45
16	136	15	250	26	750	886	10	44
17	151	15	276	25	724	875	11	43
18	166	16	301	26	699	865	10	42
19	182	15	327	26	673	855	10	41
20	9.80 197	16	9.91 353	26	0.08 647	9.88 844	11	40
21	213	15	379	25	621	834	10	39
22	228	16	404	26	596	824	10	38
23	244	15	430	26	570	813	11	37
24	259	15	456	26	544	803	10	36
25	274	16	482	25	518	793	10	35
26	290	15	507	26	493	782	11	34
27	305	15	533	26	467	772	10	33
28	320	16	559	26	441	761	11	32
29	336	15	585	25	415	751	10	31
30	9.80 351	15	9.91 610	26	0.08 390	9.88 741	10	30
31	366	16	636	26	364	730	11	29
32	382	15	662	26	338	720	10	28
33	397	15	688	25	312	709	11	27
34	412	16	713	26	287	699	10	26
35	428	15	739	26	261	688	11	25
36	443	15	765	26	235	678	10	24
37	458	15	791	25	209	668	10	23
38	473	16	816	26	184	657	11	22
39	489	15	842	26	158	647	10	21
40	9.80 504	15	9.91 868	25	0.08 132	9.88 636	11	20
41	519	15	893	26	107	626	10	19
42	534	16	919	26	081	615	11	18
43	550	15	945	26	055	605	10	17
44	565	15	971	25	029	594	11	16
45	580	15	996	26	004	584	10	15
46	595	15	9.92 022	26	0.07 978	573	11	14
47	610	15	048	25	952	563	10	13
48	625	16	073	26	927	552	11	12
49	641	15	099	26	901	542	10	11
50	9.80 656	15	9.92 125	25	0.07 875	9.88 531	11	10
51	671	15	150	26	850	521	10	9
52	686	15	176	26	824	510	11	8
53	701	15	202	25	798	499	11	7
54	716	15	227	26	773	489	10	6
55	731	15	253	26	747	478	11	5
56	746	16	279	25	721	468	10	4
57	762	15	304	26	696	457	11	3
58	777	15	330	26	670	447	10	2
59	792	15	356	25	644	436	11	1
60	9.80 807		9.92 381		0.07 619	9.88 425		0
'	L. Cos.	d.	L. Cotg.	c.d.	L. Tang.	L. Sin.	d.	'

P. P.

1'	26
1"	0.4
2"	0.9
3"	1.3
4"	1.7
5"	2.2
6"	2.6
7"	3.0
8"	3.5
9"	3.9

1'	25
1"	0.4
2"	0.8
3"	1.3
4"	1.7
5"	2.1
6"	2.5
7"	2.9
8"	3.3
9"	3.8

1'	16
1"	0.3
2"	0.5
3"	0.8
4"	1.1
5"	1.3
6"	1.6
7"	1.9
8"	2.1
9"	2.4

1'	15
1"	0.3
2"	0.5
3"	0.8
4"	1.0
5"	1.3
6"	1.5
7"	1.8
8"	2.0
9"	2.3

1'	10	11
1"	0.2	0.2
2"	0.3	0.4
3"	0.5	0.6
4"	0.7	0.7
5"	0.8	0.9
6"	1.0	1.1
7"	1.2	1.3
8"	1.3	1.5
9"	1.5	1.7

Logarithmic Functions
40°

′	L. Sin.	d.	L. Tang.	c.d.	L. Cotg.	L. Cos.	d.	′	P. P.		
0	9.80 807	15	9.92 381	26	0.07 619	9.88 425	10	60	1′	26	
1	822	15	407	26	593	415	11	59	1″	0.4	
2	837	15	433	25	567	404	10	58	2″	0.9	
3	852	15	458	26	542	394	11	57	3″	1.3	
4	867	15	484	26	516	383	11	56	4″	1.7	
5	882	15	510	25	490	372	10	55	5″	2.2	
6	897	15	535	26	465	362	11	54	6″	2.6	
7	912	15	561	26	439	351	11	53	7″	3.0	
8	927	15	587	25	413	340	10	52	8″	3.5	
9	942	15	612	26	388	330	11	51	9″	3.9	
10	9.80 957	15	9.92 638	25	0.07 362	9.88 319	11	50			
11	972	15	663	26	337	308	10	49			
12	987	15	689	26	311	298	11	48	1′	25	
13	9.81 002	15	715	25	285	287	11	47	1″	0.4	
14	017	15	740	26	260	276	10	46	2″	0.8	
15	032	15	766	26	234	266	11	45	3″	1.3	
16	047	14	792	25	208	255	11	44	4″	1.7	
17	061	15	817	26	183	244	10	43	5″	2.1	
18	076	15	843	25	157	234	11	42	6″	2.5	
19	091	15	868	26	132	223	11	41	7″	2.9	
20	9.81 106	15	9.92 894	26	0.07 106	9.88 212	11	40	8″	3.3	
21	121	15	920	25	080	201	10	39	9″	3.8	
22	136	15	945	26	055	191	11	38			
23	151	15	971	25	029	180	11	37			
24	166	14	996	26	004	169	11	36			
25	180	15	9.93 022	26	0.06 978	158	10	35	1″	15	
26	195	15	048	25	952	148	11	34	1″	0.3	
27	210	15	073	26	927	137	11	33	2″	0.5	
28	225	15	099	25	901	126	11	32	3″	0.8	
29	240	14	124	26	876	115	10	31	4″	1.0	
30	9.81 254	15	9.93 150	25	0.06 850	9.88 105	11	30	5″	1.3	
31	269	15	175	26	825	094	11	29	6″	1.5	
32	284	15	201	26	799	083	11	28	7″	1.8	
33	299	15	227	25	773	072	11	27	8″	2.0	
34	314	14	252	26	748	061	10	26	9″	2.3	
35	328	15	278	25	722	051	11	25			
36	343	15	303	26	697	040	11	24	1′	14	
37	358	14	329	25	671	029	11	23	1″	0.2	
38	372	15	354	26	646	018	11	22	2″	0.5	
39	387	15	380	26	620	007	11	21	3″	0.7	
40	9.81 402	15	9.93 406	25	0.06 594	9.87 996	11	20	4″	0.9	
41	417	14	431	26	569	985	10	19	5″	1.2	
42	431	15	457	25	543	975	11	18	6″	1.4	
43	446	15	482	26	518	964	11	17	7″	1.6	
44	461	14	508	25	492	953	11	16	8″	1.9	
45	475	15	533	26	467	942	11	15	9″	2.1	
46	490	15	559	25	441	931	11	14			
47	505	14	584	26	416	920	11	13			
48	519	15	610	26	390	909	11	12			
49	534	15	636	25	364	898	11	11	1′	10	11
50	9.81 549	14	9.93 661	26	0.06 339	9.87 887	10	10	1″	0.2	0.2
51	563	15	687	25	313	877	11	9	2″	0.3	0.4
52	578	14	712	26	288	866	11	8	3″	0.5	0.6
53	592	15	738	25	262	855	11	7	4″	0.7	0.7
54	607	15	763	26	237	844	11	6	5″	0.8	0.9
55	622	14	789	25	211	833	11	5	6″	1.0	1.1
56	636	15	814	26	186	822	11	4	7″	1.2	1.3
57	651	14	840	25	160	811	11	3	8″	1.3	1.5
58	665	15	865	26	135	800	11	2	9″	1.5	1.7
59	680	14	891	25	109	789	11	1			
60	9.81 694		9.93 916		0.06 084	9.87 778		0			
′	L. Cos.	d.	L. Cotg.	c.d.	L. Tang.	L. Sin.	d.	′			

49°

′	L. Sin.	d.	L. Tang.	c.d.	L. Cotg.	L. Cos.	d.	′		P. P.	
0	9.81 694	15	9.93 916	26	0.06 084	9.87 778	11	60	1′	26	
1	709	14	942	25	058	767	11	59	1″	0.4	
2	723	15	967	26	033	756	11	58	2″	0.9	
3	738	14	993	25	007	745	11	57	3″	1.3	
4	752	15	9.94 018	26	0.05 982	734	11	56	4″	1.7	
5	767	14	044	25	956	723	11	55	5″	2.2	
6	781	5	069	26	931	712	11	54	6″	2.6	
7	796	14	095	25	905	701	11	53	7″	3.0	
8	810	15	120	26	880	690	11	52	8″	3.5	
9	825	14	146	25	854	679	11	51	9″	3.9	
10	9.81 839	15	9.94 171	26	0.05 829	9.87 668	11	50			
11	854	14	197	25	803	657	11	49			
12	868	14	222	26	778	646	11	48	1′	25	
13	882	15	248	25	752	635	11	47	1″	0.4	
14	897	14	273	26	727	624	11	46	2″	0.8	
15	911	15	299	25	701	613	12	45	3″	1.3	
16	926	14	324	26	676	601	11	44	4″	1.7	
17	940	15	350	25	650	590	11	43	5″	2.1	
18	955	14	375	26	625	579	11	42	6″	2.5	
19	969	14	401	25	599	568	11	41	7″	2.9	
20	9.81 983	15	9.94 426	26	0.05 574	9.87 557	11	40	8″	3.3	
21	998	14	452	25	548	546	11	39	9″	3.8	
22	9.82 012	14	477	26	523	535	11	38			
23	026	15	503	25	497	524	11	37			
24	041	14	528	26	472	513	12	36			
25	055	14	554	25	446	501	11	35	1′	15	
26	069	15	579	25	421	490	11	34	1″	0.3	
27	084	14	604	26	396	479	11	33	2″	0.5	
28	098	14	630	25	370	468	11	32	3″	0.8	
29	112	14	655	26	345	457	11	31	4″	1.0	
30	9.82 126	15	9.94 681	25	0.05 319	9.87 446	12	30	5″	1.3	
31	141	14	706	26	294	434	11	29	6″	1.5	
32	155	14	732	25	268	423	11	28	7″	1.8	
33	169	15	757	26	243	412	11	27	8″	2.0	
34	184	14	783	25	217	401	11	26	9″	2.3	
35	198	14	808	26	192	390	12	25			
36	212	14	834	25	166	378	11	24	1′	14	
37	226	14	859	25	141	367	11	23	1″	0.2	
38	240	15	884	26	116	356	11	22	2″	0.5	
39	255	14	910	25	090	345	11	21	3″	0.7	
40	9.82 269	14	9.94 935	26	0.05 065	9.87 334	12	20	4″	0.9	
41	283	14	961	25	039	322	11	19	5″	1.2	
42	297	14	986	26	014	311	11	18	6″	1.4	
43	311	15	9.95 012	25	0.04 988	300	12	17	7″	1.6	
44	326	14	037	25	963	288	11	16	8″	1.9	
45	340	14	062	26	938	277	11	15	9″	2.1	
46	354	14	088	25	912	266	11	14			
47	368	14	113	26	887	255	12	13			
48	382	14	139	25	861	243	11	12			
49	396	14	164	26	836	232	11	11	1′	11	12
50	9.82 410	14	9.95 190	25	0.04 810	9.87 221	12	10	1″	0.2	0.2
51	424	15	215	25	785	209	11	9	2″	0.4	0.4
52	439	14	240	26	760	198	11	8	3″	0.6	0.6
53	453	14	266	25	734	187	12	7	4″	0.7	0.8
54	467	14	291	26	709	175	11	6	5″	0.9	1.0
55	481	14	317	25	683	164	11	5	6″	1.1	1.2
56	495	14	342	26	658	153	12	4	7″	1.3	1.4
57	509	14	368	25	632	141	11	3	8″	1.5	1.6
58	523	14	393	25	607	130	11	2	9″	1.7	1.8
59	537	14	418	26	582	119	12	1			
60	9.82 551		9.95 444		0.04 556	9.87 107		0			

′	L. Cos.	d.	L. Cotg.	c.d.	L. Tang.	L. Sin.	d.	′	

′	L. Sin.	d.	L. Tang.	c.d.	L. Cotg.	L. Cos.	d.	′
0	9.82 551	14	9.95 444	25	0.04 556	9.87 107	11	60
1	565	14	469	26	531	096	11	59
2	579	14	495	25	505	085	12	58
3	593	14	520	25	480	073	11	57
4	607	14	545	26	455	062	12	56
5	621	14	571	25	429	050	11	55
6	635	14	596	26	404	039	11	54
7	649	14	622	25	378	028	12	53
8	663	14	647	25	353	016	11	52
9	677	14	672	26	328	005	12	51
10	9.82 691	14	9.95 698	25	0.04 302	9.86 993	11	50
11	705	14	723	25	277	982	12	49
12	719	14	748	26	252	970	11	48
13	733	14	774	25	226	959	12	47
14	747	14	799	26	201	947	11	46
15	761	14	825	25	175	936	12	45
16	775	13	850	25	150	924	11	44
17	788	14	875	26	125	913	11	43
18	802	14	901	25	099	902	12	42
19	816	14	926	26	074	890	11	41
20	9.82 830	14	9.95 952	25	0.04 048	9.86 879	12	40
21	844	14	977	25	023	867	12	39
22	858	14	9.96 002	26	0.03 998	855	11	38
23	872	13	028	25	972	844	12	37
24	885	14	053	25	947	832	11	36
25	899	14	078	26	922	821	12	35
26	913	14	104	25	896	809	11	34
27	927	14	129	26	871	798	12	33
28	941	14	155	25	845	786	11	32
29	955	13	180	25	820	775	12	31
30	9.82 968	14	9.96 205	26	0.03 795	9.86 763	11	30
31	982	14	231	25	769	752	12	29
32	996	14	256	25	744	740	12	28
33	9.83 010	13	281	26	719	728	11	27
34	023	14	307	25	693	717	12	26
35	037	14	332	25	668	705	11	25
36	051	14	357	26	643	694	12	24
37	065	13	383	25	617	682	12	23
38	078	14	408	25	592	670	11	22
39	092	14	433	26	567	659	12	21
40	9.83 106	14	9.96 459	25	0.03 541	9.86 647	12	20
41	120	13	484	26	516	635	11	19
42	133	14	510	25	490	624	12	18
43	147	14	535	25	465	612	12	17
44	161	13	560	26	440	600	11	16
45	174	14	586	25	414	589	12	15
46	188	14	611	25	389	577	12	14
47	202	13	636	26	364	565	11	13
48	215	14	662	25	338	554	12	12
49	229	13	687	25	313	542	12	11
50	9.83 242	14	9.96 712	26	0.03 288	9.86 530	12	10
51	256	14	738	25	262	518	11	9
52	270	13	763	25	237	507	12	8
53	283	14	788	26	212	495	12	7
54	297	13	814	25	186	483	11	6
55	310	14	839	25	161	472	12	5
56	324	14	864	26	136	460	12	4
57	338	13	890	25	110	448	12	3
58	351	14	915	25	085	436	12	2
59	365	13	940	26	060	425	12	1
60	9.83 378		9.96 966		0.03 034	9.86 413		0
′	L. Cos.	d.	L. Cotg.	c.d.	L. Tang.	L. Sin.	d.	′

P. P.

1′	26
1″	0.4
2″	0.9
3″	1.3
4″	1.7
5″	2.2
6″	2.6
7″	3.0
8″	3.5
9″	3.9

1′	25
1″	0.4
2″	0.8
3″	1.3
4″	1.7
5″	2.1
6″	2.5
7″	2.9
8″	3.3
9″	3.8

1′	14
1″	0.2
2″	0.5
3″	0.7
4″	0.9
5″	1.2
6″	1.4
7″	1.6
8″	1.9
9″	2.1

1′	13
1″	0.2
2″	0.4
3″	0.7
4″	0.9
5″	1.1
6″	1.3
7″	1.5
8″	1.7
9″	2.0

1′	12	11
1″	0.2	0.2
2″	0.4	0.4
3″	0.6	0.6
4″	0.8	0.7
5″	1.0	0.9
6″	1.2	1.1
7″	1.4	1.3
8″	1.6	1.5
9″	1.8	1.7

'	L. Sin.	d.	L. Tang.	c.d.	L. Cotg.	L. Cos.	d.	'	P. P.	
0	9.83 378	14	9.96 966	25	0.03 034	9.86 413	12	60	1′	26
1	392	13	991	25	009	401	12	59	1″	0.4
2	405	14	9.97 016	26	0.02 984	389	12	58	2″	0.9
3	419	13	042	25	958	377	11	57	3″	1.3
4	432	14	067	25	933	366	12	56	4″	1.7
5	446	13	092	26	908	354	12	55	5″	2.2
6	459	14	118	25	882	342	12	54	6″	2.6
7	473	13	143	25	857	330	12	53	7″	3.0
8	486	14	168	25	832	318	12	52	8″	3.5
9	500	13	193	26	807	306	11	51	9″	3.9
10	9.83 513	14	9.97 219	25	0.02 781	9.86 295	12	50		
11	527	13	244	25	756	283	12	49		
12	540	14	269	26	731	271	12	48	1′	25
13	554	13	295	25	705	259	12	47	1″	0.4
14	567	14	320	25	680	247	12	46	2″	0.8
15	581	13	345	26	655	235	12	45	3″	1.3
16	594	14	371	25	629	223	12	44	4″	1.7
17	608	13	396	25	604	211	11	43	5″	2.1
18	621	13	421	26	579	200	12	42	6″	2.5
19	634	14	447	25	553	188	12	41	7″	2.9
20	9.83 648	13	9.97 472	25	0.02 528	9.86 176	12	40	8″	3.3
21	661	13	497	26	503	164	12	39	9″	3.8
22	674	14	523	25	477	152	12	38		
23	688	13	548	25	452	140	12	37		
24	701	14	573	25	427	128	12	36	1′	14
25	715	13	598	26	402	116	12	35	1″	0.2
26	728	13	624	25	376	104	12	34	2″	0.5
27	741	14	649	25	351	092	12	33	3″	0.7
28	755	13	674	26	326	080	12	32	4″	0.9
29	768	13	700	25	300	068	12	31	5″	1.2
30	9.83 781	14	9.97 725	25	0.02 275	9.86 056	12	30	6″	1.4
31	795	13	750	26	250	044	12	29	7″	1.6
32	808	13	776	25	224	032	12	28	8″	1.9
33	821	13	801	25	199	020	12	27	9″	2.1
34	834	14	826	25	174	008	12	26		
35	848	13	851	26	149	9.85 996	12	25		
36	861	13	877	25	123	984	12	24	1′	13
37	874	13	902	25	098	972	12	23	1″	0.2
38	887	14	927	26	073	960	12	22	2″	0.4
39	901	13	953	25	047	948	12	21	3″	0.7
40	9.83 914	13	9.97 978	25	0.02 022	9.85 936	12	20	4″	0.9
41	927	13	9.98 003	26	0.01 997	924	12	19	5″	1.1
42	940	14	029	25	971	912	12	18	6″	1.3
43	954	13	054	25	946	900	12	17	7″	1.5
44	967	13	079	25	921	888	12	16	8″	1.7
45	980	13	104	26	896	876	12	15	9″	2.0
46	993	13	130	25	870	864	13	14		
47	9.84 006	14	155	25	845	851	12	13		
48	020	13	180	26	820	839	12	12		
49	033	13	206	25	794	827	12	11	1′	12	11
50	9.84 046	13	9.98 231	25	0.01 769	9.85 815	12	10	1″	0.2	0.2
51	059	13	256	25	744	803	12	9	2″	0.4	0.4
52	072	13	281	26	719	791	12	8	3″	0.6	0.6
53	085	13	307	25	693	779	13	7	4″	0.8	0.7
54	098	14	332	25	668	766	12	6	5″	1.0	0.9
55	112	13	357	26	643	754	12	5	6″	1.2	1.1
56	125	13	383	25	617	742	12	4	7″	1.4	1.3
57	138	13	408	25	592	730	12	3	8″	1.6	1.5
58	151	13	433	25	567	718	12	2	9″	1.8	1.7
59	164	13	458	26	542	706	13	1			
60	9.84 177		9.98 484		0.01 516	9.85 693		0			
'	L. Cos.	d.	L. Cotg.	c. d.	L. Tang.	L. Sin.	d.	'		

′	L. Sin.	d.	L. Tang.	c.d.	L. Cotg.	L. Cos.	d.	′
0	9.84 177	13	9.98 484	25	0.01 516	9.85 693	12	60
1	190	13	509	25	491	681	12	59
2	203	13	534	26	466	669	12	58
3	216	13	560	25	440	657	12	57
4	229	13	585	25	415	645	13	56
5	242	13	610	25	390	632	12	55
6	255	14	635	26	365	620	12	54
7	269	13	661	25	339	608	12	53
8	282	13	686	25	314	596	13	52
9	295	13	711	26	289	583	12	51
10	9.84 308	13	9.98 737	25	0.01 263	9.85 571	12	50
11	321	13	762	25	238	559	12	49
12	334	13	787	25	213	547	13	48
13	347	13	812	26	188	534	12	47
14	360	13	838	25	162	522	12	46
15	373	12	863	25	137	510	13	45
16	385	13	888	25	112	497	12	44
17	398	13	913	26	087	485	12	43
18	411	13	939	25	061	473	13	42
19	424	13	964	25	036	460	12	41
20	9.84 437	13	9.98 989	26	0.01 011	9.85 448	12	40
21	450	13	9.99 015	25	0.00 985	436	13	39
22	463	13	040	25	960	423	12	38
23	476	13	065	25	935	411	12	37
24	489	13	090	26	910	399	13	36
25	502	13	116	25	884	386	12	35
26	515	13	141	25	859	374	13	34
27	528	12	166	25	834	361	12	33
28	540	13	191	26	809	349	12	32
29	553	13	217	25	783	337	13	31
30	9.84 566	13	9.99 242	25	0.00 758	9.85 324	12	30
31	579	13	267	26	733	312	13	29
32	592	13	293	25	707	299	12	28
33	605	13	318	25	682	287	13	27
34	618	12	343	25	657	274	12	26
35	630	13	368	26	632	262	12	25
36	643	13	394	25	606	250	13	24
37	656	13	419	25	581	237	12	23
38	669	13	444	25	556	225	13	22
39	682	12	469	26	531	212	12	21
40	9.84 694	13	9.99 495	25	0.00 505	9.85 200	13	20
41	707	13	520	25	480	187	12	19
42	720	13	545	25	455	175	13	18
43	733	12	570	26	430	162	12	17
44	745	13	596	25	404	150	13	16
45	758	13	621	25	379	137	12	15
46	771	13	646	26	354	125	13	14
47	784	12	672	25	328	112	12	13
48	796	13	697	25	303	100	13	12
49	809	13	722	25	278	087	13	11
50	9.84 822	13	9.99 747	26	0.00 253	9.85 074	12	10
51	835	12	773	25	227	062	13	9
52	847	13	798	25	202	049	12	8
53	860	13	823	25	177	037	13	7
54	873	12	848	26	152	024	12	6
55	885	13	874	25	126	012	13	5
56	898	13	899	25	101	9.84 999	13	4
57	911	12	924	25	076	986	13	3
58	923	13	949	26	051	974	13	2
59	936	13	975	25	025	961	12	1
60	9.84 949		0.00 000		0.00 000	9.84 949		0
′	L. Cos.	d.	L. Cotg.	c.d.	L. Tang.	L. Sin.	d.	′

P. P.

1′	26
1″	0.4
2″	0.9
3″	1.3
4″	1.7
5″	2.2
6″	2.6
7″	3.0
8″	3.5
9″	3.9

1′	25
1″	0.4
2″	0.8
3″	1.3
4″	1.7
5″	2.1
6″	2.5
7″	2.9
8″	3.3
9″	3.8

1′	14
1″	0.2
2″	0.5
3″	0.7
4″	0.9
5″	1.2
6″	1.4
7″	1.6
8″	1.9
9″	2.1

1′	13
1″	0.2
2″	0.4
3″	0.7
4″	0.9
5″	1.1
6″	1.3
7″	1.5
8″	1.7
9″	2.0

1′	12
1″	0.2
2″	0.4
3″	0.6
4″	0.8
5″	1.0
6″	1.2
7″	1.4
8″	1.6
9″	1.8

NATURAL
TRIGONOMETRIC FUNCTIONS[1]

[1] From Five-Place Tables compiled by N. J. Lennes and A. S. Merrill, Harper & Brothers, Publishers.

′	0° N. sine	N. cos.	1° N. sine	N. cos.	2° N.sine	N.cos.	3° N.sine	N.cos.	4° N.sine	N.cos.	′
0	.00000	1.00000	.01745	.99985	.03490	.99939	.05234	.99863	.06976	.99756	60
1	029	000	774	984	519	938	263	861	.07005	754	59
2	058	000	803	984	548	937	292	860	034	752	58
3	087	000	832	983	577	936	321	858	063	750	57
4	116	000	862	983	606	935	350	857	092	748	56
5	145	000	891	982	635	934	379	855	121	746	55
6	175	000	920	982	664	933	408	854	150	744	54
7	204	000	949	981	693	932	437	852	179	742	53
8	233	000	978	980	723	931	466	851	208	740	52
9	262	000	.02007	980	752	930	495	849	237	738	51
10	.00291	1.00000	.02036	.99979	.03781	.99929	.05524	.99847	.07266	.99736	50
11	320	.99999	065	979	810	927	553	846	295	734	49
12	349	999	094	978	839	926	582	844	324	731	48
13	378	999	123	977	868	925	611	842	353	729	47
14	407	999	152	977	897	924	640	841	382	727	46
15	436	999	181	976	926	923	669	839	411	725	45
16	465	999	211	976	955	922	698	838	440	723	44
17	495	999	240	975	984	921	727	836	469	721	43
18	524	999	269	974	.04013	919	756	834	498	719	42
19	553	998	298	974	042	918	785	833	527	716	41
20	.00582	.99998	.02327	.99973	.04071	.99917	.05814	.99831	.07556	.99714	40
21	611	998	356	972	100	916	844	829	585	712	39
22	640	998	385	972	129	915	873	827	614	710	38
23	669	998	414	971	159	913	902	826	643	708	37
24	698	998	443	970	188	912	931	824	672	705	36
25	727	997	472	969	217	911	960	822	701	703	35
26	756	997	501	969	246	910	989	821	730	701	34
27	785	997	530	968	275	909	.06018	819	759	699	33
28	814	997	560	967	304	907	047	817	788	696	32
29	844	996	589	966	333	906	076	815	817	694	31
30	.00873	.99996	.02618	.99966	.04362	.99905	.06105	.99813	.07846	.99692	30
31	902	996	647	965	391	904	134	812	875	689	29
32	931	996	676	964	420	902	163	810	904	687	28
33	960	995	705	963	449	901	192	808	933	685	27
34	989	995	734	963	478	900	221	806	962	683	26
35	.01013	995	763	962	507	898	250	804	991	680	25
36	047	995	792	961	536	897	279	803	.08020	678	24
37	076	994	821	960	565	896	308	801	049	676	23
38	105	994	850	959	594	894	337	799	078	673	22
39	134	994	879	959	623	893	366	797	107	671	21
40	.01164	.99993	.02908	.99958	.04653	.99892	.06395	.99795	.08136	.99668	20
41	193	993	938	957	682	890	424	793	165	666	19
42	222	993	967	956	711	889	453	792	194	664	18
43	251	992	996	955	740	888	482	790	223	661	17
44	280	992	.03025	954	769	886	511	788	252	659	16
45	309	991	054	953	798	885	540	786	281	657	15
46	338	991	083	952	827	883	569	784	310	654	14
47	367	991	112	952	856	882	598	782	339	652	13
48	396	990	141	951	885	881	627	780	368	649	12
49	425	990	170	950	914	879	656	778	397	647	11
50	.01454	.99989	.03199	.99949	.04943	.99878	.06685	.99776	.08426	.99644	10
51	483	989	228	948	972	876	714	774	455	642	9
52	513	989	257	947	.05001	875	743	772	484	639	8
53	542	988	286	946	030	873	773	770	513	637	7
54	571	988	316	945	059	872	802	768	542	635	6
55	600	987	345	944	088	870	831	766	571	632	5
56	629	987	374	943	117	869	860	764	600	630	4
57	658	986	403	942	146	867	889	762	629	627	3
58	687	986	432	941	175	866	918	760	658	625	2
59	716	985	461	940	205	864	947	758	687	622	1
60	.01745	.99985	.03490	.99939	.05234	.99863	.06976	.99756	.08716	.99619	0
	N. cos.	N. sine	N. cos.	N. sine	N.cos.	N.sine	N.cos.	N.sine	N.cos.	N.sine	
′	89°		88°		87°		86°		85°		′

Natural Tangents and Cotangents

'	0° Tang	0° Cotg	1° Tang	1° Cotg	2° Tang	2° Cotg	3° Tang	3° Cotg	4° Tang	4° Cotg	'
0	.0000	Infinite	.0175	57.2900	.0349	28.6363	.0524	19.0811	.0699	14.3007	60
1	03	3437.75	77	56.3506	52	3994	27	18.9755	.0702	. 2411	59
2	06	1718.87	80	55.4415	55	1664	30	8711	05	1821	58
3	09	1145.92	83	54.5613	58	27.9372	33	7678	08	1235	57
4	12	859.436	86	53.7086	' 61	7117	36	6656	11	0655	56
5	15	687.549	89	52.8821	64	4899	39	5645	14	0079	55
6	17	572.957	92	0807	67	2715	42	4645	17	13.9507	54
7	20	491.106	95	51.3032	70	0566	44	3655	20	8940	53
8	23	429.718	98	50.5485	73	26.8450	47	2677	23	8378	52
9	26	381.971	.0201	49.8157	75	6367	50	1708	26	7821	51
10	.0029	343.774	.0204	49.1039	.0378	26.4316	.0553	18.0750	.0729	13.7267	50
11	32	312.521	07	48.4121	81	2296	56	17.9802	31	6719	49
12	35	286.478	09	47.7395	84	0307	59	8863	34	6174	48
13	38	264.441	12	0853	87	25.8348	62	7934	37	5634	47
14	41	245.552	15	46.4489	90	6418	65	7015	40	5098	46
15	44	229.182	18	45.8294	93	4517	68	6106	43	4566	45
16	47	214.858	21	2261	96	2644	71	5205	46	4039	44
17	49	202.219	24	44.6386	99	0798	74	4314	49	3515	43
18	52	190.984	27	0661	.0402	24.8978	77	3432	52	2996	42
19	55	180.932	30	43.5081	05	7185	80	2558	55	2480	41
20	.0058	171.885	.0233	42.9641	.0407	24.5418	.0582	17.1693	.0758	13.1969	40
21	61	163.700	36	4335	10	3675	85	0837	61	1461	39
22	64	156.259	39	41.9158	13	1957	88	16.9990	64	0958	38
23	67	149.465	41	4106	16	0263	91	9150	67	0458	37
24	70	143.237	44	40.9174	19	23.8593	94	8319	69	12.9962	36
25	73	137.507	47	4358	22	6945	97	7496	72	9469	35
26	76	132.219	50	39.9655	25	5321	.0600	6681	75	8981	34
27	79	127.321	53	5059	28	3718	03	5874	78	8496	33
28	81	122.774	56	0568	31	2137	06	5075	81	8014	32
29	84	118.540	59	38.6177	34	0577	09	4283	84	7536	31
30	.0087	114.589	.0262	38.1885	.0437	22.9038	.0612	16.3499	.0787	12.7062	30
31	90	110.892	65	37.7686	40	7519	15	2722	90	6591	29
32	93	107.426	68	3579	42	6020	17	1952	93	6124	28
33	96	104.171	71	36.9560	45	4541	20	1190	96	5660	27
34	99	101.107	74	5627	48	3081	23	0435	99	5199	26
35	.0102	98.2179	76	1776	51	1640	26	15.9687	.0802	4742	25
36	05	95.4895	79	35.8006	54	0217	29	8945	05	4288	24
37	08	92.9085	82	4313	57	21.8813	32	8211	08	3838	23
38	11	90.4633	85	0695	60	7426	35	7483	10	3390	22
39	13	88.1436	88	34.7151	63	6056	38	6762	13	2946	21
40	.0116	85.9398	.0291	34.3678	.0466	21.4704	.0641	15.6048	.0816	12.2505	20
41	19	83.8435	94	0273	69	3369	44	5340	19	2067	19
42	22	81.8470	97	33.6935	72	2049	47	4638	22	1632	18
43	25	79.9434	.0300	3662	75	0747	50	3943	25	1201	17
44	28	78.1263	03	0452	77	20.9460	53	3254	28	0772	16
45	31	76.3900	06	32.7303	80	8188	55	2571	31	0346	15
46	34	74.7292	08	4213	83	6932	58	1893	34	11.9923	14
47	37	73.1390	11	1181	86	5691	61	1222	37	9504	13
48	40	71.6151	14	31.8205	89	4465	64	0557	40	9087	12
49	43	70.1533	17	5284	92	3253	67	14.9898	43	8673	11
50	.0145	68.7501	.0320	31.2416	.0495	20.2056	.0670	14.9244	.0846	11.8262	10
51	48	67.4019	23	30.9599	98	0872	73	8596	49	7853	9
52	51	66.1055	26	6833	.0501	19.9702	76	7954	51	7448	8
53	54	64.8580	29	4116	04	8546	79	7317	54	7045	7
54	57	63.6567	32	1446	07	7403	82	6685	57	6645	6
55	60	62.4992	35	29.8823	09	6273	85	6059	60	6248	5
56	63	61.3829	38	6245	12	5156	88	5438	63	5853	4
57	66	60.3058	40	3711	15	4051	90	4823	66	5461	3
58	69	59.2659	43	1220	18	2959	93	4212	69	5072	2
59	72	58.2612	46	28.8771	21	1879	96	3607	72	4685	1
60	.0175	57.2900	.0349	28.6363	.0524	19.0811	.0699	14.3007	.0875	11.4301	0
	Cotg	Tang	Cotg	Tang	Cotg	Tang	Cotg	Tang	Cotg	Tang	
'	89°		88°		87°		86°		85°		'

′	5° N.sine	5° N. cos.	6° N.sine	6° N. cos.	7° N.sine	7° N. cos.	8° N.sine	8° N. cos.	9° N.sine	9° N. cos.	′
0	.08716	.99619	.10453	.99452	.12187	.99255	.13917	.99027	.15643	.98769	60
1	745	617	482	449	216	251	946	023	672	764	59
2	774	614	511	446	245	248	975	019	701	760	58
3	803	612	540	443	274	244	.14004	015	730	755	57
4	831	609	569	440	302	240	033	011	758	751	56
5	860	607	597	437	331	237	061	006	787	746	55
6	889	604	626	434	360	233	090	002	816	741	54
7	918	602	655	431	389	230	119	.98998	845	737	53
8	947	599	684	428	418	226	148	994	873	732	52
9	976	596	713	424	447	222	177	990	902	728	51
10	.09005	.99594	.10742	.99421	.12476	.99219	.14205	.98986	.15931	.98723	50
11	034	591	771	418	504	215	234	982	959	718	49
12	063	588	800	415	533	211	263	978	988	714	48
13	092	586	829	412	562	208	292	973	.16017	709	47
14	121	583	858	409	591	204	320	969	046	704	46
15	150	580	887	406	620	200	349	965	074	700	45
16	179	578	916	402	649	197	378	961	103	695	44
17	208	575	945	399	678	193	407	957	132	690	43
18	237	572	973	396	706	189	436	953	160	686	42
19	266	570	.11002	393	735	186	464	948	189	681	41
20	.09295	.99567	.11031	.99390	.12764	.99182	.14493	.98944	.16218	.98676	40
21	324	564	060	386	793	178	522	940	246	671	39
22	353	562	089	383	822	175	551	936	275	667	38
23	382	559	118	380	851	171	580	931	304	662	37
24	411	556	147	377	880	167	608	927	333	657	36
25	440	553	176	374	908	163	637	923	361	652	35
26	469	551	205	370	937	160	666	919	390	648	34
27	498	548	234	367	966	156	695	914	419	643	33
28	527	545	263	364	995	152	723	910	447	638	32
29	556	542	291	360	.13024	148	752	906	476	633	31
30	.09585	.99540	.11320	.99357	.13053	.99144	.14781	.98902	.16505	.98629	30
31	614	537	349	354	081	141	810	897	533	624	29
32	642	534	378	351	110	137	838	893	562	619	28
33	671	531	407	347	139	133	867	889	591	614	27
34	700	528	436	344	168	129	896	884	620	609	26
35	729	526	465	341	197	125	925	880	648	604	25
36	758	523	494	337	226	122	954	876	677	600	24
37	787	520	523	334	254	118	982	871	706	595	23
38	816	517	552	331	283	114	.15011	867	734	590	22
39	845	514	580	327	312	110	040	863	763	585	21
40	.09874	.99511	.11609	.99324	.13341	.99106	.15069	.98858	.16792	.98580	20
41	903	508	638	320	370	102	097	854	820	575	19
42	932	506	667	317	399	098	126	849	849	570	18
43	961	503	696	314	427	094	155	845	878	565	17
44	990	500	725	310	456	091	184	841	906	561	16
45	.10019	497	754	307	485	087	212	836	935	556	15
46	048	494	783	303	514	083	241	832	964	551	14
47	077	491	812	300	543	079	270	827	992	546	13
48	106	488	840	297	572	075	299	823	.17021	541	12
49	135	485	869	293	601	071	327	818	050	536	11
50	.10164	.99482	.11898	.99290	.13629	.99067	.15356	.98814	.17078	.98531	10
51	192	479	927	286	658	063	385	809	107	526	9
52	221	476	956	283	687	059	414	805	136	521	8
53	250	473	985	279	716	055	442	800	164	516	7
54	279	470	.12014	276	744	051	471	796	193	511	6
55	308	467	043	272	773	047	500	791	222	506	5
56	337	464	071	269	802	043	529	787	250	501	4
57	366	461	100	265	831	039	557	782	279	496	3
58	395	458	129	262	860	035	586	778	308	491	2
59	424	455	158	258	889	031	615	773	336	486	1
60	.10453	.99452	.12187	.99255	.13917	.99027	.15643	.98769	.17365	.98481	0
	N.cos.	N. sine	N.cos.	N. sine	N.cos.	N. sine	N.cos.	N. sine	N.cos.	N. sine	
′	84°		83°		82°		81°		80°		′

′	5°		6°		7°		8°		9°		′
	Tang.	Cotg.	Tang.	Cotg	Tang.	Cotg.	Tang.	Cotg.	Tang.	Cotg.	
0	.0875	11.4301	.1051	9.5144	.1228	8.1443	.1405	7.1154	.1584	6.3138	60
1	78	11.3919	54	9.4878	31	248	08	004	87	019	59
2	81	540	57	614	34	054	11	7.0855	90	6.2901	58
3	84	163	60	352	37	8.0860	14	706	93	783	57
4	87	11.2789	63	090	40	667	17	558	96	666	56
5	90	417	66	9.3831	43	476	20	410	99	549	55
6	92	048	69	572	46	285	23	264	.1602	432	54
7	95	11.1681	72	315	49	095	26	117	05	316	53
8	98	316	75	060	51	7.9906	29	6.9972	08	200	52
9	.0901	11.0954	78	9.2806	54	718	32	827	11	085	51
10	.0904	11.0594	.1080	9.2553	.1257	7.9530	.1435	6.9682	.1614	6.1970	50
11	07	237	83	302	60	344	38	538	17	856	49
12	10	10.9882	86	052	63	158	41	395	20	742	48
13	13	529	89	9.1803	66	7.8973	44	252	23	628	47
14	16	178	92	555	69	789	47	110	26	515	46
15	19	10.8829	95	309	72	606	50	6.8969	29	402	45
16	22	483	98	065	75	424	53	828	32	290	44
17	25	139	.1101	9.0821	78	243	56	687	35	178	43
18	28	10.7797	04	579	81	062	59	548	38	066	42
19	31	457	07	338	84	7.7882	62	408	41	6.0955	41
20	.0934	10.7119	.1110	9.0098	.1287	7.7704	.1465	6.8269	.1644	6.0844	40
21	36	10.6783	13	8.9860	90	525	68	131	47	734	39
22	39	450	16	623	93	348	71	6.7994	50	624	38
23	42	118	19	387	96	171	74	856	53	514	37
24	45	10.5789	22	152	99	7.6996	77	720	55	405	36
25	48	462	25	8.8919	.1302	821	80	584	58	296	35
26	51	136	28	686	05	647	83	448	61	188	34
27	54	10.4813	31	455	08	473	86	313	64	080	33
28	57	491	33	225	11	301	89	179	67	5.9972	32
29	60	172	36	8.7996	14	129	92	045	70	865	31
30	.0963	10.3854	.1139	8.7769	.1317	7.5958	.1495	6.6912	.1673	5.9758	30
31	66	538	42	542	19	787	97	779	76	651	29
32	69	224	45	317	22	618	.1500	646	79	545	28
33	72	10.2913	48	093	25	449	03	514	82	439	27
34	75	602	51	8.6870	28	281	06	383	85	333	26
35	78	294	54	648	31	113	09	252	88	228	25
36	81	10.1988	57	427	34	7.4947	12	122	91	124	24
37	83	683	60	208	37	781	15	6.5992	94	019	23
38	86	381	63	8.5989	40	615	18	863	97	5.8915	22
39	89	080	66	772	43	451	21	734	.1700	811	21
40	.0992	10.0780	.1169	8.5555	.1346	7.4287	.1524	6.5606	.1703	5.8708	20
41	95	483	72	340	49	124	27	478	06	605	19
42	98	187	75	126	52	7.3962	30	350	09	502	18
43	.1001	9.9893	78	8.4913	55	800	33	223	12	400	17
44	04	601	81	701	58	639	36	097	15	298	16
45	07	310	84	490	61	479	39	6.4971	18	197	15
46	10	021	87	280	64	319	42	846	21	095	14
47	13	9.8734	89	071	67	160	45	721	24	5.7994	13
48	16	448	92	8.3863	70	002	48	596	27	894	12
49	19	164	95	656	73	7.2844	51	472	30	794	11
50	.1022	9.7882	.1198	8.3450	.1376	7.2687	.1554	6.4348	.1733	5.7694	10
51	25	601	.1201	245	79	531	57	225	36	594	9
52	28	322	04	041	82	375	60	103	39	495	8
53	30	044	07	8.2838	85	220	63	6.3980	42	396	7
54	33	9.6768	10	636	88	066	66	859	45	297	6
55	36	493	13	434	91	7.1912	69	737	48	199	5
56	39	220	16	234	94	759	72	617	51	101	4
57	42	9.5949	19	035	97	607	75	496	54	004	3
58	45	679	22	8.1837	99	455	78	376	57	5.6906	2
59	48	411	25	640	.1402	304	81	257	60	809	1
60	.1051	9.5144	.1228	8.1443	.1405	7.1154	.1584	6.3138	.1763	5.6713	0
	Cotg.	Tang.	Cotg.	Tang.	Cotg.	Tang.	Cotg.	Tang.	Cotg.	Tang.	
′	84°		83°		82°		81°		80°		′

′	10° N.sine	10° N. cos.	11° N.sine	11° N. cos.	12° N.sine	12° N. cos.	13° N.sine	13° N. cos.	14° N.sine	14° N. cos.	′
0	.17365	.98481	.19081	.98163	.20791	.97815	.22495	.97437	.24192	.97030	60
1	393	476	109	157	820	809	523	430	220	023	59
2	422	471	138	152	848	803	552	424	249	015	58
3	451	466	167	146	877	797	580	417	277	008	57
4	479	461	195	140	905	791	608	411	305	001	56
5	508	455	224	135	933	784	637	404	333	.96994	55
6	537	450	252	129	962	778	665	398	362	987	54
7	565	445	281	124	990	772	693	391	390	980	53
8	594	440	309	118	.21019	766	722	384	418	973	52
9	623	435	338	112	047	760	750	378	446	966	51
10	.17651	.98430	.19366	.98107	.21076	.97754	.22778	.97371	.24474	.96959	50
11	680	425	395	101	104	748	807	365	503	952	49
12	708	420	423	096	132	742	835	358	531	945	48
13	737	414	452	090	161	735	863	351	559	937	47
14	766	409	481	084	189	729	892	345	587	930	46
15	794	404	509	079	218	723	920	338	615	923	45
16	823	399	538	073	246	717	948	331	644	916	44
17	852	394	566	067	275	711	977	325	672	909	43
18	880	389	595	061	303	705	.23005	318	700	902	42
19	909	383	623	056	331	698	033	311	728	894	41
20	.17937	.98378	.19652	.98050	.21360	.97692	.23062	.97304	.24756	.96887	40
21	966	373	680	044	388	686	090	298	784	880	39
22	995	368	709	039	417	680	118	291	813	873	38
23	.18023	362	737	033	445	673	146	284	841	866	37
24	052	357	766	027	474	667	175	278	869	858	36
25	081	352	794	021	502	661	203	271	897	851	35
26	109	347	823	016	530	655	231	264	925	844	34
27	138	341	851	010	559	648	260	257	954	837	33
28	166	336	880	004	587	642	288	251	982	829	32
29	195	331	908	.97998	616	636	316	244	.25010	822	31
30	.18224	.98325	.19937	.97992	.21644	.97630	.23345	.97237	.25038	.96815	30
31	252	320	965	987	672	623	373	230	066	807	29
32	281	315	994	981	701	617	401	223	094	800	28
33	309	310	.20022	975	729	611	429	217	122	793	27
34	338	304	051	969	758	604	458	210	151	786	26
35	367	299	079	963	786	598	486	203	179	778	25
36	395	294	108	958	814	592	514	196	207	771	24
37	424	288	136	952	843	585	542	189	235	764	23
38	452	283	165	946	871	579	571	182	263	756	22
39	481	277	193	940	899	573	599	176	291	749	21
40	.18509	.98272	.20222	.97934	.21928	.97566	.23627	.97169	.25320	.96742	20
41	538	267	250	928	956	560	656	162	348	734	19
42	567	261	279	922	985	553	684	155	376	727	18
43	595	256	307	916	.22013	547	712	148	404	719	17
44	624	250	336	910	041	541	740	141	432	712	16
45	652	245	364	905	070	534	769	134	460	705	15
46	681	240	393	899	098	528	797	127	488	697	14
47	710	234	421	893	126	521	825	120	516	690	13
48	738	229	450	887	155	515	853	113	545	682	12
49	767	223	478	881	183	508	882	106	573	675	11
50	.18795	.98218	.20507	.97875	.22212	.97502	.23910	.97100	.25601	.96667	10
51	824	212	535	869	240	496	938	093	629	660	9
52	852	207	563	863	268	489	966	086	657	653	8
53	881	201	592	857	297	483	995	079	685	645	7
54	910	196	620	851	325	476	.24023	072	713	638	6
55	938	190	649	845	353	470	051	065	741	630	5
56	967	185	677	839	382	463	079	058	769	623	4
57	995	179	706	833	410	457	108	051	798	615	3
58	.19024	174	734	827	438	450	136	044	826	608	2
59	052	168	763	821	467	444	164	037	854	600	1
60	.19081	.98163	.20791	.97815	.22495	.97437	.24192	.97030	.25882	.96593	0
′	N.cos.	N. sine	N.cos.	N. sine	N.cos.	N. sine	N.cos.	N. sine	N.cos.	N. sine	′
	79°		78°		77°		76°		75°		

′	10°		11°		12°		13°		14°		′
	Tang.	Cotg.	Tang.	Cotg.	Tang.	Cotg.	Tang.	Cotg.	Tang.	Cotg.	
0	.1763	5.6713	.1944	5.1446	.2126	4.7046	.2309	4.3315	.2493	4.0108	60
1	66	617	47	366	29	4.6979	12	257	96	058	59
2	69	521	50	286	32	912	15	200	99	009	58
3	72	425	53	207	35	845	18	143	.2503	3.9959	57
4	75	329	56	128	38	779	21	086	06	910	56
5	78	234	59	049	41	712	24	029	09	861	55
6	81	140	62	5.0970	44	646	27	4.2972	12	812	54
7	84	045	65	892	47	580	30	916	15	763	53
8	87	5.5951	68	814	50	514	33	859	18	714	52
9	90	857	71	736	53	448	36	803	21	665	51
10	.1793	5.5764	.1974	5.0658	.2156	4.6382	.2339	4.2747	.2524	3.9617	50
11	96	671	77	581	59	317	42	691	27	568	49
12	99	578	80	504	62	252	45	635	30	520	48
13	.1802	485	83	427	65	187	49	580	33	471	47
14	05	393	86	350	68	122	52	524	37	423	46
15	08	301	89	273	71	057	55	468	40	375	45
16	11	209	92	197	74	4.5993	58	413	43	327	44
17	14	118	95	121	77	928	61	358	46	279	43
18	17	026	98	045	80	864	64	303	49	232	42
19	20	5.4936	.2001	4.9969	83	800	67	248	52	184	41
20	.1823	5.4845	.2004	4.9894	.2186	4.5736	.2370	4.2193	.2555	3.9136	40
21	26	755	07	819	89	673	73	139	58	089	39
22	29	665	10	744	93	609	76	084	61	042	38
23	32	575	13	669	96	546	79	030	64	3.8995	37
24	35	486	16	594	99	483	82	4.1976	68	947	36
25	38	397	19	520	.2202	420	85	922	71	900	35
26	41	308	22	446	05	357	88	868	74	854	34
27	44	219	25	372	08	294	92	814	77	807	33
28	47	131	28	298	11	232	95	760	80	760	32
29	50	043	31	225	14	169	98	706	83	714	31
30	.1853	5.3955	.2035	4.9152	.2217	4.5107	.2401	4.1653	.2586	3.8667	30
31	56	868	38	078	20	045	04	600	89	621	29
32	59	781	41	006	23	4.4983	07	547	92	575	28
33	62	694	44	4.8933	26	922	10	493	95	528	27
34	65	607	47	860	29	860	13	441	99	482	26
35	68	521	50	788	32	799	16	388	.2602	436	25
36	71	435	53	716	35	737	19	335	05	391	24
37	74	349	56	644	38	676	22	282	08	345	23
38	77	263	59	573	41	615	25	230	11	299	22
39	80	178	62	501	44	555	28	178	14	254	21
40	.1883	5.3093	.2065	4.8430	.2247	4.4494	.2432	4.1126	.2617	3.8208	20
41	87	008	68	359	51	434	35	074	20	163	19
42	90	5.2924	71	288	54	374	38	022	23	118	18
43	93	839	74	218	57	313	41	4.0970	27	073	17
44	96	755	77	147	60	253	44	918	30	028	16
45	99	672	80	077	63	194	47	867	33	3.7983	15
46	.1902	588	83	007	66	134	50	815	36	938	14
47	05	505	86	4.7937	69	075	53	764	39	893	13
48	08	422	89	867	72	015	56	713	42	848	12
49	11	339	92	798	75	4.3956	59	662	45	804	11
50	.1914	5.2257	.2095	4.7729	.2278	4.3897	.2462	4.0611	.2648	3.7760	10
51	17	174	98	659	81	838	65	560	51	715	9
52	20	092	.2101	591	84	779	69	509	55	671	8
53	23	011	04	522	87	721	72	459	58	627	7
54	26	5.1929	07	453	90	662	75	408	61	583	6
55	29	848	10	385	93	604	78	358	64	539	5
56	32	767	13	317	96	546	81	308	67	495	4
57	35	686	16	249	99	488	84	257	70	451	3
58	38	606	19	181	.2303	430	87	207	73	408	2
59	41	526	23	114	06	372	90	158	76	364	1
60	.1944	5.1446	.2126	4.7046	.2309	4.3315	.2493	4.0108	.2679	3.7321	0
	Cotg.	Tang.	Cotg.	Tang.	Cotg.	Tang.	Cotg.	Tang.	Cotg.	Tang.	
′	79°		78°		77°		76°		75°		′

′	15° N.sine	15° N. cos.	16° N.sine	16° N. cos.	17° N.sine	17° N. cos.	18° N.sine	18° N. cos.	19° N.sine	19° N. cos.	′
0	.25882	.96593	27564	.96126	.29237	.95630	.30902	.95106	.32557	.94552	60
1	910	585	592	118	265	622	929	097	584	542	59
2	938	578	620	110	293	613	957	088	612	533	58
3	966	570	648	102	321	605	985	079	639	523	57
4	994	562	676	094	348	596	.31012	070	667	514	56
5	.26022	555	704	086	376	588	040	061	694	504	55
6	050	547	731	078	404	579	068	052	722	495	54
7	079	540	759	070	432	571	095	043	749	485	53
8	107	532	787	062	460	562	123	033	777	476	52
9	135	524	815	054	487	554	151	024	804	466	51
10	.26163	.96517	.27843	.96046	.29515	.95545	.31178	.95015	.32832	.94457	50
11	191	509	871	037	543	536	206	006	859	447	49
12	219	502	899	029	571	528	233	.94997	887	438	48
13	247	494	927	021	599	519	261	988	914	428	47
14	275	486	955	013	626	511	289	979	942	418	46
15	303	479	983	005	654	502	316	970	969	409	45
16	331	471	.28011	.95997	682	493	344	961	997	399	44
17	359	463	039	989	710	485	372	952	.33024	390	43
18	387	456	067	981	737	476	399	943	051	380	42
19	415	448	095	972	765	467	427	933	079	370	41
20	.26443	.96440	.28123	.95964	.29793	.95459	.31454	.94924	.33106	.94361	40
21	471	433	150	956	821	450	482	915	134	351	39
22	500	425	178	948	849	441	510	906	161	342	38
23	528	417	206	940	876	433	537	897	189	332	37
24	556	410	234	931	904	424	565	888	216	322	36
25	584	402	262	923	932	415	593	878	244	313	35
26	612	394	290	915	960	407	620	869	271	303	34
27	640	386	318	907	987	398	648	860	298	293	33
28	668	379	346	898	.30015	389	675	851	326	284	32
29	696	371	374	890	043	380	703	842	353	274	31
30	.26724	.96363	.28402	.95882	.30071	.95372	.31730	.94832	.33381	.94264	30
31	752	355	429	874	098	363	758	823	408	254	29
32	780	347	457	865	126	354	786	814	436	245	28
33	808	340	485	857	154	345	813	805	463	235	27
34	836	332	513	849	182	337	841	795	490	225	26
35	864	324	541	841	209	328	868	786	518	215	25
36	892	316	569	832	237	319	896	777	545	206	24
37	920	308	597	824	265	310	923	768	573	196	23
38	948	301	625	816	292	301	951	758	600	186	22
39	976	293	652	807	320	293	979	749	627	176	21
40	.27004	.96285	.28680	.95799	.30348	.95284	.32006	.94740	.33655	.94167	20
41	032	277	708	791	376	275	034	730	682	157	19
42	060	269	736	782	403	266	061	721	710	147	18
43	088	261	764	774	431	257	089	712	737	137	17
44	116	253	792	766	459	248	116	702	764	127	16
45	144	246	820	757	486	240	144	693	792	118	15
46	172	238	847	749	514	231	171	684	819	108	14
47	200	230	875	740	542	222	199	674	846	098	13
48	228	222	903	732	570	213	227	665	874	088	12
49	256	214	931	724	597	204	254	656	901	078	11
50	.27284	.96206	.28959	.95715	.30625	.95195	.32282	.94646	.33929	.94068	10
51	312	198	987	707	653	186	309	637	956	058	9
52	340	190	.29015	698	680	177	337	627	983	049	8
53	368	182	042	690	708	168	364	618	.34011	039	7
54	396	174	070	681	736	159	392	609	038	029	6
55	424	166	098	673	763	150	419	599	065	019	5
56	452	158	126	664	791	142	447	590	093	009	4
57	480	150	154	656	819	133	474	580	120	.93999	3
58	508	142	182	647	846	124	502	571	147	989	2
59	536	134	209	639	874	115	529	561	175	979	1
60	.27564	.96126	.29237	.95630	.30902	.95106	.32557	.94552	.34202	.93969	0
′	N.cos.	N. sine	N.cos.	N. sine	N.cos.	N. sine	N.cos.	N. sine	N.cos.	N. sine	′
	74°		73°		72°		71°		70°		

′	15° Tang.	15° Cotg.	16° Tang.	16° Cotg.	17° Tang.	17° Cotg.	18° Tang.	18° Cotg.	19° Tang.	19° Cotg.	′
0	.2679	3.7321	.2867	3.4874	.3057	3.2709	.3249	3.0777	.3443	2.9042	60
1	83	277	71	836	60	675	52	746	47	015	59
2	86	234	74	798	64	641	56	716	50	2.8987	58
3	89	191	77	760	67	607	59	686	53	960	57
4	92	148	80	722	70	573	62	655	56	933	56
5	95	105	83	684	73	539	65	625	60	905	55
6	98	062	86	646	76	506	69	595	63	878	54
7	.2701	019	90	608	80	472	72	565	66	851	53
8	04	3.6976	93	570	83	438	75	535	69	824	52
9	08	933	96	533	86	405	78	505	73	797	51
10	.2711	3.6891	.2899	3.4495	.3089	3.2371	.3281	3.0475	.3476	2.8770	50
11	14	848	.2902	458	92	338	85	445	79	743	49
12	17	806	05	420	96	305	88	415	82	716	48
13	20	764	08	383	99	272	91	385	86	689	47
14	23	722	12	346	.3102	238	94	356	89	662	46
15	26	680	15	308	05	205	98	326	92	636	45
16	29	638	18	271	08	172	.3301	296	95	609	44
17	33	596	21	234	11	139	04	267	99	582	43
18	36	554	24	197	15	106	07	237	.3502	556	42
19	39	512	27	160	18	073	10	208	05	529	41
20	.2742	3.6470	.2931	3.4124	.3121	3.2041	.3314	3.0178	.3508	2.8502	40
21	45	429	34	087	24	008	17	149	12	476	39
22	48	387	37	050	27	3.1975	20	120	15	449	38
23	51	346	40	014	31	943	23	090	18	423	37
24	54	305	43	3.3977	34	910	27	061	22	397	36
25	58	264	46	941	37	878	30	032	25	370	35
26	61	222	49	904	40	845	33	003	28	344	34
27	64	181	53	868	43	813	36	2.9974	31	318	33
28	67	140	56	832	47	780	39	945	35	291	32
29	70	100	59	796	50	748	43	916	38	265	31
30	.2773	3.6059	.2962	3.3759	.3153	3.1716	.3346	2.9887	.3541	2.8239	30
31	76	018	65	723	56	684	49	858	44	213	29
32	80	3.5978	68	687	59	652	52	829	48	187	28
33	83	937	72	652	63	620	56	800	51	161	27
34	86	897	75	616	66	588	59	772	54	135	26
35	89	856	78	580	69	556	62	743	58	109	25
36	92	816	81	544	72	524	65	714	61	083	24
37	95	776	84	509	75	492	69	686	64	057	23
38	98	736	87	473	79	460	72	657	67	032	22
39	.2801	696	91	438	82	429	75	629	71	006	21
40	.2805	3.5656	.2994	3.3402	.3185	3.1397	.3378	2.9600	.3574	2.7980	20
41	08	616	97	367	88	366	82	572	77	955	19
42	11	576	.3000	332	91	334	85	544	81	929	18
43	14	536	03	297	95	303	88	515	84	903	17
44	17	497	06	261	98	271	91	487	87	878	16
45	20	457	10	226	.3201	240	95	459	90	852	15
46	23	418	13	191	04	209	98	431	94	827	14
47	27	379	16	156	07	178	.3401	403	97	801	13
48	30	339	19	122	11	146	04	375	.3600	776	12
49	33	300	22	087	14	115	08	347	04	751	11
50	.2836	3.5261	.3026	3.3052	.3217	3.1084	.3411	2.9319	.3607	2.7725	10
51	39	222	29	017	20	053	14	291	10	700	9
52	42	183	32	3.2983	23	022	17	263	13	675	8
53	45	144	35	948	27	3.0991	21	235	17	650	7
54	49	105	38	914	30	961	24	208	20	625	6
55	52	067	41	879	33	930	27	180	23	600	5
56	55	028	45	845	36	899	30	152	27	575	4
57	58	3.4989	48	811	40	868	34	125	30	550	3
58	61	951	51	777	43	838	37	097	33	525	2
59	64	912	54	743	46	807	40	070	36	500	1
60	.2867	3.4874	.3057	3.2709	.3249	3.0777	.3443	2.9042	.3640	2.7475	0
′	Cotg.	Tang.	Cotg.	Tang.	Cotg.	Tang.	Cotg.	Tang.	Cotg.	Tang.	′
	74°		73°		72°		71°		70°		

′	20° N.sine	N. cos.	21° N.sine	N. cos.	22° N.sine	N. cos.	23° N.sine	N. cos.	24° N.sine	N. cos.	′
0	.34202	.93969	.35837	.93358	.37461	.92718	.39073	.92050	.40674	.91355	60
1	229	959	864	348	488	707	100	039	700	343	59
2	257	949	891	337	515	697	127	028	727	331	58
3	284	939	918	327	542	686	153	016	753	319	57
4	311	929	945	316	569	675	180	005	780	307	56
5	339	919	973	306	595	664	207	.91994	806	295	55
6	366	909	.36000	295	622	653	234	982	833	283	54
7	393	899	027	285	649	642	260	971	860	272	53
8	421	889	054	274	676	631	287	959	886	260	52
9	448	879	081	264	703	620	314	948	913	248	51
10	.34475	.93869	.36108	.93253	.37730	.92609	.39341	.91936	.40939	.91236	50
11	503	859	135	243	757	598	367	925	966	224	49
12	530	849	162	232	784	587	394	914	992	212	48
13	557	839	190	222	811	576	421	902	.41019	200	47
14	584	829	217	211	838	565	448	891	045	188	46
15	612	819	244	201	865	554	474	879	072	176	45
16	639	809	271	190	892	543	501	868	098	164	44
17	666	799	298	180	919	532	528	856	125	152	43
18	694	789	325	169	946	521	555	845	151	140	42
19	721	779	352	159	973	510	581	833	178	128	41
20	.34748	.93769	.36379	.93148	.37999	.92499	.39608	.91822	.41204	.91116	40
21	775	759	406	137	.38026	488	635	810	231	104	39
22	803	748	434	127	053	477	661	799	257	092	38
23	830	738	461	116	080	466	688	787	284	080	37
24	857	728	488	106	107	455	715	775	310	068	36
25	884	718	515	095	134	444	741	764	337	056	35
26	912	708	542	084	161	432	768	752	363	044	34
27	939	698	569	074	188	421	795	741	390	032	33
28	966	688	596	063	215	410	822	729	416	020	32
29	993	677	623	052	241	399	848	718	443	008	31
30	.35021	.93667	.36650	.93042	.38268	.92388	.39875	.91706	.41469	.90996	30
31	048	657	677	031	295	377	902	694	496	984	29
32	075	647	704	020	322	366	928	683	522	972	28
33	102	637	731	010	349	355	955	671	549	960	27
34	130	626	758	.92999	376	343	982	660	575	948	26
35	157	616	785	988	403	332	.40008	648	602	936	25
36	184	606	812	978	430	321	035	636	628	924	24
37	211	596	839	967	456	310	062	625	655	911	23
38	239	585	867	956	483	299	088	613	681	899	22
39	266	575	894	945	510	287	115	601	707	887	21
40	.35293	.93565	.36921	.92935	.38537	.92276	.40141	.91590	.41734	.90875	20
41	320	555	948	924	564	265	168	578	760	863	19
42	347	544	975	913	591	254	195	566	787	851	18
43	375	534	.37002	902	617	243	221	555	813	839	17
44	402	524	029	892	644	231	248	543	840	826	16
45	429	514	056	881	671	220	275	531	866	814	15
46	456	503	083	870	698	209	301	519	892	802	14
47	484	493	110	859	725	198	328	508	919	790	13
48	511	483	137	849	752	186	355	496	945	778	12
49	538	472	164	838	778	175	381	484	972	766	11
50	.35565	.93462	.37191	.92827	.38805	.92164	.40408	.91472	.41998	.90753	10
51	592	452	218	816	832	152	434	461	.42024	741	9
52	619	441	245	805	859	141	461	449	051	729	8
53	647	431	272	794	886	130	488	437	077	717	7
54	674	420	299	784	912	119	514	425	104	704	6
55	701	410	326	773	939	107	541	414	130	692	5
56	728	400	353	762	966	096	567	402	156	680	4
57	755	389	380	751	993	085	594	390	183	668	3
58	782	379	407	740	.39020	073	621	378	209	655	2
59	810	368	434	729	046	062	647	366	235	643	1
60	.35837	.93358	.37461	.92718	.39073	.92050	.40674	.91355	.42262	.90631	0
	N.cos.	N. sine	N.cos.	N. sine	N.cos.	N. sine	N.cos.	N. sine	N.cos.	N. sine	
′	69°		68°		67°		66°		65°		′

′	20° Tang.	20° Cotg.	21° Tang.	21° Cotg.	22° Tang.	22° Cotg.	23° Tang.	23° Cotg.	24° Tang.	24° Cotg.	′
0	.3640	2.7475	.3839	2.6051	.4040	2.4751	.4245	2.3559	.4452	2.2460	60
1	43	50	42	28	44	30	48	39	56	43	59
2	46	25	45	06	47	09	52	20	59	25	58
3	50	00	49	2.5983	50	2.4689	55	01	63	08	57
4	53	2.7376	52	61	54	68	58	2.3483	66	2.2390	56
5	56	51	55	38	57	48	62	64	70	73	55
6	59	26	59	16	61	27	65	45	73	55	54
7	63	02	62	2.5893	64	06	69	26	77	38	53
8	66	2.7277	65	71	67	2.4586	72	07	80	20	52
9	69	53	69	48	71	66	76	2.3388	84	03	51
10	.3673	2.7228	.3872	2.5826	.4074	2.4545	.4279	2.3369	.4487	2.2286	50
11	76	04	75	04	78	25	83	51	91	68	49
12	79	2.7179	79	2.5782	81	04	86	32	94	51	48
13	83	55	82	59	84	2.4484	89	13	98	34	47
14	86	30	85	37	88	64	93	2.3294	.4501	16	46
15	89	06	89	15	91	43	96	76	05	2.2199	45
16	92	2.7082	92	2.5693	95	23	.4300	57	08	82	44
17	96	58	95	71	98	03	03	38	12	65	43
18	99	34	99	49	.4101	2.4383	07	20	15	48	42
19	.3702	09	.3902	27	05	62	10	01	19	30	41
20	.3706	2.6985	.3906	2.5605	.4108	2.4342	.4314	2.3183	.4522	2.2113	40
21	09	61	09	2.5583	11	22	17	64	26	2.2096	39
22	12	37	12	61	15	02	20	46	29	79	38
23	16	13	16	39	18	2.4282	24	27	33	62	37
24	19	2.6889	19	17	22	62	27	09	36	45	36
25	22	65	22	2.5495	25	42	31	2.3090	40	28	35
26	26	41	26	73	29	22	34	72	43	11	34
27	29	18	29	52	32	02	38	53	47	2.1994	33
28	32	2.6794	32	30	35	2.4182	41	35	50	77	32
29	36	70	36	08	39	62	45	17	54	60	31
30	.3739	2.6746	.3939	2.5386	.4142	2.4142	.4348	2.2998	.4557	2.1943	30
31	42	23	42	65	46	22	52	80	61	26	29
32	45	2.6699	46	43	49	02	55	62	64	09	28
33	49	75	49	22	52	2.4083	59	44	68	2.1892	27
34	52	52	53	00	56	63	62	25	71	76	26
35	55	28	56	2.5279	59	43	65	07	75	59	25
36	59	05	59	57	63	23	69	2.2889	78	42	24
37	62	2.6581	63	36	66	04	72	71	82	25	23
38	65	58	66	14	69	2.3984	76	53	85	08	22
39	69	34	69	2.5193	73	64	79	35	89	2.1792	21
40	.3772	2.6511	.3973	2.5172	.4176	2.3945	.4383	2.2817	.4592	2.1775	20
41	75	2.6488	76	50	80	25	86	2.2799	96	58	19
42	79	64	79	29	83	06	90	81	99	42	18
43	82	41	83	08	87	2.3886	93	63	.4603	25	17
44	85	18	86	2.5086	90	67	97	45	07	08	16
45	89	2.6395	90	65	93	47	.4400	27	10	2.1692	15
46	92	71	93	44	97	28	04	09	14	75	14
47	95	48	96	23	.4200	08	07	2.2691	17	59	13
48	99	25	.4000	02	04	2.3789	11	73	21	42	12
49	.3802	02	03	2.4981	07	70	14	55	24	25	11
50	.3805	2.6279	.4006	2.4960	.4210	2.3750	.4417	2.2637	.4628	2.1609	10
51	09	56	10	39	14	31	21	20	31	2.1592	9
52	12	33	13	18	17	12	24	02	35	76	8
53	15	10	17	2.4897	21	2.3693	28	2.2584	38	60	7
54	19	2.6187	20	76	24	73	31	66	42	43	6
55	22	65	23	55	28	54	35	49	45	27	5
56	25	42	27	34	31	35	38	31	49	10	4
57	29	19	30	13	34	16	42	13	52	2.1494	3
58	32	2.6096	33	2.4792	38	2.3597	45	2.2496	56	78	2
59	35	74	37	72	41	78	49	78	60	61	1
60	.3839	2.6051	.4040	2.4751	.4245	2.3559	.4452	2.2460	.4663	2.1445	0
′	Cotg.	Tang.	Cotg.	Tang.	Cotg.	Tang.	Cotg.	Tang.	Cotg.	Tang.	′
	69°		68°		67°		66°		65°		

′	25° N.sine	25° N. cos.	26° N.sine	26° N. cos.	27° N.sine	27° N. cos.	28° N.sine	28° N. cos.	29° N.sine	29° N. cos.	′
0	.42262	.90631	.43837	.89879	.45399	.89101	.46947	.88295	.48481	.87462	60
1	288	618	863	867	425	087	973	281	506	448	59
2	315	606	889	854	451	074	999	267	532	434	58
3	341	594	916	841	477	061	.47024	254	557	420	57
4	367	582	942	828	503	048	050	240	583	406	56
5	394	569	968	816	529	035	076	226	608	391	55
6	420	557	994	803	554	021	101	213	634	377	54
7	446	545	.44020	790	580	008	127	199	659	363	53
8	473	532	046	777	606	.88995	153	185	684	349	52
9	499	520	072	764	632	981	178	172	710	335	51
10	.42525	.90507	.44098	.89752	.45658	.88968	.47204	.88158	.48735	.87321	50
11	552	495	124	739	684	955	229	144	761	306	49
12	578	483	151	726	710	942	255	130	786	292	48
13	604	470	177	713	736	928	281	117	811	278	47
14	631	458	203	700	762	915	306	103	837	264	46
15	657	446	229	687	787	902	332	089	862	250	45
16	683	433	255	674	813	888	358	075	888	235	44
17	709	421	281	662	839	875	383	062	913	221	43
18	736	408	307	649	865	862	409	048	938	207	42
19	762	396	333	636	891	848	434	034	964	193	41
20	.42788	.90383	.44359	.89623	.45917	.88835	.47460	.88020	.48989	.87178	40
21	815	371	385	610	942	822	486	006	.49014	164	39
22	841	358	411	597	968	808	511	.87993	040	150	38
23	867	346	437	584	994	795	537	979	065	136	37
24	894	334	464	571	.46020	782	562	965	090	121	36
25	920	321	490	558	046	768	588	951	116	107	35
26	946	309	516	545	072	755	614	937	141	093	34
27	972	296	542	532	097	741	639	923	166	079	33
28	999	284	568	519	123	728	665	909	192	064	32
29	.43025	271	594	506	149	715	690	896	217	050	31
30	.43051	.90259	.44620	.89493	.46175	.88701	.47716	.87882	.49242	.87036	30
31	077	246	646	480	201	688	741	868	268	021	29
32	104	233	672	467	226	674	767	854	293	007	28
33	130	221	698	454	252	661	793	840	318	.86993	27
34	156	208	724	441	278	647	818	826	344	978	26
35	182	196	750	428	304	634	844	812	369	964	25
36	209	183	776	415	330	620	869	798	394	949	24
37	235	171	802	402	355	607	895	784	419	935	23
38	261	158	828	389	381	593	920	770	445	921	22
39	287	146	854	376	407	580	946	756	470	906	21
40	.43313	.90133	.44880	.89363	.46433	.88566	.47971	.87743	.49495	.86892	20
41	340	120	906	350	458	553	997	729	521	878	19
42	366	108	932	337	484	539	.48022	715	546	863	18
43	392	095	958	324	510	526	048	701	571	849	17
44	418	082	984	311	536	512	073	687	596	834	16
45	445	070	.45010	298	561	499	099	673	622	820	15
46	471	057	036	285	587	485	124	659	647	805	14
47	497	045	062	272	613	472	150	645	672	791	13
48	523	032	088	259	639	458	175	631	697	777	12
49	549	019	114	245	664	445	201	617	723	762	11
50	.43575	.90007	.45140	.89232	.46690	.88431	.48226	.87603	.49748	.86748	10
51	602	.89994	166	219	716	417	252	589	773	733	9
52	628	981	192	206	742	404	277	575	798	719	8
53	654	968	218	193	767	390	303	561	824	704	7
54	680	956	243	180	793	377	328	546	849	690	6
55	706	943	269	167	819	363	354	532	874	675	5
56	733	930	295	153	844	349	379	518	899	661	4
57	759	918	321	140	870	336	405	504	924	646	3
58	785	905	347	127	896	322	430	490	950	632	2
59	811	892	373	114	921	308	456	476	975	617	1
60	.43837	.89879	.45399	.89101	.46947	.88295	.48481	.87462	.50000	.86603	0
′	N.cos.	N. sine	N.cos.	N. sine	N.cos.	N. sine	N.cos.	N. sine	N.cos.	N. sine	′
	64°		63°		62°		61°		60°		

′	25°		26°		27°		28°		29°		′
	Tang.	Cotg.	Tang.	Cotg.	Tang.	Cotg.	Tang.	Cotg.	Tang.	Cotg.	
0	.4663	2.1445	.4877	2.0503	.5095	1.9626	.5317	1.8807	.5543	1.8040	60
1	67	29	81	2.0488	99	12	21	1.8794	47	28	59
2	70	13	85	73	.5103	1.9598	25	81	51	16	58
3	74	2.1396	88	58	06	84	28	68	55	03	57
4	77	80	92	43	10	70	32	55	58	1.7991	56
5	81	64	95	28	14	56	36	41	62	79	55
6	84	48	99	13	17	42	40	28	66	66	54
7	88	32	.4903	2.0398	21	28	43	15	70	54	53
8	91	15	06	83	25	14	47	02	74	42	52
9	95	2.1299	10	68	28	00	51	1.8689	77	30	51
10	.4699	2.1283	.4913	2.0353	.5132	1.9486	.5354	1.8676	.5581	1.7917	50
11	.4702	67	17	38	36	72	58	63	85	05	49
12	06	51	21	23	39	58	62	50	89	1.7893	48
13	09	35	24	08	43	44	66	37	93	81	47
14	13	19	28	2.0293	47	30	69	24	96	68	46
15	16	03	31	78	50	16	73	11	.5600	56	45
16	20	2.1187	35	63	54	02	77	1.8598	04	44	44
17	23	71	39	48	58	1.9388	81	85	08	32	43
18	27	55	42	33	61	75	84	72	12	20	42
19	31	39	46	19	65	61	88	59	16	08	41
20	.4734	2.1123	.4950	2.0204	.5169	1.9347	.5392	1.8546	.5619	1.7796	40
21	38	07	53	2.0189	72	33	96	33	23	83	39
22	41	2.1092	57	74	76	19	99	20	27	71	38
23	45	76	60	60	80	06	.5403	07	31	59	37
24	48	60	64	45	84	1.9292	07	1.8495	35	47	36
25	52	44	68	30	87	78	11	82	39	35	35
26	55	28	71	15	91	65	15	69	42	23	34
27	59	13	75	01	95	51	18	56	46	11	33
28	63	2.0997	79	2.0086	98	37	22	43	50	1.7699	32
29	66	81	82	72	.5202	23	26	30	54	87	31
30	.4770	2.0965	.4986	2.0057	.5206	1.9210	.5430	1.8418	.5658	1.7675	30
31	73	50	89	42	09	1.9196	33	05	62	63	29
32	77	34	93	28	13	83	37	1.8392	65	51	28
33	80	18	97	13	17	69	41	79	69	39	27
34	84	03	.5000	1.9999	20	55	45	67	73	27	26
35	88	2.0887	04	84	24	42	48	54	77	15	25
36	91	72	08	70	28	28	52	41	81	03	24
37	95	56	11	55	32	15	56	29	85	1.7591	23
38	98	40	15	41	35	01	60	16	88	79	22
39	.4802	25	19	26	39	1.9088	64	03	92	67	21
40	.4806	2.0809	.5022	1.9912	.5243	1.9074	.5467	1.8291	.5696	1.7556	20
41	09	2.0794	26	1.9897	46	61	71	78	.5700	44	19
42	13	78	29	83	50	47	75	65	04	32	18
43	16	63	33	68	54	34	79	53	08	20	17
44	20	48	37	54	58	20	82	40	12	08	16
45	23	32	40	40	61	07	86	28	15	1.7496	15
46	27	17	44	25	65	1.8993	90	15	19	85	14
47	31	01	48	11	69	80	94	02	23	73	13
48	34	2.0686	51	1.9797	72	67	98	1.8190	27	61	12
49	38	71	55	82	76	53	.5501	77	31	49	11
50	.4841	2.0655	.5059	1.9768	.5280	1.8940	.5505	1.8165	.5735	1.7437	10
51	45	40	62	54	84	27	09	52	39	26	9
52	49	25	66	40	87	13	13	40	43	14	8
53	52	09	70	25	91	00	17	27	46	02	7
54	56	2.0594	73	11	95	1.8887	20	15	50	1.7391	6
55	59	79	77	1.9697	98	73	24	03	54	79	5
56	63	64	81	83	.5302	60	28	1.8090	58	67	4
57	67	49	84	69	06	47	32	78	62	55	3
58	70	33	88	54	10	34	35	65	66	44	2
59	74	18	92	40	13	20	39	53	70	32	1
60	.4877	2.0503	.5095	1.9626	.5317	1.8807	.5543	1.8040	.5774	1.7321	0
	Cotg.	Tang.	Cotg.	Tang.	Cotg.	Tang.	Cotg.	Tang.	Cotg.	Tang.	
′	64°		63°		62°		61°		60°		′

′	30°		31°		32°		33°		34°		′
	N.sine	N. cos.	N.sine	N. cos.	N.sine	N. cos.	N.sine	N. cos.	N.sine	N. cos.	
0	.50000	.86603	.51504	.85717	.52992	.84805	.54464	.83867	.55919	.82904	60
1	025	588	529	702	.53017	789	488	851	943	887	59
2	050	573	554	687	041	774	513	835	968	871	58
3	076	559	579	672	066	759	537	819	992	855	57
4	101	544	604	657	091	743	561	804	.56016	839	56
5	126	530	628	642	115	728	586	788	040	822	55
6	151	515	653	627	140	712	610	772	064	806	54
7	176	501	678	612	164	697	635	756	088	790	53
8	201	486	703	597	189	681	659	740	112	773	52
9	227	471	728	582	214	666	683	724	136	757	51
10	.50252	.86457	.51753	.85567	.53238	.84650	.54708	.83708	.56160	.82741	50
11	277	442	778	551	263	635	732	692	184	724	49
12	302	427	803	536	288	619	756	676	208	708	48
13	327	413	828	521	312	604	781	660	232	692	47
14	352	398	852	506	337	588	805	645	256	675	46
15	377	384	877	491	361	573	829	629	280	659	45
16	403	369	902	476	386	557	854	613	305	643	44
17	428	354	927	461	411	542	878	597	329	626	43
18	453	340	952	446	435	526	902	581	353	610	42
19	478	325	977	431	460	511	927	565	377	593	41
20	.50503	.86310	.52002	.85416	.53484	.84495	.54951	.83549	.56401	.82577	40
21	528	295	026	401	509	480	975	533	425	561	39
22	553	281	051	385	534	464	999	517	449	544	38
23	578	266	076	370	558	448	.55024	501	473	528	37
24	603	251	101	355	583	433	048	485	497	511	36
25	628	237	126	340	607	417	072	469	521	495	35
26	654	222	151	325	632	402	097	453	545	478	34
27	679	207	175	310	656	386	121	437	569	462	33
28	704	192	200	294	681	370	145	421	593	446	32
29	729	178	225	279	705	355	169	405	617	429	31
30	.50754	.86163	.52250	.85264	.53730	.84339	.55194	.83389	.56641	.82413	30
31	779	148	275	249	754	324	218	373	665	396	29
32	804	133	299	234	779	308	242	356	689	380	28
33	829	119	324	218	804	292	266	340	713	363	27
34	854	104	349	203	828	277	291	324	736	347	26
35	879	089	374	188	853	261	315	308	760	330	25
36	904	074	399	173	877	245	339	292	784	314	24
37	929	059	423	157	902	230	363	276	808	297	23
38	954	045	448	142	926	214	388	260	832	281	22
39	979	030	473	127	951	198	412	244	856	264	21
40	.51004	.86015	.52498	.85112	.53975	.84182	.55436	.83228	.56880	.82248	20
41	029	000	522	096	.54000	167	460	212	904	231	19
42	054	.85985	547	081	024	151	484	195	928	214	18
43	079	970	572	066	049	135	509	179	952	198	17
44	104	956	597	051	073	120	533	163	976	181	16
45	129	941	621	035	097	104	557	147	.57000	165	15
46	154	926	646	020	122	088	581	131	024	148	14
47	179	911	671	005	146	072	605	115	047	132	13
48	204	896	696	.84989	171	057	630	098	071	115	12
49	229	881	720	974	195	041	654	082	095	098	11
50	.51254	.85866	.52745	.84959	.54220	.84025	.55678	.83066	.57119	.82082	10
51	279	851	770	943	244	009	702	050	143	065	9
52	304	836	794	928	269	.83994	726	034	167	048	8
53	329	821	819	913	293	978	750	017	191	032	7
54	354	806	844	897	317	962	775	001	215	015	6
55	379	792	869	882	342	946	799	.82985	238	.81999	5
56	404	777	893	866	366	930	823	969	262	982	4
57	429	762	918	851	391	915	847	953	286	965	3
58	454	747	943	836	415	899	871	936	310	949	2
59	479	732	967	820	440	883	895	920	334	932	1
60	.51504	.85717	.52992	.84805	.54464	.83867	.55919	.82904	.57358	.81915	0
	N. cos.	N. sine	N.cos.	N. sine	N.cos.	N. sine	N.cos.	N. sine	N.cos.	N. sine	
′	59°		58°		57°		56°		55°		′

′	30° Tang.	30° Cotg.	31° Tang.	31° Cotg.	32° Tang.	32° Cotg.	33° Tang.	33° Cotg.	34° Tang.	34° Cotg.	′
0	.5774	1.7321	.6009	1.6643	.6249	1.6003	.6494	1.5399	.6745	1.4826	60
1	77	09	13	32	53	1.5993	98	89	49	16	59
2	81	1.7297	17	21	57	83	.6502	79	54	07	58
3	85	86	20	10	61	72	06	69	58	1.4798	57
4	89	74	24	1.6599	65	62	11	59	62	88	56
5	93	62	28	88	69	52	15	50	66	79	55
6	97	51	32	77	73	41	19	40	71	70	54
7	.5801	39	36	66	77	31	23	30	75	61	53
8	05	28	40	55	81	21	27	20	79	51	52
9	08	16	44	45	85	11	31	11	83	42	51
10	.5812	1.7205	.6048	1.6534	.6289	1.5900	.6536	1.5301	.6787	1.4733	50
11	16	1.7193	52	23	93	1.5890	40	1.5291	92	24	49
12	20	82	56	12	97	80	44	82	96	15	48
13	24	70	60	01	.6301	69	48	72	.6800	05	47
14	28	59	64	1.6490	05	59	52	62	05	1.4696	46
15	32	47	68	79	10	49	56	53	09	87	45
16	36	36	72	69	14	39	60	43	13	78	44
17	40	24	76	58	18	29	65	33	17	69	43
18	44	13	80	47	22	18	69	24	22	1.4659	42
19	47	02	84	36	26	08	73	14	26	50	41
20	.5851	1.7090	.6088	1.6426	.6330	1.5798	.6577	1.5204	.6830	1.4641	40
21	55	79	92	15	34	88	81	1.5195	34	32	39
22	59	67	96	04	38	78	85	85	39	23	38
23	63	56	.6100	1.6393	42	68	90	75	43	14	37
24	67	45	04	83	46	57	94	66	47	05	36
25	71	33	08	72	50	47	98	56	51	1.4596	35
26	75	22	12	61	54	37	.6602	47	56	86	34
27	79	11	16	51	58	27	06	37	60	77	33
28	83	1.6999	20	40	63	17	10	27	64	68	32
29	87	88	24	29	67	07	15	18	69	59	31
30	.5890	1.6977	.6128	1.6319	.6371	1.5697	.6619	1.5108	.6873	1.4550	30
31	94	65	32	08	75	87	23	1.5099	77	41	29
32	98	54	36	1.6297	79	77	27	89	81	32	28
33	.5902	43	40	87	83	67	31	80	86	23	27
34	06	32	44	76	87	57	36	70	90	14	26
35	10	20	48	65	91	47	40	61	94	05	25
36	14	09	52	55	95	37	44	51	99	1.4496	24
37	18	1.6898	56	44	99	27	48	42	.6903	87	23
38	22	87	60	34	.6403	17	52	32	07	78	22
39	26	75	64	23	08	07	57	23	11	69	21
40	.5930	1.6864	.6168	1.6212	.6412	1.5597	.6661	1.5013	.6916	1.4460	20
41	34	53	72	02	16	87	65	04	20	51	19
42	38	42	76	1.6191	20	77	69	1.4994	24	42	18
43	42	31	80	81	24	67	73	85	29	33	17
44	45	20	84	70	28	57	78	75	33	24	16
45	49	08	88	60	32	47	82	66	37	15	15
46	53	1.6797	92	49	36	37	86	57	42	06	14
47	57	86	96	39	40	27	90	47	46	1.4397	13
48	61	75	.6200	28	45	17	94	38	50	88	12
49	65	64	04	18	49	07	99	28	54	79	11
50	.5969	1.6753	.6208	1.6107	.6453	1.5497	.6703	1.4919	.6959	1.4370	10
51	73	42	12	1.6097	57	87	07	10	63	61	9
52	77	31	16	87	61	77	11	00	67	52	8
53	81	20	20	76	65	68	15	1.4891	72	44	7
54	85	09	24	66	69	58	20	82	76	35	6
55	89	1.6698	28	55	73	48	24	72	80	26	5
56	93	87	33	45	78	38	28	63	85	17	4
57	97	76	37	34	82	28	32	54	89	08	3
58	.6001	65	41	24	86	18	37	44	93	1.4299	2
59	05	54	45	14	90	08	41	35	98	90	1
60	.6009	1.6643	.6249	1.6003	.6494	1.5399	.6745	1.4826	.7002	1.4281	0
	Cotg.	Tang.	Cotg.	Tang.	Cotg.	Tang.	Cotg.	Tang.	Cotg.	Tang.	
′	59°		58°		57°		56°		55°		′

Natural Sines and Cosines

′	35°		36°		37°		38°		39°		′
	N.sine	N. cos.	N.sine	N. cos.	N.sine	N. cos.	N.sine	N. cos.	N.sine	N. cos.	
0	.57358	.81915	.58779	.80902	.60182	.79864	.61566	.78801	.62932	.77715	60
1	381	899	802	885	205	846	589	783	955	696	59
2	405	882	826	867	228	829	612	765	977	678	58
3	429	865	849	850	251	811	635	747	.63000	660	57
4	453	848	873	833	274	793	658	729	022	641	56
5	477	832	896	816	298	776	681	711	045	623	55
6	501	815	920	799	321	758	704	694	068	605	54
7	524	798	943	782	344	741	726	676	090	586	53
8	548	782	967	765	367	723	749	658	113	568	52
9	572	765	990	748	390	706	772	640	135	550	51
10	.57596	.81748	.59014	.80730	.60414	.79688	.61795	.78622	.63158	.77531	50
11	619	731	037	713	437	671	818	604	180	513	49
12	643	714	061	696	460	653	841	586	203	494	48
13	667	698	084	679	483	635	864	568	225	476	47
14	691	681	108	662	506	618	887	550	248	458	46
15	715	664	131	644	529	600	909	532	271	439	45
16	738	647	154	627	553	583	932	514	293	421	44
17	762	631	178	610	576	565	955	496	316	402	43
18	786	614	201	593	599	547	978	478	338	384	42
19	810	597	225	576	622	530	.62001	460	361	366	41
20	.57833	.81580	.59248	.80558	.60645	.79512	.62024	.78442	.63383	.77347	40
21	857	563	272	541	668	494	046	424	406	329	39
22	881	546	295	524	691	477	069	405	428	310	38
23	904	530	318	507	714	459	092	387	451	292	37
24	928	513	342	489	738	441	115	369	473	273	36
25	952	496	365	472	761	424	138	351	496	255	35
26	976	479	389	455	784	406	160	333	518	236	34
27	999	462	412	438	807	388	183	315	540	218	33
28	.58023	445	436	420	830	371	206	297	563	199	32
29	047	428	459	403	853	353	229	279	585	181	31
30	.58070	.81412	.59482	.80386	.60876	.79335	.62251	.78261	.63608	.77162	30
31	094	395	506	368	899	318	274	243	630	144	29
32	118	378	529	351	922	300	297	225	653	125	28
33	141	361	552	334	945	282	320	206	675	107	27
34	165	344	576	316	968	264	342	188	698	088	26
35	189	327	599	299	991	247	365	170	720	070	25
36	212	310	622	282	.61015	229	388	152	742	051	24
37	236	293	646	264	038	211	411	134	765	033	23
38	260	276	669	247	061	193	433	116	787	014	22
39	283	259	693	230	084	176	456	093	810	.76996	21
40	.58307	.81242	.59716	.80212	.61107	.79158	.62479	.78079	.63832	.76977	20
41	330	225	739	195	130	140	502	061	854	959	19
42	354	208	763	178	153	122	524	043	877	940	18
43	378	191	786	160	176	105	547	025	899	921	17
44	401	174	809	143	199	087	570	007	922	903	16
45	425	157	832	125	222	069	592	.77988	944	884	15
46	449	140	856	108	245	051	615	970	966	866	14
47	472	123	879	091	268	033	638	952	989	847	13
48	496	106	902	073	291	016	660	934	.64011	828	12
49	519	089	926	056	314	.78998	683	916	033	810	11
50	.58543	.81072	.59949	.80038	.61337	.78980	.62706	.77897	.64056	.76791	10
51	567	055	972	021	360	962	728	879	078	772	9
52	590	038	995	003	383	944	751	861	100	754	8
53	614	021	.60019	.79986	406	926	774	843	123	735	7
54	637	004	042	968	429	908	796	824	145	717	6
55	661	.80987	065	951	451	891	819	806	167	698	5
56	684	970	089	934	474	873	842	788	190	679	4
57	708	953	112	916	497	855	864	769	212	661	3
58	731	936	135	899	520	837	887	751	234	642	2
59	755	919	158	881	543	819	909	733	256	623	1
60	.58779	.80902	.60182	.79864	.61566	.78801	.62932	.77715	.64279	.76604	0
	N.cos.	N. sine	N.cos.	N. sine	N.cos.	N. sine	N.cos.	N. sine	N.cos.	N. sine	
′	54°		53°		52°		51°		50°		′

′	35°		36°		37°		38°		39°		′
	Tang.	Cotg.	Tang.	Cotg.	Tang.	Cotg.	Tang.	Cotg.	Tang.	Cotg.	
0	.7002	1.4281	.7265	1.3764	.7536	1.3270	.7813	1.2799	.8098	1.2349	60
1	06	73	70	55	'40	62	18	92	.8103	42	59
2	11	64	74	47	45	54	22	84	07	34	58
3	15	55	79	39	49	46	27	76	12	27	57
4	19	46	83	30	54	38	32	69	17	20	56
5	24	37	88	22	58	30	36	61	22	12	55
6	28	29	92	13	63	22	41	53	27	05	54
7	32	20	97	05	68	14	46	46	32	1.2298	53
8	37	11	.7301	1.3697	72	06	50	38	36	90	52
9	41	02	06	88	77	1.3198	55	31	41	83	51
10	.7046	1.4193	.7310	1.3680	.7581	1.3190	.7860	1.2723	.8146	1.2276	50
11	50	85	14	72	86	82	65	15	51	68	49
12	54	76	19	63	90	75	69	08	56	61	48
13	59	67	23	55	95	67	74	00	61	54	47
14	63	58	28	47	.7600	59	79	1.2693	65	47	46
15	67	50	32	38	04	51	83	85	70	39	45
16	72	41	37	30	09	43	88	77	75	32	44
17	76	32	41	22	13	35	93	70	80	25	43
18	80	24	46	13	18	27	98	62	85	18	42
19	85	15	50	05	23	19	.7902	55	90	10	41
20	.7089	1.4106	.7355	1.3597	.7627	1.3111	.7907	1.2647	.8195	1.2203	40
21	94	1.4097	59	88	32	03	12	40	99	1.2196	39
22	98	89	64	80	36	1.3095	16	32	.8204	89	38
23	.7102	80	68	72	41	87	21	24	09	81	37
24	07	71	73	54	46	79	26	17	14	74	36
25	11	63	77	55	50	72	31	09	19	67	35
26	15	54	82	47	55	64	35	02	24	60	34
27	20	45	86	39	59	56	40	1.2594	29	53	33
28	24	37	91	31	64	48	45	87	34	45	32
29	29	28	95	22	69	40	50	79	38	38	31
30	.7133	1.4019	.7400	1.3514	.7673	1.3032	.7954	1.2572	.8243	1.2131	30
31	37	11	04	06	78	24	59	64	48	24	29
32	42	02	09	1.3498	83	17	64	57	53	17	28
33	46	1.3994	13	90	87	09	69	49	58	09	27
34	51	85	18	81	92	01	73	42	63	02	26
35	55	76	22	73	96	1.2993	78	34	68	1.2095	25
36	59	68	27	65	.7701	85	83	27	73	88	24
37	64	59	31	57	06	77	88	19	78	81	23
38	68	51	36	49	10	70	92	12	83	74	22
39	73	42	40	40	15	62	97	04	87	66	21
40	.7177	1.3934	.7445	1.3432	.7720	1.2954	.8002	1.2497	.8292	1.2059	20
41	81	25	49	24	24	46	07	89	97	52	19
42	86	16	54	16	29	38	12	82	.8302	45	18
43	90	08	58	08	34	31	16	75	07	38	17
44	95	1.3899	63	00	38	23	21	67	12	31	16
45	99	91	67	1.3392	43	15	26	60	17	24	15
46	.7203	82	72	84	47	07	31	52	22	17	14
47	08	74	76	75	52	00	35	45	27	09	13
48	12	65	81	67	57	1.2892	40	37	32	02	12
49	17	57	85	59	61	84	45	30	37	1.1995	11
50	.7221	1.3848	.7490	1.3351	.7766	1.2876	.8050	1.2423	.8342	1.1988	10
51	26	40	95	43	71	69	55	15	46	81	9
52	30	31	99	35	75	61	59	08	51	74	8
53	34	23	.7504	27	80	53	64	01	56	67	7
54	39	14	08	19	85	46	69	1.2393	61	60	6
55	43	06	13	11	89	38	74	86	66	53	5
56	48	1.3798	17	03	94	30	79	78	71	46	4
57	52	89	22	1.3295	99	22	83	71	76	39	3
58	57	81	26	87	.7803	15	88	64	81	32	2
59	61	72	31	78	08	07	93	56	86	25	1
60	.7265	1.3764	.7536	1.3270	.7813	1.2799	.8098	1.2349	.8391	1.1918	0
	Cotg.	Tang.	Cotg.	Tang.	Cotg.	Tang.	Cotg.	Tang.	Cotg.	Tang.	
′	54°		53°		52°		51°		50°		′

′	40°		41°		42°		43°		44°		′
	N.sine	N. cos.	N.sine	N. cos.	N.sine	N. cos.	N.sine	N. cos.	N.sine	N. cos.	
0	.64279	.76604	.65606	.75471	.66913	.74314	.68200	.73135	.69466	.71934	60
1	301	586	628	452	935	295	221	116	487	914	59
2	323	567	650	433	956	276	242	096	508	894	58
3	346	548	672	414	978	256	264	076	529	873	57
4	368	530	694	395	999	237	285	056	549	853	56
5	390	511	716	375	.67021	217	306	036	570	833	55
6	412	492	738	356	043	198	327	016	591	813	54
7	435	473	759	337	064	178	349	.72996	612	792	53
8	457	455	781	318	086	159	370	976	633	772	52
9	479	436	803	299	107	139	391	957	654	752	51
10	.64501	.76417	.65825	.75280	.67129	.74120	.68412	.72937	.69675	.71732	50
11	524	398	847	261	151	100	434	917	696	711	49
12	546	380	869	241	172	080	455	897	717	691	48
13	568	361	891	222	194	061	476	877	737	671	47
14	590	342	913	203	215	041	497	857	758	650	46
15	612	323	935	184	237	022	518	837	779	630	45
16	635	304	956	165	258	002	539	817	800	610	44
17	657	286	978	146	280	.73983	561	797	821	590	43
18	679	267	.66000	126	301	963	582	777	842	569	42
19	701	248	022	107	323	944	603	757	862	549	41
20	.64723	.76229	.66044	.75088	.67344	.73924	.68624	.72737	.69883	.71529	40
21	746	210	066	069	366	904	645	717	904	508	39
22	768	192	088	050	387	885	666	697	925	488	38
23	790	173	109	030	409	865	688	677	946	468	37
24	812	154	131	011	430	846	709	657	966	447	36
25	834	135	153	.74992	452	826	730	637	987	427	35
26	856	116	175	973	473	806	751	617	.70008	407	34
27	878	097	197	953	495	787	772	597	029	386	33
28	901	078	218	934	516	767	793	577	049	366	32
29	923	059	240	915	538	747	814	557	070	345	31
30	.64945	.76041	.66262	.74896	.67559	.73728	.68835	.72537	.70091	.71325	30
31	967	022	284	876	580	708	857	517	112	305	29
32	989	003	306	857	602	688	878	497	132	284	28
33	.65011	.75984	327	838	623	669	899	477	153	264	27
34	033	965	349	818	645	649	920	457	174	243	26
35	055	946	371	799	666	629	941	437	195	223	25
36	077	927	393	780	688	610	962	417	215	203	24
37	100	908	414	760	709	590	983	397	236	182	23
38	122	889	436	741	730	570	.69004	377	257	162	22
39	144	870	458	722	752	551	025	357	277	141	21
40	.65166	.75851	.66480	.74703	.67773	.73531	.69046	.72337	.70298	.71121	20
41	188	832	501	683	795	511	067	317	319	100	19
42	210	813	523	664	816	491	088	297	339	080	18
43	232	794	545	644	837	472	109	277	360	059	17
44	254	775	566	625	859	452	130	257	381	039	16
45	276	756	588	606	880	432	151	236	401	019	15
46	298	738	610	586	901	413	172	216	422	.70998	14
47	320	719	632	567	923	393	193	196	443	978	13
48	342	700	653	548	944	373	214	176	463	957	12
49	364	680	675	528	965	353	235	156	484	937	11
50	.65386	.75661	.66697	.74509	.67987	.73333	.69256	.72136	.70505	.70916	10
51	408	642	718	489	.68008	314	277	116	525	896	9
52	430	623	740	470	029	294	298	095	546	875	8
53	452	604	762	451	051	274	319	075	567	855	7
54	474	585	783	431	072	254	340	055	587	834	6
55	496	566	805	412	093	234	361	035	608	813	5
56	518	547	827	392	115	215	382	015	628	793	4
57	540	528	848	373	136	195	403	.71995	649	772	3
58	562	509	870	353	157	175	424	974	670	752	2
59	584	490	891	334	179	155	445	955	690	731	1
60	.65606	.75471	.66913	.74314	.68200	.73135	.69466	.71934	.70711	.70711	0
	N. cos.	N. sine	N. cos.	N. sine	N. cos.	N. sine	N. cos.	N. sine	N. cos.	N. sine	
′	49°		48°		47°		46°		45°		′

′	40° Tang.	40° Cotg.	41° Tang.	41° Cotg.	42° Tang.	42° Cotg.	43° Tang.	43° Cotg.	44° Tang.	44° Cotg.	′
0	.8391	1.1918	.8693	1.1504	.9004	1.1106	.9325	1.0724	.9657	1.0355	60
1	96	10	98	1.1497	09	00	31	17	63	49	59
2	.8401	03	.8703	90	15	1.1093	36	11	68	43	58
3	06	1.1896	08	83	20	87	41	05	74	37	57
4	11	89	13	77	25	80	47	1.0699	79	31	56
5	16	82	18	70	30	74	52	92	85	25	55
6	21	75	24	63	36	67	58	86	91	19	54
7	26	68	29	56	41	61	63	80	96	13	53
8	31	61	34	50	46	54	69	74	.9702	07	52
9	36	54	39	43	52	48	74	68	08	01	51
10	.8441	1.1847	.8744	1.1436	.9057	1.1041	.9380	1.0661	.9713	1.0295	50
11	46	40	49	30	62	35	85	55	19	89	49
12	51	33	54	23	67	28	91	49	25	83	48
13	56	26	59	16	73	22	96	43	30	77	47
14	61	19	65	10	78	16	.9402	37	36	71	46
15	66	12	70	03	83	09	07	30	42	65	45
16	71	06	75	1.1396	89	03	13	24	47	59	44
17	76	1.1799	80	89	94	1.0996	18	18	53	53	43
18	81	92	85	83	99	90	24	12	59	47	42
19	86	85	90	76	.9105	83	29	06	64	41	41
20	.8491	1.1778	.8796	1.1369	.9110	1.0977	.9435	1.0599	.9770	1.0235	40
21	96	71	.8801	63	15	71	40	93	76	30	39
22	.8501	64	06	56	21	64	46	87	81	24	38
23	06	57	11	49	26	58	51	81	87	18	37
24	11	50	16	43	31	51	57	75	93	12	36
25	16	43	21	36	37	45	62	69	98	06	35
26	21	36	27	29	42	39	68	62	.9804	00	34
27	26	29	32	23	47	32	73	56	10	1.0194	33
28	31	22	37	16	53	26	79	50	16	88	32
29	36	15	42	10	58	19	84	44	21	82	31
30	.8541	1.1708	.8847	1.1303	.9163	1.0913	.9490	1.0538	.9827	1.0176	30
31	46	02	52	1.1296	69	07	95	32	33	70	29
32	51	1.1695	58	90	74	00	.9501	26	38	64	28
33	56	88	63	83	79	1.0894	06	19	44	58	27
34	61	81	68	76	85	88	12	13	50	52	26
35	66	74	73	70	90	81	17	07	56	47	25
36	71	67	78	63	95	75	23	01	61	41	24
37	76	60	84	57	.9201	69	28	1.0495	67	35	23
38	81	53	89	50	06	62	34	89	73	29	22
39	86	47	94	43	12	56	40	83	79	23	21
40	.8591	1.1640	.8899	1.1237	.9217	1.0850	.9545	1.0477	.9884	1.0117	20
41	96	33	.8904	30	22	43	51	70	90	11	19
42	.8601	26	10	24	28	37	56	64	96	05	18
43	06	19	15	17	33	31	62	58	.9902	1.0099	17
44	11	12	20	11	39	24	67	52	07	94	16
45	17	06	25	04	44	18	73	46	13	88	15
46	22	1.1599	31	1.1197	49	12	78	40	19	82	14
47	27	92	36	91	55	05	84	34	25	76	13
48	32	85	41	84	60	1.0799	90	28	30	70	12
49	37	78	46	78	66	93	95	22	36	64	11
50	.8642	1.1571	.8952	1.1171	.9271	1.0786	.9601	1.0416	.9942	1.0058	10
51	47	65	57	65	76	80	06	10	48	52	9
52	52	58	62	58	82	74	12	04	54	47	8
53	57	51	67	52	87	68	18	1.0398	59	41	7
54	62	44	72	45	93	61	23	92	65	35	6
55	67	38	78	39	98	55	29	85	71	29	5
56	72	31	83	32	.9303	49	34	79	77	23	4
57	78	24	88	26	09	42	40	73	83	17	3
58	83	17	94	19	14	36	46	67	88	12	2
59	88	10	99	13	20	30	51	61	94	06	1
60	.8693	1.1504	.9004	1.1106	.9325	1.0724	.9657	1.0355	1.0000	1.0000	0
	Cotg.	Tang.	Cotg.	Tang.	Cotg.	Tang.	Cotg.	Tang.	Cotg.	Tang.	
′	49°		48°		47°		46°		45°		′

SOME IMPORTANT CONSTANTS AND THEIR LOGARITHMS

$\pi = 3.14159265$
$2\pi = 6.28318531$
$\dfrac{\pi}{2} = 1.57079633$
$\dfrac{\pi}{4} = 0.78539816$
$\pi^2 = 9.86960440$
$\sqrt{\pi} = 1.77245385$
$\sqrt{2\pi} = 2.50662827$
$\dfrac{1}{\pi} = 0.318309886$
$e = 2.718281829$
$M = 0.434294482$
$\dfrac{1}{M} = 2.302585092$

$\log \quad \pi = 0.497149873$
$\log \quad 2\pi = 0.798179868$
$\log \quad \dfrac{\pi}{2} = 0.196119877$
$\log \quad \dfrac{\pi}{4} = 9.895089881 - 10$
$\log \quad \pi^2 = 0.994299745$
$\log \quad \sqrt{\pi} = 0.248574936$
$\log \sqrt{2\pi} = 0.399089934$
$\log \quad \dfrac{1}{\pi} = 9.502850127 - 10$
$\log \quad e = 0.434294482$
$\log \quad M = 9.637784311 - 10$
$\log \quad \dfrac{1}{M} = 0.362215699$

1 radian $= 57°.2957795$
1 radian $= 3437'.74677$
1 radian $= 206264''.8062$
1 degree $= 0.017453293$ radians
1 minute $= 0.000290888$ radians
1 second $= 0.000004848$ radians

$\log \quad 57.2957795 = 1.758122632$
$\log \quad 3437.74677 = 3.536273883$
$\log \ 206264.8062 = 5.314425133$
$\log \quad 0.01745293 = 8.241877368 - 10$
$\log \quad 0.000290888 = 6.463726117 - 10$
$\log \quad 0.000004848 = 4.685562611 - 10$